the psychology of health and health care

A CANADIAN PERSPECTIVE   FIFTH EDITION

the psychology of health and health care

A CANADIAN PERSPECTIVE   FIFTH EDITION

GARY POOLE

UNIVERSITY OF BRITISH COLUMBIA

DEBORAH HUNT MATHESON

VANCOUVER ISLAND UNIVERSITY

DAVID N. COX

SIMON FRASER UNIVERSITY

Toronto

Vice-President, CMPS: Gary Bennett
Editorial Director: Claudine O'Donnell
Acquisitions Editor: Matthew Christian
Marketing Manager: Claire Varley
Program Manager: Madhu Ranadive
Project Manager: Susan Johnson
Developmental Editor: Cheryl Finch
Production Services: Kailash Jadli, iEnergizer Aptara®, Inc.
Permissions Project Manager: Kathryn O'Handley
Photo Permissions Research: Nazveena Begum Syed, Lumina Datamatics Ltd.
Text Permissions Research: Anjana Ragavendran, Lumina Datamatics Ltd.
Cover Designer: iEnergizer Aptara®, Inc.
Cover Image: Vetre/Shutterstock

Library and Archives Canada Cataloguing in Publication

Poole, Gary, 1950–, author
　　The psychology of health and health care : a Canadian perspective /
Gary Poole (University of British Columbia), Deborah Hunt Matheson (Vancouver Island University), David N. Cox (Simon Fraser University).—Fifth edition.

Includes bibliographical references and index.
ISBN 978-0-13-309827-3 (pbk.)

　　1. Medicine and psychology—Textbooks.　2. Medical care—Psychological aspects—Textbooks.　I. Matheson, Deborah Hunt, 1966–, author　II. Cox, David Neil, 1947–, author　III. Title.

R726.7.P66 2015　　　　　　　　610.1'9　　　　　　　　C2014-908508-7

2 2019

ISBN 13: 978-0-13-309827-3

For our families:

Marsha, Colleen, and Graeme Poole
Wyatt Matheson
Susan, Kelsi, Kieran, and Dylan Cox

Brief Contents

Preface   *xii*

Chapter 1   Welcome to Health Psychology   1

Part 1 The Connections between Our Physical and Psychological Worlds

Chapter 2   Stress and Coping   25

Chapter 3   Psychoneuroimmunology   51

Part 2 The Psychology of Wellness and Illness

Chapter 4   Health Communication   76

Chapter 5   Health and Physical Activity   106

Chapter 6   Health-Compromising Behaviours   135

Chapter 7   Chronic and Life-Threatening Illnesses   176

Chapter 8   Pain   206

Chapter 9   The World of Health Care: Places, Procedures, and People   241

Part 3 Bigger Pictures: The Health of Populations

Chapter 10   From One to Many: Health on a Large Scale   279

Chapter 11   Health Promotion   302

Index   395

Contents

Preface   xii

Acknowledgements   xv

About the Authors   xvi

1 Welcome to Health Psychology   1
What Is Health Psychology?   2
The Roots and Branches of Health Psychology   3
The Early Stages of Health Psychology: Applying the Principles of Behaviourism to Health   3
Health Psychology Expands to Include Cognition and Personality Factors   5
More Attention Is Paid to the Ways People Cope   6
The Introduction of Psychoneuroimmunology: Finding Links between Psychological and Biological Processes   6
Summary   7
The Birth of Health Psychology   7
Changing Profiles of Illness and Health in Canada   7
Multiple Perspectives Are Needed to Understand Health and Health Statistics   9
Health Psychology Today   10
The Biopsychosocial Approach to Health   10
Prominent Theories in Health Psychology   12
Working in Health Psychology   22
Clinical and Counselling Psychologists Working in Health Psychology   22
Research Careers in Health Psychology   23
Chapter Summary   23

Part 1 The Connections between Our Physical and Psychological Worlds

2 Stress and Coping   25
Issues of Definition   26
The Physiology of Stress   30
The General Adaptation Syndrome   32
Cognitive Transactional Models   34
The Role of Personality in Stress and Coping   37
Coping   39
East and West: Now the Twain Shall Meet   43
Relaxation   45
Behaviour Therapy and Cognitive Therapy   46

The Relaxation Responses: A Personal Guide   48
Chapter Summary   50

3 Psychoneuroimmunology   51
The Importance of PNI to Health Psychology   52
How Immune-System Functioning Is Measured in PNI Research   53
Counting Cells to Measure Immunocompetence   53
Functional Tests of Immunocompetence: Measuring Cells in Action   54
Methodological Issues in the Measurement of Immune-System Function   55
Research in PNI: Providing Evidence for a Biological Link between Psychology and Health   57
The Effect of Stress on Immune Functioning   58
The Effect of Depression on Immune Functioning   64
Biological Mechanisms to Explain Why Psychological States Affect the Immune System   73
Chapter Summary   75

Part 2 The Psychology of Wellness and Illness

4 Health Communication   76
Physician-Patient Interaction   78
Basic Models of Physician-Patient Interaction   78
Physician-Patient Communication   82
Adhering to Medical Advice   92
Assessing Adherence   92
Frequency and Cost of Non-Adherence   93
What Factors Predict Adherence?   94
Improving Patient Adherence   96
Dr. Google: Health and the Internet   100
Health-Related Resources Available on the Internet   100
Assessing the Quality of Health Information on the Internet   102
Implications for Patient-Physician Relationships   103
Chapter Summary   105

5 Health and Physical Activity   106

The Nature of Physical Activity   108
Physical Activity and the Five Components of Health   112
Levels of Physical Activity   112
The Five Forms of Physical Activity   114
Psychological Benefits of Physical Activity   115
Physical Activity and Sense of Self   116
Physical Activity and Cognitive Functioning   119
Physical Activity and Mood   120
Physical Benefits of Physical Activity   122
Adherence to Physical Activity   124
Psychological Factors Affecting Performance in Exercise and Sport   126
Relaxation   128
Self-Talk   128
Imagery   129
Goal Setting   130
Mindfulness and Acceptance-Based Interventions   131
Physical Activity and Injury   132
Chapter Summary   134

6 Health-Compromising Behaviours   135

Substance Abuse   136
Smoking   136
Alcohol Use   147
Illicit Drug Use   153
Unsafe Sexual Behaviours   157
Obesity   158
Biological Factors That Contribute to Obesity   162
Psychosocial Factors That Contribute to Obesity   163
Sociocultural Factors That Contribute to Obesity   163
Prevention and Treatment of Obesity   164
Eating disorders   168
Biological, Cultural, and Psychological Contributors to Eating Disorders   170
Treatment for Eating Disorders   171
Chapter Summary   174

7 Chronic and Life-Threatening Illnesses   176

Cancer   178
Some Statistics   178
Illness Burden for Cancer   179
Physical Problems   179
Psychological Distress   180

Cancer Treatment   182
Helping People Cope with Cancer   186
Diabetes   189
Diabetes and Psychological Distress   190
Helping People Cope with Diabetes   192
Diseases of the Cardiovascular System   192
Cardiovascular Disease and Psychological Distress   193
Helping People Cope with Cardiovascular Disease   194
HIV and AIDS   195
HIV/AIDS and Psychological Distress   197
Helping People Cope with HIV and AIDS   197
A Final Word about Our Discussion of HIV and AIDS   198
Other Chronic Conditions   199
Quality of Life   199
The Tradeoff between Duration and Quality of Life   200
Quality of Life as a Subjective Phenomenon   201
Death and Dying   202
Patients' Reactions to Death   202
Bereavement and Grief   204
Chapter Summary   204

8 Pain   206

The Significance of Pain   208
Pain Perception   209
Theories of Pain   210
Gate Control Theory   210
Neuromatrix Theory   211
Neurochemical Basis of Pain and Pain Inhibition   211
Acute versus Chronic Pain   213
Psychosocial Factors and Pain   216
Gender Differences   216
Cultural Differences   219
The Measurement of Pain   220
Psychophysiological Measures   220
Behavioural Assessment   220
Self-Reports of Pain   221
Assessing Pain in Infants and Children   225
Assessing Pain in Older Adults   226
Pain Control Techniques   227
Pharmacological Control of Pain   227
Surgical Control of Pain   228
Transcutaneous Electrical Nerve Stimulation   229
Acupuncture   230
Physical Therapy   230

Massage 231
Relaxation 232
Distraction 233
Hypnosis 236
Multidisciplinary Pain Management Programs 238
Chapter Summary 240

9 The World of Health Care: Places, Procedures, and People 241
Seeking Medical Care 242
Perceiving Symptoms 242
Interpreting Symptoms 244
Seeking Help from the Health Care System 245
Delaying Medical Care 245
The Hospital 247
A Hospital Patient's Loss of Control 248
Patient-Centred Care: An Ideal in the Hospital 253
Spending Time in Hospital 253
The Emergency Department 253
Recovering from Surgery 254
The Intensive Care Unit 255
Discharge 259
Palliative Care 260
The Psychological Impact of Medical Procedures 261
The Psychology of Colonoscopy 261
The Psychology of Mammography 262
People 263
Physicians 264
Physicians' Emotional Involvement in Their Work 264
Physicians and Stress 265
Gender Issues in Medical Practice 268
Nurses 270
The Nature of Modern Nursing 270
Stress in Nursing 272
Others 274
Physiotherapists 274
Chapter Summary 277

Part 3 Bigger Pictures: The Health of Populations

10 From One to Many: Health on a Large Scale 279
The Social Ecological Model: Building on the Biopsychosocial Approach to Understand Big Pictures 280

Tracking Health and Illness at the Population Level 282
Social Determinants of Health in Canada 283
The Vulnerability of Populations 284
Culture and Health 287
What Is Culture? 288
How Culture Affects Health 289
What Is Required to Ensure the Best Possible Health for All, Regardless of Culture? 290
The Health of Canada's Aboriginal Peoples 291
Who Are Canada's Aboriginal Peoples? 291
Health Challenges 292
Addressing the Challenges 293
Harm Reduction as a Treating and Preventing Illness at the Population Level 294
Reducing the Harm of Injection Drug Use 295
The Psychology of Vaccination 296
Health and the Built Environment 298
Chapter Summary 300

11 Health Promotion 302
Canada as a Worldwide Leader in Health Promotion 304
The Goals of Health Promotion in Canada 306
Health Promotion Mechanisms 307
Using Psychological Principles to Promote Healthy Living 310
Prominent Theories in Health Psychology Applied to Health Promotion 310
The Social Psychology of Health Promotion 311
Look Before You Leap: The Precede-Proceed Model 317
Assessing the Effectiveness of Health Promotion Programs 319
A Final Word about Health Promotion 321
Chapter Summary 321

Glossary 323

References 333

Index 395

Preface

With each new edition of *The Psychology of Health and Health Care: A Canadian Perspective*, we as authors learn more and more about this fascinating field of health psychology. In writing this fifth edition, we have reinforced our belief that the field continues to mature and expand, learning from other branches of psychology and from other disciplines.

As learners and as authors, we continue to feel very fortunate to be able to work in a country in which issues, opinions, and data are so very accessible. In the late 1990s, when we first began conceptualizing this book, we were convinced that the topics of health psychology manifest themselves in unique ways in Canada. After writing this fifth edition, we hold fast to that conviction. While many psychological theories developed in the United States and elsewhere apply well internationally, it is still the case that, when it comes to health and health care, our geography, demography, history, and health care system make Canadians unique, even in the face of significant, though debated, reforms to the American health care system. Our experience in writing this edition continues to confirm that Canadians are very active in research that goes beyond descriptions of our health to explore the factors affecting it. Again, you will find hundreds of new references as this research is discussed throughout the book.

HOW BEST TO USE THIS BOOK

The fifth edition of *The Psychology of Health and Health Care: A Canadian Perspective* is organized into major parts and chapters. The division of topics into major parts is a new addition to the book. You will see that we are continuing to place the work of health psychology in larger disciplinary and societal contexts, especially in Part 3 entitled Bigger Pictures: The Health of Populations. Chapters continue to be the traditionally used organizational elements. This book presents topics that are commonly found in most health psychology textbooks. Stress and coping, health communication, pain, and chronic and life-threatening illnesses are examples of such topics. However, this edition also contains chapters on some topics that are often covered in less detail by other texts. Examples include psychoneuroimmunology, health promotion, and health and physical activity.

Instructors are invited to use the book's chapters as they see fit for their educational context. For example, nursing and medical students may want to focus more on chapters such as Psychoneuroimmunology, Health Communication, The World of Health Care, Pain, and Chronic and Life-Threatening Illnesses.

Health psychology is essentially an applied discipline, and each chapter of our book opens with a vignette intended to provide students with a realistic context for what they are about to read. In this way, we begin each chapter with an applied focus. Students will also find case studies throughout the book. In addition to the analysis we provide, students can discuss these case studies in lectures and seminars.

WHAT'S NEW IN THE FIFTH EDITION

This fifth edition includes new features that highlight the key concepts for each chapter. We have rethought the structure of our "advance organizers" that help students start thinking about a chapter before delving into it. Correspondingly, we have restructured our chapter reviews to enhance students' recall and help them think about the material in deeper rather than surface ways.

The most noticeable expansion found in this fifth edition is Part 3: The Bigger Picture: The Health of Populations. The material in this section reflects health psychologists' growing appreciation for the interdisciplinary nature of their work—that no challenge in health can be understood solely from one perspective. The section also acknowledges that, while working with individuals is still a fundamental reality in health care, health is more dramatically improved by focusing on populations. No single health care practitioner can have as much impact as can one well-implemented and thoughtful policy on clear drinking water.

SUPPLEMENTS

The following instructor supplements are available for downloading from a password-protected section of Pearson Canada's online catalogue. Navigate to your book's catalogue page to view a list of those supplements that are available. See your local Pearson sales representative for details and access.

Test Item File   Available in Microsoft Word, the test bank includes a wide variety of questions that will help you create meaningful student tests and assessments.

PowerPoints   The PowerPoint presentations highlight the key concepts in each chapter and will enhance classroom lectures and discussion.

CourseSmart for Instructors   CourseSmart goes beyond traditional expectations—providing instant, online access to the textbooks and course materials you need at a lower cost for students. And even as students save money, you can save time and hassle with a digital eTextbook that allows you to search for the most relevant content at the very moment you need it. Whether it's evaluating textbooks or creating lecture notes to help students with difficult concepts, CourseSmart can make life a little easier. See how when you visit **http://instructors.coursesmart.com**.

Learning Solutions Managers   Pearson's Learning Solutions Managers work with faculty and campus course designers to ensure that Pearson technology products, assessment tools, and online course materials are tailored to meet your specific needs. This highly qualified team is dedicated to helping schools take full advantage of a wide range of educational resources, by assisting in the integration of a variety of instructional materials and media formats. Your local Pearson Education sales representative can provide you with more details on this service program.

Pearson Custom Library   For enrollments of at least 25 students, you can create your own textbook by choosing the chapters that best suit your own course needs. To begin building your custom text, visit www.pearsoncustomlibrary.com. You may also work with a dedicated Pearson Custom editor to create your ideal text—publishing your own original content or mixing and matching Pearson content. Contact your local Pearson Representative to get started.

peerScholar   Firmly grounded in published research, peerScholar is a powerful online pedagogical tool that helps develop students' critical and creative thinking skills through creation, evaluation, and reflection. Working in stages, students begin by submitting written assignments. peerScholar then circulates their work for others to review, a process that can be anonymous or not, depending on instructors' preferences. Students immediately receive peer feedback and evaluations, reinforcing their learning and driving development of higher-order thinking skills. Students can then re-submit revised work, again depending on instructors' preferences.

Contact your Pearson representative to learn more about peerScholar and the research behind it.

Acknowledgements

We are very grateful for the help we received from Sean Benay, who provided a very careful reading of our first edition, and from Caroline Murphy of the University of British Columbia, who pointed us in the right direction regarding the content for the focused module on Health and the Internet.

We also continue to be very grateful to Peter Gibson for sharing and updating his remarkable story with us in chapter 5. For their feedback on the first edition, we would also like to thank Lois Hunt and Dennis Krebs of Simon Fraser University, Tina Niwinska and Jody L. Bain of the University of Victoria, Kathleen A. Martin Ginis of McMaster University, Dean Tripp of Queen's University, and Angie MacKewn of the University of New Brunswick.

Pearson Canada and the authors would like to thank the following individuals for their reviews during the development phase of this title: Judith Andersen, University of Toronto Mississauga; Theresa Bianco, Concordia University; Yves Bureau, Western University; Nukte Edguer, Brandon University; Kyoko Hattori, Carleton University; Cameron Muir, Brock University; and Randall Tonks, Camosun College.

Gary Poole
Deborah Hunt Matheson
David N. Cox

About the Authors

Gary Poole is a Professor in the School of Population and Public Health in the University of British Columbia's Faculty of Medicine. He received his Ph.D. in Psychology from Simon Fraser University. He has won numerous awards for his teaching, and he is Past President of the International Society for the Scholarship of Teaching and Learning. In addition to his publications in the area of health psychology, he is the co-author of "Effective Teaching with Technology in Higher Education" (Bates, A.W., & Poole, G. (2003). *Effective teaching with technology in higher education: Foundations for Success*. San Francisco, CA: Jossey-Bass.)

Deborah Hunt Matheson is Chair of the Department of Psychology at Vancouver Island University. She received her B.A. (Hons) from Simon Fraser University and did her M.A. and Ph.D. graduate work at the University of Victoria. Her research interests are in health psychology, especially on factors that motivate people to commit to an exercise program. In addition, she is interested in communication in the medical setting. Her research has been published in journals such as *Behavioral Medicine*; the *British Journal of Health Psychology*; the *Canadian Journal of Communication*; the *Journal of Nonverbal Behavior*; the *Journal of Sport and Exercise Psychology*; *Measurement in Physical Education and Exercise Science*; *Psychology and Health*; *Psychology, Health and Medicine*; and the *Psychology of Sport and Exercise*.

David N. Cox is a professor in the Department of Psychology at Simon Fraser University where he has just completed a term as the Director of Clinical Training. He received his M.A. and Ph.D. from the University of British Columbia in Clinical Psychology. His research and applied interests currently focus on health psychology, human performance, and sport psychology. He is currently the Chair of the Sport Medicine Council of British Columbia. His most recent research has been published in journals such as the *Journal of Clinical and Experimental Neuropsychology*, the *International Journal of Sports Physiology and Performance*, the *International Journal of Mental health and Addictions*, the *Journal of Pediatric Psychology*, and the *Journal of Adolescent Health*.

Chapter 1
Welcome to Health Psychology

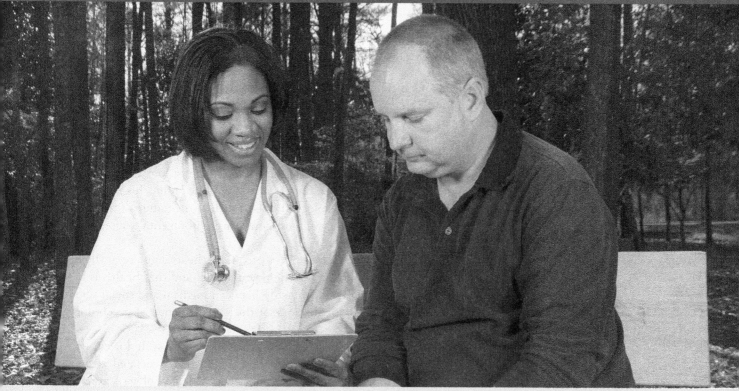

Learning Objectives

After studying this chapter, you will be able to:

1. define health psychology.
2. outline how the field grew in terms of the range of important topics addressed and the move to augment behavioural perspectives with those taken from cognitive psychology.
3. explain why health psychology has grown so quickly as a field.
4. describe and apply fundamental theories in health psychology.
5. describe different careers pursued by people who have studied health psychology.

Alan was admitted to a hospital with classic heart-attack symptoms, though that wasn't how he explained his chest pain, breathing difficulties, and profuse sweating. He had been suffering from a cold for the past week and thought the virus had flared up badly. However, Alan was wrong. Tests revealed an *infarct*—tissue that has died because of a lack of oxygen. Other tests showed the reason for the infarct: a coronary artery was completely blocked. In fact, so were two others—not the stuff of viruses. Alan was advised that he needed emergency bypass surgery.

WHAT IS HEALTH PSYCHOLOGY?

What might have caused Alan's heart attack? We might conclude that the cause was the arterial blockage, and this would certainly be correct. But is that *all* that caused it? Why did bypass surgery like Alan's become so common in the latter half of the twentieth century? Did millions of people in North America develop blocked coronary arteries because of some colossal biological coincidence? No. To understand Alan's heart attack and the growth industry that bypass surgery has become, we must look beyond biology. We must consider psychological causes, such as Alan's outlook on life, his lifestyle, and his stress level. We must consider sociological causes, such as the nature of his employment and his social network. Finally, we must consider environmental causes, such as the air he breathes.

This collection of causes is relevant not only to Alan's heart, but also at the heart of this book. The goal of this chapter is to help you understand that health is better understood and achieved through a partnership between medical and social science. We will explore, in detail, the contributions of the social science of psychology to this understanding.

Clinical psychologists have long recognized that there are psychological consequences associated with ill health, as well as physical consequences associated with many psychological disorders. It wasn't until the 1970s, however, that psychologists from other non-clinical subdisciplines began to recognize the many ways psychological principles could be applied to health and health care. It was out of this recognition that the fields of behavioural medicine and, ultimately, health psychology emerged.

behavioural medicine: a branch of medicine concerned with the relationship between health and behaviour. The focus is usually on remediation.

health psychology: the application of psychological principles to the diagnosis and treatment of illness as well as to people's attempts to maintain health and well-being.

One of the first terms to be used in the 1970s to describe the relationship between psychology and health was **behavioural medicine**, stressing an integration of biomedical and behavioural approaches. Psychology achieved prominence among these behavioural approaches with the emergence of the term **health psychology**, for which Matarazzo (1980) proposed the following definition:

> Health psychology is the aggregate of the specific educational, scientific and professional contributions of the discipline of psychology to the promotion and maintenance of health, the prevention or treatment of illness, and the identification of etiologic and diagnostic correlates of health, illness, and related dysfunction. (p. 815)

Note that this definition includes not just maintenance of health but also treatment of illness. Health psychology, then, is the compilation of all that psychology has to offer to the diagnosis and treatment of illness as well as to people's attempts to maintain health and well-being. In this context, the word *health* means more than just the absence of illness. As far back as the 1940s, the World Health Organization (WHO) promoted the notion that being "healthy" also means being able to enjoy a desired quality of life in terms of physical, mental, and social functioning. Today, WHO espouses the same definition it presented in 1946: "Health is a state of complete physical, mental and social well-being and not merely the absence of disease or infirmity" (WHO, 1946).

We can apply this notion of health to Alan, who has just had a heart attack. We can, with some accuracy, assess the extent of his tissue damage. However, what will it take to help Alan be *healthy* again, and what does this mean? If we adopt the WHO definition of health, our role as health psychologists becomes clearer. We must help Alan return to a level of functioning that restores his sense of quality of life. This may include addressing his fears of having another heart attack, helping him change his approach to life so that it is less hostile, and helping him develop the conviction that these changes are possible. In this example and in Matarazzo's definition of *health psychology*, we form an image of psychologists working at the interface of medicine and psychology. This work has been recognized by the Canadian Psychological Association (CPA) in its creation of a section on health psychology, and by the American Psychological Association through its creation of Division 38, the Division of Health Psychology.

THE ROOTS AND BRANCHES OF HEALTH PSYCHOLOGY

A subdiscipline has truly "arrived" in psychology when the *Annual Review of Psychology* begins publishing articles summarizing its development. Thus, Neal Miller's 1983 article on behavioural medicine (Miller, 1983) marked the arrival of health psychology. This article was followed over the years by a number of reviews that, taken collectively, provide a good overview of how the field has developed, especially in light of the topics given prominence.

The Early Stages of Health Psychology: Applying the Principles of Behaviourism to Health

In 1983, Neal Miller traced the development of the biomedical perspective on illness, starting with the invention of the microscope and moving to the development of **germ theory**, which is based on the discovery that many illnesses are caused by the activity of microorganisms, such as bacteria. From germ theory came the development of antibiotics to fight these germs. The biomedical perspective took full flight, realizing considerable success by reducing illnesses to a cellular level and treating them with medicines.

At least two important developments resulted from these discoveries. First, the success of antibiotics brought about a change in the profile of life-threatening illnesses, and lifestyle replaced infection as the number one killer. Second, an emphasis on the technical aspects of medicine replaced a consideration for emotional factors in health. The paradox is that technical medicine, so revered for its success in treating germ-based conditions, is relatively ineffective against health problems caused by lifestyle and other psychosocial factors. As a result, these two developments gave rise to behavioural medicine.

Psychologists adopting a behavioural perspective believe that our health is affected primarily by what we *do* rather than what we *think*. You will see later in this chapter how

germ theory: the discovery that many illnesses are caused by the activity of microorganisms, such as bacteria.

this perspective has been expanded with the introduction of theories such as the health belief model, which emphasizes the way our thinking can affect the decisions we make.

In Miller's article, the key issues of the day were explained using the language of behaviourism. For example, Miller identified *non-compliance* with medical regimens as an important problem. Today, we are more likely to use terms such as *adherence* or *co-operation* to describe people's decisions to follow medical regimens. He explained non-compliance in terms of what he called a **gradient of reinforcement**. By this, he meant that the greater the lag time between behaviour and reinforcement, the weaker the behaviour will be. Non-compliance can be explained in these terms because the reinforcement for following a medical regimen is often delayed. When we exercise, we don't suddenly get fit. High blood pressure doesn't drop to a normal range after one low-sodium meal. These benefits take time to realize. Behaviourists call this time lag between behaviour and reinforcement **delayed gratification**. Returning to our opening story, for example, Alan must contend with problems of delayed gratification as he recovers from his heart attack and tries to change his behaviour and thinking.

There is research support for the delayed gratification explanation of Miller's concept of non-compliance. Specifically, we know that compliance rates are higher for regimens bringing about a rapid reduction in symptoms than they are for those in which improvement takes longer. Lowest of all are compliance rates for conditions that are **asymptomatic**—that is, conditions accompanied by no palpable symptoms or sensations (Buckalew, 1991). For example, after 1 year, about 40 percent of people who were prescribed a medication for high blood pressure no longer take the prescribed medicine (Hong, Oddone, Dudley, & Bosworth, 2006).

The delayed gratification theory helps to explain why significantly more people will follow instructions to take an antibiotic to relieve a painful ear infection than will follow instructions to change their lifestyle to reduce hypertension. According to the behavioural explanation, this is because taking the antibiotic is reinforced almost immediately by pain relief. Lifestyle changes for the usually asymptomatic condition of high blood pressure are reinforced by longer life expectancy, which is far less immediate. This problem is further compounded by the fact that behaviours that worsen hypertension, such as eating a high-fat diet, are immediately reinforced—these foods taste good. Miller provided a similar analysis to explain why people find it difficult to quit smoking cigarettes.

Miller addressed a number of other conditions, including alcohol abuse, obesity, stress, and the Type A behaviour pattern first described in the late 1950s by two cardiologists who identified behaviour patterns that they claimed were more common among their cardiac patients than in the general population (Friedman & Rosenman, 1959). At the time of Miller's article (1983), psychologists believed that the entire constellation of attributes identified by the Type A pattern were linked to heart disease. These attributes included time urgency, achievement orientation, and hostility. Large-scale studies, such as the Framingham study, published around the time of Miller's article, showed that people exhibiting the Type A pattern were generally at greater risk for coronary heart disease (CHD) (Haynes, Feinleib, & Kannel, 1980). Other studies that followed large samples of men over a 7-year period found that those prone to anger were three times more likely to die from heart disease or suffer a non-fatal heart attack (Kawachi, Sparrow, Spiro, Vokonas, & Weiss, 1996). We will review the balance of these findings

gradient of reinforcement: the gradual weakening of a behaviour the further it gets in time from the reinforcement of that behaviour.

delayed gratification: term used by behaviourists to describe a situation in which there is a time lag between a behaviour and its reinforcement.

asymptomatic: conditions that are not accompanied by palpable symptoms or sensations.

in chapter 3 in our discussion of stress and coping. For now, it is important to understand that the Type A construct was a catalyst for general research attempting to link psychology with health.

Health Psychology Expands to Include Cognition and Personality Factors

Shortly after Miller's article, Krantz and colleagues (1985) published another major review that identified a number of key areas in which health psychology had made contributions and others in which more research was needed. Closely related to the investigations in the mid-1980s was the study of the relationship between behaviour and cardiovascular health. The link between cigarette smoking and disease had been sufficiently established, so the next logical step was to study the psychology of smoking. To this end, studies examined the ages at which people (usually young people) started smoking (Kozlowski, 1979; Pomerleau, 1979), how they maintained the habit (Kozlowski & Herman, 1984), and why smoking cessation programs were less successful than they might be (Schachter, 1981).

By the mid-1980s, psychologists were working with physiologists and others to identify the mechanisms whereby stressful environments put people at risk for health problems. Further, Miller's behavioural perspective was expanded to study the cognitive and personality factors that cause some people to view a situation as being stressful while others may not. By 2002, approximately 80 percent of the articles published in *Health Psychology* emphasized cognitive processes (Montgomery, 2004).

As cognitive factors rose in prominence during this period, psychologists were also studying ways that stress could be reduced. For example, social support grew as a significant area of study, as did therapeutic interventions such as *cognitive restructuring*, which was aimed at changing people's stress-prone interpretations of events. (For a review, see Matarazzo, Weiss, Herd, Miller, & Weiss, 1984.)

Eating disorders were another topic that rose to prominence in the 1980s, specifically obesity, anorexia, and cachexia (malnourishment). Obesity was studied from biological,

Hostility, as identified by the Type A behaviour pattern, can take the form of road rage.
Magmaphoto.com/Corbis

behavioural, and social perspectives; today, we call this a *biopsychosocial approach*, and it will be discussed later in this chapter.

Finally, Krantz and colleagues discussed communication issues as they are related to compliance (as they called it) by introducing perspectives other than behaviourism. The work of Howard Waitzkin in the United States (Waitzkin, 1985), Philip Ley in Great Britain (Ley, 1977), and others showed that communication between physicians and their patients often lacked clarity and relevance. Through this work, physicians discovered that their impression of an interview with a patient could be quite different from the patient's impression. Specifically, less information was being conveyed, and patients' understanding of that information was poorer than what physicians realized. Communication in medical settings continues to be an important topic in health psychology (see chapter 4).

Thus, the study of compliance was also important because it led to a more in-depth study of the patient-physician relationship. Indeed, the term *compliance* has come under fire specifically because of its implication that the physician-patient relationship is unidirectional (DiMatteo, 1991). Health psychologists criticized the expectation that the physician should give the orders and that patients should passively follow those orders.

More Attention Is Paid to the Ways People Cope

Four years after the review paper by Krantz and colleagues, Rodin and Salovey (1989) published another review of health psychology. By 1989, some new topics had emerged. For example, research attention was being paid to the ways in which people *coped* with illness and everything that went along with it, such as hospital stays and the impact of illness on relationships with others. At this time, health psychologists were attempting to identify coping styles—patterns in the ways people deal with difficult situations.

One good example of coping styles is Suzanne Miller's notion of *monitors* and *blunters* (Miller, 1980). Monitors are information seekers; blunters are information avoiders. The coping style of each type of person is consistent with that person's desire for receiving or avoiding information. This is just one example of how people differ in the ways they cope with illness and the challenges it brings. We will look more closely at these and other coping styles in chapter 9, when we talk about hospital stays and medical procedures, and again in chapter 7 in our discussion of chronic and life-threatening illness.

The Introduction of Psychoneuroimmunology: Finding Links between Psychological and Biological Processes

In 1996, Cohen and Herbert approached health psychology by focusing exclusively on **psychoneuroimmunology (PNI)**. This is the study of the relationship between our psychological state and the functioning of our immune system, a relationship alluded to by Miller in 1983 and studied in more detail in recent years. The breakthrough in this area came with the development of techniques to quantify the status of our immune systems (called **immunocompetence**) through blood tests and saliva samples. This advance made PNI extremely important because it provided an opportunity for health psychology to produce empirical proof of hypothesized relationships between mind and body.

psychoneuroimmunology (PNI): the study of the relationship between psychological states and the functioning of the immune system.

immunocompetence: the extent to which our immune system is functioning properly to ward off microorganisms.

In truth, PNI had been introduced well before the mid-1990s. In fact, a prominent book on the subject was published in 1981 (Ader, Felton, & Cohen, 1981). Since then, our knowledge of PNI has been significantly advanced by a number of researchers. One of the more prolific is Janice Kiecolt-Glaser, who has been publishing extensively on the subject of PNI since the mid-1980s. She has looked at such diverse psychological states and situations as marital conflict (Kiecolt-Glaser, Fisher et al., 1987) and caregiving for patients with Alzheimer's disease (Kiecolt-Glaser, Glaser et al., 1987) in terms of their effects on the immune system. (For a review of research linking social relationships and immune functioning, see Kiecolt-Glaser, Gouin, & Hantsoo, 2010.) We present a detailed examination of PNI in chapter 3.

An article by Andrew Baum and Donna Posluszny (1999) in the *Annual Review of Psychology* summarized the field of PNI. Their paper provided an excellent overview of the ways in which all the major relevant topics since Miller's 1983 article had coalesced and evolved into the current perspective on health psychology. Baum and Posluszny covered the following topics, all of which we discuss in the following chapters: stress and coping (chapter 2), health-compromising behaviours (chapter 6), and behaviours related to seeking and consuming health care (chapter 9). A more recent review has focused on the contributions psychological theory can make to the self-management of chronic illness (Leventhal et al., 2008).

Summary

When we compare these approaches to health psychology, it becomes clear that the topics being studied have changed much less than the ways in which we view them. From the strong behavioural roots of Miller and others, our thinking has expanded to include theories featuring a more cognitive approach. Today, health psychologists use interventions that combine behavioural and cognitive theories, evidence of which you will see in this book.

THE BIRTH OF HEALTH PSYCHOLOGY

The Health Psychology section of the CPA is one of the association's larger sections. There are many reasons for its importance, not the least of which are the changes in health and illness patterns in this country and elsewhere in the second half of the twentieth century.

Changing Profiles of Illness and Health in Canada

A comparison of mortality statistics over the course of the twentieth century reveals that the major causes of death today are quite different from those of just 50 or 100 years ago. In 1900, the most common cause of death in North America was acute, infectious disease—namely, respiratory diseases such as influenza and pneumonia (Sexton, 1979) (see Figure 1-1). By 1950, the leading cause of death in Canada had become circulatory disease (heart and cerebrovascular disease), while cancer had become the second leading cause, ahead of respiratory diseases (Wilkins, 1995). This was still true in 2003, with circulatory illnesses and cancer accounting for 60 percent of all deaths in Canada in that year. In 2012, cancers were the leading cause of death, followed by heart disease and stroke (Statistics Canada, 2012a).

Deaths per 100 000

Figure 1-1 Death Rates per 100 000, 1900

Source: Sexton, M. M. (1979). Behavioral epidemiology. In O. F. Pomerleau & J. P. Brady (Eds.), *Behavioral medicine: Theory and practice* (pp. 3–22). Baltimore, MD: Lippincott, Williams & Wilkins.

When psychologists look at this change, they focus on the *preventability* of these diseases. As Neal Miller pointed out in 1983, it was around the middle of the twentieth century that lifestyle replaced microbiology as a major source of life-threatening conditions. Hence, we see the rationale for behavioural medicine, which is concerned with the relationship between health and behaviour. It should also be noted, however, that comparing the Canadian death rates in 1950 and 1993 reveals a dramatic 57 percent drop in deaths from circulatory disease, a trend that continued to the end of the century. Much of this decline can be attributed to lifestyle change, so it becomes clear that the increased propensity for diseases that are triggered by lifestyle can also be reduced by different lifestyle choices—lifestyle choices that are, in many ways, a psychological phenomenon. Returning once again to Alan, it is possible that lifestyle change will be the most pressing challenge facing him as he approaches life after his heart attack.

In Canada, 53 percent of men and 49 percent of women report being active or moderately active (Shields & Tremblay, 2008). This means that they engage in vigorous activities, such as calisthenics, jogging, racquet sports, team sports, dance classes, or brisk walking for a period of at least 30 minutes, three times or more per week. Men who are inactive by these criteria are 1.4 times more likely to be obese. Inactive women are 2.3 times as likely to be obese (Shields & Tremblay, 2008). Even with encouraging activity statistics, 23 percent of Canadian adults were obese in 2004, as measured by the Canadian Community Health Survey. In the United States, 30 percent of adults were obese (Statistics Canada, 2004a).

While the data on adult activity levels does offer some encouragement, the data on childhood and adolescent obesity is now very worrisome. In 1978, 3 percent of children between the ages of 2 and 17 were obese. In 2004, 8 percent of that age group

Comparing Canadian Health Status to Other OECD Countries

The Organisation for Economic Co-operation and Development (OECD) was founded by 12 countries in 1960. Currently, the OECD comprises 30 countries, all producing comparative research and publications on economic and social issues. OECD members are often used as comparison points for countries like Canada.

In 2008, Canadian's life expectance was 80.8 years. The OECD average in 2010 was 79.8. Also in 2008,

Canada spent 11.8 percent of its gross domestic product on health, the third highest among OECD countries. By comparison, the United States was first, spending 17.6 percent of its GDP on health. In terms of burden of illness, Canadian survival rates for cancer were third highest among OECD countries, although wait times for breast cancer care were longer than the OECD average (OECD, 2011).

were obese (Shields, 2006). In 2011, 13 percent of children aged 5 to 11 were obese and 10 percent of those aged 12 to 17 (Statistics Canada, 2012b). In Canada, this equates to 500 000 children (Statistics Canada, 2004a). To demonstrate the behavioural and socio-economic components of these statistics, research has shown that being overweight or obese is 39 percent more common among children who buy their lunch than among those who take a packed lunch to school from home (Canadian Institute for Health Information, 2005c). Also, rates of obesity are increasing more rapidly among children from lower income families (Oliver & Hayes, 2008).

If you have ever tried to quit smoking or make some other significant and lasting change to your lifestyle, it is likely that you encountered some psychological barriers along the way. Of those Canadians who have successfully quit smoking, the average number of attempts before stopping for good is 3.2 (Health Canada, 2004). To successfully quit, you must *learn* new behaviours and *unlearn* old ones. You have to *believe* that you are capable of making the change. Other people might be involved who could make the change easier or more difficult. Even from this brief analysis, we can see that learning theory, cognitive psychology, and social psychology are all relevant to lifestyle change, which has become an integral part of our health and wellness in the new millennium.

Alan, from our case study, will be encouraged to learn new ways of thinking and behaving that will result in reduced stress, greater relaxation, and improved fitness. These changes will also have a social component, as family and friends will be called upon for support.

Multiple Perspectives Are Needed to Understand Health and Health Statistics

Another reason for the growth of health psychology is that it provides helpful ways to understand the statistics describing our health. For example, male deaths from cancer in Canada rose by over 35 percent in the second half of the twentieth century (Wilkins, 1995). Which perspective provides us with the best way to respond to this new reality in ways that will affect that statistic? Biomedical research, for example, may focus on the biology of **malignant neoplasms**, cancerous growths that may be treated by radiation and

malignant neoplasms: cancerous growths that may be treated by radiation and chemical therapy.

chemical therapy. This is a valuable perspective, but is there more to the story? Just as we discovered when talking about Alan's heart attack, there are additional perspectives that will help us better understand cancer statistics.

Perhaps we can learn more by looking at the *types* of cancer that account most for this 35 percent increase. Lung cancer had the highest mortality rate of all cancers, accounting for 27 percent of all cancer deaths in 2012 in Canada. This indicates that there is more at work than a random and unfortunate growth of neoplasms. Lung cancer is linked to a behaviour—smoking. Psychologists can make valuable contributions to the modification of this behaviour from what they know about attitude change, persuasion, and addiction. They can help reduce the number of smokers and thus reduce death rates resulting from lung cancer. In fact, lung cancer deaths for men fell slightly from 2002 to 2003.

We have shown that patterns of illness and health are changing in Canada. Also, there has been a change in emphasis from cure to prevention. To understand these changes and to improve health and health care, we need to acquire the knowledge of many disciplines. This is the essence of the **biopsychosocial approach** (Engel, 1977). As the term implies, this model considers biological, psychological, and social factors affecting health. We will take a close look at this approach in the next section. At this point, it is important to understand that psychology has much to offer in our attempt to understand health and illness.

biopsychosocial approach:
a model that suggests that biological, psychological, and social factors are all involved in any given state of health or illness.

HEALTH PSYCHOLOGY TODAY

In this section, we will begin by introducing the most fundamental assumption of the field, as captured by the biopsychosocial approach. We'll then look at what this approach means for psychologists working in health care settings. From there, we'll move to an overview of prominent theories informing the biopsychosocial approach and conclude with a look at what people with training in health psychology actually do.

The Biopsychosocial Approach to Health

It is essential to understand that both good health and poor health can be attributed to a multitude of causes. Further, these causes are varied enough that they cannot be understood from any one perspective, whether in medicine or the social sciences. The biopsychosocial approach to health takes all of these various perspectives into account, acknowledging that biological, psychological, and social factors combine to influence our health.

The term *biopsychosocial* refers to three major perspectives on the causes of health and illness. As we move from the biological to the psychological to the social, we move from a microscopic perspective to a macroscopic one. For example, we can study cancer at a biological cellular level by analyzing neoplasms (new growths), at a psychological level by assessing patients' coping abilities and the correlations between stress and immune function, and at a sociological level by identifying government policies that affect environmental toxins or hospital regulations that affect the nature of treatment.

Why Is a Biopsychosocial Approach So Important? Mortality statistics make it clear that many life-threatening conditions are preventable, in some cases by inoculation, in others by lifestyle changes, and in others by government policies such as seat belt legislation. Only the biopsychosocial approach encompasses all these levels. Even the common cold has psychological and sociological causes. Our immune systems are affected by our psychological state (for a review, see Cohen & Herbert, 1996), so we are more likely to catch a cold when we have endured something stressful, and we often catch colds from people with whom we interact at work and in other social settings.

What Are the Implications of the Biopsychosocial Approach? Today, the adoption of the biopsychosocial approach demands clear communication between health care practitioners and social scientists as well as a mutual respect for the potential contributions each can make to health and health care. It makes no more sense for a physician to downplay psychological factors affecting patients than it does for psychologists to say that viruses, tissue damage, and neoplasms are of little consequence.

Clear communication between practitioners and social scientists requires mutual understanding. This doesn't mean that social scientists must have all the knowledge of a physician or that physicians must be trained psychologists, but it does require a mutual appreciation for each other's potential contributions to the understanding of health and illness. For a number of reasons, however, achieving this mutual appreciation can be difficult because of the different ways in which health care professionals are trained.

Medical practitioners are trained primarily in the **biomedical model**. According to this model, as the name implies, health is best understood in terms of our biology. Students of the biomedical model are taught that the model is precise and concrete, which might make this model easier to understand; however, it is a daunting task to learn enough human biology to be able to practise medicine. The time required often results in the exclusion of other models of health and well-being. It stands to reason, then, that the dedication required to cope with the reams of material presented in medical school also demands a strong belief in the efficacy of the biomedical model.

biomedical model: an approach suggesting that health is best understood in terms of biology.

The end result, understandably, is that most medical school graduates are firmly entrenched in that model. Other approaches—for example, those from the social sciences—seem much less precise and far too abstract by comparison. The psychosocial causes of disease cannot be viewed under a microscope or measured directly via blood tests or a CT scan. This abstractness can undermine a physician's view of the credibility of disciplines such as health psychology.

For their part, psychologists also have beliefs specific to their discipline that are not always considered legitimate by people outside the field. For example, psychologists are trained to believe that behavioural phenomena can be reliably measured, that correlations as small as 0.3 can be meaningful, and that there are attributes shared by large groups of people that go beyond how many kidneys or lungs they have.

The different emphases in training result in graduates with different perspectives, a conclusion that is well illustrated by health psychologist Robin DiMatteo, who describes a tour a physician gave her through a hospital's intensive care unit (ICU). The physician was justifiably excited by the recent acquisition of new equipment for the ICU. Dr. DiMatteo, on the other hand, had her attention drawn in different directions:

> I remember feigning interest in the newly acquired machinery, little of which I understood, and I congratulated everyone on this up-to-date facility. But as I looked around to where the loved ones of the intubated people were waiting, I tried to catch a glimpse of their faces. My concern was not with the tremendous technical advances in the intensive care unit (ICU). As a psychologist, my focus was on the loved ones of those

in the ICU, people who were suddenly forced to have their lives revolve around the ICU, where they waited day after day for some news that their child, spouse, relative, or friend might survive and someday be normal again. (DiMatteo, 1995, p. 217)

The point of this example isn't that the physician's focus was misguided in concentrating on the new equipment in the ICU but that many phenomena need attention in a place like the ICU. Robin DiMatteo and other health psychologists provide expertise that fills in other pieces of the puzzle implied by the biopsychosocial approach.

As we mentioned earlier, the biopsychosocial approach grew in part from a change in the causes of life-threatening illnesses. Psychological and behavioural factors became more significant, and it became clear that psychological causes and consequences are associated with *many* aspects of our health, not just those that result in mortality statistics. As a result, the way we train people to become psychologists working in health care needs to reflect the biopsychosocial approach (Levant, 2005).

Prominent Theories in Health Psychology

We began this chapter by defining health psychology. We then looked at how it developed from its early years and why it has grown so rapidly. Next, we looked at the overarching model in modern health psychology—the biopsychosocial approach. Now it is time to look into the "tool kit" of today's health psychologists. In it are a number of useful theories that help health psychologists understand health issues so that they can help people recover from illness or injury and stay healthy.

Quite a few theories have emerged to help us understand, predict, and affect health behaviour. It is helpful to be able to group these theories into categories as Christopher Armitage and Mark Conner do in their review of social cognition models of health behaviour (Armitage & Conner, 2000). They present three categories: motivational models, behavioural enaction models, and multi-stage models.

To illustrate these models, we return to our case study of Alan, who, as you will see below, is home from the hospital and has been put on a rehabilitative recovery plan.

Health care professionals are asking Alan to rethink his life's priorities, change the way he ate, and start the Healthy Heart program. Will Alan do all these things? It is an important question, since his life might depend on it. The theories we look at in this section will help us predict the answer.

Motivational Models   Motivational models of health behaviour are based on the assumption that behaviour follows *intention*—we must intend to do something before we

Alan Revisited: The Road Back

Alan spent 5 days in the cardiac care unit of the hospital. His moods swung between fear and frustration. He certainly didn't want another heart attack, but he had a business to run and countless other responsibilities. He felt that the people in cardiac care didn't appreciate this. They kept telling him to try and relax—easy for them to say.

Now that he was home convalescing, it was even harder to "relax." He had so much to do and think about. On top of it all, the cardiologist had given him a bunch of pills to take and a strict diet to follow. And then there was the Healthy Heart program that he was expected to start attending on a weekly basis at the hospital.

will actually do it. For example, a study of pregnant women found that their intentions (whether or not they intended to breastfeed their babies and, if so, for how long) were predictive of their actual behaviour, in combination with their early breastfeeding experiences (DiGirolamo et al., 2005).

However, while there is some correspondence between intention and action, the fact that this correspondence is far from perfect is a source of criticism for these models, because they attempt to predict intention and not actual behaviour.

The Health Belief Model One of the most well-developed and useful contributions psychology has made to the understanding of health is the **health belief model** (Becker, 1974; Rosenstock, 1974). This model represents a good entry point for our exploration of the psychological component of the biopsychosocial approach. A *health belief* is something we think to be true concerning our health. For example, we might believe that a low-fat diet will improve cardiovascular health or that modern medicine can cure most ailments. There are many different health beliefs.

> **health belief model:** a model that analyzes health behaviour in terms of the belief that a health threat exists and the belief that a given course of action will affect the threat.

The health belief model starts with the reasonable assumption that health behaviours are explained by our health beliefs. This is a good start, but we really need to know *which* specific health beliefs are most closely linked to behaviour if the model is to be of value.

To this end, the health belief model is valuable because it identifies a manageable number of relevant, measurable types of health beliefs that can predict health behaviour. In its most basic form, the model focuses on two beliefs—the belief that a health threat exists and the belief that a given course of action will affect the threat. Perceived threat is determined by our beliefs about vulnerability and the possible severity of an outcome.

Here is an everyday example. When the weather channel reports a 100 percent chance of rain on a day when you must go outdoors, you know you are personally vulnerable to rain, but the *consequence* isn't particularly severe, so you don't believe a threat exists. On the other hand, if you read that one in three people will get cancer, you develop a belief regarding the likelihood that you could be that one (personal vulnerability), as well as a belief regarding how bad it would be to get cancer (severity of consequences). These beliefs affect your perception of threat and, in turn, affect your cancer-preventing behaviours, such as using sunscreen.

There are two types of beliefs that influence the fundamental confidence you have that a course of action will *reduce* a threat. First, the **response efficacy belief** refers to the extent to which you think a course of action (e.g., a preventive behaviour or treatment) will actually work. Second, there is a **cost–gain belief**, which refers to your assessment of the costs associated with this action (e.g., effort, discomfort, embarrassment, or inconvenience) compared to the benefit of the behaviour to your health. For example, if someone believes that the gains of exercise seem distant and minor compared to the costs, such as effort and short-term fatigue, then exercise behaviour is unlikely.

> **response efficacy belief:** the perception that a threat-reducing strategy will work.
>
> **cost–gain belief:** an individual's assessment of the costs associated with a course of action (e.g., effort, discomfort, embarrassment, or inconvenience) compared to the benefit of the behaviour to the individual's health.

Table 1-1 contrasts the beliefs of two people (Person A and Person B). In this case, we use the model to predict condom usage. At the top of the table are two general beliefs: that a health threat exists and that behaviour can affect the threat. Beneath that is a list of specific beliefs related to these general beliefs. The next two rows provide examples of those related beliefs for each of these fictitious people.

Person A believes himself to be somewhat vulnerable and that the consequences of contracting acquired immunodeficiency syndrome (AIDS) are severe (i.e., fatal). He also

Table 1-1 The Health Belief Model Applied to Condom Usage

General Belief	A health threat exists		A behaviour will affect the threat		Result
Related Beliefs	Beliefs regarding personal vulnerability to the threat	Beliefs about the severity of the consequences	The belief that a course of action will actually work or not	The assessment of the costs and benefits associated with this action	
Person A	"I could get AIDS."	"AIDS is a fatal disease."	"Using condoms will greatly reduce my chances of getting AIDS."	"I get embarrassed when I buy condoms, but they will reduce the risk of getting AIDS."	Condoms are used
Person B	"Other people might get AIDS but I won't."	"With new drugs, AIDS isn't as life-threatening as it once was."	"Condoms don't always work."	"I feel very embarrassed when I buy condoms and using them ruins sex."	Condoms are not used

believes that condoms work and that the benefits of using them outweigh the costs. As a result, Person A uses condoms. In contrast, Person B feels little vulnerability, doesn't think AIDS is necessarily fatal, does not believe in the effectiveness of condoms, and thinks the personal costs of using them are high. Not surprisingly, this person doesn't use condoms.

The beliefs in this example have been intentionally polarized to make the contrast clear. In reality, a person may hold a range of beliefs working together in such a way that prediction of behaviour is more difficult. For example, a woman might believe that she could get cervical cancer and that it could be fatal. She might think the costs of screening are low but lacks confidence in the accuracy of the Pap test used in the screening, so she doesn't think screening is effective. What could we predict here? Perhaps sporadic Pap tests? It is difficult to be certain.

And what about Alan? The health belief model can help us predict the likelihood that he will attend the Healthy Heart program. To start, we need to know if Alan believes he is vulnerable to a second heart attack, and if so, whether he thinks its consequences would be severe. In fact, he does believe that people who have had one heart attack are at increased risk for a second heart attack and are much less likely to survive it.

Now we move to his beliefs regarding the behaviour that is supposed to affect that threat—the Healthy Heart program. We already know that he has considered the costs of attending. He is busy and thinks it will be inconvenient. And what about his efficacy belief? Does he think the program will reduce the threat of a second heart attack? If he does, then he might attend. The problem is that he must *keep attending*; therefore, his belief in the efficacy of the program must be strong enough to keep him going.

Health Beliefs and Health Values   The health belief model attempts to predict behaviour using a person's specific beliefs. There is one more important factor to consider, however: the extent to which the person values good health. Even if a person's beliefs appear to predict a particular behaviour, such as condom use or screening for cancer, the behaviour will not follow unless the person values his or her health.

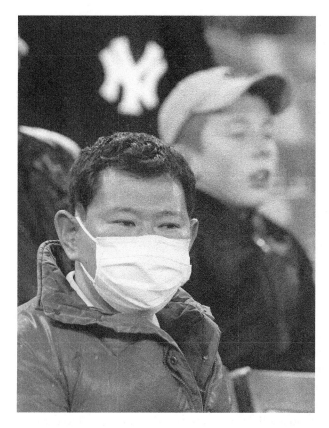

According to the health belief model, this person felt vulnerable to SARS and believed that it was serious and that wearing a surgical mask would reduce his chances of contracting SARS at a Toronto Blue Jays game.

Frank Gunn/Canadian Press Images

It may be difficult to imagine that there are people who do not place a high value on their health. However, research indicates that people do indeed vary in terms of their health values. To understand this, we must view values as being relative to each other. For example, an adolescent might value health to a certain extent, but he or she might value group acceptance more. This person might take up smoking, in spite of the fact that it compromises health, to achieve the more valued outcome of group acceptance.

It is also possible that some people can *afford* to place health values high on their list, while other people must be more concerned with basic survival. This does not mean that people living in poverty do not value their health. A study of homeless women, for example, found that health and self-respect were two commonly held values (Rosengard et al., 2001). In fact, women generally tend to value their health more than men do (Felton, Parsons, & Bartoces, 1997). Clear reasons exist, then, for individual differences in health values. These differences are important to consider because research has shown that the health belief model is most predictive for people who place a high value on their health (Lau, Hartman, & Ware, 1986).

How Well Does the Health Belief Model Predict Behaviour? If the health belief model is to be useful, it must do a better-than-chance job of explaining and predicting health-related behaviour for those individuals who place a relatively high value on their health. For health psychologists, it is important to investigate the model's utility because the model has the potential to make significant contributions to the biopsychosocial understanding of health and illness. Given this importance, it is not surprising that a great deal of research has been conducted over the years testing the ability of the health belief model to explain and predict behaviour in a wide variety of health-related contexts, from youth cigarette smoking (Li et al., 2003) to obesity during pregnancy (Sui, Turnbull, & Dodd, 2013).

One area in which the health belief model has been used extensively is in risky behaviours related to AIDS. Fraze et al. (2009) used the health belief model to gauge intentions to get HIV testing. The health belief model has also been used to explain some of the variance in sexual risk behaviours among college students, such as having multiple partners and being intoxicated or high during sexual encounters. It was less helpful, however, when it came to predicting condom usage for this group (Lollis, Johnson, & Antoni, 1997).

The health belief model has also been used extensively in predicting behaviours associated with screening for cancer. In general, these behaviours can be analyzed reasonably well using the health belief model, given that important issues of perceived vulnerability and belief in the value of early detection fit well within the model. For example, a study in Ontario has shown that, consistent with the model, women with a relative who has had breast cancer are more likely to be interested in genetic testing for cancer than are women without this family history (Cappelli et al., 2001). The model is far less than perfect in this context, though, because of other psychological factors. Perhaps the most notable is the role that *emotion* plays in cancer screening. People might believe in the accuracy of a given screening technique and see cancer as a threat. However, they might not want to know if they have cancer (Cameron, 1997). Such a discovery would constitute too great a cost of the behaviour (e.g., Millar, 1997). For another example, see Table 1-2 for an application of the health belief model to the decision to have back surgery.

The Theory of Reasoned Action

theory of reasoned action: a theory that behaviour is preceded by intention and that our intention is influenced by beliefs about the behaviour and subjective norms.

subjective norms: beliefs regarding what others think we should do and the extent to which we are motivated to go along with these people.

The Theory of Reasoned Action The **theory of reasoned action** (Ajzen & Fishbein, 1980; Fishbein & Ajzen, 1975) has a number of elements in common with the health belief model and adds some other considerations. The two main elements of the theory of reasoned action are a person's attitudes toward a behaviour and a person's beliefs regarding other people's thoughts about the behaviour. It is this introduction of other people's beliefs that most strongly differentiates the theory of reasoned action from the health belief model. In the language of the theory, other people's beliefs help us to develop **subjective norms**—what we think other people want us to do.

Table 1-2 The Health Belief Model Applied to the Decision to Have Back Surgery

General Belief	A health threat exists		A behaviour will affect the threat		Result
Related Beliefs	Beliefs regarding personal vulnerability to the threat	Beliefs about the severity of the consequences	The belief that a course of action will actually work or not	The assessment of the costs and benefits associated with this action	
Stan	*"I definitely have a back problem."*	*"I am in pain I can't work and I can't enjoy my life."*	*"Surgery will correct this problem."*	*"I'm nervous about the possibility of being paralyzed but the risk is low."*	Surgery chosen

Baby Think It Over®: A Program Encouraging Teens to Rethink Their Chances of Getting Pregnant

One reason why teens might engage in unprotected sex is that they have an "it can't happen to me" belief regarding pregnancy. Using the language of the health belief model, they have low perceived vulnerability to pregnancy. But what if they had the chance to experience what it was like to look after a baby? Would this change their beliefs? Two researchers from the University of Windsor, Jennifer Out and Kathryn Lafreniere, have tested the effect of a program called Baby Think It Over, which is intended to address these questions (Out & Lafreniere, 2001).

In this program, teens work with infant simulators (essentially, high-tech dolls) for two or three days to develop an appreciation for what it is like to have to look after a baby. After going through the program, a group of males and females aged 14 to 19 were more accurate at assessing the risk of unplanned pregnancy and at producing real examples of the consequences related to raising children than were a control group of teens. In other words, an experience that simulated the responsibilities of child-rearing affected their perceptions of vulnerability to pregnancy and the consequences of having a child.

According to the theory of reasoned action, our attitudes toward a behaviour and our subjective norms determine our intention regarding the behaviour. As in the health belief model, we have related beliefs to consider for each of these two main elements of the theory of reasoned action. Specifically, our attitudes toward a behaviour are influenced by our beliefs regarding the *outcomes* that behaviour will yield and the extent to which we *value* that outcome.

Subjective norms are composed of beliefs regarding what others think we should do and the extent to which we are motivated to go along with these people. To put all this together and apply the theory to health, we will look at Table 1-3, which charts two people facing a decision regarding treatment of back pain. Person A believes that the surgery will work, so she sees a connection between the behaviour (surgery) and the outcome (pain relief). She values a pain-free existence. Her friends and family are in favour of surgery, and she wants them to have a favourable impression of her. These beliefs lead to a decision to choose surgery.

In contrast, Person B is not convinced of the efficacy of the surgery, nor does he place as high a value on being pain free. His subjective norms oppose surgery; namely, his wife favours exercise over surgery, and he values her opinion. Consistent with these beliefs, he does not choose surgery.

As we did in Table 1-2 with relation to the health belief model, in Table 1-3 we present two people with diametrically opposed views. In reality, our beliefs are more mixed than this. We may really want to engage in a health-related behaviour (be it surgery, a low-sodium diet, etc.) but find that our friends are opposed to it. The process by which we *choose* the people whose opinions we will consider can also be quite complicated (Kahneman & Miller, 1986). For example, we take into account such things as friendship and how similar these people are to us. This is part of the social component of the biopsychosocial approach.

Table 1-3 The Theory of Reasoned Action

General Beliefs	Attitudes toward the behaviour		Subjective norms		Result
Related Beliefs	Belief that the behaviour will produce given outcome	The value placed on the outcome	Beliefs regarding what other people think regarding the behaviour	Motivation to do what other people think should be a done	
Person A	"Surgery will relieve the pain in my back."	"I would love to be pain free again."	"My friends and family think I should have the back operation."	"I want my friends and family to know I have the courage to have the operation."	Surgery chosen
Person B	"Surgery might not work. There's no guarantee."	"Being pain free isn't really possible. Everyone lives with some degree of pain."	"My wife thinks I should try bed rest before risking surgery."	"My wife is usually right."	Surgery not chosen

How Well Does the Theory of Reasoned Action Predict Health Behaviour?

Modern research has used the theory of reasoned action to address many of the same phenomena as the health belief model. Thus, we find studies testing the power of the theory of reasoned action for predicting HIV risk and prevention behaviours (for a comprehensive review, see Crepaz & Marks, 2002), teen sexual behaviour (Frigon, 2004), and cancer-screening behaviours (Ham, 2005). (For a review of the applications of the theory of reasoned action, see Bogart & Delahanty, 2004.)

The literature indicates that the theory of reasoned action does a good job of predicting behaviours related to HIV and AIDS prevention. The addition of social norms tends to increase its predictive power compared to the predictive power of the health belief model. For example, the theory of reasoned action worked well to predict both intention and actual condom use among high-risk heterosexual teens (Morrison, Baker, & Gillmore, 2000).

In terms of cancer-screening behaviour, the theory of reasoned action quite accurately predicts the intention to perform self-examination (breast and testicular) (Moore, Barling, & Hood, 1998). The theory has also been used to explain differences in women's intentions to be screened for cervical cancer via a Pap smear test (Barling & Moore, 1996). The theory of reasoned action has also been used to help understand gender differences in such health behaviours as sunscreen use (Abroms, Jorgensen, Southwell, Geller, & Emmons, 2003); females are more likely than males to use sunscreen (Campbell & Birdsell, 1994) and to be influenced by subjective norms as derived from family members. Abroms and colleagues found that young adults' beliefs about sunscreen use were divided along traditional gender lines. Females talked about the importance of skin care, which motivated them to use sunscreen. Males talked about skin care as being a feminine concern and thus something that would not motivate them to use sunscreen.

The Theory of Planned Behaviour
The predictive power of the theory of reasoned action is generally improved with the addition of the notion of **perceived behavioural control** (Millstein, 1996). In other words, beliefs about the effectiveness and costs of a given behaviour are augmented by beliefs about one's ability to actually carry off the behaviour. This is consistent with the thinking of Fishbein and Ajzen, the psychologists who proposed the theory of reasoned action in 1975. In fact, Fishbein and Ajzen developed a hybrid theory that included perceived behavioural control and named it the **theory of planned behaviour** (Fishbein & Ajzen, 1975).

The only difference between the two theories is the addition of the belief that the person is actually capable of performing the behaviour. "Can I really quit smoking?" "Can I go through with the operation?" These are questions about perceived behavioural control. The answer must be "yes" for the theory of planned behaviour to predict that intention will follow belief.

The theory of planned behaviour can be a powerful tool to help explain variation in health-related intention and behaviour. For example, the theory helped predict binge drinking among university students (Johnston & White, 2003). In other words, the elements of the theory combine to correlate significantly with adolescents' reports of intention to drink. As one might expect, the theory of planned behaviour has been used as often as the theory of reasoned action to analyze a wide range of behaviours, including condom use and drinking and driving (Armitage, Norman, & Conner, 2002) and the use of dental floss (Lavin & Groarke, 2005). Also, interventions intended to help people with issues such as rehabilitation after cancer have been shown by researchers at the University of Alberta to be effective when perceived control was one of the targets of that intervention (Jones, Courneya, Fairey, & Mackey, 2005).

How can the theory of planned behaviour help us predict whether our case study subject, Alan, will attend the Healthy Heart program? To answer this question, consider each of the elements of the theory. First, like the theory of reasoned action, there are Alan's beliefs regarding the efficacy of the program and the value he places on not having another heart attack. Then there are the subjective norms. Would other people want him to go to the program? For example, his wife might really encourage him to attend, or she might see it as an unnecessary inconvenience, as Alan does. Also, we must know whether Alan is motivated to do what his wife thinks he should do or whether he would rather assert his independence and either not go or go in opposition to her wishes. Finally, there is perceived behavioural control. Does Alan really believe that he can do the things the Healthy Heart program will expect of him in terms of exercise, diet, tests, and so on? According to the theory of planned behaviour, the answers to these questions will determine whether Alan intends to go to the program. Research has shown that heart patients' beliefs about subjective norms and perceived behavioural control accounted for 69 percent of the variance in exercise rates (Prapavessis et al., 2005).

Behavioural Enaction Models
You may have heard the saying, "The road to ruin is paved with good intentions," implying that there is often a considerable gap between what we *intend* to do and what we *actually* do. For the most part, motivational models address intention, while behavioural enaction models attempt to improve our ability to predict and affect behaviour by addressing the gap between intention and behaviour. Behaviour enaction models add elements that bridge this gap.

perceived behavioural control: the belief that a specific behaviour is within one's control.

theory of planned behaviour: behaviour is preceded by intention and that intention is influenced not only by subjective norms and beliefs about the efficacy of the behaviour, but also by the belief that one is actually capable of performing the behaviour.

Gollwitzer's Implementation Intentions Model Gollwitzer's model (1993) contains many of the same elements as the motivational models but posits that people who have an implementation plan are much more likely to engage in the behaviour. Such a plan indicates a higher level of commitment, just as when an organization strikes an implementation committee with a mandate to make something happen. Not surprisingly, research shows that such implementation plans do increase the likelihood that a behaviour will be enacted (Verplanken & Faes, 1999).

Bagozzi's Goal Theory Bagozzi's goal theory (1992) is similar to Gollwitzer's model but also considers a person's thoughts about the nature of the goal and the expression of intentions about the goal. Is the goal something I can attain—for example, reduced alcohol consumption (Murgraff, Walsh, & McDermott, 2000)? How would I feel if I succeeded? If I failed? You will recognize these as questions about perceived control and cost–gain analysis. This form of cost–gain thinking, however, entertains the possibility of fear of success and fear of failure.

Multi-Stage Models Multi-stage models provide a step-by-step explanation for how someone develops intention and then carries the intention through to behaviour, both short term and long term. Like all stage models, the ones that are used to analyze health behaviour are questioned regarding their rigidity. Do people have to go through these stages in this order? Can't someone skip a stage? Regress backward? And so on. In spite of these questions, stage theories have been influential in health psychology because they help us understand the progression of an individual's thinking and behaviour.

When we look at the topic of health promotion in chapter 11, we will see that an important challenge for health psychologists involves helping people make changes to their lives. In many cases, these changes involve aspects of lifestyle, as we have seen with Alan. In others, changes are forced upon us by illness, accident, or aging. Because change is such a major topic, models that describe the ways people go about effecting change (or not) are most helpful. Multi-stage models provide just such descriptions.

Health Action Process Approach (HAPA): approach that divides health behaviours into a motivational phase and a volitional phase.

In the **Health Action Process Approach (HAPA)**, Schwarzer (1992) divides health behaviours into a motivational phase and a volitional phase. In the former, the person develops expectations regarding the outcomes being considered. Will I feel better if I engage in this behaviour? Will I be supported in my change? The person also perceives control. Am I capable of making this change? If the answers to these questions are positive, the person moves to the volitional phase, featuring planning, action, and maintenance of the change.

stages of change model: model containing six linear stages: precontemplation, contemplation, action, maintenance, termination, and relapse.

The **stages of change model** (Prochaska & DiClemente, 1983, 1986), sometimes called the transtheoretical model, contains many of the same elements as HAPA, but provides six linear stages to help understand change: precontemplation, contemplation, action, maintenance, termination, and relapse. These stages are relatively simple to comprehend, and they can be valuable as a way to understand health behaviour—in particular, behaviour involving a lifestyle change. One of the most common applications of the stages of change model is to smoking cessation. Smokers in the precontemplation stage have not thought about quitting and see no need to do so. Smokers in the contemplation stage may have some symptom or nagging thought that has them considering quitting. In the next stage, they take action. Perhaps they visit their physician, or use

Stages of Change and Support for Government Quit-Smoking Programs

Researchers at the University of Toronto have applied the stages of change model to assess smokers' and former smokers' knowledge of the health consequences of smoking (Cohen et al., 2002). They hypothesized that the higher a person's stage in the model, the more knowledge the person would have regarding health consequences.

Remember that current smokers will be placed at one of two stages when it comes to quitting smoking: precontemplation or contemplation. Former smokers, on the other hand, could be placed at either of three different stages: action, maintenance, or termination. (Relapse was not included in this study.)

Cohen and colleagues provided operational definitions of each stage and then collected survey data from 846 people in Ontario to determine their knowledge of the health consequences of smoking. They asked questions about such things as smoking and lung cancer, chronic bronchitis, pregnancy complications, heart attacks, and environmental tobacco smoke. They did not stop there, however. They also reasoned that smokers' or former smokers' positions on the stages of change model would be related to their attitudes toward and support for government legislation regarding tobacco control measures. To test this, they also asked questions about these attitudes.

The researchers did indeed find that the further along the stage model the person was placed, the more knowledge the person had regarding health consequences. This was particularly true for the current smokers, who showed greater knowledge on seven of eight knowledge questions the further they were along the stages that applied to them. For the former smokers, this increase in knowledge across the stages applied to only two of the knowledge questions. The Cohen group also found that attitudes toward tobacco control and support for government control measures increased along the stages of the model.

These findings are interesting for at least two reasons. First, the study has implications for the health promotion programs designed to help people quit smoking. We will look closely at health promotion in chapter 11. It is simplistic to assume that smokers are not receptive to stop-smoking messages. Rather, precontemplative smokers are most likely to be unreceptive. Also, people in this category are the least well informed regarding health consequences. Second, this study extends the stages of change model. The model was originally introduced to help explain *behaviour*. Cohen and colleagues have used the model to help understand *cognition*.

patches, or make a pact with a friend. If the action works, then they must maintain their non-smoking behaviour. Eventually, after 3 years or more of abstinence, they would be considered to be in the termination stage (Gilpin, Pierce, & Parkas, 1997).

One of the most valuable contributions of the model is the acknowledgement of relapse as a stage rather than as failure. This allows people to deal with a bout of cigarette smoking as something that is part of the process, rather than as a sign that the entire lifestyle change has failed. They can then get back into the maintenance stage, rather than starting over.

Summary of the Models   You may have wondered, as you read through these theories, just how well they apply across different cultures. For example, the notion of internal perceived behavioural control tends to make more sense to people who have been raised in **individualist** rather than **collectivist** cultures (Hart & Poole, 1995; Triandis, Bontempo, Villareal, Asai, & Lucca, 1988). Individualists focus on independence and self-reliance, whereas collectivists see themselves as part of a greater whole in which individualism is less important than allegiance to the group.

individualist: one who focuses on independence and self-reliance rather than placing group needs above his or her own.

collectivist: one who considers him- or herself to be part of a greater whole and who considers individualism to be less important than allegiance to the group.

The theory of reasoned action and the theory of planned behaviour have been tested with Latin American, English-speaking Caribbean, and South Asian participants (Godin et al., 1996). The study concluded that the theory of planned behaviour was more useful in these three cultures than the theory of reasoned action, even though these cultures would be considered more collectivist than most Western cultures. The theory of reasoned action has also been used successfully to analyze breastfeeding patterns in the United States and Colombia (Ramirez, Bravo, & Katsikas, 2005).

We introduced you to some of the major theories and models common to health psychology to give you an idea of some of the ways psychological theory has been applied to health and health care. The theories and models presented in this chapter grow, for the most part, from a cognitive perspective, with their focus on people's thought processes, attitudes, and beliefs. Of course, there are many other theories, some with a stronger behavioural emphasis, others more humanistic or psychodynamic. We refer to such models and theories throughout the remaining chapters of this book. We invite you to think critically about their utility and the ways in which they could be further developed to be even more useful.

WORKING IN HEALTH PSYCHOLOGY

Health psychology is a field that offers a number of interesting career opportunities, the vast majority of which require a graduate degree, usually a Ph.D. There are two main paths you can take when preparing for a career in health psychology: one is to be trained as a clinical or counselling psychologist and the other is to be trained as a researcher.

Clinical and Counselling Psychologists Working in Health Psychology

Clinical psychologists and counselling psychologists require different training and perform different roles in health psychology. Clinical psychologists must have either a master's or a doctoral degree, depending on the province or territory in which they are practising. The CPA has recommended that all clinical psychologists hold a Ph.D. Clinical training usually involves a year of internship, and in some jurisdictions students must pass a certification exam in order to practise clinical psychology.

Counselling psychologists do not require a Ph.D., though some have one. The certification process for counselling psychologists tends to be less rigorous than for clinical psychologists. In fact, in some jurisdictions no formal training is required to call oneself a counsellor. Usually, however, counsellors working in health settings have formal training, at least at the master's level.

Clinical health psychologists work with people who are experiencing psychological problems that are either the result of illness or a cause of it. For example, they may work with cancer patients who are suffering from depression or breast reconstruction patients who are grappling with issues related to self-image. They may also work with people who suffer from anxiety and, as a result, are dealing with psychosomatic disorders.

Two major surveys have been conducted to learn more about the work these psychologists do. The first survey was conducted in 1982 (Arnett, Martin, Streiner, & Goodman, 1987) and the second in 1999 (Humbke et al., 2004). A comparison of the two studies reveals a considerable increase over time in the number of psychologists working in acute-care hospitals. In 1982, 54 percent of acute-care hospitals employed at least one full-time psychologist. By 1999, that number had jumped to 68 percent (Humbke et al., 2004). This means that, in 1982, there was one psychologist for every 131 acute-care hospital beds. In 1999, there was one psychologist for every 53 beds (Humbke et al., 2004). One of many reasons for this increase in the number of psychologists working in health care is the growing emphasis on prevention and health promotion in Canadian health care (Kenkel, Deleon, Mantel, & Steep, 2005).

The three most common topics addressed by these hospital psychologists were pain, eating disorders, and cancer. Within those topics, mental health and rehabilitation were the most common areas where challenges were addressed. Over 80 percent of these referrals to psychologists came from physicians, and the majority of the hospital psychologists' work involved individual psychotherapy (Humbke et al., 2004).

Counselling psychologists work with people facing similar challenges. For example, a counselling psychologist might work with a family in which a member is seriously ill. Another might work with someone who is recovering from an injury or illness and is trying to integrate back into work and society. As is the case with clinical health psychologists, there is plenty of work for a skilled counselling psychologist in health-related settings. Counselling psychologists' salaries tend to be somewhat lower than those of clinical psychologists, though they can still do very well financially. Similar work might also be conducted by people in other helping professions, such as social work.

Research Careers in Health Psychology

Not all people working in health psychology have clinical training. Some are trained in other fields, such as social or developmental psychology, and they apply the theories of those disciplines to health and health care. Indeed, some of the major theories we introduced earlier in the chapter were forwarded by social psychologists. A good example is the theory of reasoned action developed by Fishbein and Ajzen. Instead of providing clinical services, psychologists from these other areas conduct research and consult with health professionals regarding aspects of health care delivery.

Most people conducting research in health psychology hold academic appointments at universities, though some are employed by other institutions, such as hospitals and cancer agencies. Most hold doctoral degrees. Those working in universities combine their research duties with teaching and other academic responsibilities. Of course, clinical work and research are not mutually exclusive; many people do both, within private practice, institutional appointments, or university positions.

CHAPTER SUMMARY

■ Define health psychology.

Health psychology is the application of psychological principles to the diagnosis and treatment of an illness as well as to people's attempts to maintain health and well-being.

- Outline how the field grew in terms of the range of important topics addressed and the move to augment behavioural perspectives with those taken from cognitive psychology.

  Health psychology grew from behavioural and cognitive perspectives. The early focus was on affecting health-related behaviour. This expanded to include the relationship between people's thinking and their health. Behaviour, thought, and emotion have all been tied to physiological processes through the study of psychoneuroimmunology.

- Explain why health psychology has grown so quickly as a field.

  Health psychology has grown quickly due to the changing nature of modern health problems. Over the last hundred years, the main causes of death have changed; today more people die from lifestyle choices than from bacterial infections. As a result, a comprehensive understanding of health requires a multi-disciplinary approach that includes social sciences such as psychology.

- Describe and apply fundamental theories in health psychology.

  The Health Belief Model analyzes health behaviour in terms of the belief that a health threat exists and the belief that a given course of action will affect the threat.

  The Theory of Reasoned Action posits that behaviour is preceded by intention and that intention is influenced by beliefs about the behaviour and subjective norms.

  The Theory of Planned Behaviour is similar to the Theory of Reasoned Action but adds that intention is influenced not only by subjective norms and beliefs about the efficacy of the behaviour, but also by the belief that one is actually capable of performing the behaviour.

- Describe different careers pursued by people who have studied health psychology.

  Career opportunities in health psychology include clinical psychologist (requiring a Ph.D.), counselling psychologist, and research psychologist. Some people with advanced degrees in health psychology work in hospitals; others work in higher education.

Chapter 2
Stress and Coping

Learning Objectives

After studying this chapter, you will be able to:

1. define stress and coping.
2. understand the physiology of stress.
3. understand the cognitive components of stress.
4. appreciate the role of personality in stress and coping.
5. identify different coping styles.
6. identify strategies for coping with stress.

John, a young business executive, is awakened by his alarm. He hits the snooze button, but his relief lasts only 10 minutes. He snaps to attention, realizing that he is now running late. He was out until 1:00 a.m. at a social function, and although he understands that these events are important for his work, he wishes he had not had so much to drink and had come home earlier. He rushes to shower and shave and in his haste cuts his chin. Leaving his apartment, he runs to his car through heavy rain only to discover that he has left his briefcase back inside his apartment.

Once on the road, he aims for his local coffee shop for his morning dose of caffeine. He arrives to find a long lineup, but the alternative—a commute without coffee—is not an option he would even consider. This is the first of approximately 20 cups of coffee he will have today, and he wants it to be a good one. His impatience is visible, and he curses under his breath at the woman at the head of the line who he feels is taking too long to order. As he jumps back into his car he spills coffee on his pants.

He endures the heavy rush hour by riding the bumper of the car in front of him and yelling at those around him who seem oblivious to his urgency. His cell phone is in constant use. Periodically, he has to slam on the brakes in order to avoid rear-ending the vehicle ahead of him. He has difficulty finding a parking spot and, after running through the rain, he arrives at his office 45 minutes late for an important meeting. His boss tells him not to bother coming into the meeting and suggests that he should attend instead to some of the accumulated work on his desk.

He pours himself another coffee and sneaks a doughnut from a box in the coffee room. As he sits down at his desk his heart is racing, his stomach is churning, his jaw is clenched, he is sweating profusely, he is hyperventilating, and he feels a muscle-tension headache coming on. He is so angry, frustrated, and worried by his boss's response to his lateness that he has difficulty focusing on the tasks in front of him. His enthusiasm for his work has decreased dramatically. He longs to return home and curl up in his bed. There is nowhere to run to and no one to fight.

ISSUES OF DEFINITION

Throughout this text, we provide many definitions for the terms we use. This is to ensure clarity regarding the meaning of the concepts presented. There is usually considerable agreement concerning the correct definition for a particular term. However, when it comes to the topics of this chapter, **stress** and **coping**, this is not the case. If we compared your definition of these terms with those of other students, there would likely be considerable variability. Definitions of stress and coping are highly personalized and reflect an individual's unique life experiences.

Brannon and Feist (2000) have compared the concept of *stress* to that of *love*. Everyone seems to know what the word means and the role it plays in their lives, and they are sure that they know it when they feel it. Yet the concept is difficult to define. We do, however, have a commonsense understanding of these terms. When someone tells us they feel stressed, we empathize because we believe that we have experienced similar feelings. Some of us would even describe ourselves as being "experts" in the field. We believe that

stress: the non-specific mental or somatic result of any demand upon the body.

coping: strategies that an individual employs to deal with stresses caused by the ever-changing demands of the environment.

we have attained a high level of stress competency through one of the acknowledged avenues by which this can occur—personal experience.

A similar inconsistency exists with regard to how we define *coping*. To say we "cope with stress" is a highly individualized statement that reflects the variability of human experience. There is obviously no "right" way to cope with stress, there are many different ways. Our stress is not your stress, and our coping strategies are not yours.

Answers to questions such as the following demonstrate that we do not experience stress in the same way: Is stress always a bad thing? How stressful are positive events, such as getting married or having a child? How much more stressful is it to lose a close relative than to receive a speeding ticket? Are the strategies one person uses to cope with stress applicable to another? Can some coping strategies actually increase the stress we experience? Why do we continue to use coping strategies that appear to be quite ineffective?

Given the number of times we use the terms *stress* and *coping* in describing our daily activities, it is remarkable how little consensus exists as to how to define them.

Our opening vignette reminds us that while stress and coping are concepts that have always existed, sabre-toothed tigers have been replaced by the paper tigers of today's world. Only recently, however, have they been the object of research and systematic efforts at conceptualization. What we are struggling with is what Smith (1993) has described as **stress literacy**. He considers this an issue of considerable importance, as the alternative is confusion, and he suggests that the "popular culture provides volumes of conflicting bits of stress wisdom" (p. 5). For example, is it better to face your problems or ignore them? Do we perform better when we are "psyched up" or when we are relaxed? The contradictions are many, and Smith suggests that "stress literacy begins with a useful definition of stress" (p. 6).

stress literacy: the degree to which an individual (or community) understands the effects of stress.

One might expect that, in an empirical world, this issue would be somewhat more straightforward; however, considerable confusion exists. Haan (1993) addresses this concern directly. She believes that those studying stress are "handicapped by a lack of consensus on the meaning of these terms. The concept of stress is used and understood by laypersons, but its scientific study has proven difficult" (p. 256). She suggests that this same level of controversy and confusion is attached to definitions of coping. She argues that if we acknowledged "that our knowledge of stress arises from common, shared understandings and not from objective reality, the insight would be liberating" (p. 260).

The lack of consensus in defining these terms has led some researchers to ask if the concept of stress is worth retaining. Pearlin (1993) believes that the very nature of stress dictates that it is a diffuse, multidimensional phenomenon that cannot be reduced to one element. He believes that our efforts should be directed toward examining the interconnections among its multiple dimensions. This process is proceeding slowly, as it requires an interdisciplinary focus that is difficult to create. Pearlin laments that "firmly and actively engaged in his chosen research, each investigator is convinced that the manifestation of stress that he is examining represents 'real' stress" (p. 305). He argues that we should, instead, work with the concept of stress in an interdisciplinary fashion.

Aldwin (1994) suggests that even through stress is difficult to define, the term should be retained. She states that "stress refers to that quality of experience, produced through a person-environment transaction that, through either overarousal or underarousal, results in psychological or physiological distress" (p. 22). DiMatteo and Martin (2002) conclude that as the concept of stress has developed and become more popular it has also become more imprecise. Marks, Murray, Evans, and Estacio (2011) review a literature that suggests that "stress is an umbrella term that has been applied to so many quite different phenomena as to become virtually meaningless from a scientific point of view" (p. 282).

Clearly this debate continues as Schwarzer and Luszczynska (2013) conclude that while it is a universal component of daily life "there is little agreement among researchers about the definition of stress" (p. 29). They identify three approaches that can be taken in the study of stress: response based, stimulus based and cognitive-transactional.

Hans Selye, the originator of the biological concept of the term *stress* (see Focus on Canadian Research 2-1), defined it as "the nonspecific result of any demand upon the body, be the effect mental or somatic" (1993, p. 7). He recognized that, for most people, stress is viewed as a negative experience that is equated with *distress*. To counter this position, he coined the term *eustress* to reflect a positive yet stressful experience. **Eustress** (like its related word, *euphoria*) is a state of physical and psychological well-being that is associated with increased motivation and the acceptance of challenge. Perhaps the ultimate expression of this positive state is found in the title of a book by the Canadian physician Peter Hanson, *The Joy of Stress* (1986). Selye argued that a sense of balance is essential, that we function best when stress is used to produce an optimal level of arousal. The implication is that too little stress can be as harmful as too much, that distress can result from being over- *or* understimulated. Selye described stress as "the spice of life" (1974, p. 83).

Lazarus and Folkman (1984), and more recently Lazarus (1999), have provided us with descriptions of stress and coping that have received wide acceptance in the field. *Stress* is described in terms of a relationship that exists between a "person and the environment that is appraised by the person as taxing or exceeding his or her resources and endangering his or her well-being" (1984, p. 21). An individual's cognitive appraisal of a situation will determine the level of stress he or she will experience. It is interesting to note that Lazarus (2006), in discussing the development of stress as an interdisciplinary concept, suggests that overlapping terms such as *anxiety, frustration, conflict, trauma,* and *emotional distress* are unified under this rubric. He states that "stress became the dominant term for uniting these concepts, and for identifying the causes and emotional consequences of the struggle to manage the pressures of daily living" (p. 30). *Coping* is defined as "constantly changing cognitive and behavioral efforts to manage specific external and/ or internal demands that are appraised as taxing or exceeding the resources of the person" (Lazarus & Folkman, 1984, p. 141).

Central to our understanding of stress are the contributions of Walter Cannon. In 1939, he introduced the concept of **homeostasis**, which describes the body's attempt to maintain a stable internal state. This is a dynamic physiological response on the part of the body to the demands of the environment. The body seeks balance, and stress presents a challenge to homeostasis. It was Cannon who articulated the concept of the **fight-or-flight response**, which describes a complex autonomic reaction. The sympathetic nervous system and hormones secreted by the adrenal glands interact in an adaptive response developed through evolution. This response helps us to cope with potential attacks from a threatening world.

eustress: a positive, yet stressful, experience.

homeostasis: the dynamic physiological response on the part of the body to maintain a stable internal state in spite of the demands of the environment.

fight-or-flight response: the body's complex autonomic reaction when faced with a perceived threat.

A Great Canadian

Hans Selye has been described as "the grand master of stress research and theory." Born in Vienna in 1907, Selye lived and worked in Montreal for 50 years until his death in 1982. He first used the term *stress* in 1936 to describe the non-specific result, either mental or physical, of demands placed on the body. Close to 40 years later, Selye indicated that, if his English had been better at the time, he would probably have chosen the word *strain* to describe this response. He had taken the idea of stress from the field of physics, where it describes the force exerted by one body against another. The response to this tension is strain and, as what Selye was describing was a response, he acknowledged that he probably should have used this term. Rather than correct him, we have adjusted our definition to fit his model.

Selye initially observed a consistent pattern of responses in rats when these animals were exposed to diverse noxious stimuli. He called this a "stereotypic response," which he had first observed in human patients some 10 years earlier (the "general adaptation syndrome" or "biologic stress syndrome") and for which he now had experimental evidence. He also identified an initial "alarm reaction" in which the organism's defences were activated. If the organism survived this initial attack, Selye identified an adaptive phase or rebound effect that occurs, which he called the "the stage of resistance." Eventually, if the demands on the organism were of sufficient severity or length, a "stage of exhaustion" occurred.

In 1956, Selye published *The Stress of Life*, in which he translated the concept of stress for the layperson. He dedicated his life to the study of stress and wrote more than 1700 articles and 39 books on the topic. He was a scientist, trained as both a physician and an endocrinologist. He served as a professor and director of the Institute of Experimental Medicine and Surgery at the University of Montreal. He also served the non-scientific world through texts such as that mentioned above and *Stress without Distress* (1974), which he wrote to help us better understand the impact of the stress response on humans throughout their lifespans. He was made a Companion of the Order of Canada, the highest honour this country can bestow upon an individual, and has been described as a "Canadian resource to the world."

Cannon (1939) expressed concern about the implications for physical illness through the continuous activation of the fight-or-flight reaction in response to the chronic pressures and demands of the contemporary world. The actions implied by the term *fight-or-flight* are simply not always appropriate in our contemporary world. In fact, to engage in either of these responses in today's world could have disastrous consequences. Our young businessman could neither fight nor flee. He had to sit at his desk while his body experienced the same physiological responses as his ancestors (churning stomach, tightening muscles, pounding heart, soaring blood pressure, grinding teeth, hyperventilation, profuse sweating) while his emotions were running wild. It is not difficult to understand how the continual stimulation of this response could eventually result in physical illness.

A challenge to the universality of the fight-or-flight response has been made by Taylor et al. (2000), who propose that although the physiological component of the fight-or-flight response may be common to both males and females, the female behavioural component will also involve social and nurturant behaviours. These responses are described as "tend and befriend" behaviours. The implication is that the female response to stress has evolved to increase the likelihood of survival of both the self and offspring. *Tending* is associated with nurturing activities, and *befriending* involves establishing social networks. This attachment–caregiving response in females may be triggered by neuroendocrine responses to stress. This theory is described as "a biobehavioural alternative to the fight-or-flight response" (Cannon, 1932), which has dominated stress research for the past five decades and has been "disproportionately based on studies of males" (Taylor et al., 2000, p. 422). Taylor and Sirois (2012) state that this approach emphasizes social behaviour in the stress process as "we are affiliative creatures who respond to stress collectively, as well as individually, and these responses are characteristic of men as well as women" (p. 157).

Rice (1999) describes several distinct meanings attached to stress. One has to do with external causes. These are the environmental demands placed upon us that cause us to feel stressed. As such, these should be described as *stressors*, rather than *stress*. It is in response to these external stressors that we invoke coping strategies to reduce their impact. Stress is concerned with subjective responses and refers to the interpretive mental state of the individual. Stress allows us to react cognitively to diminish, augment, or distort the impact of external events. Another term used in this context is *strain*, which describes the long-term consequences of exposure to stress and can result in physiological problems, such as cardiovascular disease; psychological concerns, such as depression; and cognitive concerns (Francis & Barling, 2005).

The belief that stress is somehow "all in our minds" has been expressed by writers and philosophers throughout history. Epictetus, for example, said some 2000 years ago that "Humans are not disturbed by events, but by the view they take of them." Shakespeare wrote in *Hamlet* that "There is no such thing as good or bad, but thinking makes it so." Milton suggested in *Paradise Lost* that "The mind is its own place, and in itself can make a Heaven of Hell, a Hell of Heaven." And Mark Twain said, "I am an old man and have known a great many troubles—but most of them never happened."

Rice (1999) points out that even though stress may be a subjective experience, we frequently use physical terms to explain its impact. We speak of being on the "edge" of a breakdown, of feeling the "weight" of the world, of not being sure that we can cope with "the pressure", or of "exploding" if we are exposed to any more stress, and we use phrases such as "it was the straw that broke the camel's back" to describe the precarious balance we maintain with the stress in our lives. Regardless of our personal views of what stress feels like, the fact is that stress imposes a physiological challenge that, if prolonged, can result in a decreased capacity to cope physiologically (Rice, 1999).

THE PHYSIOLOGY OF STRESS

There are two major components of the physical response to stress—the **nervous system** and the **endocrine system**. The nervous system is composed of two divisions, the **central nervous system** and the **peripheral nervous system**. The former is made up of the brain and the spinal cord, while the latter is made up of the somatic nervous system and the autonomic nervous system, which is further divided into the sympathetic and parasympathetic nervous systems. The physiology of stress creates a highly complex response that begins when an individual perceives a threat, real or imagined. The perception of stress mobilizes the body to act through two interrelated systems (Kemeny, 2005). One is the sympathetic adrenomedullary (SAM) system, in which the sympathetic nervous system and the adrenal medulla are most important. The second is the hypothalamic-pituitary-adrenal (HPA) axis, which initiates a response in the hypothalamus. The SAM system initiates the body's rapid *fight-or-flight* response to stress through the release of adrenaline and noradrenaline from the adrenal medulla as mediated by the sympathetic nervous

nervous system: one of two major components of the physical response to stress; made up of the central nervous system and the peripheral nervous system.

endocrine system: a system of the body that controls glandular responses to stress; responds more slowly than the nervous system but the effects can persist for weeks.

central nervous system: division of the nervous system that is composed of the brain and the spinal cord.

peripheral nervous system: division of the nervous system that is made up of the somatic nervous system and the autonomic nervous system (which is further divided into the sympathetic and parasympathetic nervous systems).

system. The HPA system, on the other hand, is a delayed response to stress that attempts to minimize the initial impact of stress and restore the body to a balanced state. It involves activation of the adrenal cortex and the secretion of corticosteroids, the most important of which is cortisol. The levels of circulating cortisol in the blood and saliva frequently serve as a physiological indicator of stress. Prolonged or repeated activation of the HPA system can lead to dysregulation in the body's responses to stress, which can have both physical and psychological consequences.

More specifically, the stress response begins in the **hypothalamus**, which is located in the central core of the brain. It initiates the stress response in both the nervous system and the endocrine system. The hypothalamus helps maintain homeostasis in the body through its many regulatory functions. As well, it controls activities such as eating, drinking, and sexual behaviour, all of which are greatly affected by stress. The activities of the hypothalamus increase arousal in the sympathetic nervous system in the form of the previously described fight-or-flight response (Cannon, 1939). The heart beats faster and blood pressure increases at the same time as peripheral blood vessels, in areas such as the hands and feet, constrict to ensure sufficient blood supplies for the brain and skeletal muscles. Stored fats and glucose flow into the bloodstream to provide fuel for necessary actions. Respiration rate increases and the bronchial tubes dilate to help increase oxygen flow for the metabolism of fuel. Pupils dilate to allow more light to enter the eyes and improve vision. The efficiency of the process is demonstrated when non-essential activities, such as digestion, decrease.

As a part of this response, the hypothalamus causes the **adrenal medulla**, located above the kidneys, to secrete *catecholamines*, which contain the hormones adrenaline and noradrenaline (also known as epinephrine and norepinephrine). Catecholamines affect the response of the **sympathetic nervous system**, and the level of these two hormones increases with the severity of the stress. The actions of adrenaline and noradrenaline are different, however. The former is fast-acting and increases with mental stress; the effect of the latter is more prolonged and increases with physical activity.

Adrenaline has a powerful impact on heart function and blood pressure. Presumably it is this experience that finds popular expression in the phrase "adrenaline rush." It is interesting that this phrase is usually viewed in positive terms as something that people seek. We even go so far as to ascribe an addictive quality to it by describing people who purposefully seek the physiological "high" that adrenaline brings as "adrenaline junkies." These stimulation seekers may engage in extreme activities to purposefully initiate the fight-or-flight response and the flow of adrenaline.

Also involved in the stress response is the **limbic system** of the brain, which adds an element of *emotion* to the response that goes beyond the identified dimensions of fight-or-flight. The feelings triggered by the limbic system include aggression, anger, fear, anxiety, sexual arousal, and pain. In addition, the **reticular formation** is a complex system running through the middle of the brain stem that performs several functions during the stress response. It serves as a communication network that filters messages between the brain and the body, which is most important when we consider the impact that the brain's perception of psychosocial stressors can have on physical systems in the body. The reticular formation receives input from all the sensory systems and influences which sensory information is processed or blocked.

Such selectivity results in increased efficiency in the system, which can become apparent to us in quite dramatic ways. For example, in high-arousal situations we may find

hypothalamus: a portion of the brain that initiates the stress response in both the nervous system and the endocrine system.

adrenal medulla: the central portion of the adrenal gland; secretes catecholamines (containing both adrenaline and noradrenaline) when the hypothalamus initiates the stress response.
sympathetic nervous system: the system responsible for the "fight-or-flight" response when triggered by the hypothalamus (faster heartbeat, increased blood pressure).

limbic system: a system of the brain that is responsible, in part, for emotion in the stress response.

reticular formation: complex system running through the middle of the brain stem that serves as a communication network to filter messages between the brain and the body.

ourselves remarkably able to selectively attend to a specific task while ignoring irrelevant distractions. A basketball player, given the opportunity to win a game by sinking a last-second foul shot, needs to focus his attention on the front rim of the hoop. He does not want to be distracted by the noise of the crowd and the movement of those behind the basket, who will often go to considerable extremes in an attempt to distract him. The reticular formation helps us attend to what matters and ignore that which doesn't. It also serves an important role in modulating the brain's levels of arousal or alertness in preparation for action.

In contrast to the sympathetic nervous system, the **parasympathetic** component of the autonomic system is activated by the hypothalamus to re-establish homeostasis in the system and to promote the reconstructive process following a stressful experience. It is associated with a relaxed or hypometabolic state in which the heart rate slows and blood pressure drops. Muscle tension decreases and respiration is slow and easy.

The endocrine system responds to stress more slowly than does the nervous system, but the effects associated with it can persist for weeks. The **pituitary gland**, which is located in the brain close to the hypothalamus, is described as the "master" gland because of its controlling effect on other glands. Most of the hormones secreted by the pituitary gland have an indirect impact on stress. The most important of these is adrenocorticotropic hormone (ACTH), which acts on the adrenal glands and is eventually involved in the release of up to 30 stress hormones (Smith, 1993).

The **adrenal cortex** secretes **glucocorticoids** and mineralocorticoids. One of the glucocorticoids is cortisol, an important stress hormone that provides energy to the system by converting stored protein and fats into glucose. If stress is prolonged, glucocorticoids can adversely affect the body's ability to resist disease and recover from injury. Cortisol levels are often used as an index of stress. Aldosterone is an important mineralocorticoid that regulates minerals in the body during stress by increasing blood pressure.

The **thyroid gland** functions in the stress response by producing thyroxine, which increases the release of fatty-acid fuels that are metabolized in the stress process. Elevated thyroxine levels increase blood pressure and respiration rate. Mental processes are also affected, in that individuals feel more anxious or agitated.

The **pancreas**, which lies close to the stomach, secretes insulin and glucagon in response to blood sugar levels. Insulin decreases blood sugar by storing it, whereas glucagon stimulates increases in blood sugar, which is an energy source during times of stress.

The autonomic nervous system responds rapidly in response to stress and the endocrine system responds more slowly, although its impact usually continues much longer. Acting together, these two systems provide a physiological response to stress that can be both adaptive and maladaptive.

The General Adaptation Syndrome

Initially, Selye conducted his research on laboratory animals. He observed that animals exposed to chronic stress demonstrated physical distress that included organic pathology and, ultimately, death. This work and that of others, such as Brady's work on executive monkeys (Brady, Porter, Conrad, & Mason, 1958), resulted in Selye's conceptualization of the **General Adaptation Syndrome (GAS)** (Selye, 1956). This is a three-stage response of the body to stressors. In the initial phase, the body goes into **alarm** as it mobilizes its

parasympathetic nervous system: the component of the autonomic system that re-establishes homeostasis in the system and promotes the reconstructive process following a stressful experience.

pituitary gland: a gland in the brain described as the "master" gland because it controls other glands through the hormones it secretes; most of these hormones have an indirect impact on stress.

adrenal cortex: the outer portion of the adrenal gland; at times of stress supplies hormones to the body that provide energy and increase blood pressure, but that can adversely affect the body's ability to resist and recover from disease.

glucocorticoids: substances released by the adrenal glands upon stimulation from the sympathetic division when one is under stress.

thyroid gland: an important gland in the stress response because it produces thyroxine, which increases blood pressure and respiration rate, and affects mental processes.

pancreas: a gland that secretes insulin and glucagon in response to blood sugar levels.

General Adaptation Syndrome (GAS): the three-stage response of the body to stressors as identified by Selye: alarm, resistance, and exhaustion.

alarm: the initial phase of Selye's General Adaptation Syndrome in which the body mobilizes its defences against a stressor.

defences against the stress. This involves many of the processes involved in the fight-or-flight response. As experience will often confirm, this acute response is usually enough to allow us to deal successfully with the impact of a stressor and then allow homeostasis to be re-established.

If a source of stress moves from acute to chronic, the body enters the second phase of adaptation, which Selye called **resistance**. Here the body mobilizes its resources over an extended period of time. Initially, the individual will appear as normal. If the stress continues for too long, however, the body's resources are depleted and resistance decreases.

The result of neurological and hormonal changes can be what Selye described as **diseases of adaptation**, which includes cardiovascular disease, hypertension, peptic ulcers, bronchial asthma, and the increased risk of infection.

The resources our bodies use to resist stress are clearly finite. Eventually, if the stressor is too severe or too long, the body enters what Selye called **exhaustion**. This is an endpoint at which the body's ability to resist the stressor breaks down and might even result in death if a return to homeostasis is not possible.

An extension of the body's attempt to maintain homeostasis is the concept of **allostatic load** as described by McEwen and Stellar (1993). This "refers to the price the body pays for being forced to adapt to adverse psychosocial or physical situations, and it represents either the presence of too much stress or the inefficient operation of the stress hormone response system" (McEwen, 2000, p. 110). In this context, homeostasis is seen as a mechanism that functions within an optimal physiological set point that is critical for survival, whereas allostasis promotes coping and adaptation by maintaining stability through change. If this adaptive process is called upon too frequently, or is not managed well, the consequence is allostatic load.

Criticisms of Selye's theory centre on its narrowness because it is concerned only with physical responses to stress and does not account for psychosocial factors that influence the human stress response. This emphasis may have derived from his initial work with animals; his critics suggest that he neglected the emotional and cognitive processes unique to humans (Brannon & Feist, 2007; Schwarzer & Luszczynska, 2013).

Other biologically based models have been proposed to explain our ability to resist the impact of stress. The emphasis may be placed on genetic influences that predispose an individual to increased risk for specific diseases or to vulnerabilities or reductions in resistance that may be expressed under certain conditions. Closely linked to this is the **stress-diathesis model**, which examines the interaction between the environment and heredity, often referred to as *nature versus nurture*. This model proposes that people may be predisposed to experience a physical effect in the presence of stressful events. Thus, individuals with a genetic predisposition for a particular condition may never display signs of that condition if they are not exposed to the precipitating stress. However, high levels of stress may test the limits of invulnerability even in those who are genetically robust. This evokes a sense of adaptability or "survival of the fittest." The implication is that stress forces an individual to adapt and evolve or run the risk of being selected against. Certainly many of us, when we consider our own vulnerability to disease, are quick to blame or flaunt our genes. We boast to others that we will never develop cardiovascular disease no matter how much we abuse our bodies with environmental stressors such as a poor diet or lack of exercise, as we are blessed with "good genes." We may develop an inappropriate sense of invulnerability. The stress-diathesis model (or

resistance: a set of physiological responses that allow a person to deal with a stressor; the second phase of Selye's General Adaptation Syndrome in which the body mobilizes its resources if the source of stress moves from acute to chronic.

diseases of adaptation: health problems that are the result of long-term neurological and hormonal changes caused by ongoing stress.

exhaustion: the third stage in Selye's General Adaptation Syndrome; the body experiences fatigue and immunocompromise because of the severity or duration of a stressor.

allostatic load: the long-term physiological impact of chronic exposure to stress.

stress-diathesis model: model that examines the interaction between the environment and heredity, often referred to as *nature versus nurture*; this model proposes that predisposing factors in an individual may determine whether or not a physical effect is experienced in the presence of stressful events.

diathesis-stress model, as Grossarth-Maticek & Eysenck, 1990, call it) is also discussed in chapter 3 in our examination of psychoneuroimmunology.

COGNITIVE TRANSACTIONAL MODELS

Selye's popularization of the idea of stress can't be underestimated. It's hard to imagine where we would be today without the contributions he made to the field. However, as we have indicated, his theory is limited by its reliance on physiological processes based on an animal model of behaviour. In this regard, his theory fails to take into account the higher-level cognitive abilities that are distinctly human and allow us to interpret our vulnerability to a particular stressor both now and in the future. Compared to Selye's model, **cognitive transactional models** of stress hold far more appeal for psychologists. As indicated in the definition provided by Lazarus and Folkman earlier in this chapter (Lazarus & Folkman, 1984), these models, described more recently by Lazarus (2006), emphasize the relationship existing between individuals and the environment and the appraisals individuals make of that relationship. Personal **cognitive appraisals** determine whether or not an event will be perceived as stressful. These are based on an individual's unique social learning history.

Lazarus and Folkman (1984) describe the process of cognitive appraisal as one that is "largely evaluative, focused on meaning or significance, and takes place continuously during waking hours" (p. 31). They distinguish among three forms of appraisal that influence the coping process: **primary appraisal**, **secondary appraisal**, and **reappraisal**. They acknowledge that these are somewhat unfortunate terms, as one form of appraisal (e.g., primary as compared to secondary) is neither superior to, nor precedes, the other.

Primary appraisals are concerned with the initial evaluation of a situation. Three kinds of primary appraisal are identified—**irrelevant**, **benign-positive**, and **stressful**. The first involves a cognitive process by which an event is appraised as having no implications for the individual's well-being; it is irrelevant and requires no response. Benign-positive appraisals involve outcomes appraised to be positive and that may increase well-being. They are associated with pleasurable emotions, such as happiness, joy, or love. The only demand benign-positive appraisals place on the individual is the awareness that these feelings will end.

There are three types of stressful appraisal—**harm/loss**, **threat**, and **challenge**. Harm/loss appraisals involve the possibility of significant physical or psychological loss, such as might be experienced through a serious illness or the loss of one's job. Threat involves the anticipation of situations of harm or loss. When an individual has experienced harm/loss, threat is involved, as it has implications for the future. Perceptions of threat allow a person to anticipate and prepare for the impact of an event. Challenge appraisals involve events perceived to be stressful, but the focus is one of positive excitement and anticipation of the potential for growth contained in the situation. Having to speak in front of a class may be perceived as threatening by a person with anxieties about public speaking but as an opportunity to test one's public-speaking abilities by an individual who has worked on these skills. Clearly, it is possible to experience threat and challenge in the same situation. The confident speaker may experience some threat in the speaking opportunity, which is expressed in the form of anxiety and some fear; however, the dominant emotions are confidence and anticipation. The overall emotional tone is positive, and the

cognitive transactional models: models that emphasize the relationship between a person and his or her environment and the appraisal that the individual makes of the situation.

cognitive appraisal: assessment of whether or not an event is stressful.

primary appraisal: the initial evaluation of a situation.

secondary appraisal: an individual's evaluation of their ability to cope with a situation following the primary appraisal.

reappraisal: a continuous experience in which existing appraisals of situations are changed or modified on the basis of new information.

irrelevant appraisal: a cognitive process by which an event is appraised as having no implications for the individual's well-being.

benign-positive appraisal: a cognitive process by which an event is appraised to involve outcomes that are positive and may enhance well-being.

stressful appraisal: a cognitive process by which an event is appraised to involve harm/loss, threat, or challenge at the time of the primary appraisal.

harm/loss appraisal: a type of stressful appraisal at the time of primary appraisal that involves significant physical or psychological loss.

threat appraisal: an appraisal at the time of the primary appraisal that involves the anticipation of harm or loss.

challenge appraisal: appraisal in which, though an event is perceived to be stressful, the focus is one of positive excitement and the potential for growth.

individual actively employs available resources in preparing to meet the demands imposed by the presentation.

Secondary appraisal is concerned with people's evaluations of their ability to cope with a situation. After the initial evaluation of the nature of the event, which is *primary appraisal,* individuals consider their options. As Lazarus and Folkman (1984) make clear, this is not simply an intellectual exercise. It is "a complex evaluative process that takes into account which coping options are available, the likelihood that a given coping option will accomplish what it is supposed to, and the likelihood one can apply a particular strategy" (p. 35). They point out that this is very similar to the distinction Bandura (1986) makes between outcome and efficacy judgments. Bandura states that "efficacy and outcome judgments are differentiated because individuals can believe that a particular course of action will produce certain outcomes, but they do not act on that outcome belief because they question whether they can actually execute the necessary activities" (1986, p. 392).

The interaction between secondary appraisals of coping options and primary appraisals of the situation will determine an individual's emotional reaction to the event. If the consequences of an event are perceived as important, individuals may experience considerable stress if they believe they cannot cope with the event; a state of helplessness may result. Conversely, *challenge appraisals* are more likely to result when an individual feels in control of the situation, even if this means overcoming extreme adversity.

We are all aware that some individuals, when faced with a devastating situation such as an illness or loss of a relationship, articulate their efforts to cope in very positive ways. They describe the challenge of *confronting* through their own behaviour what others would perceive as overwhelming odds. They know they may not ultimately have an outcome others would consider desirable, but they focus their attention on elements of the situation that are under their control. For example, they may talk of the challenge of coping with pain, either physical or psychological, to the best of their ability while recognizing that there are elements of the situation that are outside their control. Even though a situation may appear hopeless, they search for challenges.

Reappraisal is a continuous experience in which existing appraisals are changed or modified on the basis of new information. Reappraisal simply follows an earlier appraisal of an event and results in a new appraisal. What may vary is the direction of the outcome of the appraisal. For example, an irrelevant situation may now be perceived in terms of threat, or a harm/loss situation may now be appraised as a challenge. Lazarus and Folkman (1984) also identify what they call a *defensive reappraisal.* They describe this as a self-generated coping strategy in which an attempt is made to reinterpret past events more positively or to view current threats or losses as being less threatening.

Also of importance in the cognitive appraisal process is the concept of **vulnerability**, which reflects the adequacy of an individual's resources. This is a concept that, like so many in this context, is defined within a relationship. With regard to physical issues, it is possible to think of vulnerability only in terms of resources. A physical injury can increase vulnerability to further injury. However, deficiencies in resources will result in a psychological vulnerability only when resource deficiency threatens which is valued by the individual. Therefore, an individual may have resource deficiencies but not experience vulnerability, if the deficiencies do not threaten domains that are important to him or her.

vulnerability: physically, the adequacy of an individual's resources; psychologically, a threat to something that an individual values.

person variables: variables, particularly commitments and beliefs, that interact with situation variables to affect the appraisal of a situation's stressfulness.

situation variables: variables that interact with person variables to influence the appraisal of a situation.

commitments as person variables: values that influence appraisal by determining the importance of a particular encounter and that affect the choices made to achieve a desired outcome.

beliefs as person variables: pre-existing notions, both personal and cultural, that influence appraisal, and thus stress, by determining the meaning given to the environment.

novelty: the extent to which an individual's previous experience with a situation influences the appraisal process.

predictability: a characteristic of the environment that allows an individual to prepare for an event and therefore reduce the stress involved.

event uncertainty: the inability to predict the probability of an event, which, as a result, increases the stress response.

imminence: interval during which an event is being anticipated; the more imminent an event, the more intense the appraisal.

duration: situational factor involved in stress appraisal.

temporal uncertainty: lack of knowledge about when an event will occur, which can result in stress.

The cognitive transactional model also identifies **person** and **situation variables** that influence appraisal. The impact of these variables is in the individual's assessment of the salience of an event, an individual's understanding of the event, the possible consequences of an event, and ultimately, the possible outcomes (Lazarus & Folkman, 1984). Person and situation variables are interdependent and involve transactions between individuals and their environments.

The person variables of importance are **commitments** and **beliefs**. *Commitments* are concerned with what is important to an individual. Commitments influence appraisal by determining the importance of a particular encounter and will affect the decisions made to achieve a desired outcome. As well, they interact with concepts we discussed in the context of primary appraisal, such as challenge, threat, benefit, or harm, to determine if an individual will engage in or avoid an encounter. *Beliefs* are pre-existing notions that determine the meaning given to the environment. They can be both personal and cultural. Their impact, which is often difficult to observe, is most obvious when there is a sudden change in the belief system.

Numerous factors influencing the appraisal process have been identified. **Novelty** refers to an individual's previous experience with a situation. **Predictability** identifies characteristics of the environment that can be learned or discerned, which allows an individual to prepare for an event and therefore reduce the stress involved. Of more relevance to appraisal is the concept of **event uncertainty**, which involves issues of probability. High levels of uncertainty can be extremely stressful.

Temporal situational factors are also important in stress appraisal. **Imminence** concerns the time interval during which an event is being anticipated. Typically, the more imminent an event, the more intense the appraisal. **Duration** refers to the time period during which a stressful event occurs. The implication is that the longer the duration, the more stressful the event. This concept is reminiscent of Selye's General Adaptation Syndrome, in which the duration of stress plays an important role; continued exposure to stress compromises resistance and leads ultimately to exhaustion. **Temporal uncertainty** is concerned with the stress involved in *not knowing* when an event will occur.

A final concern here relates to the *timing* of stressful events in the context of the life cycle. The implication is that there are appropriate or "usual" times for events to occur over one's lifespan. If these expectations are violated, it may result in the event being appraised as more stressful. We have a sense of an order as we move through our lives, and this master calendar allows us to develop expectations and prepare for events. When the timing is "wrong", normal life events may become sources of stress. We all know individuals who have been affected by life events in this way, such as the couple who have a child later in life, the athlete whose career comes to an abrupt end due to injury, or the individual who is unexpectedly terminated in what they had perceived to be their life's work.

The model developed by Lazarus and his colleagues views stress as a complex, dynamic process in which individuals' experience of stress is determined by their own unique cognitive appraisal of the event and their ability to cope with it. Recent research by Keller et al. (2012) provides intriguing support for this position that it is the perception that stress affects one's health that is most important. Specifically, they found that there was a synergistic effect in individuals who reported high levels of stress combined with the perception that stress affects health. This resulted in an increased risk for premature mortality over those who did not display this form of stress appraisal. They state that "reporting a lot of stress and perceiving that stress affected one's health a lot increased the risk of premature death by 43%" (p. 681). This finding may have extremely important clinical implications. As Schwarzer and Luszczynska (2013) indicate, "stress has to be analyzed and investigated as an active, unfolding process" (2013, p. 30).

THE ROLE OF PERSONALITY IN STRESS AND COPING

If a particular temperament or set of personality traits predisposed an individual to a specific disease, then given the stable, enduring qualities of personality it might be possible to intervene and reduce the risk. There are a number of ways these interactions might occur (Rice, 1999). A specific personality profile might predispose one to the development of a specific disease, as is indicated with Type A personality and coronary heart disease (CHD). A second possibility is that a particular disease process may result in a particular personality profile—as when depression follows the diagnosis of a serious illness. A third possibility is that personality affects or filters the response to an illness. An individual receiving the news of a serious illness might respond in an optimistic and active manner compared to another person who responds passively and pessimistically. In a fourth possibility, personality may interact with the disease process in a feedback loop that affects the individual's physiology and influences the disease process itself. Ultimately, the question centres on whether there are personality traits that predict behaviours, such as smoking or alcohol use, or disease processes, such as cancer or coronary disease.

The most extensively studied set of personality traits in connection with disease is the **Type A behaviour pattern** which was first described by two cardiologists, Meyer Friedman and Ray Rosenman, in 1974. They identified patients they saw frequently in their medical practice whom they believed were at a much higher risk for cardiovascular disease. Such "Type A" individuals display a sense of time urgency, are impatient and very competitive, and can be aggressive and hostile. They exhibit behavioural characteristics such as rapid, explosive, clipped speech; frequent interruptions of another speaker; speech-hurrying techniques (e.g., nodding the head while another person speaks); vehement reactions to time impedance; emphatic one-word responses; and finger-pointing to emphasize speech.

They stand in comparison to "Type B" individuals, who give the impression of being relaxed and calm, are less competitive, are not overly reactive to time impediments, and rarely display hostility. Powerful empirical support has emerged for the suggestion that Type A behaviours are linked to an increased risk for coronary disease. Indeed, this set of behaviours has been identified as a risk factor for all forms of morbidity (Shoham-Yakubovich, Ragland, Brand, & Syme, 1988). However, some inconsistencies in the findings have led to a search for the toxic core of Type A behaviours. This work initially identified the components of hostility and anger to be the crucial elements. Wright (1988) expanded it to describe a multi-causal pathway that identifies Type A behaviour in combination with family history, lifestyle risks, and anger as being the core risk factors. Williams et al. (2000) report that individuals with high anger-scale scores have a greatly elevated risk of heart attack in comparison to those with low scores. Also of interest is work summarized by Smith and Ruiz (2002) that has identified **social dominance** as a risk factor for coronary disease that is independent of hostility. Social dominance is described as "a set of controlling behaviours, including the tendency to cut off and talk over the interviewer" (p. 552).

Type A behaviour pattern: behaviours include impatience, time urgency, aggressiveness, hostility, and competitiveness; originally believed to be predictive of coronary heart disease.

social dominance: a risk factor for coronary disease that is independent of hostility; social dominance is described as "a set of controlling behaviours, including the tendency to cut off and talk over the interviewer."

Being able to identify the risk factors of CHD increases the likelihood of designing interventions that may successfully modify or eliminate destructive behaviours (Straub, 2007). These could involve a variety of activities such as making philosophical decisions about one's lifestyle, training in relaxation techniques, or specific behavioural management programs. The latter are designed to help people learn to modify emotional responses, such as hostility and anger, and control environmental conditions through techniques such as practising time management, engaging in problem solving, beginning an exercise program, developing communication skills, and managing diet. You might find it relevant at this point to read "Peter's Story" in chapter 5 of this book. Peter would have been described as a classic Type A individual prior to having a heart attack. After surviving this scare and subsequent bypass surgery he has made significant lifestyle changes that have resulted in remarkable improvements to his health.

It is interesting that programs designed to change maladaptive behaviours are not usually described in terms of coping but are more likely to be described as being programs in "stress management." This suggests that it is easier to sell the concept of *stress* than it is the concept of *coping*. The term *stress management* permeates our culture. We are taught to "manage" our stress rather than to cope. This sounds like an active, dynamic, even aggressive response to the situation in which we will overwhelm the stress. Coping, on the other hand, suggests a more passive, reflective stance. To say that you are in a stress management program implies that you are still in control of your situation and are learning techniques to help you maintain your position, whereas coping suggests that things have deteriorated for you and you are in need of help.

Research that examines the relationship between health outcomes and personality has focused primarily on negative traits (Kern & Friedman, 2008). In 1993, Friedman et al. suggested that conscientiousness, as measured in childhood, is predictive of longevity. Specifically, the indication is that higher levels of conscientiousness are significantly related to a longer life and more positive health behaviours. A meta-analysis of 194 studies by (Bogg & Roberts, 2004) indicated that "conscientiousness-related traits were negatively related to all risky health-related behaviors and positively related to all beneficial health-related behaviors" (p. 887). The behavioural contributors to mortality that were looked at include tobacco use, levels of physical activity, diet, alcohol use, sexual behaviour, vehicular behaviours, and illicit drug use, which are related to longevity through illnesses such as cardiovascular disease, cancer, AIDS, and accidental deaths. This may occur because a lack of conscientiousness is related to disinhibition and impulsive, reckless, present-centred behaviours as compared to the planned, risk-avoidant, long-term behaviours of conscientious individuals. Conscientiousness is also related to conventionality, which suggests that individuals displaying this trait are more likely to "uphold social norms and traditions (i.e. traditionalism), avoid trouble, and not let others down (i.e. responsibility)" (Bogg & Roberts, 2004, p. 890). Ultimately the value in this type of research may lie in interventions that focus on individuals who display a lack of conscientiousness or in attempting to enhance behaviours related to conscientiousness.

It appears that personality is an important determinant of health-related behaviours, and consideration should be given to how personality may positively or negatively affect our health. Kubzansky, Martin, and Buka (2009) conclude that a life course perspective "dovetails nicely with other research on personality and health which has posited cumulative effects via biological pathways, effects on stress, coping, and emotional responses, and health or illness behaviours" (p. 370). Again, the value of interventions which focus on early childhood characteristics is emphasized, particularly as it relates to the cumulative effect on adult health outcomes.

COPING

This discussion of the Type A behaviour pattern and its modification provides a transition into a discussion of specific coping behaviours. Sarafino (1998) states that as individuals make the "effort to neutralize or reduce stress, coping activities are geared toward decreasing the person's appraisal of or concern for this discrepancy. Thus coping is the process by which people try to manage the perceived discrepancy between the demands and resources they appraise in a stressful situation" (p. 133). These efforts may not necessarily improve the person's situation. As Rice (1999) points out, it has not always been clear whether we are talking about the process or outcome of coping. He cites research by Rudolph, Dennig, and Weisz (1995) that identifies three components of coping. They distinguish between a **coping response** and a **stress response**. A coping response is an intentional physical or mental act that is initiated in response to a stressor. It can be directed toward either external events or internal states. A stress response is defined as "any response that reflects a spontaneous emotional or behavioral reaction to stress, rather than a deliberate attempt to cope" (p. 329). The objective of a coping response, which is usually to reduce the impact of stress, is described as a **coping goal**. The specific or actual outcomes of a coping response are called **coping outcomes**. As Xanthopoulos and Daniel (2013) indicate, it is a "dynamic process influenced by temperament, developmental stage, personality disposition, past experience, situational characteristics such as demands, and environmental features" (p. 74).

Lazarus and his colleague have proposed that coping can serve two functions (Lazarus & Folkman, 1984). **Problem-focused coping** is concerned with managing the situation by defining the problem, looking at alternative solutions, evaluating the implications of the alternatives, and choosing the best one to act on. It is a rational approach, similar to problem solving. However, it also includes solutions that are focused inward as well as those directed at the environment. In our daily existence, we use problem-focused coping strategies frequently as we take action to reduce the demands placed upon us. Students who feel overwhelmed with assignments may seek out the professor to discuss how they can reduce the impact of their workload. As part of this process, they might focus on what material to study, use time management procedures to plan their study time more efficiently and reorganize their approach to preparing for the exams. Two types of problem-focused coping have been identified—*proactive coping* and *combative coping* (Aspinwall & Taylor, 1997). In proactive coping, potential stressors are anticipated and acted on in advance to either prevent or decrease their impact. In combative coping, people react to an unavoidable stress in a manner designed to help better cope with the stress. For example, the relaxation technique outlined at the end of this chapter can be used as a combative coping skill to help deal with physiological arousal and muscle tension.

Emotion-focused coping involves modifying emotional responses to an event. This could consist of using cognitive processes, such as avoidance or minimization, to decrease emotional distress, or using techniques to increase emotional intensity, as one might do in preparation for an athletic competition. Some forms of emotion-focused coping change

coping response: an intentional physical or mental act that is initiated in response to a stressor.

stress response: a response that reflects a spontaneous emotional or behavioural reaction to stress, rather than a deliberate attempt to cope.

coping goal: the objective of a coping response (which is usually to reduce the impact of stress).

coping outcomes: the specific outcomes of a coping response.

problem-focused coping: coping by actively addressing the stressors associated with a disease, such as cancer and its treatment.

emotion-focused coping: coping by focusing on ways to reduce the emotional impact of a disease without trying to cure it.

nothing about the objective situation. They change only the manner in which an event is perceived and, as such, constitute reappraisal.

The emotional response to a situation can be regulated through both behavioural and cognitive strategies. Cognitive strategies change the way we think about a situation. There is a tendency to use emotion-focused coping when the individual believes there is nothing that can be done to change the stressful situation. Lazarus and Folkman (1984) have indicated that problem-focused and emotion-focused coping strategies can be used at the same time and can either facilitate or impede each other in the coping process.

personal resources: resources that are available to people in their own lives to help them reduce the potential for stressful events and cope with stressful situations as they occur.

social support: a collection of interpersonal resources people have at their disposal to help them avoid or cope with difficult times in their lives.

In our efforts to cope with stress, we often call upon the **personal resources** available to us to help prevent the occurrence of stressful events and to help us cope with stressful situations if they occur. One of these personal resource mechanisms is **social support**, which we discuss on a number of occasions in this book. In times of stress we have all benefitted from support received from friends, family, and institutions such as social agencies, the health care system, and the church. For example, it has been reported that 80 percent of Americans believe that prayer can have a positive impact on the course of an illness (Levin & Puchalski, 1997). In a general sense, spirituality is a frequent coping response to stress. Gall et al. (2005), in a recent review of the relevant literature, suggest that "the construct of spirituality is congruent with the basic tenets of the transactional model of coping. Specifically, this framework is seen to be dynamic and relational, phenomenological, transactional, and process-oriented" (p. 90). We, in turn, provide assistance to family and friends when they are experiencing stress in their lives. That we can turn to others, and they to us, is an expectation of the human condition and, as a first line of defence, it is a highly effective and widely used resource.

emotional support: support provided by people who take the time to understand our fears and frustrations, who help calm us during anxious times, who help lift our moods, or who distract us from our worries.

informational support: the provision of information that might include such things as treatment options or typical recovery times from a treatment or injury.

tangible support: help with the demands of daily living, such as getting meals and rides to the doctor.

stress-buffering hypothesis: the theory that social support has an indirect effect and acts as a buffer to protect individuals from the negative effects of stress.

Social support takes different forms. **Emotional support** implies being cared for and loved; **informational support** comes in the form of advice and information made available to us concerning a particular event; **tangible support** concerns the direct aid or services we receive to assist us in coping with stress. Each of these forms of support is more relevant at different times in the coping process. However, it is clearly the *perception* of social support rather than the *objective situation* that is most important (Coyne, Aldwin, & Lazarus, 1981).

Social support is believed to exert its effect on stress in one of two ways (Cohen & Wills, 1985). The **stress-buffering hypothesis** suggests that social support has an indirect effect and acts as a buffer to protect individuals from the negative effects of stress. This means that when people are exposed to stress, the social support they receive from others serves to buffer and therefore reduce the impact of the event. Social support acts between the event and the recipient, or between the response to the stress and the outcome. As a result, the effect of social support should be most noticeable at higher levels of stress, and social support should have little impact on lower levels of stress. Alternatively, social support may have direct effects that are independent of stress and serve to enhance an individual's general sense of well-being and self-esteem, thereby increasing their sense of control, decreasing anxiety, and increasing health-promoting behaviours—all of which help to reduce stress.

Kaplan, Sallis, and Patterson (1993) suggest that more complex models will ultimately be required to explain the relationship between social support and the impact of stress. One possibility is a direct-effect model incorporating the functional effects of the social support system (which may affect health either positively or negatively). These researchers "would expect that close, caring relationships would play a stronger role in reinforcing health behavior and in enhancing use of the health care system. At the other extreme, social isolation might contribute to disconnection with services, poor nutrition, and inadequate responses to emergency" (p. 145). It is clear that lack of social support is a risk factor for illness. For example, a lack of social support is reported to be as important a risk factor for cardiovascular disease as are cigarette smoking, poor diet, and inadequate physical activity (Kaplan et al., 1993). The exact mechanisms by which social support impacts psychological well-being and health outcomes will require more longitudinal research that evaluates "an individual's ability to receive and benefit from social support" (Xanthopoulos & Daniel, 2013, p. 74).

Another factor that may influence one's ability to cope with stress is a sense of **personal control**. Feeling in control of a situation appears to reduce the impact of stressful events. As Bandura (1986) has indicated, one's sense of control over events can be achieved either behaviourally, by taking actions to reduce stress, or cognitively, by believing in one's ability to control the impact of stressful events. Bandura points out that it is important to distinguish between these two forms of control, as the relationship between actual and perceived coping efficacy is often not perfect. He states that "there are many competent people who are plagued by a sense of inefficacy and many less competent ones who remain unperturbed by impending threats because they are self-assured of their coping capabilities" (p. 440).

Behavioural control has been demonstrated to greatly reduce the impact of stressful events. To have behavioural control over an event increases one's sense of predictability, which reduces stress. With regard to cognitive control, individuals who believe they can effect control over stressful events have demonstrated that they will be less affected physiologically and behaviourally than those who believe they have no personal control over the situation. Bandura (1997) suggests that the "intensity and chronicity of human stress is governed largely by perceived control over the demands of one's life" (p. 262). He cites epidemiological and correlational evidence, which suggests that a lack of behavioural, or even perceived, control over such demands increases our risk of infection, contributes to the development of physical disorders, and accelerates the rate at which disease progresses.

The role of perceived behavioural and cognitive control over stressful events is of importance to the developing field of **positive psychology**, which encourages psychologists to use fewer negative, deficit-oriented, or problem-focused frameworks and to focus more on effective human functioning (Sheldon & King, 2001). The emphasis here is on what has been described as strength-based assessment (Tedeschi & Kilmer, 2005).

Fundamental to this new interest is the concept of **resilience**, which Masten (2001) describes as "a class of phenomena characterized by good outcomes in spite of serious threats to adaptation or development" (p. 228). Schwarzer and Luszczynska (2013) suggest that "resilient persons bend without breaking, and they quickly rebound from adversity" (p. 40). Research in this area attempts to understand better the process by which resilience is developed and can be enhanced (Alvord & Grados, 2005). Positive emotions can have a powerful undoing effect on negative emotions and individuals should be encouraged to cultivate positive emotional experiences to help them cope with stress and adversity (Fredrickson, 2001; Zautra, Arewasikporn, & Davis, 2010).

Lyubomirsky (2001) discusses cognitive and motivational strategies that have been demonstrated to increase happiness and reduce the impact of stress. These include developing positive perceptions of one's self, learning to derive positive meanings from

personal control: a factor that influences a person's ability to cope with stress; personal control can be achieved either behaviourally or cognitively.

positive psychology: approach that encourages psychologists to use fewer negative or problem-focused frameworks and to focus more on effective human functioning.

resilience: concept in positive psychology that describes "good outcomes in spite of serious threats to adaptation or development."

negative experiences, using humour and faith, not engaging in self-rumination, and using social comparison selectively in a manner designed to protect one's sense of well-being.

In their research on the relationship between positive emotions and health, Richman et al. (2005) conclude that "the consistency of effects across diseases that involve different physiological systems (cardiovascular, metabolic, and respiratory) strongly suggests broad-based effects of positive emotion on health. Moreover, the prospective analyses suggest the possibility of a protective role for positive emotion in the development of disease" (p. 427). The two positive emotions they examined were hope and curiosity, which were found to have a protective impact across multiple disease outcomes. They also concluded that the impact of positive emotions is not simply equivalent to "the absence of negative emotion" (p. 427), but rather there appears to be an increase in resilience and health promotion suggesting a unique protective role for positive emotions. Following an extensive review of the literature, Lyubomirsky, King, and Diener (2005) conclude that "happy individuals are more likely than their less happy peers to have fulfilling marriages and relationships, high incomes, superior work performance, community involvement, robust health, and a long life" (p. 846). In reviewing the empirical support for the importance of positive emotion as a resilience resource, Zautra et al. (2010) suggest that the unresolved issue is whether or not it is possible to enhance positive emotions. It is important to distinguish the value of happiness per se as compared to happy people who may differ from those who are less happy on many characteristics that have positive health outcomes (p. 227). To this end, Boehm, Peterson, Kivimaki, and Kubzansky (2011) carried out prospective research on the impact of psychological well-being on the incidence of CHD in middle-aged men and women. Specifically, they report that over a period of five years, emotional vitality and optimism were associated with a reduced risk of CHD that could not be explained by biological risk or health behaviours.

Social support and personal control are resources that increase one's ability to cope with stress. However, at times such resources are unavailable or insufficient to cope with high levels of stress. It is often necessary to seek the assistance of techniques that have been specifically developed to help people cope with stress either directly or indirectly. These are techniques that are considered adaptive compared to strategies such as alcohol or drug use, which, although effective in some ways, are *not* adaptive and ultimately increase stress. Although adaptive techniques are coping strategies, they are often labelled **stress management techniques**.

Some of the most widely used and effective interventions against stress are the various **relaxation techniques** that have been developed throughout history. These are strategies based on a simple principle—that we cannot be relaxed and tense at the same time. It is the antidote to the fight-or-flight response, which is under the control of the sympathetic nervous system, whereas the relaxation response is under the control of the parasympathetic nervous system. In a relaxed state, the heart slows, blood pressure drops, breathing is slow and easy, and muscle tension decreases. This response, described earlier as **hypometabolic**, is the opposite of the **hypermetabolic** fight-or-flight response. These responses reciprocally inhibit one another. One of the implications of understanding this inhibitory process is that it may allow us to gain some control over the autonomic nervous system, which has long been considered an involuntary system (i.e., outside of volitional control). Demonstrations of physiological control by highly trained individuals have provided support for this possibility and have further expanded our understanding of physiological control.

stress management techniques: techniques that have been developed specifically to help people cope with stress either directly or indirectly.

relaxation techniques: techniques to reduce anxiety to manageable levels so that the energy can be used to positively influence performance; based on the principle that we cannot be relaxed and tense at the same time.

hypometabolic: a state of the body in which the heart slows, blood pressure drops, breathing is slow and easy, and muscle tension decreases.

hypermetabolic: a physiological state in which the metabolic rate is higher than normal, as occurs in the fight-or-flight response.

East and West: Now the Twain Shall Meet

Since the mid-1960s, Western culture has shown an increased interest in Eastern philosophies and meditative disciplines. This enthusiasm, shared by many, has largely focused on techniques designed to promote psychological and physical well-being; this interest forms an important component of the stress and coping literature. Many researchers have been intrigued by accounts of bodily control often difficult for us to comprehend (Brunton, 1972; Murray, 1980; Yogananda, 1969). Brunton, in a book first published in 1934, describes his travels to discover a "secret" India. He speaks of a culture described under the generic term of *Yoga* that "proffers benefits to mankind as valuable in their own way as any proffered by the Western sciences. It can bring our bodies nearer the healthy condition which nature intended them to possess; it can bestow one of modern civilization's most urgent needs—a flawless serenity of mind" (p. 6).

The philosopher Harvey Cox believes that the "mystics and contemplatives have served as the guardians of that uniquely human realm called interiority" (1973, p. 93). He suggests that our renewed interest in this realm represents a survival instinct intended to turn our attention from without to within.

Our fascination with these traditions is important in a health psychology context, as it has caused us to question our understanding of the mind–body interaction. Our ability to control physiological processes has been challenged by reports of individuals who have claimed they can control or even stop their hearts, survive lengthy pit burials, regulate their body temperatures, or allow their skins to be penetrated without bleeding. It is quite reasonable to suggest that it was these early investigations that provided the foundation for many of the stress-management techniques we practise today. Techniques such as biofeedback and many of the secular relaxation strategies we use are firmly rooted in the belief that we can gain control of physiological variables previously thought to be outside our control.

Therese Brousse was a pioneer in this field. In 1935 she took a crude, portable electrocardiograph to India to record attempts by yogis to achieve voluntary control of cardiovascular activity. One of her published records indicates that for one individual, heart potentials and pulse waves recorded from the radial artery decreased almost to zero and remained there for several seconds. More than 20 years later, Wenger, Bagchi, and Anand (1961) returned to India with more sophisticated equipment to record cardiovascular activity in four individuals who claimed to be able to slow or stop their hearts. One of them was the person previously investigated by Brousse.

It became obvious that these individuals did not directly control the functioning of their hearts; rather, they used striate muscle control to produce changes in circulatory patterns. The technique is called the Valsalva manoeuvre, which involves an increase in muscle tension in the abdominal and thoracic muscles, closure of the glottis, and development of intrathoracic pressure. This interferes with venous return to the heart, so that heart sounds are diminished and masked by muscular sounds, and the radial pulse seems to disappear. The increased sophistication of the equipment in the study by Wenger and his colleagues indicated that normal cardiac activity continued to occur. The results Brousse had reported were an artifact of the crude recording techniques she used and did not take into account the impact of the Valsalva manoeuvre. Although these individuals did not stop their hearts, they demonstrated a remarkable level of muscular control.

Anand and Chhina (1961) carried out a similar investigation with three yogis who claimed to be able to stop their hearts. Rather than supporting their claim, the electrocardiogram (EKG) indicated that their heart rate actually increased while the yogis held their breaths. This finding is supported by accounts of research done on Swami Rama at the Menninger Foundation (Luce & Peper, 1971). Physiological recordings indicated that when the Swami "stopped" his heart, his heart rate actually increased to approximately 300 beats a minute over a period of 17 seconds. This sudden atrial fibrillation, a dangerous cardiac condition that prevents the necessary volume of blood from being pumped to the body, would normally render a person unconscious and, if continued, would soon lead to death. Apparently the Swami was intrigued by this result, as he indicated that he experienced a "fluttering" in his chest. It is also reported that he was able to produce a temperature difference of 10 degrees between two spots on his hand.

An interesting extension of this work was done by Anand, Chhina, and Singh (1961a), who conducted experiments on Sri Ramanand Yogi while he was sealed in an airtight box for two periods of 8 and 10 hours. It was reported that he was able to reduce his oxygen intake and carbon dioxide output beyond his requirements under basal conditions. Even when he was breathing air with decreased oxygen and increased carbon dioxide content, his heart rate did not increase, nor did his respiratory activity increase or deepen. The electroencephalograph (EEG) indicated brain waves suggestive of early stages of sleep, despite there being no evidence that he actually slept.

EEG measures can also be used to assess the ability to maintain attention without being distracted. Anand, Chhina, and Singh (1961b) used EEG to test the assertion that, during meditation, highly trained yogis are oblivious to external stimulation. They examined four such individuals and found that they were indeed able to achieve this state. The yogis did not demonstrate the expected blocking of the EEG alpha waves in response to stimulation during meditation. Two of the subjects kept their hands immersed in cold water for 45 to 55 minutes with no apparent discomfort. During this experience, they displayed persistent EEG alpha wave activity, which is associated with a state of wakeful relaxation.

Swami Rama, while at the Menninger Foundation, experimented with EEG recordings and is reported to have produced alpha and theta waves with ease. The latter are slow waves associated with sleep states. He is also said to have entered a state he called "yogi sleep," which appeared, on the basis of the EEG, to be much like deep sleep, and yet he was able to repeat, almost verbatim, statements made to him during this state upon awakening 25 minutes later. Luce and Peper (1971), commenting on these findings, stated that "our idea of a 'normal' EEG is based upon the particular, limited, habitual use that a person makes of his brain. Swami Rama's agile and controlled transitions from one state of consciousness to another would, no doubt, be considered abnormal" (p. 43).

It is this final point that is important. As indicated earlier, this research raised questions about what our physiological and psychological limitations really are. When we think of stress and coping, we often think of physiological and psychological processes that are out of our control. Research such as that just described has considerable significance as it resulted in the development, over a very short period of time, of highly effective techniques oriented more to the Western mind and lifestyle. The impact of these techniques on our ability to regain control of our lives and effectively cope with stress has been profound.

Relaxation

There are many different relaxation techniques. One of the most popular is **progressive muscular relaxation (PMR)**. This technique originated in the 1930s with Edmund Jacobson, who spent 50 years of his life developing it. The literature abounds with variations on Jacobson's original relaxation strategies. For example, work done by Bernstein and Borkovec (1973) is widely cited. (We provide you with the opportunity to practise this technique through instructions provided at the end of this chapter.) Another method, autogenic training, is an imagery-based relaxation technique developed in Europe by Schutz and Luthe (1959). As well, Herbert Benson, as a result of his interest in transcendental meditation, developed a secular form of meditation that he described as being based on achieving the "relaxation response" (1975).

Although there are many different relaxation techniques, they share many similar features. Generally they recommend a quiet, undisturbed setting, where one can sit passively, usually with eyes closed, and allow the muscles to completely relax. It is of major importance that patterns of deep, rhythmical breathing be observed, although variations on breathing are often used.

Meditation has been used throughout history to reduce stress, and there are many different forms of meditation practised throughout the world. Again, they usually share common features, such as positioning and attention to the *process* of thought rather than its *outcome*. There are differences in approach though, particularly as many of these forms of meditation are based on religious belief systems. A system that has greatly influenced Western culture recently is **transcendental meditation (TM)**. An important aspect of TM is the extensive body of empirical research that has accumulated regarding the efficacy of the meditative practice. A consistent picture emerges indicating that the practice of TM has a beneficial physiological and psychological impact on an individual and that its benefits accrue with time (Alexander, Robinson, Orme-Johnson, Schneider, & Walton, 1994; Dillbeck & Orme-Johnson, 1987). Techniques such as this have important implications for stress and coping. **Biofeedback** is another technique that has received significant attention with regard to the possibility of modifying physiological processes. This involves recording physiological measures with electronic instruments that provide immediate information or feedback concerning the subject's physiological state. The implication is that, since it has been shown that we may be able to exercise conscious control over aspects of our physiology, this feedback could allow us to make beneficial alterations where necessary.

This observation has led to the extensive development of a biofeedback technology aimed at controlling physiological variables, such as muscle tension, heart rate, blood pressure, brain wave activity, and skin temperature. For example, electromyography (EMG) has been widely used to record and modify muscle tension in specific muscle groups in the body. Temperature control of blood flow has been examined in the context of migraine headaches and Raynaud's disease (Blanchard & Haynes, 1975; Green, Green, & Walters, 1972). The initial enthusiasm for biofeedback was considerable; however, this enthusiasm has since been somewhat tempered by realistic evaluations of its efficacy. It appears that many of the effects attributed to biofeedback have more to do with the general state of relaxation, or the relaxation response, experienced during the procedure than the specific feedback provided (Straub, 2007). This development has been disappointing,

progressive muscular relaxation (PMR): a technique in which a person achieves relaxation by flexing and gradually relaxing muscle groups.

meditation: a form of relaxation in which one attempts to focus attention fully on a single thought or image.

transcendental meditation (TM): a technique of meditation to reduce stress introduced by Maharishi Mahesh Yogi in the late 1950s.

biofeedback: the recording of physiological measures through electronic instruments that provide immediate feedback concerning a subject's physiological state in an attempt to modify physiological processes.

particularly given the promise the technique held for teaching individuals to gain control of their physical and psychological states and thereby being able to effect important changes in lifestyle and subsequently their health.

Behaviour Therapy and Cognitive Therapy

In the fields of behaviour therapy and cognitive therapy, numerous strategies have been developed that have direct relevance for coping with stress. For example, Wolpe (1958) developed the technique of **systematic desensitization** to help people cope with fear and anxiety. It is based on the principle of reciprocal inhibition between the sympathetic and parasympathetic nervous systems and the position that anxiety and relaxation are incompatible responses. The client is initially trained in a relaxation technique and asked to construct a hierarchy of events that elicit increasing levels of anxiety. The client is then encouraged by the therapist to imagine or visualize these events from the least to the most anxiety-provoking. The technique assumes that imagining the feared event results in significant anxiety.

Our ability to create high levels of stress as a function of our thinking is a fundamental principle underlying our discussions in this chapter. Through cognitive exposure to the feared situation we enter into the process of *desensitization*. At the point at which the anxiety attached to imagining a particular event becomes unpleasant, the client is encouraged to use relaxation to decrease arousal. The process of pairing these two inhibiting responses can lead to a significant reduction in the stress associated with the event that might involve situations such as undergoing a medical procedure, such as an MRI or an injection, flying on an airplane, speaking in public, or writing an exam. It is clear that a crucial component of this process is the repeated exposure to the feared situation, which ultimately leads to fear reduction (Newman, Hofmann, Trabert, Roth, & Taylor, 1994).

Modelling is another procedure that can be used effectively to reduce stress associated with fear-provoking situations. Bandura (1986, 1997), who has described this process in detail, points out that most human behaviour is learned through the observation of models. We acquire cognitive skills and new behaviours through observing others. The influence of a model can serve to instruct, inhibit, disinhibit, facilitate, enhance environmental effects, and arouse emotions. Individuals can learn to cope with stressful situations by observing models. The process is similar to that of desensitization in that observing a model coping well with an anxiety-provoking situation serves to reduce fear.

In **participant modelling**, the individual observes a model coping with the anxiety-evoking situation. The individual is then encouraged to imitate the model and engage in the behaviour while receiving reassurance from the model (Ritter, 1968). The model may also be presented symbolically through videos or films. This procedure has been used effectively by Melamed and her colleague to help reduce children's anxieties about hospitalization and medical procedures (Melamed & Siegal, 1975). It has also been used with adults to prepare them for the stress of aversive medical procedures. Bandura argues that modelling is an effective intervention because it increases the individual's sense of self-efficacy (1997).

In **cognitive restructuring**, maladaptive, stress-producing cognitions are identified and replaced with ones that are more appropriate. A well-known approach to cognitive restructuring is based on the work of Albert Ellis, who developed *Rational Emotive Behaviour*

systematic desensitization: a technique to help people cope with fear and anxiety by combining relaxation with gradual exposure to the fear-inducing stimulus.

modelling: a technique used to reduce stress associated with fear-provoking situations, in which observing a model coping well with a situation facilitates a similar response by the observer in a similar situation.

participant modelling: a technique used to reduce stress in which, subsequent to an individual's observing a model coping with an anxiety-evoking situation, the person is encouraged to engage in the behaviour while receiving reassurance from the model.

cognitive restructuring: a technique whereby maladaptive, stress-producing cognitions are identified and replaced with ones that are more appropriate.

Therapy (REBT) (Ellis, 1962; Ellis & Grieger, 1977). Ellis posits that it is our beliefs about events, not the events themselves, that create stressful emotional reactions. The sequence proceeds in the following manner: an event occurs, it is interpreted irrationally, and negative emotions and inappropriate behaviours follow. Ellis has identified specific logical errors that form the basis of this irrational thinking, such as overgeneralization, catastrophizing, and absolute thinking. To reduce the stress of the experience, it is necessary to identify the thoughts that are based on irrational beliefs, challenge the irrational beliefs, and replace them with thoughts based on rational beliefs. This approach has been used effectively in managing stress-related emotional states, such as anxiety, anger, fear, and depression, as well as in dealing with behavioural concerns, such as Type A behaviour and obesity.

The work of Beck is similar to that of Ellis in its emphasis on helping people to modify distorted cognitions (Beck, 1963, 1976). Beck describes his approach as *cognitive therapy*. Although it was initially developed to treat depression, cognitive therapy has now been applied to a wide variety of psychological problems. It differs from REBT in encouraging people to identify their dysfunctional beliefs and then to put these beliefs through a process of hypothesis testing, or what Beck calls "collective empiricism," to test their validity.

The final behavioural stress management technique we will consider here is based on the work of Donald Meichenbaum and is appropriately called **stress inoculation training** (Meichenbaum, 1977, 1985). This is a package of procedures designed to help people cope effectively with stressful events.

stress inoculation training: a technique designed to help people cope effectively with stressful events; includes reconceptualizing events in less stressful ways, improving coping strategies, and applying the reconceptualized cognitive and behavioural approach to relevant stressors.

Initially, individuals are asked to examine how they conceptualize stressful events and are taught that those events can be reconceptualized in less stressful ways. They are encouraged to view coping as a process in which they can prepare for, confront, and cope with stressful events. In the second phase, they learn and rehearse coping strategies such as relaxation training, problem solving, and self-reinforcement. In the third phase, this reconceptualized approach, both cognitive and behavioural, is applied to relevant situations. This can be done initially through imagery and role-playing and then applied gradually to situations eliciting increasingly higher levels of stress.

Like many cognitive and behavioural strategies, stress inoculation training has been applied with success to a wide variety of problems within the health psychology realm. For example, Vocks, Ockenfels, Jurgensen, Mussgay, and Ruddel (2004) demonstrated that blood pressure reactivity was effectively reduced using a cognitive behavioural stress management program in comparison to training in progressive muscular relaxation. The components of the program included the following: psychoeducation regarding stress and its impact, a behavioural analysis of individual patterns of stress-related behaviours, time management, cognitive restructuring, problem solving, assertiveness training, the use of positive affirmations, and the identification of short- and long-term stress management strategies.

The last 15 years have seen a dramatic increase in the development and practice in psychology of mindfulness and acceptance-based behavioural interventions such as acceptance and commitment therapy (ACT; Hayes, Strosahl, & Wilson, 1999) and mindfulness-acceptance-commitment (MAC; Gardner & Moore, 2012). These approaches promote the development of "mindful nonjudgemental awareness of internal experiences, acceptance of internal states, and a willingness to experience these states while engaging in behaviors that are congruent with one's personal life values" (Gardner & Moore, 2010, p. 187).

An important technique in enhancing mindfulness is meditation which helps to bring about an awareness of immediate experience and focus on the present moment.

Self-help manuals that provide do-it-yourself instruction in coping with stress abound in our culture today (e.g., Abascal, Brucato, & Brucato, 2001; Davis, Eshelman, & MacKay, 2008; Girdano, Dusek, & Everly, 2005; Romas & Sharma, 2004; Tompkins, 2013). Although they provide evidence about the pervasiveness of stress in today's world, they serve a very useful function in allowing individuals to self-regulate their own behaviour and to actively engage in what is usually described as a positive process. Girdano et al. (2005) state that "stress is a gift of motivation and a compass to remind us we are off course. However, your whole life is your journey, so there is no need to hurry—if you miss this bus (or lesson) or if this bus takes you only part of the way, there will be another along shortly" (p. xix).

As part of this self-help process and as we bring this chapter to an end, we thought that, after speaking so much about stress and coping, we should provide you with the opportunity to experience the benefits of relaxation for yourself. So read on.

The Relaxation Responses: A Personal Guide

You can have someone else read the relaxation script to you, you can make a tape of it, or you can commit it to memory and take yourself through it. We'll provide you with a general overview and the specifics of the technique. It's based on the original procedure developed by Jacobson in the 1930s and subsequently modified by Bernstein and Borkovec (1973) and Bernstein and Given (1984). A basic component of the procedure is learning to identify the sensations associated with muscular tension and relaxation through tensing and then relaxing different muscle groups in the body. It's important to realize that learning relaxation skills is like learning any other skill—no one else can do it for you; it's not a matter of desire, it's a skill that needs to be learned. This means learning the technique and practising it.

You will be asked to tense a specific muscle group initially to become aware of what muscle tension feels like and to be able to compare it to the experience of relaxation. As well, if the muscle group is tensed prior to relaxation a greater reduction in muscle tension will occur upon relaxation.

Rest in a comfortable position such as in a recliner or lying down, with support for your head and spine. Do not cross your legs or arms, and try to minimize body movements. Close your eyes so as to be less aware of your external surroundings and loosen any tight items of clothing. During the relaxation session, breathe slowly and regularly. Tense each muscle group for 5 to 7 seconds and relax it on cue for 30 to 40 seconds. If you have a tape of the procedure or someone is guiding you through it, a cue word such as "tense" can be used to signal the beginning of the tension phase and "relax" to signal the relaxation phase.

The tension phase need not be extreme and should not involve any pain to the muscle. If you feel pain or cramping, shorten the period of tension. You only need to tighten the muscles, not strain them. At the beginning of the relaxation phase, you should focus your attention on the sensations attached to the reduction in tension and the increase in relaxation in the muscles.

It's usual to relax each muscle group twice, although it's not inappropriate to continue the tension/relaxation sequence in a particular muscle group several times until a desired depth of relaxation is obtained. There are many variations on the sequence and methods used; the following is one example. As you practise and develop your relaxation skills, it's important to remember that you do not need to try to relax—you just let it happen. Increased effort is not the key to success; rather, you need to take a passive stance, let go, and enjoy the experience.

1. Dominant hand and forearm: make your hand into a tight fist, then relax.
2. Non-dominant hand and forearm; make your hand into a tight fist, then relax.
3. Dominant upper arm: bend your arm at the elbow and bring your hand toward your shoulder, then relax.
4. Non-dominant upper arm: bend your arm at the elbow and bring your hand toward your shoulder, then relax.
5. Forehead: raise your eyebrows and wrinkle your forehead, then relax.
6. Eyes: close your eyes tighter, then relax.
7. Lower face and jaws: clench your teeth and tighten the corners of your mouth, then relax.
8. Shoulders: raise your shoulders as if to touch your ears, then relax.
9. Chest: take a deep breath and hold it, then relax.
10. Abdomen: tighten the stomach muscles, then relax.
11. Legs one: point your toes downward, away from your body, then relax.
12. Legs two: bring your toes upward, toward your body, then relax.
13. Scan your body for residual tension: if tension is experienced in a muscle group, repeat the tension/relaxation sequence for that muscle group.
14. Take some time to enjoy the feelings of relaxation in your body.
15. You can end the session by counting backward from five to one, becoming more alert as you count down. When you get to one, open your eyes.

The procedure will take approximately 30 minutes. You should practise the technique regularly for optimal effectiveness; every day would be ideal. When you begin to learn a relaxation procedure, it's best to do so in a setting that is quiet and comfortable, where distractions are minimal, and in which you are not likely to be disturbed. This may require some preparation on your part, but it will make it easier to focus your attention on learning the technique.

As you become more skilled at relaxation, you'll want to generalize the learning experience to those places in your life where relaxation is most needed (e.g., your workplace, a performance activity, social situations). When you become more familiar with the relaxation experience, as indicated by greater levels of relaxation both during and outside the relaxation sessions, you can cut out the tension phase of the sequence and focus only on the relaxation of the muscle. Increased familiarity with the sensations of relaxation will make it unnecessary for you to have the feeling of tension to compare them to.

With time, you'll be able to combine muscle groups in obvious ways. For example, the four-group procedure involves the following groups: (1) hands and arms; (2) head; (3) chest, shoulders, and abdomen; and (4) legs. Combining muscle groups will reduce the time of the procedure to less than 10 minutes. Eventually, you will be able to achieve a relaxed state simply by recalling the sensations of the relaxed muscle groups together with deep breathing and a cue word such as "relax" or "let go." Ultimately, you should be able to achieve this relaxed state simply through a countdown in combination with deep breathing. When you have arrived at this level, you will have achieved the desired skill level. You should continue to practise and use this skill. It is a powerful resource for coping with stress.

CHAPTER SUMMARY

- Define stress and coping.

  The terms *stress* and *coping* are somewhat difficult to define as they have a highly idiosyncratic meaning for each of us. My stress is not your stress and your coping strategies may not be the same as mine. It is important to achieve some consensus regarding the meaning of these concepts.

- Understand the physiology of stress.

  Central to our understanding of stress is the concept of *homeostasis*, which describes the body's attempt to maintain a stable physiological internal environment. In this context, Cannon articulated the *fight or flight response*, which describes a complex autonomic response to perceived threat.

  The physiology of stress involves a highly complex response to perceived threat that involves the *nervous system* and the *endocrine system*. The nervous system is composed of the *central nervous system* and the *peripheral nervous system*. The former is made up of the brain and spinal cord, while the latter is made up of the sympathetic and parasympathetic nervous systems. The endocrine system responds to stress more slowly but its effects may persist for much longer.

- Understand the cognitive components of stress.

  General Adaptation Syndrome describes a three-stage response to stress made up of *alarm, resistance,* and *exhaustion,* which focuses essentially on physiological processes. Alternatively *cognitive transactional models* focus more on the role of *cognitive appraisals* in determining whether or not an event will be perceived as stressful.

- Appreciate the role of personality in stress and coping.

  It is possible that certain personality styles predispose an individual to specific stress responses and specific illnesses. A widely researched set of personality traits, the *Type A behaviour pattern,* has been identified as a risk factor for coronary cardiovascular disease.

- Identify different coping styles.

  Coping is the process by which individuals attempt to manage stress. This can be achieved through *problem-focused coping* or *emotion-focused coping*. The former involves identifying the problem and choosing a solution, whereas the latter focuses more on managing emotional responses to stress.

- Identify strategies for coping with stress.

  Highly effective procedures are available to help us cope, both physiologically and psychologically, with stress. These include strategies such as relaxation techniques, biofeedback, meditation, and behavioural and cognitive approaches to stress management.

Chapter 3
Psychoneuroimmunology

Yuri Arcurse/Shutterstock

Learning Objectives

After studying this chapter, you will be able to:

1. explain why psychoneuroimmunology (PNI) is important to health psychology.
2. read and understand research papers on PNI.
3. cite research evidence to show that there is a biological relationship between psychological state and health.
4. explain fundamental biological mechanisms linking psychological state and health.

Lori's last exam was scheduled for December 11. She was flying home the next day and was really looking forward to being home for a while. However, she expected she would spend the first few days with a bad cold or maybe the flu. Lori was a third-year student who was experienced with final exams and flying home, but didn't know why she got sick every year after December exams.

Was there something about being home that made Lori sick? That didn't seem likely. She got along well with her family and loved her parents' cooking. Maybe it was the airplane. She had heard about "bad air" on planes. But Lori played university volleyball and flew with the team all the time without ever getting sick.

Could it be the exams? That seemed more likely, since Lori often got sick right after April finals, too, and she didn't fly home until mid-May. Lori finally concluded that writing exams somehow affected her immune system.

Lori is not alone. Many university students get sick either during or just after exams. Indeed, research has shown that immune-system functioning is altered during exam time (e.g., Glaser et al., 1993; Lester et al., 2010). Glaser and colleagues measured immune-system functioning in medical students 1 month before an exam period and then again on the last day of that exam period. They found significant declines in a number of indicators of **immunocompetence**—the extent to which our immune system is functioning properly to ward off microorganisms that invade our bodies. Researchers have also found that self-hypnosis and massage therapy can actually reduce these exam-related effects on the immune system by reducing stress (Gruzelier, 2003; Kiecolt-Glaser, Marucha, Atkinson, & Glaser, 2001; Zeitlin, Keller, Shiflett, Schleifer, & Bartlett, 2000).

immunocompetence: the extent to which an immune system is functioning properly to ward off microorganisms.

This sort of research raises a number of important questions for students of health psychology. How is immunocompetence assessed in studies like this? What biological mechanisms link a psychological state, such as stress, to immune-system functioning? How strong is this link? These are some of the key questions addressed by **psychoneuroimmunology (PNI)**, which is the study of the relationship between psychological states and the functioning of the immune system.

psychoneuroimmunology (PNI): the study of the relationship between psychological states and the functioning of the immune system.

The term *psychoneuroimmunology* is best understood by dividing it into its three component parts. Our psychology (*psycho*) affects nervous system functioning (*neuro*), which, in turn, affects our immunity to disease (*immunology*). PNI is interested in the interaction among three of the body's major systems: the nervous system, the endocrine system, and the immune system (Glaser & Kiecolt-Glaser, 2005). In this chapter, you will learn how research has explored the interactions among these systems and how the systems are affected by a number of psychological states. We begin with an explanation of why PNI is so important to the discipline of health psychology.

THE IMPORTANCE OF PNI TO HEALTH PSYCHOLOGY

In chapter 1, we traced the development of health psychology from its roots. Many of the people participating in this early development cautioned that, while health psychology held considerable promise, it would be essential to avoid extravagant and unsubstantiated claims regarding what was known and what could be achieved in terms of improving health through psychological interventions. One important piece of the puzzle missing in those days was empirical proof that psychological states were directly linked to biological processes. Psychoneuroimmunology has uncovered that piece.

PNI research not only provides much-needed information linking psychology and health, but also provides data in a form that makes sense to people whose training is biomedical in nature. As such, PNI research represents an invaluable bridge between social scientists and health care providers and increases the credibility of health psychology in the eyes of health care providers.

HOW IMMUNE-SYSTEM FUNCTIONING IS MEASURED IN PNI RESEARCH

One of our main objectives in presenting this section on measuring immune-system function is to help you develop a familiarity with the language used in PNI research, without which the research can be confusing to read. With this objective in mind, we will focus on the *language* of PNI research as well as the *processes* involved in assessing immune-system function.

The *dependent variable* in an experiment is the variable we measure to determine if our treatment or manipulation has had any effect. In PNI research, dependent variables take the form of measures of immunocompetence. The manipulation, or *independent variable*, is usually some psychological state. This can be naturally occurring, as was the case with the stress caused by Lori's exams in our opening example, or it can be experimentally induced by putting people through stressful experiences or presenting them with stimuli aimed at eliciting positive moods, such as happiness.

For several reasons, measuring the impact of psychological state on immune functioning is a complex business. First, immune-system cells are located in a number of places throughout the body, such as the tonsils, appendix, small intestine, spleen, and bone marrow. This makes it difficult to just go to the source and measure activity. Instead, we must assess cellular activity in the bloodstream or mucus. Second, there are a variety of forms this cellular activity can take, and these operate independently of each other. So it is possible that a psychological state might influence one aspect of immune functioning and not another. This means that researchers must assess a number of immune-system cellular functions to ascertain the potential impact of a situation or mood state. It also means that two studies assessing the impact of the same psychological variable, such as exam stress, might come to different conclusions depending on which aspect of immune functioning is being assessed—that which fights off colds or that which kills tumour cells, for example.

Counting Cells to Measure Immunocompetence

Immune-system function is dependent on the system's ability to produce, or *proliferate*, cells to do its work. One simple way of measuring immunocompetence is to count these cells (typically white blood cells) as they exist in the bloodstream. This cell counting is called an **enumerative assay** and is common in PNI research. In studies using cell counts, you will see lymphocyte measures taken from blood samples, counting such white blood cells as NK, T, and B cells. Researchers look for two things in these counts—a minimum number of cells for adequate immune function and a balance between various cell types, such as different types of T cells (Herbert & Cohen, 1993).

enumerative assay: a lab test done to count cells (typically white blood cells) as they exist in the bloodstream.

In general, the better the immune system functions, the higher these counts are. Studies using cell counts will often report lower cell counts in blood samples taken from groups of individuals who have been exposed to a stressor, such as an exam.

Functional Tests of Immunocompetence: Measuring Cells in Action

functional tests of immunity: tests done to assess the immune system at work.

Counting cells can be informative, but it is even more important to assess the immune system *at work*. This is what **functional tests of immunity** do (Cohen & Herbert, 1996). We can perform these functional tests inside the body, though this can be difficult because it is hard to localize the sites of the immune system. However, we can also measure cell functions by *removing* them from the body and incubating them with other cells to see how the immune-system cells respond. Functional tests performed on cells outside the body are called *in vitro* tests. Those performed inside the body are called *in vivo* tests.

mitogen: a relatively harmless substance that stimulates immune cell activity as though the immune cell were acting against an invading cell or antigen.

In vitro tests of immunocompetence start with a blood sample that is combined with a substance called a **mitogen**. A mitogen is a substance that stimulates immune-cell activity as though the immune cell were acting against an invading cell, or antigen. Three of the most common mitogens used in PNI research are concanavalin A (Con A), phytohemagglutinin (PHA), and pokeweed mitogen (PWM).

A PNI study might say "people whose interactions with others were less confrontational showed greater lymphocyte proliferation in response to PHA." Translated, this means that blood samples taken from people who differed in the amount of confrontation they experienced in their interactions with others were incubated with PHA. From this, researchers discovered that the blood of people whose interactions were less confrontational produced more lymphocytes when exposed to PHA. Other studies using this general design might substitute Con A or PWM as the mitogen, or they might run a number of tests (or *assays* as they are sometimes called) using two or more different mitogens. In these studies, you will see data reported separately for each mitogen.

Natural killer (NK) cell activity is also measured through *in vitro* techniques. Because NK cells perform a "seek and destroy" function, researchers measure their activity by exposing NK cells to diseased cells, usually tumour cells. For this reason, PNI research linking psychological variables to cancer often measures NK cell activity.

NK cell cytotoxic activity assay: test in which the proliferation and effectiveness of NK cells is measured after they have been exposed to diseased cells.

NK cell lysis: destroying tumour cells by exposing them to NK cells.

After exposure, NK cells are assessed in two ways. In one, *proliferation* is measured through cell counts taken after the introduction of tumour cells. In the other, NK cell *effectiveness* is assessed by measuring the destruction of the tumour cells. In PNI literature, this second method is often called an **NK cell cytotoxic activity assay**. This process of killing tumour cells is called **NK cell lysis** because to *lyse* a tumour cell means to destroy it. PNI researchers, especially those dealing with cancer, might talk of "a decrease (or increase) in NK cytotoxic activity," or "a significant effect on NK cell lysis." It is important to note that NK cells aren't the only immune-system cells capable of cytotoxic activity. However, they are commonly measured in PNI studies involving cancer.

There are also a number of *in vivo* functional tests of immunocompetence. Here, we will look at two of the more common types. One takes advantage of the fact that almost everyone carries herpesviruses. The other uses injections of small dosages of antigens.

Once you have been exposed to a herpesvirus, you carry it with you for life. The virus is usually present in such small quantities that you don't experience any symptoms, but it is there all the same. There are many different types of herpesviruses, from cold sores to Epstein–Barr virus. One reason you don't have to spend much time worrying about herpesviruses is that your immune system does the worrying for you by producing antibodies (Ab) whose job it is to "flag" herpesviruses for destruction, thus keeping their numbers under control. Herpesviruses will multiply, however, when the immune system is suppressed, thus creating the need for more Ab. Therefore, we can determine immunocompetence by measuring Ab. Be careful when you read studies that use this measure, though. The more suppressed the immune system, the more herpesviruses, and thus the more Ab. This means that, when herpesvirus-specific antibodies are being measured, the *higher* the Ab count, the *poorer* the immune-system function.

Researchers can also introduce an antigen into the body and measure the specific Ab activity meant to deal with that intrusion. In these studies, small quantities of an antigen are introduced by injection or nasal spray. After this is done, scientists measure immune-system activity in two ways. In the simplest, the skin is observed at the site of the injection. If the immune system is working properly, there should be swelling and redness. Appropriate amounts of inflammation are signs of a properly functioning immune system.

We can also count antigen-specific Ab produced in response to the injection. This can be done through blood samples or mucous secretions that are measured most often in the saliva. One antibody commonly measured in the saliva or mucus is called sIgA, which stands for *secretory* or *salivary immunoglobulin* A antibody. Because it exists in saliva and mucus, it represents one of the body's first lines of defence against antigens (Tomasi, 1971). But measuring salivary sIgA isn't always as easy as it sounds. What happens when we want to measure sIgA levels during times of stress? Many people experience "dry mouth" at these times; that is, they don't produce much saliva.

Again, be careful when you read studies about tests that measure Ab production to assess immunocompetence. It is easy to get confused about the meaning of Ab counts, because they have opposite meanings depending upon whether the count is herpesvirus-specific or in response to an injection. In herpesvirus studies, higher Ab counts indicate *immunosuppression*. An increase in that virus comes about because of suppression of the immune system. In the case of injection studies, more Ab indicates *better* immunocompetence. In these studies, the antigen is introduced into the body. This means that Ab is being produced by a *competent* immune system that is dealing with an invading antigen. These herpesvirus studies have proven important, since this virus is linked to shingles, a painful condition found primarily in older adults (Irwin, Pike, Cole, & Oxman, 2003), and Epstein–Barr virus, considered a precursor to mononucleosis. Also, medical students experiencing exam stress (Glaser et al., 2005) and people who had lived through childhood adversity (Fagundes, Glaser, Malarkey, & Kiecolt-Glaser, 2013) had elevated levels of antibodies associated with Epstein–Barr virus.

Methodological Issues in the Measurement of Immune-System Function

As you read through the preceding section on measurement, did you wonder just *how* these blood samples were taken and *when*, given that the independent variable in much PNI work is often stress related? Can we casually draw blood from someone who is in the middle of an argument with her husband or studying for final exams? Hardly. In PNI research, a sophisticated knowledge of measurement techniques and biological processes is needed. Measurement of immune functioning is intrusive, and it requires skill. Certainly, conducting research in psychoneuroimmunology is not without its challenges.

Short-Term versus Long-Term Effects

In PNI research, we must make an important distinction between short-term and long-term effects. In laboratory research, it is common for a participant to be subjected to an **acute stressor**, which is to say one that is immediate in its duration and proximity. The effects of this acute stressor are then measured through blood samples taken just before, just after, and then some time (minutes to hours) after the stressor has been introduced. Studies of this nature measure how quickly the immune system is affected. As we will see in the next section, when we look at specific studies in PNI, short-term changes in immune-system function occur quite commonly in the face of these acute stressors. The complication here lies in the fact that acute stressors can actually enhance immune function by stimulating nonspecific, or innate, immunity while suppressing immunity to specific diseases (Moraska et al., 2002). Chronic stress, on the other hand, suppresses both nonspecific and specific immunity (Mercado, Mercado, Quan, Padgett, Sheridan, & Marucha, 2002).

acute stressor: a stressor that is immediate in its duration and proximity.

Not all psychological variables occur on an acute basis. Trait anxiety, job stress, marital problems, loneliness, and many other facts of life are *chronic*, or long term. Their effects are more like a constant hum than a single blast. Psychoneuroimmunological research designed to measure the effects of chronic stressors cannot rely on well-controlled laboratory environments. Instead, field research must study people exposed to these stressors and compare their immune functioning to those who are not exposed (e.g., Barnett, Steptoe, & Gareis, 2005; Robles & Kiecolt-Glaser, 2003). It is much more difficult to ascertain definitive cause-and-effect relationships in these studies because there are so many other variables in field work that cannot be controlled.

Statistical Significance versus Clinical Significance

In any scientific endeavour, researchers need to be aware that data might be statistically significant without being clinically or socially significant. This fact is of great relevance to PNI studies attempting to determine if an aspect of the immune system has been affected by a person's psychology.

To prove that some aspect of immune functioning has been affected, we must be able to show that the difference in cell count or cytotoxic activity between groups of subjects is too large to have occurred by chance. In such a case, the results are said to be *statistically significant*. This means that there is a less than 1-in-20 chance that the differences detected would occur without the experimental manipulation.

Statistical significance may be scientifically important, but is it *clinically* important? In other words, do the statistically significant differences mean that people are actually more or less likely to get sick? Or are the differences, though statistically detectable, too small to affect our susceptibility to illness? These are important questions for PNI research, because it is entirely possible that our statistical tests are more sensitive to cellular differences than our bodies are.

PNI researchers have responded to these questions, although such studies are difficult to carry out for a multitude of reasons. If we want to study the link between immunocompromise and illnesses such as cancer that take a relatively long time to develop, then we must take our measurements regularly, on a longitudinal, prospective basis. This means that we must start with participants who are well, follow them over a long period, take regular assays, and compare the results for those who get sick with those who do not. This work isn't impossible, but it is expensive, intrusive, and fraught with extraneous variables that can account for health differences.

One way to get around these problems is to expose healthy people to antigens and psychological factors in the same study. Then we can observe the progression of symptom display while we monitor immune functioning. In studies that follow this approach, volunteers are exposed to a cold virus or similar pathogen, and the disease course is monitored for a 2- or 3-week period following exposure. Some of the volunteers in the study go through a stressful life event, such as an exam period, allowing researchers to monitor their immune cell activity as well as symptom progression.

RESEARCH IN PNI: PROVIDING EVIDENCE FOR A BIOLOGICAL LINK BETWEEN PSYCHOLOGY AND HEALTH

In the following overview of PNI research, we have organized the studies according to the psychological factors measured. Some factors, including depression, state anxiety, and short-term stress, are acute in nature. Others, including personality factors such as cynical hostility, coping styles, and social support, are more chronic or long term. As you read through the summary of these studies, keep in mind the methodological issues discussed in the previous section. We have tried to select studies that represent the field of PNI and use dependent measures and terminology consistent with those introduced earlier in this chapter. If you get confused at any point as you read this section, refer back to our explanations in the section entitled "How Immune-System Functioning is Measured in Psychoneuroimmunological Research."

Some of these students will catch a cold or flu after final exams are over because their immune systems have been compromised by stress.
Western News

The Effect of Stress on Immune Functioning

In the opening of this chapter, you read about Lori, a university student who regularly got either a cold or the flu just after exams. The assumption is that the stress of exams increased Lori's susceptibility to these illnesses by compromising her immune system. Health psychologists have studied students' immune functioning before, during, and after exams for some time (e.g., Jemmott et al., 1983; Wadee, Kuschke, Kometz, & Berk, 2001). The general finding has been that symptom complaint goes up at these times and that cellular measures of immune response indicate immunosuppression. Exams are examples of acute stressors. Chronic stress also affects immune functioning and has even been linked to premature aging (Kiecolt-Glaser, 2003), so Lori shouldn't spend her whole life writing exams!

Before we can link stress to disease using PNI research, we need to refer to the working definition of stress introduced in chapter 2. From that chapter, you might recall the work of Lazarus and Folkman (1984), who defined stress as an aversive condition in which the demands of a situation are perceived to be greater than our ability to cope with them.

In the laboratory, volunteers have been exposed to acute, short-term stressors, such as having to make speeches or perform mental tasks under time pressure. At the same time, their immune functioning was monitored. Using designs such as these, researchers can learn about the immediacy with which a stressor can affect immune functioning. Such studies have discovered that, while it may take days for the immune system to react to an antigen, it takes as little as 5 minutes for a stressor to inhibit the ability of the immune system to engage that response (Herbert et al., 1994). Laboratory studies have also shown that the effect of stressors on immune functioning is stable over time for a given individual, leading to the conclusion that there are dispositional or personality factors that influence the extent to which a stressor affects immunity (Wadee et al., 2001). Similarly, laboratory research has demonstrated that people differ in their physiological reactivity to a stressor, as measured by cortisol levels. Not surprisingly, highly reactive people show the greatest incidence of such things as upper respiratory infections in the face of real-life stressors (Cohen, Rodriguez, Feldman, Rabin, & Manuck, 2002).

In addition to laboratory studies of the effects of acute stressors, other work has investigated chronic, long-term stress as it occurs in real life. Boscarino (1997) conducted a 20-year follow-up of 332 Vietnam veterans who had presented symptoms of post-traumatic stress disorder (PTSD). He compared their health to 1067 veterans who did not suffer from PTSD. PTSD was reasoned to be evidence of severe stress exposure.

Boscarino discovered that the veterans who had suffered from PTSD were significantly more likely to suffer from a wide range of medical problems, including circulatory, digestive, musculoskeletal, and metabolic ailments. The worst problems were nervous system disorders, which PTSD veterans were 2.47 times more likely to suffer from than non-PTSD vets, and non-sexually transmitted infectious diseases, which they were 2.14 times more likely to contract.

Two aspects of this study are particularly noteworthy. First, Boscarino controlled 14 other factors that could account for increased susceptibility to illness, including substance abuse, hypochondriasis, age, and smoking history. Controlling for these external variables makes it significantly more valid to attribute the higher odds of suffering from this wide variety of illnesses to the effects of the stress. Second, the long range of the follow-up (20 years) demonstrated that severe stress exposure can have long-term effects.

Studies based on the Canadian Community Health Survey have shown that people with PTSD have higher rates of respiratory disease, cardiovascular disease, chronic pain syndromes, gastrointestinal illnesses, and cancer (Sareen et al., 2007). In the Netherlands, people who experienced PTSD after an explosion at a fireworks depot were more likely to subsequently experience vascular, musculoskeletal, and dermatological problems (Dirkzwager, van der Velden, Grievink, & Yzermans, 2007). Researchers in this study had access to people's health records from before the disaster, so they could compare pre- and post-disaster health data.

Research on clusters of symptoms experienced by veterans of the Gulf War has also implicated the immune system (Ferguson & Cassaday, 1999, 2002). The authors also hypothesize that these symptoms persist, in part, because of classically conditioned associations triggered by such stimuli as smells and tastes.

Other research has shown that immune function is affected by exposure to natural disasters. Survivors of Hurricane Andrew in the United States, for example, showed disruption in their sIgA counts (Rotton & Dubitsky, 2002), and those who lived through an earthquake in Northridge, California, showed a positive correlation between immunocompromise and the degree of distress experienced up to 4 months after the quake (Solomon, Segerstrom, Grohr, Kemeny, & Fahey, 1997).

In another study of real-life stressors and their effect on general health and the immune system, Kiecolt-Glaser and colleagues (1987) took multiple measures of immune functioning from women who were divorced or separated within the past year. They found that these women had significantly poorer functioning on five of the six immune-system measures compared with women who were neither divorced nor separated. In a subsequent study of men, it was found that those who initiated the divorce reported better health than those whose partner had initiated it (Kiecolt-Glaser et al., 1988).

It is clear from this collection of work that stress affects health through the immune system in acute and immediate ways, as well as on a long-term basis. (For a comprehensive review of 30 years of research linking stress to the immune system, see Segerstrom & Miller, 2004). We turn now to a discussion of the link between specific illnesses and stress.

Long-term Effects of Stress: Linking Childhood Adversity with Poor Adult Health
There is a large and continually growing body of evidence to indicate that our early childhood experiences affect our health across our entire lifespan (Mulvihill, 2005). Research from the Human Early Learning Partnership (HELP) in Canada and from the studies of Adverse Childhood Experiences (ACE) in the United States is particularly telling. For example, people exposed to stress in early childhood, caused by such factors as poverty and abuse, are 1.5 to 2 times more likely to develop cardiovascular disease, cancer, and autoimmune disorders in adulthood (Anda et al., 2009; Dube et al., 2009; Fagundes, Glaser, & Kiecolt-Glaser, 2013; Miller, Chen, & Parker, 2011).

We have already discussed numerous studies documenting the relationship between stress and disease, but here we are talking about something more dramatic—effects that last a lifetime. Still, when we search for explanations for these effects, we return to PNI, while also considering the biology of genetic expression. Researchers at the University of British Columbia and elsewhere have posited a model utilizing the science of PNI and genetics to help explain the long-term effects of poverty and maltreatment in early childhood. In the words of researchers in this area, we need to know how stress gets "under the skin" (Hertzman & Boyce, 2010; Miller et al., 2011) to produce these lifelong effects.

At the heart of this model is the concept of **biological imbedding**. This is the process by which experience has permanent effects on the expression of our genetic coding and, subsequently, on a range of biological processes this coding affects. This is not the place to present a detailed explanation of these biological processes. For now, it is important to know that the DNA in our cells can be modified by epigenetic pathways that either remodel cell structures or wrap around cells that affect genetic expression. The important discovery has been that these processes are influenced by experience.

Via these epigenetic processes, the development and workings of immune cells can be permanently altered. One immune response that is particularly affected concerns the production and regulation of inflammation. As you will see in the final section of this chapter, inflammatory responses provide important clues to how stress affects immunity and our susceptibility to disease. Specifically, while we need a certain amount of inflammatory response, it is important to be able to regulate this—to shut it off. Excessive inflammation is linked to many difficulties, including cardiovascular disease.

Thus, the Biological Embedding of Childhood Adversity Model (Miller et al., 2011) posits that adverse experiences in the particularly sensitive period of early childhood impinge upon our DNA and subsequently our immune systems in ways that permanently alter cells responsible for the regulation of inflammation. The model adopts a biopsychosocial perspective in that it also states that cellular alterations manifest themselves in other ways, including what Miller and colleagues (2011) call "behavioral proclivities" (p. 966). In other words, children who have experienced adversity become predisposed to behaviours that further increase their risk for ill health. These behaviours include mistrust of others and a difficulty establishing constructive social ties. You will discover in a number of places in this book that strong social ties are an important determinant of good health. These effects are further exacerbated by a dysregulation of hormones that also accentuate inflammatory responses.

We have long known that early childhood is a formative time, featuring rapid development. We are now learning, thanks to PNI research, just how dramatic the influences of early childhood can be. Adversity quite literally lasts a lifetime.

Stress and Upper Respiratory Tract Infection

Many people doing PNI research believe that, of all the medical conditions brought on or worsened by stress, **upper respiratory tract infection (URTI)** might be the most common. Upper respiratory infection refers to a collection of common illnesses, such as colds, coughs, flu, and bronchitis. This is the category into which Lori's illness in our opening example would fall. If you have ever developed sniffles and sneezes or a nagging cough during or after exams, you may well have been a walking demonstration of the well-established relationship between stress and URTI. You might also have been producing low levels of sIgA, which provides immune defence in the mucus and saliva (thus implicating sIgA when we come down with URTI). In fact, research has shown that people who experienced high levels of stress over a 2-year period had lower secretion levels of sIgA (Phillips et al., 2006).

In field studies, we can get self-report measures of the intensity of the stress being experienced, but we can't control the event. As such, we can't know for sure whether we are dealing with the kind of events most people would find stressful, or if we have a volunteer who is particularly vulnerable to stress. Is the variable a *situational* one that might affect most people the same way, or is it a *dispositional* one that can be generalized only to certain types of people? Some might argue that it doesn't matter—if a person reports

Have You Had Your Flu Shot? Using Vaccinations to Measure Immune Responses within the Body

Many studies that investigate the relationship between stress and immune function use *in vitro* methods. While much has been learned from *in vitro* studies of this kind, concerns have been expressed about whether or not they reflect what is actually going on inside the body. In people's bodies, these cells exist in a biological milieu that is quite different from the lab dish (Fleshner & Laudenslager, 2004).

In response to this concern, a number of studies have introduced antigens into the body and then assessed immune function via blood samples (e.g., Smith, Kennedy, & Fleshner, 2004; Smith, Vollmer-Conna et al., 2004). These *in vivo* studies have the advantage of allowing immune cells to function in their normal internal environments, but how can researchers ethically introduce antigens into human participants? The answer is via routine vaccination. Vaccinations work by introducing non-toxic amounts of certain antigens into the body so that the immune system can develop specific immunities toward them. We know that poor immune responses to vaccination indicate a greater susceptibility to illness (Plotkin, 2001).

At the University of British Columbia and Carnegie Mellon University, Greg Miller, Sheldon Cohen, and colleagues have used this vaccination method. In one study (Miller et al., 2004), 83 first-year university students were given handheld computers to carry for 2 days before receiving a flu vaccine (not for H1N1) and then for 10 days after. Four times per day, the computer would sound an alarm and students responded to a series of questions about mood state, perceived stress, health behaviours, and physical symptoms. On the day of their vaccination, a 20-mL blood sample was taken to be used as a baseline for immune system measures. Students also provided saliva samples (via a chewable cotton dental roll) on 4 of the 13 days in order to assess cortisol levels.

After they received their flu shot, participants returned to the lab twice—after 1 month and again after 4 months. In each of these visits, researchers took a blood sample to assess the immune system's response to the antigen presented in the flu shot.

Miller and colleagues had a measure of perceived stress, cortisol levels, symptom experience, and immune functioning. The hypothesis was that those students reporting higher stress and cortisol levels after receiving the shot would exhibit poorer immune responses to the flu shot antigen. Their hypothesis was supported in that higher reports of stress were associated with lower levels of antibody production (though all students produced adequate responses to the shot for it to be an effective vaccination). This effect was not influenced by the health practices the students reported prior to receiving the shot, although it *was* related to reports of the amount of sleep the students were getting. Sleep reports were also correlated with stress reports.

Miller and colleagues discovered a critical period during which the stressors appeared to have the most detrimental effect on immune response. Specifically, stressors experienced before or on the day of the shot were not related to immune response. Instead, the effect started to be observed after the shot, peaking at between 8 and 10 days after the shot had been administered.

stress, then there is stress. The fact that immune functioning clearly fluctuates with self-reports of stress supports the view that these subjective reports are a valid way of assessing stress for the purposes of PNI research.

Some people are more prone to stress than others. From the perspective of PNI, we should be able to learn something about the effects of stress by studying the URTI experiences of these types of people. This is just what La Via and his colleagues (1996) set out to do. They studied 14 people with generalized anxiety disorder, a disorder characterized by excessive and chronic apprehension about a wide variety of aspects of life, such as work, family, and social contacts.

stress-intrusion scores:
a measure of the impact a stressful
event has on a person's life.

People with generalized anxiety disorder experience greater impact from stressful events, or, in the language of stress research, their **stress-intrusion scores** are high. La Via and his team members measured stress intrusion in these 14 people using the Impact of Events Scale. To measure immune functioning, they took *in vitro* measures of lymphocyte activity and kept track of the number of URTI-related sick days the subjects reported. They began by confirming that the people with generalized anxiety disorder had higher stress-intrusion scores. The researchers discovered that the anxiety group had less lymphocyte activity and almost three times more sick days than a control group. In fact, the anxiety group averaged 24.8 URTI sick days in a 12-month period, compared to only 9 days among the non-anxious control participants. The study showed that lymphocyte activity was correlated with URTI sick days and with stress intrusion.

At least one study has found that *positive* life events can also increase vulnerability to URTI (Evans, Doyle, Hucklebridge, & Clow, 1997). University students were asked to complete the Life Experience Survey as well as other measures, such as personality and stress experience. They were then monitored for just over 6 weeks for URTI episodes, which were verified with body temperature readings. It was discovered that positive life events were most closely related to URTI, independent of personality measures or health-related behaviours. This means that we need to consider the effect of *any* major event, not just the negative ones, when conducting PNI research.

Thus far, we have assumed that stress works alone to influence URTI. In the language of statistics, we have assumed a *main effects* model. However, while main effects models allow us to isolate a factor to determine its unique contribution to illness, they also oversimplify the realities of health and well-being. Stress rarely works in isolation. Instead, it *interacts* with other factors, such as social support, demographics, and personality.

In recognition of this fact, Miyazaki and colleagues (2003) have investigated the possible moderating effects of social support. Their predictor variables were perceived stress *and* perceived social support. They found that social support did help reduce the harmful effects of stress on the immune system. In particular, social support was positively correlated with NK cell production.

What can we conclude about the extent to which stress puts us at risk for upper respiratory infection? Major life event stress often results in immunosuppression. If a person is exposed to a respiratory virus at the same time, it is likely that the person will get sick. These stressful events don't all have to be recent, though they probably have an additive effect if several of them "pile up" over time.

Stress and Autoimmune Disease   When people have autoimmune diseases, their own immune systems becomes their worst enemy. These diseases cause the immune system to produce antibodies that attack the body's own tissue. In other words, the system fails at one of its hallmarks—*tolerance*. Autoimmune diseases include rheumatoid arthritis, insulin-dependent diabetes, and multiple sclerosis.

Research indicates that stress can put people at greater risk for contracting these diseases and for suffering more once they have contracted them (Homo-Delarche et al., 1991). People with PTSD are more likely to report a host of illnesses, including arthritis (Pietrzak, Goldstein, Southwick, & Grant, 2012).

For those with arthritis not associated with trauma, both relaxation and hypnosis have been effective in reducing patients' physical pain, as has the use of analgesic medication (Gay, Philippot, & Luminet, 2002). Potential exists, therefore, for these therapies to be applied successfully to other autoimmune diseases.

Stress and Cancer   A great amount of research on the relationship between stress and cancer exists in the health psychology literature. Of course, many of these studies discuss the stress brought on by cancer rather than the possibility that the cancer was brought on by stress. However, others have looked at stress as a possible risk factor for cancer (Reiche, Morimoto, & Nunes, 2005). (See Kiecolt-Glaser et al., 2002b, for a review of research linking stress to cancer and the immune system.)

One approach to understanding the relationship between stress and cancer is to conduct prospective studies: People who are cancer-free are followed over time, and their perceptions of stress and their incidence of cancer are measured. Another approach looks at the extent to which a diagnosis of, and initial treatment for, cancer are perceived to be stressful and then charts the progression of disease correlated with those perceptions of stress.

Using this latter approach, research has shown that patients reporting high perceived stress just after diagnosis and first treatment also showed poorer immune functioning (Anderson et al., 1998). Following this finding, Thornton and colleagues conducted longitudinal research in which they compared what they called the trajectory of stress following cancer diagnosis and early treatment with the trajectory of immune functioning (Thornton, Andersen, Crespin, & Carson, 2007). Not surprisingly, Thornton found that the patterns, or trajectories, of stress and immune functioning were mirror opposites of each other. In some people, as the high stress associated with initial diagnosis and treatment subsided, immune functioning improved. In those whose stress did not subside, immune function remained compromised. Thus, those who could better cope with the stress of cancer and its treatment had better prognoses.

Remember that NK cells are primarily responsible for seeking out and destroying abnormal cells. This function makes NK cells crucial in the body's ability to remain cancer free. Numerous *in vitro* studies have clearly established the relationship between stress (and other psychological factors) and NK cell activity (Herbert & Cohen, 1993). It is believed that hormones produced during stress, such as cortisol, may suppress the production of T-lymphocytes and NK cells (Maier, Watkins, & Fleshner, 1994; McEwen, 1998).

These mixed findings indicate that the progression of cancer is not always adversely affected by major life stressors. One reason for this might be that the immune system cannot detect all tumour types. Spiegel Sephton, Terr, and Stites (1998) also point out that the cause-and-effect relationship between immune-cell activity and cancer progression isn't one way. That is, while compromised immune systems may put the body at greater risk for tumour growth, the presence of cancerous cells may also bring on immunosuppression. They conclude that "the role of stress in immunosuppression and tumor progression may be central to *potentiating* existing tumor rather than *initiating* primary carcinogenesis" (p. 679). In other words, stress may worsen existing cancer but not make a person more susceptible to getting it. Further investigation is certainly warranted.

Stress-Reduction Interventions and Immune Functioning   Given the well-documented effects of stress on the immune system and illness and the clear biological links between stress response and immune function, it would make sense to study the potential immunologic benefits of psychological interventions designed to reduce stress. For example, Michael Antoni has presented a model that links the beneficial effects of cognitive-behavioural stress management to its effects on the immune systems of HIV-positive men (2003).

Greg Miller and Sheldon Cohen (2001) performed a meta-analysis using the results of 59 studies of stress-reducing interventions featuring more than 2000 participants, all of whom had chronic illnesses. Interestingly, Miller and Cohen discovered mixed results. Effects varied depending on the nature of the intervention and the form of immune response being measured. For example, interventions that featured relaxation techniques had a positive effect on sIgA production but not on any other elements of immune functioning. Hypnosis fared slightly better. Interventions using disclosure of emotions did not affect immune functioning. Furthermore, there was no *dose-response effect*, which in this case means that the length of the intervention was unrelated to its effect on the immune system.

Studies have also shown that pharmacological treatment of depression has a positive effect on NK activity (Frank, Hendricks, Johnson, Wieseler, & Burke, 1999; Irwin, Lacher, & Caldwell, 1992; Schleifer, Keller, & Bartlett, 1999). In each of these studies, it was the reduction of depressive symptoms that correlated with improvements in immune function and not the mere presence of the medication in the system. Physical exercise and diet have also been shown to moderate the negative effects of depression on immune function to combat cancer and upper respiratory tract infection (Nieman et al., 1990). Similarly, a stress reduction program was associated with an improvement in NK levels in women recently diagnosed with breast cancer (Witek-Janusek, Gabram, & Mathews, 2007).

The Effect of Depression on Immune Functioning

A body's physiological responses to stress may be adaptive in the face of the stressor, but in the long run stressors compromise its immune system. It is the *arousal* associated with stress that puts strain on our bodies. What effect, if any, do the opposite feelings associated with *under*-arousal, such as depression or sadness or loneliness, have on the immune system?

We have seen in our discussion of stress and immunity that so-called major negative life events affect immunity (see Figure 3-1). One reason for this is that these events are stressful. But another reason may relate to the impact of these events on mood (or *affect*), as they often elicit strong, unpleasant emotions, such as depression, sorrow, anger, grief, and helplessness. The death of a loved one is a clear example of such a life event. Most health psychologists believe that coping with a seriously ill loved one brings on *stress*. Coping with their death, on the other hand, brings on *negative mood*. This is why studies that measure immune functioning of a caregiver when the loved one is very ill and then again if the loved one dies allow us to differentiate between stress and mood in terms of their impact on our immune system.

An early study (Irwin, Daniels, Smith, Bloom, & Weiner, 1987) measured immune functioning in three groups of wives: (1) wives whose husbands were in good health, (2) wives whose husbands were being treated for lung cancer that had spread to other parts of the body, and (3) wives whose husbands had died from lung cancer up to

Depression

Moderating Factors
- age - stress - sleep - physical activity
- sex - body mass - smoking - alcohol
- socioeconomic status

Biological Mechanisms
- ↑corticotropin releasing hormone
- ↑hypothalamic-pituitary-adrenal axis
- ↑sympathetic nervous system

Immunologic Alterations

Immunosuppression
- altered immune cell distribution
- ↓lymphocyte proliferation
- ↓virus-specific T cell responses
- ↓memory T cell responses

Immune Activation/Inflammation
- ↑proinflammatory cytokines
- ↑acute phase proteins
- ↑chemokines
- ↑adhesion molecules

Clinical Implications

Disease Relevance
- infectious diseases
  - viruses (e.g., HIV, HCV)
  - bacteria
- cancer

Disease Relevance
- cardiovascular disease
- autoimmune disorders
- inflammatory disorders
- cancer
- sickness behaviour/depression

Figure 3-1 How Depression Affects Health

Source: Irwin, M. R., & Miller, A. H. (2007). Depressive disorders and Immunity: 20 years of progress and discovery. *Brain, Behavior, and Immunity, 21*(4), 374–383. Copyright 2007 by ELSEVIER SCIENCE & TECHNOLOGY JOURNALS. Reproduced with permission via Copyright Clearance Center.

6 months previously. It was discovered that this third group was the most depressed and also had the poorest immune functioning. A similar study of men whose wives were dying of breast cancer found that lymphocyte proliferation was better in pre-bereavement husbands than among those in the group whose wives had died (Schleifer et al., 1983).

Longitudinal work supports the conclusion that depression compromises the immune system. Having discovered that almost 25 percent of hospital patients had abnormally high depression scores, a group of researchers set out to measure the relationship between this depression and mortality. They measured depression in 454 people when they were admitted to hospital (Herrmann et al., 1998) and then monitored them for the next 22 months. Fifteen percent of them died. The strongest predictors of mortality were then identified through statistical analysis. After the expected variables of age and the nature of the illness, depression scores taken upon admission were the best predictors of mortality. When the other factors were controlled for, it was discovered that people scoring high in depression were more than three times as likely to die as those scoring low. Kinder and colleagues (2008) looked at over 35 000 U.S. military veterans, discovering that depressed patients were at increased risk of dying over a period of 5 years.

Depression has been shown to predict mortality in hospital patients, independent of age and nature of illness.
Dean Mitchell/Getty Images

By a wide range of cell counts, immune function is compromised by depression (Zorilla et al., 2001). However, this effect is more pronounced in some people than others, suggesting that other factors also come into play. For example, the effect of depression on immunity appears worse for older adults (Andreoli et al., 1993). Also, NK cell counts are more severely affected in men with depression than in women with depression (Evans et al., 1992). Not surprisingly, depression interacts with stress to increase the negative effects of each (Irwin et al., 1990).

In the Herrmann study, depression increased mortality risk for all types of patients, regardless of their age or sex. However, depression had its strongest impact on patients with cardiopulmonary disease, which is consistent with research showing that depression increases mortality risk after myocardial infarction (heart attack). (See, for example, Parker et al., 2006.) Herrmann and colleagues also found that depression increased mortality risk for patients with hematological diseases and cancer.

These studies linking mortality rates and mood provide an important first step, but because they do not measure immune functioning, we cannot conclude from them that the link is due to immunocompromise. However, other research has shown that certain components of the immune system do fluctuate along with mood (Stone, Cox, Valdimarsdottir, Jandorf, & Neale, 1987). For example, the relatively short life span of sIgA makes it more susceptible to daily mood fluctuations. To demonstrate this, research subjects completed checklists of adjectives describing mood three times per week for 8 weeks. Their responses were divided into positive and negative moods. Two weeks prior to all this, they started to ingest a harmless antigen. It was discovered that negative moods suppressed immune function and positive moods improved it (see Figure 3-2). More recent work has hypothesized that cytokines, specifically interleukin-6 (IL-6), may provide the pathway between mood and health (Kiecolt-Glaser, McGuire, Robles, & Glaser, 2002b).

Negative Mood and Upper Respiratory Infection   One of the conceptual problems encountered when studying negative mood is that it can be difficult to distinguish between mood and personality characteristics. In the language of psychology, we are talking about a distinction between **states**, which are short-term conditions, and **traits**, which are enduring characteristics. This distinction might be particularly relevant if one of your dependent measures were symptom reporting, because increased reporting could just as easily be an indication of chronic complaining as it is of genuine symptom experience.

states and traits: psychological concepts that distinguish between short-term conditions (states) and enduring characteristics (traits).

Figure 3-2 The Relationship between Daily Mood and sIgA Production

Source: Stone et al. (1987). Evidence that secretory sIgA antibody is associated with daily mood. *Journal of Personality and Social Psychology, 52*(5), 988–993. Adapted by permission from the American Psychological Association.

A study by Cohen and colleagues (1995) made the distinction between state- and trait-negative affect, including anxiety, anger, depression, and fatigue. The main purpose of the study was to sort out whether negative states or negative traits had more influence on the development of colds and flu.

At the start of the study, blood samples were taken to establish baseline measures of specific antibody levels. The participants were then exposed to either a cold or influenza virus by way of nasal drops. Measures of state- and trait-negative affect were also taken at the start of the study. To do this, participants filled out a scale called the Profile of Mood States (POMS). They did this twice—once for how they felt in the preceding 24 hours (state) and once for how they felt generally (trait).

The participants were then quarantined in hotel rooms for the duration of the study, and their URTI symptoms were monitored daily via assessments of nasal secretions and self-reports of symptoms. Finally, a second blood sample was taken 4 weeks after exposure to the virus.

The researchers wanted to know to what extent symptom severity and frequency were related to negative affect. The answer is interesting, because it underscores the importance of drawing a distinction between state and trait affect. Both state-negative affect and trait-negative affect were correlated with symptom reporting; however, only state-negative affect was correlated with objectively confirmed symptoms. This means that higher state-negative affect at the outset of the study predicted the actual symptoms a person would experience upon exposure to a virus. It also means that people with high trait-negative affect reported symptoms that could not be verified objectively.

This illustrates why we must make the distinction between personality and state in this work. Interestingly, people who scored high on trait-negative affect didn't start complaining until they actually started experiencing something. The question is: What was that "something?" In fact it was concluded that their complaints were a result of *misinterpretation* of sensations. The authors suggest that this misinterpretation is due to an inability to accurately discriminate between real symptoms and other sensations, rather than to an oversensitivity to actual URTI symptoms.

At least three important points must be noted concerning the design of this study. First, the authors demonstrated statistically that state-negative affect and trait-negative affect are different things. Second, in their design they did not correlate antibody proliferation with symptoms. This means that we can only infer that the high-state-negative-affect people had compromised immune systems, although it is arguably a reasonable inference in this case. Third, this study used a *prospective* design, starting with healthy individuals and charting the course of their URTIs. This is important because the relationship between mood and URTI is bidirectional (Hall & Smith, 1996).

In subsequent work, Pressman and Cohen (2005) have looked at state and trait distinctions in positive emotions. In this work, the authors point out that trait-positive mood is more predictive of good health outcomes than is induced state-positive mood. In fact, the latter can have negative effects on immune function due to the physiological arousal accompanying it. In support, Marsland, Cohen, Rabin, and Manuck (2006) found that people with higher dispositional positive affect produced more antibodies in response to hepatitis B vaccination.

CASE 3-1 TWO DIFFERENT REACTIONS TO A DIAGNOSIS OF CANCER

Jack and Stephen had never met but found themselves sitting across from each other in a waiting room at the cancer clinic, leafing through magazines. Both had recently been diagnosed with prostate cancer and were very upset. However, from the moment their respective family physicians told them the news, each reacted quite differently. In this case study, we will describe these different reactions and speculate on the effect these reactions might have on the progression of the disease for each man. We will base our speculation on what we know from PNI research with cancer patients.

Both men were in their early sixties. Both were happily married. Jack kept in close contact with his two children, who were both married and had children of their own. Stephen didn't hear from his children much since they had started lives of their own. He saw them on major holidays, and that was about it.

The most significant difference between the two men was in the way they took the news that they had cancer. Jack was upset, of course, but he considered himself to be relatively young and determined. He went to the library and took out books on prostate cancer to learn more about the disease and what his options were. He also checked out the Internet for information. He felt thankful that he wasn't in very much pain at this point, and he was confident that he could handle the treatment and that it would work.

Stephen responded differently. When he was told he had prostate cancer, he suddenly felt very old. He had heard of others with the disease, and they were all in their seventies and eighties. He felt bitter that he had contracted a disease that put him in such an infirmed category. He decided that this would be the way his life would end—prematurely and terribly. Sure, he would go through with the treatments, but he had no confidence that they would work. He was convinced that his quality of life was about to decline, that the decline would be permanent, and that there was nothing he could do about it. He began to feel depressed much of the time.

Other aspects of these men's lives were different as well. When Jack told his wife about the diagnosis, she responded that the two of them were going to grow old together and that was that. She maintained an upbeat attitude and helped Jack through the times when he got discouraged or was in discomfort. Jack's friends and neighbours responded the same way.

Stephen had a different experience. His wife was devastated by the news that her husband had cancer. They had both just retired and had plans to travel and enjoy life. Now, in her mind, all of those plans would come to nothing. When Stephen would get depressed, he was difficult to be around. At these times, his wife would leave him alone. Stephen didn't have many friends, and he now felt awkward around those he had because he believed he had a horrible disease that made him different from them.

If Jack and Stephen were at the same stage of illness when diagnosed and were similar in all other aspects of their health, PNI research findings would suggest a more favourable prognosis for Jack. He had an optimistic attitude and believed in the efficacy of the treatment. These cognitions helped him avoid getting depressed, and depression has been shown to accelerate cancer progression. Jack also had a strong support system in the form of family, friends, and neighbours. This support is associated with better survival rates for cancer patients.

Stephen was on a much less encouraging course. His depression had the potential to suppress his immune system to the extent that his cancer could worsen over time. This, of course, would only depress him more. Stephen needed to get help for his depression in order to break this cycle. His social support network wasn't strong—another disadvantage—and Stephen needed to change his thinking in this regard as well. Perhaps if he gave his friends more of a chance, they would be more supportive of him, which would help him feel less depressed. Also, as difficult as it may have seemed for him, Stephen needed to be a more positive companion for his wife. For her part, she needed to persevere through the difficult times brought on by Stephen's depression and try to maintain an optimistic and positive approach to his treatment and their future together.

Although Stephen's response and that of his wife were understandable, such responses would not help Stephen. The couple had to try to make changes in the way they were reacting to Stephen's illness, which was easier said than done. Fortunately, there are counsellors who specialize in helping families cope with illness. We emphasize the need for such counselling here, because an improvement in Stephen's mood and thinking would likely increase the competence of his immune system and thus improve his chances of survival, not to mention his overall quality of life.

Depression and Cancer   There is considerable evidence to indicate that Jack can expect a better outcome for his cancer. At the beginning of this section on depression, we showed that depression was a significant predictor of mortality for a number of illnesses, including cancer. Here, we will take a closer look at the possibility that negative moods such as depression, hopelessness, and pessimism increase the risk of getting cancer or of shortening the patient's survival time. Of course, all research in this area must be prospective in nature. A diagnosis of cancer is depressing for most people. As such, we know about that causal direction. What we need to know is the impact of depression in causing or accelerating cancer.

Like research on the relationship between stress and cancer, prospective studies looking at depression and cancer take one of two forms. Researchers may begin with cancer-free people, measure their levels of negative mood, and then monitor them for cancer onset; or they may assess the moods of people with cancer and then monitor the *progression* of their cancer. In this latter type of study, researchers must control for the type and severity of cancer at the outset of the study in order to make meaningful comparisons among people regarding survival.

Interest in the relationship between depression and cancer progression was fuelled in the 1960s, when Arthur Schmale identified what he and George Engel called the "giving up–given up" complex (Schmale & Engel, 1967). This term referred to the accelerated rate of decline they observed in cancer patients after these patients gave up hope for survival. Because these observations were anecdotal rather than empirical, it is difficult to sort out cause and effect. Evidence for causal links between mood and cancer came some 15 years later from a study in which cancer-free participants were monitored for 17 years to assess the extent to which depression predicted cancer deaths (Shekelle et al., 1981).

In this large prospective study of male employees at the Western Electric Company in the 1950s, more than 2000 cancer-free men were administered a battery of psychological tests, including the Minnesota Multiphasic Personality Inventory (MMPI). The MMPI is a comprehensive measure that is often used in the diagnosis of psychological disorders. Its subscale, measuring levels of depression, provided the main predictor variable for this study. Once the study began, the participants were given annual physical exams for each of the next 11 years. Then, 17 years after the start of the study, mortality statistics were collected from the sample.

The study discovered that those who showed evidence of clinical depression on the MMPI were 2.3 times more likely to have died of cancer at some point in the 17 years covered by the study than those who did not show evidence of depression. This effect was independent of age, cigarette smoking, alcohol use, family history of cancer, occupational status, or type of cancer contracted. Furthermore, depression was not related to any other cause of death. These results were replicated in a follow-up study 20 years later (Persky, Kempthorne-Rawson, & Shekelle, 1987). More recently, a study of women with abnormal results on a Pap smear found that depressive symptoms were associated with poorer immune-system functioning, specifically lower CD3+ CD8+ cell counts (Savard et al., 1999), thus suggesting a biological link between depression and disease.

Researchers have also discovered that pessimism, independent of depression, is related to decreased survival rates among younger people who already have cancer (Schulz, Bookwalla, Knapp, Scheier, & Williamson, 1996). A study involving patients who were receiving palliative radiation treatment for either recurrent or metastasized cancer showed that, for patients aged 30 to 59 years, pessimism was a significant predictor of mortality, regardless of type of cancer (see Figure 3-3). Here again it can be difficult to distinguish between a psychological state and a personality trait. We all feel pessimistic from time to time (state), but that does not mean that we are *pessimists* (trait). There are at least two reasons why this study does not lead to the conclusion that pessimists are more likely to get cancer. First, the design did not begin with cancer-free participants. Second, pessimism was conceptualized more as a state than a trait.

Figure 3-3 Pessimism Scores for Survivors and Non-Survivors of Cancer by Age

Younger patients who survived with recurrent or metastasized cancer had significantly lower pessimism scores than those in that age group who did not survive.

Source: Schultz et al. (1996). Pessimism, Age, and Cancer Mortality. *Psychology and Aging, II*, 304–309. Adapted by permission.

In summary, it is safe to say that depression and other negative mood states are related to increased risk of contracting cancer and of dying from it once it is contracted. It is also likely that immunocompetence provides one explanation for these increased risks. Some researchers have suggested that cancers related to viruses such as Epstein–Barr would be more susceptible to mood fluctuation than would cancers that are induced by chemical carcinogens, such as lung cancer (Kiecolt-Glaser, McGuire, Robles, & Glaser, 2002a).

However, immunocompetence doesn't provide the whole explanation; we must remember that negative mood states are related to a number of other behavioural

Depression has been shown to more than double a person's chances of dying of cancer.
Johan Larson/Fotolia

phenomena that can affect the experience of cancer, especially its progression. People experiencing depression or hopelessness are less likely to follow medical regimens and generally take care of themselves. Also, they tend to sleep poorly and have less energy (Jenkins, 1996). So it would be an oversimplification to say that the negative impact of mood on the immune system is the sole reason that negative mood is associated with increased cancer risk. However, whatever the actual mechanisms involved, health psychologists, counsellors, and others working in a psychosocial capacity with cancer patients must pay close attention to patients' moods and help patients to be optimistic and hopeful.

Depression and Heart Health

As we saw earlier in our discussion of research on negative mood, depression is often studied as an *outcome* rather than a *cause*. Still, there are some prospective studies indicating that depression is a risk factor for heart disease and related mortality.

One such study, after following people for 13 years, concluded that people with major depression had a 4.5 times greater risk of heart attack than those without depression (Pratt et al., 1996). Other studies measuring depressive symptoms as opposed to major depression estimated the risk of first heart attack for those with higher depression scores to be 1.5 to 2 times higher (Glassman & Shapiro, 1998).

Another prospective study followed more than 3700 adults who were over the age of 70 at the start of the study. The researchers made a distinction between what they called "new depression" and "chronic depression". Newly depressed participants were those who were depressed at the outset of the study but had not been either 3 or 6 years before. Chronically depressed participants were depressed at the outset *and* either 3 or 6 years before. It was discovered that for men, "new depression" (but not chronic depression) increased the risk of contracting heart disease and dying from it. In fact, it was concluded that newly depressed older men were twice as likely to have a cardiovascular disease event than were men who were either chronically depressed or not depressed at all (Penninx et al., 1998). Because these studies statistically controlled correlated risk factors (including age), we can conclude that depression increases risk of heart disease, *independent of these other factors.*

Depression is associated with a reduced responsiveness of the immune system, such as lower lymphocyte proliferation (Maes, 1995). This, in turn, compromises the body's ability to deal with inflammation, which can be a good thing for the cardiovascular system as a short-term response, but if depression persists it can cause damage. This is but one of a number of ways in which the immune system is involved in cardiovascular health (Kop & Gottdiener, 2005).

Depression and HIV Infection

Given what we know about the general effects of mood on the immune system, and given that AIDS is an immune-system disease, we might expect significant effects of negative mood on HIV infection and AIDS. There have been several fairly large studies in this area. For example, in a study of over 1700 HIV-positive women, depression was associated with shorter time to AIDS-related death (Cook et al., 2004).

Burack and colleagues (1993) measured depression in a group of 277 HIV-positive men. They then tracked T-helper-cell activity in these men for 5 years (T-helper-cell activity is an important predictor of prognosis for people who are HIV positive).

Stress and Immune Function for Persons Living with AIDS

Leserman et al. (1999) have shown that HIV-positive men living with above-median stress for 5 or more years are two to three times more likely to progress to AIDS than HIV-positive men living with below-median stress levels, and Fumaz et al. (2012) have shown that stress reduces the effectiveness of anti-retroviral treatment for HIV infection. Thus, it makes sense that researchers at an Ottawa hospital have investigated the link between emotional states, such as stress and depression, on immune functioning among people living with AIDS (Balfour et al., 2003).

Sixty-one people took part in the study, in which they were asked to complete the Perceived Stress Scale and a measure of depression. Outcome measures included HIV disease progression, and CD4 counts in particular. CD4 refers to helper T cells that are believed to be particularly important in the progression of HIV.

It was found that stress and depression together accounted for 17 percent of the variance in CD4 counts, thus supporting a growing body of literature linking psychological state with symptoms associated with AIDS.

The depressed men showed a significantly greater decline in this cell activity than did the non-depressed men.

BIOLOGICAL MECHANISMS TO EXPLAIN WHY PSYCHOLOGICAL STATES AFFECT THE IMMUNE SYSTEM

We have reviewed studies indicating that psychological states and traits can influence our immune system in a variety of ways. This influence increases or decreases our susceptibility to a range of medical conditions and helps or hinders our ability to cope with these conditions once we have them. An important question remains to be answered, however: Just how does our biological makeup allow for this influence? When looking for mechanisms that link psychological factors to health, researchers tend to cite four possible sources—the endocrine system, which controls hormones; the sympathetic nervous system; the immune system; and behaviour. (See Stowell, Robles, & Kane, 2013, for a more detailed explanation of the biological mechanisms associated with PNI.)

In terms of the endocrine system, researchers have cited the hypothalamic-pituitary-adrenal (HPA) axis to help explain the biology behind the stress-immunity link (Kendall-Tackett, 2009). The hypothalamus and pituitary gland are located within the brain. When we experience stress, the hypothalamus releases a hormone that causes the pituitary gland to release yet another hormone, which, in turn, causes the adrenal cortex to release cortisol. The immune system is affected by cortisol. Thus, this "axis" produces a chain of events that link stress to immune functioning.

When the stressor is particularly strong, as in the case of psychological trauma, the HPA axis is "chronically activated" (Kendall-Tackett, 2009, p. 37), as is the sympathetic nervous system, which has extensive nerve fibres in areas of high immune cell concentration (Evans, Hucklebridge, & Clow, 2003). This over-activity has adverse effects on the immune system, specifically by causing it to release an abundance of **cytokines**. Cytokines

cytokines: increase the body's capacity to produce inflammation, and help heal wounds and fight infection.

increase the system's capacity to produce inflammation and help heal wounds and fight infection. Cortisol usually helps keep the inflammatory response in check so that it doesn't go overboard and cause problems. Unfortunately stress reverses the effect of cortisol. Ultimately, severe stress results in excessive inflammation, which results in disease.

Kendall-Tackett (2009) makes the case that excessive inflammation provides the explanation for many of the ways psychological state affects health, from coronary heart disease to impaired wound healing (e.g., Surtees et al., 2008).

Inflammation has also been cited to explain the relationship between depression and health. Another indicator of inflammation is C-reactive protein. Elevated levels of this protein have been found in depressed patients with heart disease (Surtees et al., 2008; Taylor et al., 2006). We also know that inflammation is an important contributor to coronary artery disease (Zouridakis, Avanzas, Arroyo-Espliguero, Fredericks, & Kaski, 2004).

Even some of the behavioural explanations of PNI can be traced back to inflammation. For example, disturbed sleep, which is not uncommon among people with depression, is associated with increased inflammation. To make matters worse, inflammation can disrupt sleep, thus creating a negative cycle (Suarez & Goforth, 2010). The good news is that stress, and inflammatory responses, can be affected by diet and exercise. Students with diets high in omega-3s (long-chain fatty acids) were found to have lower inflammatory responses to stress (Maes, Christophe, Bosmans, Lin, & Neels, 2000). One good source of omega-3 is fish oil. Exercise has also been shown to reduce excessive inflammatory response (Starkweather, 2007).

Remember that PNI distinguishes between the effects of acute and long-term stress on health. Short-term stress can actually enhance immune functioning, whereas long-term stress is most often detrimental. This is because long-term secretion of adrenalin (remember this is the output of the HPA axis) suppresses immunity (Song & Leonard, 2000). Specifically, lymphocyte proliferation is lower, and NK cells lose their ability to destroy cancerous cells (de Kooker, 2008).

The nature of cancerous cells also provides insights into the biological relationship between psychological state and disease. Cancer cells survive by mutation and proliferation, and spread. As a result, cancer becomes progressively more serious as the cells "escape" from the primary site and mutate, so that the immune system has difficulty tracking them down and destroying them (Ben-Eliyahu, Page, & Schleifer, 2007). Competent immune systems, which most people possess, deal effectively with these escaped cells. Compromised systems do not result in the spread, or metastasizing, of the disease.

There are times during the cancer progression when a patient is at greater risk for metastatic spread. One such time is immediately following cancer surgery when there may be "shedding of tumour cells to circulation" (Ben-Eliyahu et al., 2007, p. 882). Other risky times are during exposure to carcinogens and during pregnancy. Ben-Eliyahu and colleagues suggest that these are times when it is particularly important to monitor and reduce the stress responses of cancer patients.

These explanations of the biological mechanisms linking psychological state and health are crucial to psychoneuroimmunology and, more generally, to health psychology. They prove that this link, which is at the heart of this book, stems from biological realities. The more we can learn about these mechanisms, the better we can help people stay healthy and cope with illness.

CHAPTER SUMMARY

■ Explain why psychoneuroimmunology (PNI) is important to health psychology.

PNI provides empirical proof that psychological states are directly linked to biological processes. This brings further credibility to the field of health psychology and provides the kinds of research evidence that biomedical practitioners understand.

■ Read and understand research papers on PNI.

To read and understand research papers in PNI, you must understand how immunocompetence is measured. Immunocompetence is measured in a number of ways. Some of the more common include counting cells that proliferate in the presence of an antigen or a substance that is foreign to the body. Functional tests of immunocompetence measure the extent to which these proliferated cells actually destroy, or lyse, the antigen. These measurements can be taken inside the body (*in vivo*) or outside (*in vitro*).

Research features a range of antigens, including Con A, phytohemagglutinin (PHA), and pokeweed mitogen (PWM). Cancerous cells might also be used in this research to assess the immunocompetence of natural killer (NK) cells. Alternatively, antigens, in the form of viruses, can be introduced into the body to track the progression of the virus.

■ Cite research evidence to show that there is a biological relationship between psychological state and health.

Considerable research has linked stress with a range of illnesses, from upper respiratory infections to autoimmune disease to cancer. Depression has also been linked with a range of illnesses, most notably coronary heart disease.

■ Explain fundamental biological mechanisms linking psychological state and health.

One important mechanism linking psychological state and health concerns the body's ability to produce and control inflammatory responses. During stress and depression, this ability is compromised, often producing increased inflammation, which can result in disease.

In addition, the hypothalamus-pituitary-adrenal (HPA) axis works to link psychological state and health. During times of stress, this axis produces increased amounts of hormones that can compromise immune functioning, essentially by shifting the body's priority away from immune response to fight-or-flight response.

Chapter 4
Health Communication

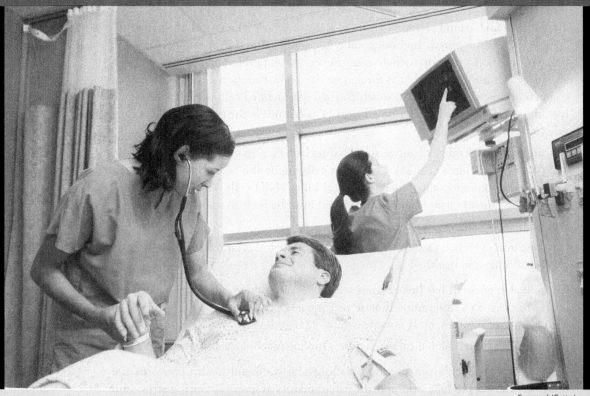

Comstock/Getty Images

Learning Objectives

After studying this chapter, you will be able to:

1. provide an overview of different models of the physician-patient relationship.

2. outline both patient and physician characteristics that lead to poor communication.

3. define patient non-adherence and list contributing factors to non-adherence.

4. outline strategies to improve patient adherence.

5. outline health-related resources available on the Internet and how one should assess the quality of those resources.

6. describe how the Internet has altered physician-patient interactions.

Lynn is visiting her physician, primarily because she has recently been experiencing a lot of stomach discomfort. However, this isn't Lynn's only complaint. In addition to her stomach problems, Lynn hasn't been sleeping, she has more blemishes on her face than usual, and her mother has recently been diagnosed with adult-onset diabetes. Lynn is quite concerned about her mother.

Upon visiting her physician, Lynn decides she will present her symptoms in order of ease of describing them. Lynn says, "My face has been worse than usual lately, I haven't been getting enough sleep, and I've had a lot of butterflies in my stomach these past few weeks." Lynn doesn't bother to mention her concern about her mother to the physician because she already has a lot of issues to discuss and knows the physician can't possibly help her mother during this visit. Lynn's physician dismisses the "butterflies" because Lynn has downplayed this symptom and hasn't reported any pain in her stomach. He also assumes Lynn hasn't been getting enough sleep simply because she has been busy lately. The doctor therefore decides that Lynn is primarily there to seek help for her "worse than usual" face. He provides her with a prescription for a topical ointment and sends her on her way. The main reason for Lynn's visiting her physician, her upset stomach, is never discussed.

Compare Lynn's physician visit to the more positive experience that Alexander and his parents have when they visit the emergency ward: Alexander is an 18-month-old toddler who just loves to run. However, running is a relatively new talent, and he sometimes forgets a few required details—such as looking where he's going. After Alexander has a head-on collision with the corner of a kitchen cupboard, resulting in a gash on his forehead, his parents take him to Emergency to get his cut sutured. As expected, there is a wait. Once Alexander sees a doctor, the stitching begins. The physician seems to realize it is a stressful situation for the young family and quietly reassures Alexander that everything is going to be okay. Then the physician tells Mom and Dad how to care for the laceration and answers all their questions. Mom and Dad are allowed to stay in the room to lessen Alexander's anxiety, and when the suturing is complete, the doctor gives Alexander a "rubber glove balloon" and a Popsicle.

Most people have had both positive and negative experiences with physicians. Lynn's experience exemplifies a situation in which a patient isn't completely satisfied with the outcome of a physician visit. In this case, the physician didn't address all of Lynn's concerns during the physician-patient interview. Indeed, her primary concern, stomach problems, wasn't even mentioned by her physician. In contrast, Alexander's parents were very satisfied with their interaction with the emergency room physician. From the moment Alexander arrived at Emergency, it was obvious why he was seeking treatment. The doctor provided treatment for Alexander and answered all of the questions posed by Alexander's parents.

Effective communication contributed to the satisfaction Alexander's parents felt with the treatment they received from their physician. The *lack* of communication between Lynn and her physician, on the other hand, resulted in a negative experience for her.

Communication is central to the physician-patient relationship. In this chapter, we will discuss how both physician and patient behaviours contribute to faulty communication. As well, we will outline the impact communication has on physician-patient relationships, adherence to medical advice, and health outcomes.

PHYSICIAN-PATIENT INTERACTION

A final, extremely important factor contributing to people's decisions to use medical services is the quality of the relationship they have with their physicians.

Basic Models of Physician-Patient Interaction

A crucial element in the typical interaction between a patient and a health care practitioner is the nature of their relationship. A classic article in the field of health psychology by Thomas Szasz and Marc Hollender, written in 1956, outlines three basic models they believed characterized the nature of the physician-patient relationship.

The **active-passive model** describes a relationship in which patients are unable to participate in their own care or to make decisions for their own welfare because of the severity of their medical conditions. For example, when patients have severe injuries or are in a coma, the physician is responsible for providing care and making decisions on their behalf; obviously, the patients are not in a position to provide any input. Consider the following situation:

Dennis gashed himself with a knife while camping in the bush. He cut an artery and the blood was spurting out. His buddies placed him in the back of their pickup truck and sped down the highway toward the nearest town. By the time they reached the hospital, Dennis was unconscious. A few seconds after they arrived at the hospital emergency ward, Dennis was placed on a gurney and wheeled to the operating room. Then Dennis's clothing was ripped off and the severed artery was found and tied. At the same time, others worked to find a vein that had not collapsed in order to put in an intravenous line. The entire emergency room staff worked with skill and speed. Dennis, who was unconscious, could neither participate in nor fight their efforts.

The **guidance-cooperation model** applies when patients seek advice from the physician. The patients answer the questions that the physician asks about their symptoms, but the physician is responsible for determining diagnosis and treatment. In essence, the physician is responsible for the thinking and decision making. This model would likely be followed if a person had an infection or a sprain. Consider the following example:

Henry was told by his physician to "take one of these little pills three times a day. If you do what I tell you to, you will be just fine." Henry was convinced that asking the physician questions would be challenging physician authority, so he simply nodded in agreement. Henry was to take the medication to control his hypertension. However, he couldn't seem to remember to take the pills. This may have been due to the fact that he didn't feel sick (hypertension is often referred to as "the silent killer"), or because he had never been told exactly what the medication would do.

In the **mutual-participation model**, the patient has more responsibility than in the other models. In this model, the physician and patient make joint decisions about every aspect of care, from deciding what diagnostic tests the patient should undergo to the

active-passive model: situation in which patients are unable to participate in their care or to make decisions because of their medical condition.

guidance-cooperation model: communication in which the patient seeks advice from the physician and answers the questions that are asked, but the physician is responsible for determining the diagnosis and treatment.

mutual-participation model: health care model in which the physician and patient make joint decisions about every aspect of care.

choice and implementation of treatment. Input and responsibility are shared equally by physician and patient. The two work together in a partnership. Here's an example:

Patient: I don't know how I'll be able to eliminate caffeine from my diet. That will be quite a challenge, especially if there needs to be an immediate reduction in my caffeine consumption.

Physician: What do you think you'll be able to manage? Can you try to reduce your caffeine intake a little bit every day?

Patient: I can try but it won't be easy. And you don't just mean reducing coffee drinking, do you? You also mean reducing the amount of chocolate I consume. I think I'm going to be pretty grumpy over the next while, perhaps you should warn my partner.

Physician: Is there anything you can think of that I might be able to do to help you?

Patient: Tell me again exactly why this is necessary. Also, is there anything else I should be doing to help my medical condition?

Do you think this scenario characterizes a typical interaction between a physician and patient? Or does the patient in this scenario seem unusually assertive? According to some researchers, assertiveness and active involvement on the part of the patient are the precursors of an effective partnership with the physician. The mutual-participation model is seen as the ideal relationship between physician and patient. However, the typical physician-patient relationship is one in which the physician possesses a greater degree of power than the patient.

Power is an issue that we will return to later in the chapter. For now, let's continue with our discussion of physician-patient relationship models. Szasz and Hollender (1956) were some of the first to provide a theoretical model of the physician-patient relationship, but they were not the last. Other models have been put forward over the years (e.g., Emanuel & Emanuel, 1992), but until recently none used empirical techniques to determine whether the patterns of interaction in the physician-patient relationship corresponded to the theoretical approaches found in the literature.

Roter and colleagues (Roter, 2000; Roter et al., 1997) used audiotape analysis to describe communication patterns in 537 patients seen at 11 outpatient, private, and group primary-care settings in the United States and Canada. Their analysis revealed five distinct communication patterns.

The first pattern, **narrowly biomedical communication**, was characterized mainly by biomedical talk (e.g., "The medication may make you sleepy"), closed-ended medical questions (e.g., "Are you in pain when you walk?"), and very little discussion of psychosocial topics (such as problems of daily living, emotions, and issues regarding social relations). The narrowly biomedical pattern occurred in 32 percent of the visits.

The second pattern was described as **expanded biomedical communication**. This pattern also included numerous closed-ended medical questions but had more moderate levels of biomedical and psychosocial exchange for both physicians and patients. This pattern was common to 33 percent of the visits. The third pattern, **biopsychosocial communication**, reflected a balance of psychosocial and biomedical communication. The biopsychosocial pattern occurred in 20 percent of visits.

narrowly biomedical communication: characterized mainly by biomedical talk, closed-ended medical questions, and very little discussion of psychosocial issues.

expanded biomedical communication: includes numerous closed-ended medical questions and moderate levels of biomedical and psychosocial exchange between physician and patient.

biopsychosocial communication: suggests that biological, psychological, and social factors are all involved in any given state of health or illness.

The **psychosocial communication** pattern was the fourth pattern identified by Roter and her colleagues. This pattern included substantially more psychosocial exchanges than the previous patterns. An example of such an exchange is the following: "It is important to get out and do something on a regular basis. The recreation centre is a great place to find the company of other seniors." Eight percent of visits are considered psychosocial. The final pattern was designated **consumerist communication**. This pattern of communication also represented 8 percent of visits. The consumerist pattern suggests the use of the physician as a consultant who answers questions rather than as one who asks them.

It is somewhat difficult to compare the model proposed by Roter (2000) and Roter and colleagues (1997) with that proposed by Szasz and Hollender (1956) because of the different terminology used in describing the models. However, it is clear that both models place the interactions on a continuum, where at one end the patient has little involvement in the decision-making process or in contributions to the interaction, and at the other end the patient is at least on par with the physician in guiding the interaction. Szasz and Hollender stated that the mutual-participation model was "essentially foreign to medicine." Now more than 50 years have elapsed, and this statement no longer seems to be true. Roter's program of research (e.g., Bensing, Roter, & Hulsman, 2003; Roter, 2000) suggests that while collaborative models do not predominate in North America, they are certainly evident in primary-care practice. In Europe, where similar studies have been conducted, far fewer physician-patient interactions are active-passive or biomedically intensive (Bensing et al., 2003; Deveugele et al., 2004).

Is the collaborative model the preferred model of physician-patient interaction? According to patients, the collaborative model—or, in Roter's terminology, the psychosocial pattern—is preferred (Bensing, Rimondini, & Visser, 2013; de Boer, Delnoij, & Rademakers, 2013; Deledda, Moretti, Rimondini, & Zimmerman, 2103; Roter et al., 1997). Somewhat surprisingly, physicians were especially satisfied with the consumerist pattern, reporting that these visits made good use of their time. Patients were moderately pleased with these interactions, although they didn't receive the highest patient satisfaction ratings. Patients who engaged in this pattern of communication were younger than others, so there may be a cohort effect, suggesting that younger generations of patients will be consumerist in their relationships with physicians. In Roter and colleagues' study, the consumerist pattern occurred in only a small proportion of visits. We might speculate that this pattern will increase as younger cohorts get older and develop more chronic conditions and therefore become more frequent users of health services. The patterns least preferred by both patients and physicians were the biomedical patterns. Biomedical patterns of communication were used most often by younger, male physicians and by those physicians interacting with patients who were more sick, were older, and had a lower income.

In a national U.S. study (Stock Keister, Green, Kahn, Phillips, McCann, & Fryer, 2004), researchers investigated "what people want from their family physician." The people surveyed for this study mirrored the general population of the United States with regard to race, ethnicity, gender, age, and location. People deemed the 10 attributes identified in Table 4-1 as those that most contributed to their satisfaction with their physician.

Table 4-1 The Top 10 Physician Attributes Contributing to Patient Satisfaction in Rank Order

1. Always honest and direct
2. Listens to me
3. Encourages me to lead healthier lifestyle
4. Does not judge; understands, supports
5. Someone I can stay with as I grow older
6. Tries to get to know me
7. Acts as partner in maintaining health
8. Treats both serious and non-serious conditions
9. Attends to emotional and physical health
10. Can help with any problem

Source: Adapted from Graham Center One-Pager #26. Stock Keister, M.C., Green, L.A., Kahn, N.B., Phillips, R.L., McCann, J., & Fryer, G.D. (2004). What people want from their family physician. *American Family Physician, 69*(10), 2310. Copyright (2004) American Academy of Family Physicians. All rights reserved. This article was reprinted from the original article published in *American Family Physician*, a publication of the American Academy of Family Physician.

Focus on Canadian Research 4-1

Patient-Centred Care

Researchers at the University of Western Ontario (McWilliam, Brown, & Stewart, 2000; Stewart, 1995; Stewart et al., 2000) have refined and tested a patient-centred model of physician-patient interaction. This model highlights the need to integrate the conventional understanding of disease with each patient's unique experience of illness. The model is viewed as a total-person approach to patient problems. Six interconnected components are included in the model (Weston & Brown, 1995).

1. *Exploring both the disease and the illness experience.* Identification of disease, or problems in terms of abnormalities of structure and/or function of body organs and systems, takes place just as it would if a physician subscribed to the biomedical model. However, the patient-centred model focuses on four key dimensions of patients' illness experience: (i) what the patients believe is wrong with them, (ii) their feelings (e.g., fears) about being ill, (iii) the impact of the illness on their daily functioning, and (iv) how they believe the physician should proceed.

2. *Understanding the whole person.* The physician should come to understand both the patient's disease and the experience of illness in the context of the patient's life

(e.g., the patient's cultural beliefs, stage of life, and family situation).

3. *Finding common ground.* Physicians and patients must reach agreement in three principal areas if they hope to develop an effective management plan: (i) the specific problems and priorities, (ii) the goals of treatment, and (iii) the role of both the physician and the patient.

4. *Incorporating prevention and health promotion.* The physician and patient must work together to enable the patient to take the steps required to control and improve his or her own health.

5. *Enhancing the patient-physician relationship.* Every patient-physician interaction provides the opportunity to build rapport. The establishment of an effective relationship will aid the physician in recognizing the specific approach that should be taken with the patient in order to meet the patient's needs (e.g., recognizing vulnerability and offering support).

6. *Being realistic.* Physicians must recognize their own limits. They must manage their time and emotional energy in a way that provides the most benefit to their patients.

Physician-Patient Communication

Information-Giving   The collaborative model of physician-patient communication preferred by most patients requires their involvement in making decisions about their treatment. But to participate in these decisions, patients need information. Physicians provide information to their patients about a number of things, including the patient's diagnosis, possible causes of the problem, and methods of treatment. Information-giving is a very important element of the physician-patient interview, and yet researchers have found that "patients tend to be more dissatisfied about the information they receive from their physicians than about any other aspect of medical care" (Waitzkin, 1985, p. 83). For their part, when questioned about the amount of time they believed they spent giving information to their patients, physicians drastically overestimated the amount of time they were engaged in this task. Specifically, in an average 20-minute interview physicians estimated that they spent approximately 9 minutes giving information to their patients. In reality, the physicians spent an average of 1 minute giving information to their patients.

Research consistently demonstrates that physicians underestimate patients' desire for information (Say, Murtagh, & Thomson, 2006). A number of studies have demonstrated that physicians sometimes choose to withhold information from their patients in an attempt to protect their patients from worry and because they find providing such information difficult (Rogg, Loge, Aasland, & Graugaard, 2009). Perhaps this is why patients who are elderly, have less education, or have a poor prognosis receive less information from physicians (Ong, Visser, Lammes, & de Haes, 2000).

In one example, family doctors who had made a diagnosis of Parkinson's disease, a degenerative nerve disorder, were very concerned about protecting their patients (Pinder, 1990). Specifically, the physicians had difficulty in deciding how, when, and whom to tell, and difficulty in deciding just how much information to share about the patient's diagnosis and prognosis. The physicians tended to be positive and overly optimistic. For instance, they avoided details about medications, were low-key about side effects, and did not explore the problems of long-term medication use.

Most patients, on the other hand, wanted to be given as much information as possible. In a sample of 141 breast cancer patients, only one did not want information about recurrence rates, yet 40 percent did not receive this information (Kelly et al., 2013). Information about medication and its side effects was lacking (Puro, Pakarinen, Korttila, & Tallgren, 2013). Providing such information to patients results in lowered blood pressure and less psychological distress as well as improvement of symptoms when the information presented is coupled with emotional support (Roter, 2000).

Participation   Although the vast majority of patients would like to be informed about what their illnesses are and how to treat them, some want more details and involvement in decisions and some prefer less. Generally, healthier, younger, and better-educated patients prefer greater involvement in health-related decisions (Hall & Roter, 2007; Perneger, Charvet-Bérard, & Perrier, 2008; Say et al., 2006). People in lower social classes tend to prefer a more passive role. Studies in the United States conducted along ethnic lines found that, compared to white patients, Hispanics and Asians are less satisfied with the involvement allowed them by their physicians (Bigby & Perez-Stable, 2004; Johnson, Saha, Arbelaez, Beach, & Cooper, 2004). African-American patients also experience less patient-centred care than do their white counterparts (Johnson, Roter, Powe, & Lisa, 2004).

Knowing patient preferences is invaluable. Research shows that providing the amount and type of participation that patients want in their health care enhances patients' adjustment to and satisfaction with medical treatment (Bennenbroek, Buunk, van der Zee, & Grol, 2002). Moreover, patients who report a preference for an active role in their treatment tend to recover faster than those who prefer an inactive role.

Just as patients differ in the amount of participation they want in managing their health, health professionals differ in the amount of involvement they are likely to encourage. As we might predict, some physicians are more inclined than others to share their authority and decision making (McKinstry, 2000; Say et al., 2006). A mismatch between the patient's and the physician's desire for participation can be detrimental to their relationship. Furthermore, as we will discuss in more detail in the next chapter, mismatches of this type will frequently result in an increase in the stress experienced by patients during medical procedures. When determining how much information and involvement to provide each patient, health professionals clearly need to consider the needs of the patient.

General Patient Satisfaction   Considering the needs of the patient is certainly an important component of a physician's role. Most people can recall both positive and negative experiences they have had with physicians. When people talk about their negative experiences, they often mention the physician's hurried manner, insensitivity, lack of responsiveness, apparently faulty diagnoses, or useless treatment. However, most people can also provide details of an interaction with a physician that was exemplary. Patients praise physicians who don't rush and answer all their questions. Many of the positive attributes patients recount include personal factors about the physician. Patients show a strong preference for practitioners who have a warm and expressive emotional style as opposed to those who are emotionally neutral (e.g., Clowers, 2002; Coulter, 2002; Zachariae et al., 2003).

Patient satisfaction with medical care is primarily influenced by the quality of the physician-patient relationship. Nonverbal behaviours are more closely related to patient satisfaction than is verbal communication. A particularly important consequence of this is that patients often judge the competence of a physician by their emotional satisfaction with care. Physicians who appear more emotionally expressive in their facial expressions, eye contact, body posture, and tone of voice typically are viewed more favourably by their patients (Roter, Frankel, Hall, & Sluyter, 2006). The important implication of this finding is that patients who are satisfied with the emotional aspects of their care are more likely to want to return to that physician and are more likely to keep future appointments (Roter et al., 2006). The effect of nonverbal behaviour is so strong, in fact, that some researchers have found a relationship between tone of voice and medical malpractice suits (Ambady et al., 2002).

Patient Satisfaction, Communication, and Malpractice Claims   In Canada, most complaints by the public about physicians deal not with clinical competency but with communication (Richards, 1990; Simpson et al., 1991). Some estimate that 70 to 80 percent of medical litigation involves relationship or communication problems (Lussier & Richard, 2006). We should point out that the number of malpractice lawsuits is decreasing in Canada (CHSRF, 2006). In 1996, 1415 lawsuits were filed, the highest in Canadian history; however, the numbers have been declining ever since. By 2004, this number had declined by 23 percent to 1083. Lawsuits that go to trial

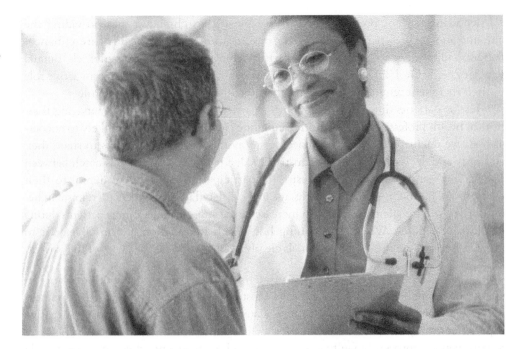

When physicians interact with patients in a warm, friendly, confident manner, they are viewed as both competent and nice.
Corbis

increasingly favour the physician—84 percent of trials in 2004. Lawsuit rates have also been declining in the United States, but in both countries when a payment is made the sums are large. In 2004, payouts averaged $300 000 per case in Canada, which is an increase of 66 percent in 10 years (CHSRF, 2006).

As we have already mentioned, patients have preferences and expectations about their interactions with physicians. The physician's awareness of the patient's expectations during a visit is critical in achieving effective communication. And only with effective communication are patients likely to be satisfied with their medical care (Stewart et al., 2000). According to Lussier and Richard (2006), sources of patient dissatisfaction arising from poor physician-patient relations and inadequate communication include physicians' failing to prepare for meetings with patients, appearing to rush through the physician-patient interview, underestimating the seriousness of the symptoms patients report, and devaluing patient and family views. The combination of patient dissatisfaction and a bad outcome is said to be "a recipe for litigation." When patients and their families feel the physician is caring and compassionate, however, malpractice suits happen less frequently (Levinson, 1994).

Levinson and colleagues (1997) were the first to identify specific communication behaviours associated with malpractice claims based on direct observation of physicians' behaviour. Physicians and surgeons were randomly selected from the databases of companies providing malpractice insurance in Oregon and Colorado. Ten routine office visits were audiotaped for each of the 124 participants. Analysis of the conversations revealed significant differences in communication behaviours between physicians who had been subjected to malpractice claims and those who had not. Roughly half of the physicians were primary-care physicians and the other half surgeons. "No-claims" primary-care physicians gave more orienting statements about the flow of a visit (e.g., "First, I will examine you, and then we will talk about your condition"), laughed and used more humour, facilitated communication (e.g., asked patients for their opinions and checked that patients understood), encouraged their patients to talk, and spent more time with their patients (18.3 against 15 minutes). Levinson and his colleagues found no behaviours that distinguished between claims and no-claims surgeons.

Undoubtedly, there is a link between communication, patient satisfaction, and malpractice claims. Although researchers have documented a number of components of poor communication possibly responsible for this link, further research is required to explain some of the anomalies (e.g., between physicians and surgeons). While studies investigating the link between communication problems and malpractice claims began relatively recently, research exploring more general communication problems during the physician-patient consultation began decades ago.

Physician Behaviours Contributing to Faulty Communication   Having exchanged introductions and established initial rapport, the next step for a physician is to determine what issues the patient wishes to discuss. What is his or her agenda for the consultation? Why has the patient come today? These are questions that cannot be addressed unless the practitioner listens to the patient. In a landmark study (Beckman & Frankel, 1984), physicians were found to interrupt their patients after only 18 seconds! In a span of 15 years, this behaviour improved only slightly; now patients are given 23 seconds to speak before they are interrupted (Marvel, Epstein, Flowers, & Beckman, 1999).

Research (Marvel et al., 1999; McDonald & Fedo, 2009) clearly demonstrates that even minimal interruptions to patients' initial statements can prevent other concerns from being mentioned at all or can make important complaints arise late in the consultation. By asking patients to provide further comment on any one problem, patients' options are restricted and they are prevented from expanding on other information. For example, a patient may have mentioned headaches but is interrupted before he or she can mention having experienced recent palpitations and marital problems. "Tell me more about your headaches" or, worse, "Where do you get the pain?" restricts the discussion to the headaches and limits both the patient's options and the effectiveness of the interview as a whole. Allowing patients to complete their opening statement without interruption should not be a difficult task for practitioners, as patients usually take less than 60 seconds to do this. In Beckman and Frankel's (1984) research, not a single patient took longer than 150 seconds to complete an opening statement, even when encouraged to continue. Yet in only 28 percent of the cases were patients given the opportunity to finish their explanations of concerns (Marvel et al., 1999). When patients are interrupted, they are given the opportunity to return to and complete their opening statement only 2 percent of the time (Frankel & Beckman, 1989).

Physicians seem to assume that the first complaint the patient mentions is the only one the patient has. However, patients come to an office visit with an average of three concerns they wish to express (Kaplan, Gandek, Greenfield, Rogers, & Ware, 1995; Stewart, Brown, Levenstein, McCracken, & McWhinney, 1986). Furthermore, the order in which patients present their problems is not related to their clinical importance; the first concern presented is no more likely than the second or third to be the most important, as judged by either the patient or the physician (Beckman & Frankel, 1984).

To make matters worse, patients and physicians do not always agree on the nature of the patient's chief complaint (Burack & Carpenter, 1983; Starfield et al., 1981). Recall Lynn from the beginning of this chapter. Her major complaint was not addressed by her physician. Lynn's primary reason for visiting her physician was to determine what was causing her stomach problems. However, this was not the first symptom Lynn described to her physician, because she also had some other concerns. Lynn left the physician's office still wondering what was responsible for her stomach ache. Stewart, McWhinney, and Buck (1979) discovered that 54 percent of patients' complaints were not elicited during the medical interview. These shocking findings have led researchers to devise interview methods, such as the Calgary-Cambridge method, that improve communication during the physician-patient interview (Kurtz, 2002; Kurtz, Silverman, Benson, & Draper, 2003; see Table 4-2 later in this chapter).

Medical Jargon Another factor that contributes to poor communication in the physician-patient interview is the physician's use of **medical jargon** and technical language (Collins et al., 2013). Numerous studies have documented that using medical jargon or technical terms without explaining the terms or checking comprehension can create confusion, misunderstandings, and negative perceptions of the physician (e.g., Castro, Wilson, Wang, & Scillinger, 2007; Collins et al., 2013; Jenkins et al., 2013). For example, the term *splenomegaly* conveys a considerable amount of information to health professionals, but very little to patients. Splenomegaly describes an enlargement of the spleen (a large glandlike organ situated in the upper left side of the abdomen that breaks down red corpuscles) often related to progressive anemia (reduction below normal in the hemoglobin, the volume of packed red blood cells) with no evidence of leukemia or disease of the lymph glands (DiMatteo, 1991). Even if the patient asks the physician for the meaning of *splenomegaly*, he or she is likely to need the physician to explain the explanation! Test *your* knowledge of common medical terms by attempting the quiz in Box 4-1.

medical jargon: technical language used by a physician that is sometimes unintelligible to the patient.

Box 4-1

Do You Know What These Medical Terms Mean?

The following 10 medical terms were used in Thompson and Pledger's (1993) study of patients' understanding of medical jargon. Match the terms with the definitions given below:

1. _____ malignant
2. _____ incubation
3. _____ acute
4. _____ abscess
5. _____ diuretic

6. _____ benign
7. _____ chronic
8. _____ cyst
9. _____ suture
10. _____ edema

A. A localized collection of pus in a cavity formed by the disintegration of tissue.

B. The accumulation of excess fluid in a fluid compartment.

C. Persisting for a long time.

D. The provision of proper conditions for growth and development.

E. Having severe symptoms and a short course.

F. Not recurrent: favourable for recovery with appropriate treatment.

G. An agent that promotes urine secretion.

H. A closed sac or capsule containing liquid or a semisolid substance.

I. A joining together of separated tissue or bone, or material used to achieve this joining.

J. Any condition that, if uncorrected, tends to worsen so as to cause serious illness or death (e.g., cancer).

The answers are provided below. Did you obtain a perfect score? If you had been asked to define each of the terms rather than simply fill in the blanks with the provided answers, do you think you would have scored as well?

1– J, 2–D, 3–E, 4–A, 5–G, 6–F, 7–C, 8–H, 9–I, 10–B

There are a number of reasons physicians use medical jargon when talking to patients. One reason is because they tend to overestimate the amount their patients can understand (Guttman, 1993). A number of studies have tested patient knowledge of medical terminology (e.g., Castro et al., 2007). In a typical study, physicians and nurses make lists of medical words that they believe patients understand. When these same words are presented to patients, surprisingly few can define the terms accurately. For example, in the study conducted by Thompson and Pledger (1993) less than half of the patients could adequately define the words *abscess, tumour, diuretic,* or *cyst.* Moreover, even simple everyday words can be ambiguous when used in a medical context (Hadlow & Pitts, 1991). For example, Mazullo, Lasagna, and Griner (1974) showed that 52 percent of those interviewed thought that a medication prescribed "for fluid retention" would cause fluid retention. More recently (Castro et al., 2007), a sample of diabetic patients were asked about their comprehension of terminology (e.g., weight is stable) that was commonplace in audiotaped physician-patient interactions. The rates of comprehension never exceeded 38 percent.

Another reason practitioners use medical jargon when speaking to patients is because patients often believe that the sophisticated vocabulary of the physician represents intelligence. Perhaps they feel that they will be better taken care of by a physician who is obviously intelligent.

A more cynical view of the reason for using medical jargon was provided by the famous heart surgeon Dr. Michael DeBakey, who said, "Most doctors don't want their patients to understand them! They prefer to keep their work a mystery. If patients don't understand what a doctor is talking about, they won't ask him questions. Then the doctor won't have to be bothered answering them" (Robinson, 1973). Another famous physician, Howard Waitzkin (1985), explained jokingly that if you wanted to forestall any additional questions from the patient you could simply connect the term *itis* (meaning "inflammation of") to whatever organ was troubled (e.g., *stomachitis*).

More commonly, however, health professionals may use medical jargon with their patients because they simply forget that their patients do not share the same medical vocabulary. Practitioners spent years in medical school learning this vocabulary, they use it when speaking with their colleagues, and they just naturally use the same vocabulary with their patients.

Unfortunately, when health care providers are aware that patients may not understand medical jargon, they sometimes go to the opposite extreme and engage in baby talk and simplistic explanations. One example comes from a surgeon who said to an elderly man, "We're just going to pop you into the operating theatre to have a little peek into your tummy." Toynbee noticed that the term *pop* was used quite frequently in the hospital by many of the hospital staff. Another physician said, "Nurse, would you just pop off her things for me? I want to examine her." Nurses also "popped" patients in and out of washrooms and wheelchairs, into and out of hospital gowns, beds, and bandages (Toynbee, 1977).

The ideal alternative to the use of medical jargon and baby talk is for practitioners to provide **non-discrepant responses** and **multilevel explanations** when speaking to their patients (Waitzkin, 1985). A non-discrepant response is one that uses the same level of vocabulary that the patient uses when asking the question. For example, if a patient asks about her "lump," the physician might reply by saying we have to remove part of the lump to determine if there is cancer in it. A multilevel explanation is one that initially uses

non-discrepant responses: physician responds to the patient's questions using the same sophistication of vocabulary that the patient uses.

multilevel explanations: explanations that use medical jargon followed by further explanation using everyday language.

medical jargon but then explains the jargon using everyday language. The use of multi-level explanations educates the patient in medical terminology, as seen in this example: "We'll have to conduct a biopsy to determine if the tumour is malignant. In other words, we'll have to remove the lump to determine if there is cancer in it." The use of medical jargon by health professionals is therefore appropriate if it is explained to the patient or if the patient is already familiar with the terminology (Thompson, 2000). Additional strategies such as asking patients to repeat information, drawing pictures, writing out instructions, or providing handouts are sometimes used by health care professionals to help with communication (Schwartzberg, Cowett, VanGeest, & Wolf, 2007).

Time Factors   Another factor thought to limit a physician's ability to communicate effectively is the time available for the consultation. In our discussion of communication issues linked to malpractice claims, we mentioned that if patients felt rushed, they were more likely to file a suit. If a physician appears hurried, then this contributes negatively to the interaction. However, overall length of the physician-patient interview does not seem to be related to general satisfaction. Mauksch, Dugdale, Dodson, and Epstein (2008) attempted to determine how much time is needed to provide quality care, as many studies suggest that more successful communication requires more time (e.g., Flocke, Miller, & Crabtree, 2002; Goedhuys & Rethans, 2001; Zyzanski, Stange, Langa, & Flocke, 1998). They identified studies that had timed the physician-patient interview in six European countries and in the United States. The length of primary-care visits ranged from 7.5 minutes in Germany to 18 minutes in the United States. However, they were unable to identify how much time was required for an optimal interview. In fact, Mauksch et al. (2008) concluded that more time does not necessarily result in good communication. They also explored whether the length of time spent in the physician-patient interview was linked to whether the interaction style was biomedical or psychosocial in nature. Their review of the literature concluded that the physicians maintained their preferred communication style and this was not dependent on the length of the interaction. Numerous studies show no difference in visit length no matter the communication style adopted according to the biomedical–psychosocial continuum (e.g., Belle Brown, 2003; Roter et al., 1997). Perhaps then, it is the perception of the physician being rushed rather than the actual time spent in the interaction that contributes the most to patient dissatisfaction related to time factors (Lussier & Richard, 2006).

Patient Behaviours Contributing to Faulty Communication   Both patient behaviours and physician behaviours contribute to faulty communication. In the next section, we discuss a number of patient behaviours that present challenges to efficient communication during physician-patient encounters.

Patient Deception   Not surprisingly, patients also find some topics difficult to discuss with physicians. Both younger and older patients may experience difficulty and embarrassment discussing topics related to sexually transmitted diseases or sexual behaviours (Gott, 2006; Pitts, Wooliscroft, Cannon, Johnson, & Singh, 2000). Patients may avoid the topic altogether, or if asked directly, they may give false information. Researchers at the University of Victoria (Lewis, Matheson, & Brimacombe, 2011) asked female patients attending a birth control clinic if they had falsified information during the preceding physician-patient consultation. Approximately one-half (46.4 percent) of female respondents admitted to withholding information or lying about their sexual histories to the physician during the consultation.

The list of topics that patients admit to lying about is long. Burgoon, Callister, and Hunsaker (1994) noted that 50 percent or more of the participants in their study admitted to lying "often" or "always" about adherence to medical regimens, exercise behaviours, the amount of stress they were under, and financial status. These participants lied about other topics with less frequency.

Lack of Information-Seeking Behaviours   Athough numerous studies (e.g., Kelly et al., 2013; Puro et al., 2013) have documented that patients are underwhelmed by the quantity and quality of information they receive from their physicians, far fewer studies have focused on the patients' contributions to this process. Given that patients want information from their physicians, we would expect them to request additional information during the medical interview. Traditionally, however, patients do not engage in many information-seeking behaviours when communicating with their physicians (Beisecker & Beisecker, 1990).

In a study conducted by Tuckett, Boulton, and Olson (1985, cited in Silverman, Kurtz, & Draper, 2005), 76 percent of patients said that they had specific doubts or questions during the interview that they did not mention to the physician. When asked why they did not ask the physician questions, patients gave the following reasons: (1) it was not up to them to ask questions, express doubts, or behave as if their view was important (36 percent); (2) they were afraid of being less well thought of by the doctor (22 percent); (3) they were frightened of a negative reaction from the doctor (14 percent); (4) they were too flustered or hurried to ask coherently (27 percent); (5) they doubted that the doctor could tell them any more at the moment (22 percent); (6) they forgot or were waiting until next time to ask, when they would be more certain of what they thought was reasonable to ask (36 percent); and (7) they feared the truth (9 percent).

This behaviour, however, may be changing. Younger and better-educated patients tend to engage in more proactive behaviour, such as asking more questions and volunteering unsolicited information to the physician (Siminoff, Graham, & Gordon, 2006). It is reassuring to know that researchers are attempting to determine the best way to achieve improved information-seeking behaviours by patients. A review of more than 20 studies found that interventions did improve patient participation in these exchanges, but the form of participation was more likely to focus on clarification of statements made rather than more fully developed questions (Harrington, Noble, & Newman, 2004). That being said, these interventions did result in other positive outcomes, including increased perceptions of control over health, greater recall of information, and greater adherence to treatment regimens (Harrington et al., 2004).

Trouble Remembering   Even if patients understand all the terminology the physician used, they may not remember everything that was said. In a review of the literature, Ley (1988) notes that, in the hospital setting, patients remember approximately 60 percent of the information a health care worker tells them. When Tuckett and colleagues (1985) looked more closely at the information patients recalled, they found that only 10 percent of patients couldn't remember the key points they had been told. That is, most patients could remember the gist of what they heard even if they could not remember all the details.

Anxiety contributes to patients' inability to remember information from a medical interview. Specifically, when people are anxious (as they often are in medical situations) they find it difficult to concentrate and to process incoming information. Again, this is true even when patients understand the information they are being told. A physician describes her experience upon being told she had cancer in just these terms: She said that even though she knew exactly what her physician was telling her, as soon as she got the "news," she zoned out. She began thinking about what this would mean in terms of all the adjustments she would have to make in her life, whether she would survive, and so on, and in doing so she didn't hear another word her physician said to her. One way of communicating where memory doesn't come into play nearly as much is when the physician and patient communicate via e-mail.

E-mail in Patient–Health Care Provider Communication   Face-to-face communication is the traditional means of communication between patients and their health care providers. However, with advances in technology and the popularity of electronic mail (e-mail) in our daily life, it may not be surprising that physicians and other health care professionals are slowly beginning to incorporate e-mail as a means of communication with their patients (Ye, Rust, Fry-Johnson, & Strothers, 2010). Both the Canadian Medical Association and the American Medical Association have already published guidelines to facilitate this process (AMA, 2013; CMA, 2005).

Analyzing 24 studies, Ye et al. (2010) discovered that the most frequently written about topics via e-mail were the exchange of medical information, an update on the patient's medical condition, medication information, and subspecialty evaluation. Roter, Larson, Sands, Ford, and Houston (2008) found that the pattern of e-mail exchanges appears similar to in-person visits—the great majority of time was spent on information exchange and the remaining communication was focused on building rapport between the doctor and patient. Physicians spend an average of 2 to 3 minutes answering questions from patients no matter what the length of the patient's question (Kummervold & Johnsen, 2011). Thus, communicating via e-mail has the potential to save time.

In addition to saving time, e-mail communication is convenient, makes patients feel more comfortable when asking questions, and allows the message to be saved (Ye et al., 2010). Thus, the problem mentioned earlier of remembering information is eliminated. At present, it is younger, better-educated patients in poor health who are accessing their physicians using technology. Yet, it is expected that this type of communication will increase (Atkins & Cullen, 2013; Ye et al., 2010). Given that most studies show that providing e-mail communication for patients increases their satisfaction, this is very good news indeed.

Patient-Physician Concordance   What much of this research shows us is the importance that both members of the dyad play in achieving successful communication. A relatively recent area of research focus in the field of health communication is patient-physician social concordance. Social concordance is based on similarity with respect to shared social characteristics (e.g., race, gender, education, and age) between dyad members in a specific interaction (Johnson Thornton, Powe, Roter, & Cooper, 2011). Admittedly, these topics have been researched in isolation over several decades. For example, we know that women physicians spend longer with their patients, ask more questions, and engage in more emotional talk than do male physicians (Roter & Hall, 2006).

Further, we know that patients self-disclose and are more assertive with female physicians than with male physicians (Roter & Hall, 2006). In addition, we know that there is a slight preference for same-sex physicians in general; however, when one is seeking help for a gender-specific problem there is a large preference for a same-sex physician (Janssen & Lagro-Janssen, 2012; Lewis et al., 2011; Roter & Hall, 2006).

Regarding race, when studied in isolation, we know that physicians are more verbally dominant with African-American patients and express a less positive tone with them when compared with their white patients (Johnson et al., 2004). African-American and Caucasian race-concordant doctor–patient interviews last longer than do non-concordant interviews even when age, socioeconomic status, and patient health are controlled for (Cooper et al., 2003). As well, these dyads depict less hurriedness in their interactions (Cooper et al., 2003). Similar findings were reported between ethnic minority patients and their Dutch physicians, compared to Dutch patient visits. Specifically, non-discordant racial dyads exhibited less friendliness by both parties, less psychosocial discussion, and lower ratings of physician concern (Van Wieringen, Harmsen, & Brujnzeel, 2002).

Age and education level have also been examined together and in isolation germane to their impact on patient-physician interaction. When we consider age and education level of the patient, we know that those patients who are younger and better educated tend to ask more questions of their physicians than do those who are older and less well educated (Roter et al., 1997). Moreover, health care providers have relatively positive appraisals of better-educated patients (Ratanawongsa et al., 2009) and less positive appraisals of older patients (Greene, Hoffman, Charon, & Adelman, 1987; Holroyd, 2006).

The study of social concordance with respect to shared social characteristics (e.g., race, gender, education, and age) between dyad members in a specific interaction is unique. The recently published study by Johnson Thornton et al. (2011) is unique in that it measured level of concordance between the patient and physician on the characteristics of gender, age, and level of education. When the patients and physicians shared three of these characteristics they were coded as high in social concordance, when they shared two characteristics they were coded as medium in concordance, and when they shared only one or fewer characteristics they were coded as low in concordance. The results indicate that lower patient-physician social concordance was associated with less favourable patient perceptions of care and less favourable patient affect. In addition, when there was less social concordance between patients and their physicians, the patients provided lower ratings of global satisfaction with office visits, and they were less likely to recommend their physician to a friend. Johnson Thornton et al. (2011) conclude that patient-physician social concordance may have a cumulative effect on the interaction; thus, future studies should move beyond measuring only a single dimension when attempting to determine the influence of social characteristics on health communication and health care quality.

Poor communication between physicians and patients is negatively correlated with patient adherence to treatment regimens. In the words of Moira Stewart and her colleagues at the University of Western Ontario, "Patient–doctor communication and patient adherence are inexorably linked because the interaction provides the context within which the recommendations to be complied with are delivered" (1999, p. 27). The next section of this chapter addresses the topic of adhering to medical advice.

ADHERING TO MEDICAL ADVICE

compliance or adherence: the degree to which patients carry out the behaviours and treatments that physicians and other health professionals recommend.

Traditionally, medical professionals have used the term **compliance** to mean the degree to which patients carry out the behaviours and treatments that physicians and other health professionals recommend. But because the term *compliance* can be interpreted as implying reluctant obedience, many health professionals prefer the term **adherence** (although some use the terms interchangeably). What does it mean to adhere to medical advice? Although we may immediately respond to this question by saying that being adherent means we take medication in the way a physician has prescribed, adherence is much more than that. Adhering to the advice of a health professional may mean maintaining healthy lifestyle practices, such as eating properly, avoiding stressful situations, getting enough sleep and exercise, abstaining from smoking, and limiting our intake of alcohol, as well as carrying out other behaviours that promote good health. Medical professionals use the term **non-adherence** to describe the practice of *not* following their advice.

non-adherence: failure to follow the advice of a health professional.

How prevalent is the problem of non-adherence? This question is actually more difficult to answer than one might first assume. Patients may fail to adhere to any of the different types of medical advice just outlined, and they can violate each of these types of advice in many different ways. Thus, failing to take one's medication as prescribed could mean taking medication in the wrong amount or at the wrong time, or discontinuing the medication before the prescribed time has elapsed.

creative non-adherence: a patient's intentional modifying or supplementing of a recommended treatment regimen.

Creative non-adherence is a particularly interesting form of non-adherence that is intentional and involves modifying or supplementing the recommended treatment regimen. These alterations are often based on private theories about a health problem and its treatment. For example, the patient may decide that particular symptoms meriting treatment were ignored by the health professional; he or she may then augment the treatment regimen, perhaps including over-the-counter medications or home remedies that interact with prescribed medication in unpredictable, even dangerous ways. Sometimes, however, these modifications are useful (Shine, 2002). For example, some patients are thought to have a better idea of how to control their blood glucose level than their health care provider does. Similarly, parents who adjust their child's asthma regimen can control asthma better than if they precisely follow a prescribed regimen. This is because there are often fluctuations in the severity of asthma (e.g., seasonal variability), and the parents can adjust the treatment in response to their child's needs at the time.

Assessing Adherence

To determine the prevalence of non-adherence, we must be able to assess the problem. There are at least seven methods researchers can use to measure patient adherence. They can (1) ask the health professional, (2) ask the patient, (3) ask other people, (4) watch for appointment non-attendance, (5) count pills, (6) watch for treatment non-response, and (7) examine biochemical evidence (Haynes, McDonald, & Garg, 2002; Turk & Meichenbaum, 1991).

One of the easiest ways to measure adherence is to ask the health professional who works with the patient to estimate it. Generally, though, health professionals' estimates of their patients' adherence are inaccurate, often only slightly better than chance (e.g., Gross, Bilker, Friedman, Coyne, & Strom, 2002; Miller et al., 2002). Typically, health professionals overestimate patient adherence. Another simple approach to measuring adherence is to ask the patient. However, patients also tend to overestimate their adherence, perhaps because they know they should follow "doctor's orders." Health professionals' and patients' reports of adherence are subjective and may be biased by lying and wishful thinking. The same bias may result when family members are asked to assess the patient's adherence.

More objective measures of patient adherence include pill counting and biochemical tests. In pill counting, the medication remaining in the dispenser is compared to the amount that should remain at this point in the treatment regimen to determine if patients have been following directions. However, even if the right quantity of medication is found, patients may not have been compliant. We would not know if the patients took the medication at the right times, in the correct amount, or if, wanting to please the health professional, they simply discarded some of the medication.

Some researchers (e.g., Kehr, 2004) have installed microprocessors in the lids of pill containers to record when the pill bottle is opened. Perhaps not surprisingly, data gathered from this device do not show high consistency with self-report (Garber, 2004). Other electronic means include simply monitoring the filling of prescriptions. A 2010 study (Fischer et al., 2010) of e-prescriptions reported that 22 percent were not filled even once! Biochemical tests can be conducted (on patients' blood or urine, for example) to determine if the patients have ingested a medication recently. This method of assessment is both time-consuming and expensive. In addition, there are problems with this technique, resulting from individual differences in absorption and metabolism of drugs (Liu et al., 2001). We should also point out that biochemical tests do not measure the degree of adherence; the presence of a drug simply identifies that the patients ingested some amount of the drug at some time. Such tests do not indicate that the patients took the proper amount at the proper time.

Frequency and Cost of Non-Adherence

Despite the difficulties in assessing adherence, researchers have been able to estimate the prevalence of non-adherence. A meta-analysis of more than 500 studies conducted over 50 years led Robin DiMatteo (2004b) to report that adherence ranges from 25 to 50 percent. However, the actual range of adherence to prescribed medications varies from zero to 100 percent (e.g., Haynes, McKibbon, & Kanani, 1996; McDonald, Garg, & Haynes, 2002). It is reported that at least 38 percent of patients do not follow short-term treatment plans (e.g., completing a prescription for medication; DiMatteo, 1994), and as many as 50 percent do not adhere to recommendations for long-term treatment (e.g., taking hypertensive medication; Wahl et al., 2005). Moreover, more than 75 percent of patients are unwilling or unable to follow suggested lifestyle changes, such as exercising regularly or eating a low-fat diet.

The cost of non-adherence is considerable. It is estimated that non-adherence costs Canadians several billion dollars annually (Coambs et al., 1995; Patodia, 2010). Both direct and indirect costs are incurred when patients fail to adhere. Direct costs result from excessive hospital expenditures (e.g., for people admitted to hospital due to non-adherence regarding prescription medications), excessive nursing home expenditures (medication non-adherence is the primary reason that elderly patients must reside in nursing homes), and excessive treatment costs of ambulatory care (e.g., additional visits to a physician). Indirect costs result from reductions in worker productivity due to sick days taken, less efficient work due to illness, and costs associated with premature death.

As you can see, the monetary costs of non-adherence are enormous. But more importantly, the personal costs of non-adherence are also immense.

What Factors Predict Adherence?

Non-adherence often results in people becoming sicker or dying. Why, then, do people fail to adhere to medical recommendations? Although researchers are not completely sure how to answer this question, they have discovered a number of factors that are linked to non-adherence.

Illness and Characteristics of the Treatment Regimen   Some medical recommendations require patients to change *longstanding habits*. For example, a physician may suggest that a patient go on a restricted diet, stop smoking cigarettes, begin a program of regular exercise, or avoid stressful situations. These changes can be thought of as life-style changes. Although some patients will adhere to these recommendations, particularly if they are at a high risk for serious illness (DiMatteo, 2004b), it is more likely that people will not make these lifestyle changes (e.g., Turk & Meichenbaum, 1991). Patients presumably do not make these changes because the effort involved seems greater than the health risks of not making such changes.

Both *complexity* and *duration* of the regimen prescribed also play a role in non-adherence. If you are told to "take one of these pills after meals, one of these other pills every 8 hours, two of these pills at bedtime, and these pills as needed," you will likely have some difficulty following the "doctor's orders." As you might predict, the greater the variety of medications one must take and the more complex the schedule, the more likely people are to make an error, thereby failing to adhere to the medical regimen (Haynes, Ackloo, Sahota, McDonald, & Yao, 2008).

Research exploring the impact of side effects on treatment is mixed. Not surprisingly, unpleasant *side effects* can lead to non-adherence. Research conducted with HIV-positive patients, for example, indicates that the more severe the side effects, the less likely the patient is to take the prescribed medication (Catz, Kelly, Bogart, Genosch, & McAuliffe, 2000; Gellaitry et al., 2005). However, other research indicates that most people who engage in non-adherence do not consider side effects to be a very important factor.

As mentioned before, the longer the *duration* of the treatment, the less likely people are to adhere to it. Researchers at McMaster University (Haynes et al., 2008) reviewed numerous studies comparing adherence rates to the length of treatment and concluded that, in most cases, non-adherence increases as duration of therapy increases. Often, long-term treatment programs are for illnesses that have no visible symptoms, such as hypertension. Understandably, people are less motivated to adhere to a treatment if there are no apparent symptoms indicating that they are unwell.

Because people are less likely to adhere to medical recommendations if they do not perceive symptoms of illness, it follows that *severity of an illness* will not lead to adherence unless symptoms are perceived by the patient. The more obvious a symptom is, the more likely people are to adhere to treatment.

Patient's Personal Characteristics   Adherence is also linked to personal attributes of patients, such as their age, gender, and cultural background. The association between adherence and age is very complex. Adherence can either increase or decrease with age, depending on the specific illness, the timeframe, and the treatment regimen prescribed. Some research has revealed a curvilinear relationship between age and adherence. In a large-scale longitudinal study (Thomas et al., 1995) investigating colorectal cancer screening, those who adhered best were approximately 70 years old; the worst adherers were younger than 50 years of age or older than 80. Another study (Park et al., 1999) revealed a surprising pattern of medication adherence in arthritis patients. This study found an age-related cognitive decline among participants. Yet, the older participants actually adhered to their treatment regimen better than middle-aged patients. A busy lifestyle associated with middle age was found to be more of a determinant of non-adherence than was cognitive functioning.

Adherence rates are also related to age in children. Both cancer patients and diabetic children are more likely to adhere to treatment regimens at younger ages (e.g., until about 9 years of age) (Jonasson et al., 1999; Manne, Jacobsen, Gorfinkle, Gerstein, & Redd, 1993; Miller & Drotar, 2003). These results may be explained by the decreasing responsibility parents have for their children's treatment as they get older.

Researchers have found very few gender differences in overall adherence rates (DiMatteo, 2004b). Some differences do emerge, however, when we look at adherence to specific medical recommendations. For instance, women seem to be better than men at adhering to dietary restrictions (Laforge, Greene, & Prochaska, 1994) and at taking medication for mental disorders (Sellwood & Tarrier, 1994). As well, young female pediatric patients are more adherent than males (DiMatteo, 2004b).

Cultural differences in adherence rates are not only rare but also have been noted (McDonald et al., 2002). Such cultural differences appear most often in patients who are from a culture that does not believe in modern medical recommendations and who prefer their own traditional healers (e.g., Novins, Beals, Moore, Spicer, & Manson, 2004). Ka'opua and Mueller (2004) note that native Hawaiians prefer holistic healing approaches that emphasize inclusion of the family. Native Hawaiians are also less likely to adhere to medical regimens prescribed to control diabetes and heart disease risk than other groups. But there are no notable differences in adherence rates by native Hawaiians in the complex pharmaceutical treatment of highly active antiretroviral therapy regimens (HAART) required to control HIV infection. Oggins (2003) provides narratives from minority group members that depict common misconceptions, often culturally based, that lead to non-adherence for other illnesses. Antshel (2002) and Hamill and Dickey (2005) outline how consideration of common elements in the minority member's culture improves treatment adherence.

Socioeconomic Factors   When considering the expense of medications, we see that seniors (4.6 percent) are less likely to report cost-related non-adherence than are young adults (8.7 percent) in Canada (Kennedy & Morgan, 2009). In the United States, studies report non-adherence due to cost to be at least three times higher than it is in Canada (Kennedy & Morgan, 2009).

Physician Characteristics   As we might predict, patients' adherence improves as confidence in their physician's competence increases (Gilbar, 1989; Wroth & Pathman, 2006).

When patients lack confidence in their physicians, or are unsatisfied with the concern demonstrated by their physicians and even the friendliness of office staff, they are less likely to adhere to prescribed medical regimens (Wroth & Pathman, 2006). However, you may remember that the physician who is perceived as having positive attributes, such as kindness, is more likely to be perceived as competent than is one who is seen as unfriendly. It follows that people are more likely to adhere to medical recommendations if their physician is viewed as warm, caring, friendly, and interested in the welfare of patients (DiNicola & DiMatteo, 1984). When physicians exhibit a good bedside manner by providing encouragement, making eye contact, smiling, and even joking and laughing, patient adherence improves (Haskard Zolnierek & DiMatteo, 2009; Haskard Zolnierek et al., 2009). In contrast, when physicians are disrespectful to their patients the patients are less likely to adhere (Blanchard & Lurie, 2004).

Physician-Patient Interaction   Earlier in the chapter, we outlined a number of elements inherent in physician-patient communication and physician-patient relationships that can also influence patient adherence. For instance, if the patient does not understand instructions (e.g., due to the use of medical jargon), does not ask questions to clarify the instructions the physician provides, or does not remember those instructions, adherence is not possible. Indeed, there is a 19 percent higher risk of non-adherence among patients whose physicians communicate poorly compared to those whose physicians communicate well (Haskard Zolnierek & DiMatteo, 2009). When the interaction between physician and patient includes the discussion of benefits, risks, and barriers to adherence and allows patient involvement in decision making, then you have set the stage for maximum patient adherence (Haskard Zolnierek & DiMatteo, 2009). If a physician's expectations and a patient's expectations about what role each party should play in the interaction differ, patients are less likely to follow the physician's medical recommendations.

Improving Patient Adherence

In this next section, we will see a number of different approaches that can be used to increase a patient's medical adherence.

In their meta-analysis of published studies between 1949 and 2008 linking patient treatment adherence to physician-patient communication, Haskard Zolnierek and DiMatteo (2009) state that providing physicians with communication skills training increases patient adherence by 12 percent. This effect is even greater when analyzing only studies that include pediatricians. However, there is less of an effect when a patient has a more severe illness. As previously mentioned, when a patient has a serious illness, adherence is greater. Thus, one would assume that there would be less room for improvement. Interestingly, providing communication training that focuses specifically on achieving adherence does not seem to provide an additional increase in adherence rates. For an example of one framework for increasing communication skills, see Table 4-2.

In addition to physicians becoming more skilled in communicating with their patients over the last several decades, patients have also begun to assert more power in the physician-patient relationship. One reason for this may be the increased level of education attained by people in Western society. The average person is better informed now than ever before about health. It is interesting to note that models of physician-patient

Table 4-2 The Calgary-Cambridge Observation Guide

1. Initiating the session
   a. establishing rapport
   b. identifying reasons for the consultation
2. Gathering information
   a. exploration of problems
   b. understanding the patient's perspective
   c. providing structure (e.g., sequencing, summarizing)
3. Building the relationship
   a. developing rapport
   b. involving the patient
4. Providing structure
   a. Summarizing what has been said
5. Explanation and planning
   a. providing the correct amount and type of information
   b. aiding accurate recall and understanding
   c. achieving a shared understanding (i.e., incorporating the patient's perspective)
6. Closing the session

Source: Based on Silverman, Kurtz, and Draper (2005).

relationships did not include a profile wherein the patient dominates until relatively recently. Roter and colleagues (1997) note that young patients often choose to interact with their physicians by controlling the consultation (e.g., asking the majority of questions). Whatever the cause of this change, it may necessitate health professionals to alter their style of social influence to maintain patient adherence. Moreover, there are additional strategies available to improve patient adherence.

Educational Strategies   Educational strategies to improve adherence are abundant. Health education is aimed at filling in the gaps in patient understanding about the need to follow medical recommendations (Ockene, 2001). Types of patient education vary considerably and include package inserts, written information sheets to reinforce verbal instructions, one-on-one counselling, small group sessions, lectures, demonstrations, and mailed information. In Canada, health education is provided by hospital, clinic, community, worksite, and private programs. As well, pamphlets and brochures are readily available to supplement and reinforce verbal instructions (Coambs et al., 1995).

Behavioural Strategies   Behavioural strategies can also be effective in increasing patients' motivation to adhere to their treatment regimens (Brondolo & Mas, 2001; DiMatteo & DiNicola, 1982; Ockene, 2001). Providing *prompts* and *reminders* as cues may encourage patients to perform recommended activities. These cues may include notes posted; certain forms of drug packaging (e.g., dispensers with dated compartments or other built-in reminders); or reminder phone calls, e-mails, or texts.

Tailoring the regimen so that activities in the treatment are fitted to habits and routines in the patient's daily life may also help. For example, taking medication is easiest to do if it is tied in with another activity, such as brushing one's teeth in the morning. *Self-monitoring* is another way to encourage patient adherence; the patient keeps a written record of regimen activities, such as monitoring his or her resting heart rate or documenting foods eaten during the day.

Contingency contracting, wherein the patient and health professional (or parent, if the patient is a child) negotiate a series of treatment activities and goals as well as rewards based on the patient's fulfillment of these activities, can also help. For example, "a diabetic child and his or her parents may enact a contract that specifies a particular reward for each day the child does his or her insulin injection without argument" (Miller & Stark, 1994, p. 81). These techniques have a clear advantage in that the patient must actively participate in their design and execution. Further, the patient can usually carry out these strategies without assistance.

Social Support   Social and emotional support can provide much-needed motivation for patient adherence, particularly when the regimen is long term or requires lifestyle changes. Family and friends can provide positive encouragement about the treatment activities and help to ensure they occur. Marital status, marital status of parents for children, and having a roommate increase adherence to medical regimens (DiMatteo, 2004a). Social support can also be provided by self-help groups, patient groups, and organizations established to help with specific health conditions. Patients who receive encouragement, inspiration, reminders, and aid in carrying out the regimen are believed to be more likely to comply than those who do not.

Research evaluating these strategies suggests that the more comprehensive the program of intervention, the more effective the outcome. Roter and colleagues (1998) contend that the most powerful interventions include combinations of all three strategies—educational, behavioural, and social or affective. Haynes and his colleagues have outlined which of these strategies is most effective for short-term (less than 2 weeks) and long-term treatment regimens (see Table 4-3).

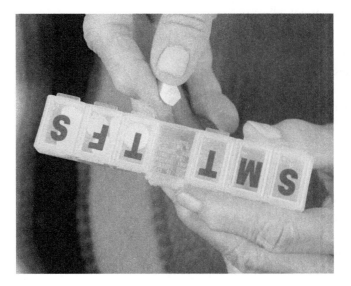

A pill organizer such as this one can help ensure patient adherence.
Jupiterimages/Stockbyte/Getty Images

Table 4-3 Methods of Increasing Adherence

Short-term treatments

- Counselling about the importance of adherence
- Written instructions about taking medicines
- Reminder packaging (e.g., calendar packs, dosettes)
- Reminders using personal phone calls or text messaging

Long-term treatments require combinations of the following for effective health outcomes:

- Instruction and instructional materials
- Simplifying the regimen (e.g., less frequent dosing, controlled release dosage forms)
- Counselling about the regimen
- Support group sessions
- Reminders for medications and appointments
- Manual telephone follow-up
- Cuing medications to daily events
- Reinforcement and rewards (e.g., explicitly acknowledging the patient's efforts to adhere)
- Self-monitoring with regular physician review and reinforcement
- Involving family members and significant others

Source: Based on Haynes, R. B., McDonald, H. P., & Garg, A. X. (2002). Helping patients follow prescribed treatment. *Journal of the American Medical Association, 288,* 2880–2883.

How important is it to adhere to medical recommendations provided by health care professionals? This is another question that is not easy to answer. By not adhering to treatment regimens, people increase their risk of developing health problems or of prolonging or worsening their current illnesses. Approximately 20 percent of hospital admissions are thought to result from patient non-adherence to medical recommendations (Ley, 1982). In general, studies show a strong relationship between loyal adherence and improved health. DiMatteo and colleagues (2002) reviewed studies of adherence involving more than 19 000 patients and concluded that 26 percent more patients experienced a good outcome by adhering than by not adhering to their treatment. This means the adherent patient's odds of having a good health outcome are three times higher than the odds for non-adherers.

This increase in health is essentially as effective as many well established medical interventions. Health outcomes were highest in studies of chronic conditions and of pediatric patient populations. Interestingly, a meta-analysis conducted by researchers (Simpson et al., 2006) at the University of Alberta noted that adherence to placebo treatment also led to lower mortality. There may be a **"healthy adherer" effect**, whereby adherence to drug therapy is indicative of overall healthy behaviour.

Another possibility to be explored in determining the importance of adherence is that complete adherence may not be necessary. Perhaps there are only certain levels of adherence that are required to obtain health benefits. If this is the case, it may explain

"healthy adherer" effect: greater adherence to health-promoting behaviours, such as medication adherence, is indicative of overall healthy behaviour.

why there are few differences between those who adhere completely and those who do not adhere. For example, consuming 80 percent of the medication prescribed has been described as the minimum rate of adherence necessary to treat hypertension effectively (Epstein & Cluss, 1982). Unhealthful non-adherence might then be defined as "the point below which the desired preventive or therapeutic result is unlikely to be achieved with the medication prescribed" (Parrish, 1986, p. 456).

In summary, non-adherence appears to be a fairly common phenomenon. There are a number of factors associated with non-adherence, including poor physician-patient communication; complexity and duration of the regimen; age, gender, and cultural background of the patient; and affective characteristics of the physician. Several strategies have been devised to increase adherence to medical regimens (e.g., educational and behavioural strategies), but researchers question their effectiveness. Furthermore, researchers have been unable to find a significant benefit to high levels of adherence. However, it may be that more moderate levels of adherence contribute to health benefits, thereby explaining the lack of differences between high- and low-level adherers.

DR. GOOGLE: HEALTH AND THE INTERNET

Internet use is having a significant impact on the way people think about their health and how they consume health services. In March 2013, when we "googled" the word diabetes, Google found 230 000 000 sites in 0.2 seconds! When we did this in 2010, we got 67 600 000 hits. These numbers are going up daily.

The Internet is particularly relevant to health in Canada. Geography provides challenges for health care access, computer technology is relatively more available than in many other countries (though disparities still exist within Canada in this regard), and a wealth of information is available on the Internet. Thus, the Internet has the potential to have a positive impact on the health of Canadians.

Here, we make reference to a number of health-related websites. Where appropriate, we also indicate the date we last accessed that site; however, websites and their addresses are subject to change. In fact, one study of website attrition found that, of 184 websites studied, 59 percent of those that existed in 1999 could not be found using the same web addresses in 2002 (Veronin, 2002).

Although it is likely that some of the sites mentioned here will be active for a long time, it is possible that some will be eliminated or that, perhaps, their addresses will change. Even if this is the case, we hope they will stand as good examples of the phenomena we discuss.

Health-Related Resources Available on the Internet

Not only is there a great deal of health information on the Internet, it also covers a wide range of topics. What follows is a description of some of the more commonly accessed resources.

Medical Articles and Reports   Health Canada is a rich source of health information. Visit www.hc-sc.gc.ca and have a look around. If you did this in March of 2010, as we did, you would find a list of advisories and warnings covering everything from eating sprouts to the purchase of children's jewellery. Some of these articles are written for the general public, others are targeted to health care professionals. Good articles are not only well written, they are also well referenced. Claims and statistics are linked to sources that the reader can find and assess. Of course, this is no different from good articles in any medium. It becomes more of an issue with the Internet, though, because of its widespread use and potential misuse.

The home page of Health Canada (or the Health on the Net foundation) features a wealth of information. Another example of an informative Canadian site is the Centre for Health Evidence, affiliated with the University of Alberta and the University of Manitoba (www.cche.net, accessed March 17, 2013). The purpose of this site is to support evidence-based practice, thus supporting medical decision making that relies on research findings and not just on intuition. As such, it is intended for patients, practitioners, and policy makers and geared primarily for practitioners and practitioners-in-training. Publications found on this site include a User's Guide to Evidence-Based Medicine, which contains information about how to calculate the benefits and risks of health decisions and interventions.

Yet another good Canadian site is run by the Canadian Institute for Health Information (CIHI) (www.cihi.ca, accessed March 17, 2013). The information found here is particularly helpful for researchers, policy makers, and practitioners. A number of the reports also provide useful information for the general public. Throughout this book, you will see information drawn from the CIHI site.

Services   Imagine the following story: Shortly after moving to Halifax, Maureen and her husband had triplets. Needless to say, this changed everything for them. At times, they found it difficult to cope, especially since they knew very few people in town. One day, while working on her computer, Maureen typed the following into her search engine: "Parents of multiple births, Halifax, Nova Scotia." This yielded 19 900 hits! The first site listed was for the Parents of Multiple Births Association—Halifax Region. There she found information on support groups and a list of activities and events for families with multiple births.

Other organizations, such as the Alzheimer Society of Canada, provide valuable information and services across the country. For example, if you lived in Manitoba, you could use the society's website to discover that there are offices in Winnipeg, Brandon, Winkler, Portage La Prairie, Dauphin, and Whitemouth. Each comes with contact information, including an e-mail address. The Society's URL is www.alzheimer.ca (accessed March 17, 2013).

Still other Internet-based services help people make treatment-related decisions. Using the tools provided by these sites, people can view interviews with practitioners and other consumers and obtain information pertaining to the specific decision they face (Schwitzer, 2002). These tools have considerable potential to provide help with difficult decisions, when used in concert with one's own physician.

Health Initiatives and Health Promotion   Not surprisingly, the Internet is a widely used vehicle for health promotion. The Health Canada home page in March of 2013 featured something called "Eat Well Central." Eat Well Central contains information about cooking and meal planning tips, grocery shopping tips, and healthy eating for kids on the go. The World Health Organization website features health initiatives on a global scale (www.who.int, accessed March 17, 2013). Good examples from 2013 include World Health Day and World Immunization Week.

If you have ever tried to quit smoking or know someone who has, you might know that you would come up with no fewer than 12 billion hits from a Google search using the words *quit smoking*. Some of these sites promote tobacco-free living, some provide free quit-smoking support, some sell smoking cessation products, and still others get you into chat rooms and newsgroups.

There are also electronic health promotion interventions available on the Internet. One Internet intervention had people record their physical activity behaviour and then feedback was provided (van den Berg, Schoones, & Vliet Vlieland, 2007). Another intervention had people self-monitor both their fat intake and physical activity. Feedback and suggestions were then given on the healthfulness of their behaviours and ways to improve them (Oenema, Brug, Dijkstra, De Weerdt, & De Vries, 2008). These types of interventions successfully increase participants healthful behaviour.

Surveys   Canada does a good job of surveying its population on issues relating to health. More important, a considerable amount of the data from these surveys is available on the Internet free of charge. These sites contain a collection of tables presenting statistics on such things as health expenditures and pregnancy outcomes. Of course, we have accessed many sites like these in writing this book.

On a provincial level, websites such as the one for The McCreary Centre Society, which addresses the health of young people in British Columbia, describe numerous health initiatives for that population. This initiative is documented on the McCreary Centre website (www.mcs.bc.ca, accessed March 17, 2013).

Support   While there are numerous services providing support on the Web, there are also groups of individuals engaged in e-mail conversations and blogs that take place outside the purview of any formal support service. It is quite possible that someone caring for a person with Alzheimer's disease could "meet" someone halfway around the world engaged in the same challenges. These relationships can be extremely important to the individuals involved (Wright & Bell, 2003).

Assessing the Quality of Health Information on the Internet

The quantity of information available on the Internet is unparalleled. The quality of that information can vary considerably, however. How, then, can we assess quality? One way is to rely on others to provide that assessment. Organizations such as the Internet Trade Bureau provide what might be called seals of approval for business-related Internet sites. Services like this one monitor complaints against sites and provide a list of these upon request.

Services also exist that provide accreditation or "seals of approval" for health-related websites. One such example is Health on the Net Foundation (HON) (www.hon.ch, accessed March 17, 2013). The HON code of conduct allows for the display of the HON code icon by websites meeting HON quality criteria, which are based on principles outlined in Table 4-4 (Health on the Net Foundation, 2014). These criteria are consistent with those recommended by other bodies, such as the World Health Organization, the Canadian Health Network (which is maintained by the federal government), and the American Accreditation Health Care Commission.

Table 4-4 Principles Used to Assess Quality in Health-Related Websites (Health on the Net Foundation)

Principle	Description
1. Authority	Advice is given by those who are medically trained and qualified, unless it is made clear that other forms of qualification apply.
2. Complementarity	The purpose of the website is to support relationships with health practitioners, not replace them.
3. Confidentiality	Any health data presented or information provided by visitors to the site is kept strictly confidential.
4. Attribution	Sources of data and claims are clearly provided.
5. Justifiability	Claims are supported by appropriate and balanced evidence.
6. Transparency of authorship	Contact addresses (including that of the webmaster) are provided so that further information can be sought.
7. Transparency of sponsorship	Any organizations, public or private, contributing funding are identified.
8. Honesty in advertising	The advertising policy of the site is described. Advertising and editorial policy will be presented so that it is clearly distinguishable from other site content.

Source: Health on the Net Foundation, http://www.hon.ch, accessed July 1, 2003.

These symbols indicate that a health website has been reviewed and approved by the Health on the Net Foundation (www.hon.ch)

Health on the Net Foundation

Implications for Patient-Physician Relationships

Internet use is having a considerable impact on the way people interact with their doctors (Iverson, Howard & Penney, 2008). A study of 266 oncologists found that 98 percent of them felt they were spending increasing amounts of time discussing information that patients derived from the Internet. The oncologists estimated that this has added about

10 minutes to each patient consultation, compared to 5 years ago (Helft, Hlubocky, & Daugherty, 2003).

Patients' increased usage of the Internet is also affecting their expectations of the health care system. A study at Princess Margaret Hospital in Toronto (Chen & Siu, 2001) discovered a gap between the number of people who wanted as much information as possible about their cancer (86 percent) and the number who believed they were getting enough information from health care professionals (54 percent). The Internet provides one way to close this information gap. Of the 191 cancer patients surveyed in the Toronto study, 88 percent felt their doctors were willing to discuss information the patients found on the Internet.

While patients in the Toronto study felt their doctors were receptive to discussions of Internet information, there were differences in patients' and physicians' views about that information. For example, of the 410 oncologists who took part in the study, only 6 percent thought their patients used Internet information correctly. Perhaps this helps explain differences in opinion regarding the helpfulness and potential negative impact of this information.

Cartoon Stock

CHAPTER SUMMARY

■ Provide an overview of different models of the physician-patient relationship.

A number of different models of the physician-patient relationship have been proposed. Szasz and Hollender outlined three basic models of the physician-patient relationship: active-passive, guidance-cooperation, and mutual-participation. Debra Roter and her colleagues outlined a model with five distinct communication patterns: narrowly biomedical, expanded biomedical, biopsychosocial, psychosocial, and consumerist. Other models have also been proposed including one entitled patient-centred care.

■ Outline both patient and physician characteristics that lead to poor communication.

Both patient and physician characteristics can lead to poor communication. Physicians may interrupt their patients or in other ways receive little input from their patients, they may use medical jargon or baby talk when conversing with patients, they may give little information to their patients, and they may appear hurried. Patients are not always forthcoming with information, and they fail to ask questions of their physicians.

■ Define patient non-adherence and list contributing factors to non-adherence.

Patient non-adherence is the failure to follow the advice of the health professional. Certain patient characteristics also contribute to adherence. For example, children, females, and those who have the socioeconomic means are most likely to adhere. When treatments are complex or when poor physician-patient communication occurs, there is greater likelihood of non-adherence.

■ Outline strategies to improve patient adherence.

Adhering to treatment regimens results in better health outcomes. To improve adherence, one should simplify the regimen, use reminders (calendar packs to automated e-mails), engage in self-monitoring, provide reinforcements, engage in counselling about the importance of adherence, and involve family members and friends. A combination of strategies is often best.

■ Outline health-related resources available on the Internet and how one should assess the quality of those resources.

Internet use is having a significant impact on the way people think about their health. There is good health-related information on the Internet, but one must be mindful of assessing the quality of this information. The Internet is a useful vehicle for health promotion and personal electronic interventions can be accessed.

■ Describe how the Internet has altered physician-patient interactions.

The Internet is having an impact on physician-patient interactions with patients now asking more questions during the interview than in the past.

Chapter 5
Health and Physical Activity

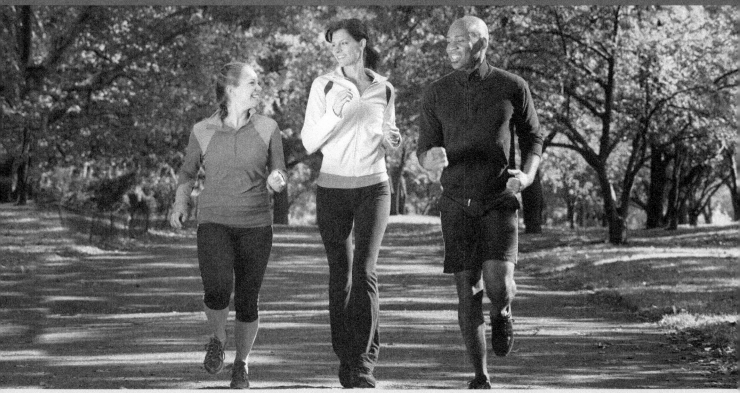

Learning Objectives

After studying this chapter, you will be able to:

1. define physical activity, exercise, and sport.
2. describe the psychological benefits of physical activity.
3. describe the physical benefits of physical activity.
4. appreciate the importance of adherence to physical activity.
5. understand some of the psychological issues involved in performance.
6. appreciate some of the psychological concerns resulting from injuries due to physical activity.

Gerry had always thought of himself as an athlete, and in high school and university this was indeed the case. He excelled in basketball, and he enjoyed snowboarding and mountain biking. He went to university on a basketball scholarship where he fully immersed himself in the life of a student athlete. He trained hard, played well, and maintained a solid academic record.

In his fourth year all of this changed. He went skiing over the winter holidays and a seemingly minor collision on the hill resulted in an awkward fall. A visit to the local clinic revealed that he had torn his anterior cruciate ligament. This required surgery followed by several weeks on crutches and 6 months of rehabilitation by which time the basketball season was well finished and he had graduated.

This experience was devastating for him, and he seemed to lose his interest in sport and physical activity as he sought to establish himself in the working world. He had less time to exercise and his eating habits deteriorated. He rationalized this shift in his priorities as being necessary to advance in his job. Over a period of 10 years, he gained weight and he did not handle stress well. Clearly his health had deteriorated.

In February of 2010 his life changed again when, like so many Canadians, he became completely absorbed in watching the Winter Olympics held in British Columbia. He was mesmerized by the performance of Canadian athletes, particularly the snowboarders as this was a sport that he had once enjoyed. He watched North Vancouver's Maelle Ricker win the gold medal in snowboard cross and was amazed to hear that she'd had eight knee operations and frequently competes with braces on both legs. At the end of the second week, he was again overwhelmed with emotion as he watched Quebec's Jasey Jay Anderson win the gold medal in alpine snowboarding. This time he was surprised to learn that Jasey Jay was 34 years old.

That evening he found himself thinking about how fortunate he was in that, although his health had deteriorated, he still had the option to change his situation. He had had seven fewer knee operations than Maelle and he was 2 years younger than Jasey Jay. The choice was his. The next day he watched the gold medal hockey game while riding an exercise bike at his fitness club. He made a decision to regain his health through regular exercise, good nutrition, and better management of the stress in his life. He continues in this program today, motivated by the improvement in both his physical and psychological well-being.

The personal choices that we make are among the most significant factors affecting our health and well-being. This chapter is about these decisions as they apply to physical activity. Most of us will admit that we often sacrifice physical activity when overwhelmed by time demands. We make comments like "I won't be able to exercise today as I have too much work to do" or "I won't be able to attend my yoga class this evening as I need to spend more time with my family." The implication is that we have little choice in the matter. As in the examples given, we may blame our jobs or our families as we are often not prepared to take responsibility for the decision. When it comes to priorities in our lives, physical activity is often low on the list. For many of us it does not occupy a line in our day planner. We tend to rationalize it: "I'll do it if time allows, and if it doesn't, I can always do it tomorrow."

THE NATURE OF PHYSICAL ACTIVITY

In this chapter, we focus on health issues relevant to physical activity, exercise, and sport. The literature indicates that one can attach quite different meanings to each of these terms. Biddle and Mutrie (2001) promote physical activity "in the belief that many forms of physical activity are healthy" (p. 3). They identify both exercise and sport as elements or sub-components of physical activity while recognizing that distinctions between these constructs are not always obvious and often overlap.

Dubbert (2002) points out that, as psychologists continue to be involved in the promotion of physical activity and exercise for disease prevention and rehabilitation, the research and intervention skills learned in these situations are now being applied to athletic performance. Hays (1999) suggests that, although exercise and sport may have different implications, the two fields are clearly related, and the effects of exercise are usually considered within the field of sport psychology. In introducing a special issue of *Canadian Psychology* (53:4, 2012) on sport and exercise psychology, the editor makes the point that psychology in general has much to learn from these two overlapping fields with particular mention being given to the speciality of health psychology (Drapeau, 2012). The leadership role that psychology can have in influencing poor lifestyle choices, including not exercising, is emphasized particularly as "public health representatives have shifted their focus from environmental causes of poor health to people's attitudes and behaviours concerning their health" (p. 259).

Sport psychology focuses on the influence of psychological factors on sport behaviour, whereas **exercise psychology** is concerned with the influence that sport and exercise have on psychological behaviour. According to Hays, "Exercise psychology attends to the body-to-mind relationship, whereas sport psychology is directed toward the mind-to-body relationship" (Hays, 1999, p. 240). Anshel (2005) suggests that exercise and sport psychology differ primarily with regard to the populations served, the type of physical activity, and the goals of the activity. However, in noting these differences, Gill (2006) observes that applied sport psychology interventions are effective in enhancing exercise activities: "Behavioural strategies and social cognitive approaches that focus on recognizing health and fitness benefits, overcoming barriers and developing self-control and perceived competence in a supportive environment are particularly appropriate" (p. 611). In 1988, one of the major journals in the field, *The Journal of Sport and Exercise Psychology*, changed its title from *The Journal of Sport Psychology* to reflect its commitment to the emerging area of physical activity and exercise.

Gauvin and Spence (1995) define exercise as "leisure activity (as opposed to occupational physical activity) undertaken with a specific external objective, such as the improvement of fitness, physical performance, or health, in which the participant is advised to conform to the recommended mode, intensity, frequency, and duration of such activity" (p. 435). Intention is important in this definition. If we go to the gym to ride a stationary bike or play basketball to improve our fitness, this would be considered exercise, but if walking is part of our work (e.g., a postal worker), it is not considered exercise as it is not being done to improve our fitness.

This would suggest that we can push a hand-mower, shovel snow, or chop wood to either get some exercise or cut the grass, clear the driveway, or get some wood for the fire. The intention is different, but the outcome is the same. Alternatively, Casperson, Powell, and Christenson (1985) have suggested that **physical activity** can be a part

sport psychology: the study of the influence of psychological factors on sport behaviour.

exercise psychology: the study of the influence that sport and exercise have on one's psychology and behaviour.

physical activity: the expenditure of energy, either purposely or without intention, as a result of bodily movements produced by skeletal muscles as part of leisure or work activities.

of either leisure or work activities, as it is a function of bodily movements produced by skeletal muscles. Whether it is purposeful or without intention, it involves the expenditure of energy.

Gauvin, Levesque, and Richard (2001) describe four parameters of physical activity: type, frequency, intensity, and duration. *Type* identifies the physiological systems that are used in a particular activity such as aerobic, strength, endurance, and flexibility. *Frequency* is concerned with how much the activity is performed over a time period. *Intensity* describes the load imposed on physiological systems by an activity (e.g., strenuousness). *Duration* indicates the temporal length of a particular activity. More recently, Cox (2007) has drawn from the work of Morgan in suggesting that for "physical activity to be meaningful it must have a 'purpose.' The purpose must be more meaningful and immediate than wanting to be physically fit or lose weight" (p. 403). His examples include getting a dog and taking it for a walk each day or riding a bike to work in order to save gas.

Physical fitness refers to physiological functioning and describes attributes we have that influence the ability to perform physical activity (Casperson et al., 1985).

Five forms of physical fitness have been identified (Hahn, Payne, Gallant, & Crawford, 2003; Kaplan, Sallis, & Patterson, 1993). These include cardiorespiratory endurance, muscular endurance, muscular strength, body composition, and flexibility.

Definitions of **sport** are often very inclusive, and it is difficult to distinguish among activities such as games, recreation, play, leisure activity, and sport. Wann (1997) suggests that most definitions of *sport* are too narrow and may exclude individuals often described as "weekend warriors." He defines sports as "activities involving powers and skills, competition and strategy, and/or chance, and engaged in for the enjoyment, satisfaction, and/or personal gain (such as income) of the participant and/or others (e.g., spectators), including organized and recreational sports, as well as sport as entertainment" (p. 3). The importance of including sports activities that fall outside the realm of competition is supported by Biddle and Mutrie (2001). It is our sense that the most appropriate definition includes both the youngster playing recreational sport for the first time motivated only by intrinsic enjoyment and the professional athlete who entertains others and makes his or her living in sport.

We now will consider the personal journey of Peter. In previous editions of this text, he has described his initial "heart attack," his second such event, his subsequent by-pass surgery, and the response he made each time with regard to his health and physical activity. In this edition, he brings us up to date on his health circumstances. This is not fiction but a Canadian's true story told in his own words.

physical fitness: physiological functioning (including cardiorespiratory endurance, muscular endurance, muscular strength, body composition, and flexibility) that influences the ability to be physically active.

sport: an activity that involves rules or limits, a sense of history, an aspect of winning and losing, and an emphasis on physical exertion in the context of competition.

CASE 5-1 PETER'S STORY

The Next Challenge.

I have had two heart attacks in my life (March, 1995, and August, 2007). This vignette is about my existing health situation and how I am going about managing it.

In December 2009, I had open-heart surgery. After the surgery, my convalescence was at home where I had to make significant adjustments to my life. For example, I learned to sleep in a chair as getting in and out of bed was difficult. Being home and alone much of the time, although I had many visitors, gave me an incredible opportunity to look at my life from all perspectives. It allowed me time to grieve over the friends and loved ones I had lost through death, and to also rejoice in the knowledge that I had some wonderful friends, a family that provided me with complete support, and a wife who sincerely wanted me to be around so that we could enjoy the rest of our lives together. I do not like the overuse of the term "bucket list" but this is just what I produced, and the list just seems to be getting longer.

In all of our lives, we may look around and think about what has made us the happiest and the saddest. Interestingly enough, I believe emotions like happiness, sadness, ecstasy, sorrow, anger, hatred, etc., revolve mostly around the people with whom we spend our time. In my recent life, I have felt attacked by some people who did this quietly but with great force. At the same time, I have been fortunate to make new friends and reacquaint myself with some old friends. I look upon myself as being fortunate to be alive, and I will share my story with whoever is interested in listening.

I was recently rearranging my home office and came across a letter that my son had given to me before my surgery with the understanding that I would not open it until after the surgery. He wrote it on December 6, 2009. It is a long letter and when I read it after my surgery, I cried openly. The following passages taken from it demonstrate the level of support that I received from my family and friends.

"The procedure is to bypass certain blockages in your heart. I am thinking of each of those bypasses to represent myself, mom, sister and the dog. I am thinking that each of us will represent a bridge to make you better, stronger, healthier, and the dad in our loving family. We are all here for you at each step of the way, no matter how minor or major. We all love you and need you in our lives. . . . I know that we have an incredibly strong family, that loves unconditionally, and I am proud to be a part of it. The support we have been receiving from our family friends has been a little overwhelming but it shows the importance of friendship and the kind of individuals that care about us. . . . you will have our family no matter what, and you will have a wonderful network of support from our friends".

What am I doing now?

In November of 2011, I elected to retire from my management position. Initially this was cause for some concern by my family as they were worried about how I would fill my days. They also worried about my emotional health. But they have been assured that I am doing very well. I have a plan that I live with every day.

When I wake up every day, the first thing I do is to look outside. This reminds me of how lucky I am to be here, alive, and feeling better than I ever have. I make breakfast for my wife and myself and then start the rest of the day. My first task is to figure out what my purpose is today. Without purpose, we just exist.

Every day is different and fulfilled. My best friend is a little Sheltie dog named Dakota. Each day we trek off for our daily walk, although I am not sure yet who walks whom. This is the time for me to reflect on the positive things in my life and to assure myself that all is well. About 45 minutes into the walk, we cross a bridge, which I find is one of the most peaceful areas in North Vancouver. I spend about 10 minutes looking out at the river water, and daydreaming. This leaves me at peace with myself. I think about what if I could do this, or that, or whom I might meet on this glorious walk. It is a time of day that I look forward too.

Some of my actions on these walks are a little difficult for some to understand. I will say that I must be an enigma to those who know me well. I can be a contradiction in my ways of thinking from one day to the next. I can be walking one day and smiling at everyone. This is a game to me to see who smiles back. When someone smiles back, it is a delightful experience. They have enhanced my life, as much as I may have enhanced theirs. The next day I may tread grudgingly in deep thought and not notice anyone else around me.

The next step in the day is to do my exercise workout. I do these with four very special friends. So that as well as getting physically fit, I also work on my emotional fitness. Reading and writing form a very large part of my day. I am learning French, as I want to become fluent in another language. It is also a good workout for the brain. I volunteer whenever I can for the Heart and Stroke Foundation. I speak to groups of volunteers about my life style changes and encourage them to help others as well. I recently had an article in the local paper talking about some of my experiences.

Forgiveness

In the second paragraph, I suggested that people are an emotional force that can make us angry, sad, or happy. However, ultimately it is up to us to make change happen. I have come to believe that the easiest way to change an outcome from anger to happiness is to forgive. This is very difficult for me. I am 61 years of age, and I am now learning that resentment, anger, and frustration do nothing to make our lives healthier. These feelings are only good for one thing, and that is to increase our stress levels. The more stressed we are, the greater is the negative impact on heart health.

Uncluttering

I use the word "uncluttering" from two perspectives. One is physically letting go of anything that is not useful to you anymore. It is amazing how much we accumulate over our lives. I was in my basement recently and found a box that had been sitting in the corner for about 25 years. I wondered what was in that box. When I opened it, I found scraps of paper that were only useful to me 25 years ago. Today they are in the garbage, and that corner now looks so appealing. No clutter. The other part of this process is letting go in your mind of useless information such as angry thoughts or unkind ways of treating others. Have you heard of people who have not spoken to each other since a disagreement many years ago? We all have. Forgive, forget, and move on. You will feel much less distress.

Bucket List

The list consists of items that I want to accomplish over the next one day to thirty years:

1. Make ten people smile today.
2. Call my mom, brother, son, and daughter at least once per week and more is better. Do as much as I can with them while we are all on this earth.
3. Forgive my wife everyday (I had to insert some humour).

4. Drink the good wine today, eat the good food today, and wear the good clothes. All of this makes you feel better—and who knows—you may not be here tomorrow to enjoy all these things.

5. Travel to as many different places as possible. Enjoy the people you meet along the way.

6. Laugh more and cry less. It feels good.

7. Help someone that is less fortunate than you are.

8. Work voluntarily for a charity that has meaning for you.

9. Live each day with passion, conviction, and strength.

I will conclude by saying this. I am blessed to have a great family and great friends. This makes my beliefs attainable. I believe the best days of my life are ahead of me. Enjoy.

PHYSICAL ACTIVITY AND THE FIVE COMPONENTS OF HEALTH

Peter's story clearly demonstrates the importance of lifestyle change. For him, the alternative has become unacceptable. The choices he faces and the decisions he must make touch on many of the issues connecting health psychology and physical activity.

Greenberg and Pargman (1989) describe a health–illness continuum anchored by four points: death, illness, health, and perfect health. Peter has moved close to the extremes of the continuum. To have been faced with the real possibility of death and to now be moving towards good health demonstrates the power of personal change processes. Each point on the continuum between death and perfect health is made up of five components: mental, physical, emotional, social, and spiritual health. Wellness is a function of the balance between the five components. The goal is to be well rounded in all areas. It is important not to invest in a component of health disproportionately (Pargman, 1998). Each component influences, and is influenced by, the others.

This reciprocity is clearly demonstrated in Peter's story, in which growth in all five areas is evident. He has not only moved a significant distance on the continuum of health and illness, but also has achieved a greater sense of balance in his life. By his own admission he has in a sense been "reborn." Although four of the components of health, other than physical (mental, social, emotional, and spiritual) are subjective, and therefore difficult to quantify, they are perhaps the most important elements of change for him as they have had the greatest impact on the quality of his life. He has discovered the joy of what Csikszentmihalyi (1997) has described as **active leisure** rather than **passive leisure**. Active leisure is an extremely positive experience associated with activities such as exercise. When people engage in these activities, they "tend to be happier, motivated, concentrated, and more often in flow than in any other part of the day. It is in these contexts that all the various dimensions of experience are most intensely focused and in harmony with one another" (p. 39).

active leisure: a positive experience that is associated with activities such as hobbies, playing a musical instrument, and exercise.

passive leisure: a positive experience that is associated with lack of activity (e.g., listening to music, daydreaming).

Levels of Physical Activity

It has been recommended for some time that we should have at least 30 minutes of moderate exercise every day (Pate et al., 1995), although there is some debate over exactly what this means. More recently, it has been recommended that adults need to have a minimum of 150 minutes of moderate to vigorous exercise each week in order to experience substantial health benefits (Statistics Canada, 2011b). Dubbert (2002) suggests that "moderate-level activity has significant health benefits but that vigorous activity should also be encouraged for those who are able and willing to increase the intensity of their effort" (p. 527). Although an appropriate program of exercise is recognized as part of a prescription for physical and psychological health, it is clear that many individuals do not get sufficient exercise and that, for those who initiate a program of exercise, the levels of adherence are low.

A frequently cited statistic in this regard is based on early research by Dishman (1988). He found that 50 percent of those who began a structured exercise program discontinued it within the first 6 months. There appears to be consistency to these findings, as Estabrooks (2000) reported that while 30 percent of North Americans exercise on a regular basis, 50 percent of those who begin an exercise program stop within 6 months. We will return to the issue of adherence later; now we will focus on the incidence of physical activity in Canadians.

Statistics Canada (2007) reported that in the decade leading up to 2005 there was an increase in the number of Canadians aged 12 or older who are at least moderately active during their leisure time. This means that they achieved the equivalent of 30–60 minutes of walking per day or a one-hour exercise class three times a week. Essentially, half of the population (52 percent) was moderately active while 48 percent were described as "inactive" which means they got less than the equivalent of half an hour of walking each day. This is an increase of 9 percent since 1996. Using the more recent recommendation of an accumulation of at least 150 minutes of moderate to vigorous exercise each week, it has been reported that 15 percent of Canadian adults are this active (Statistics Canada, 2011b).

Men were more likely to be physically active than women and the proportion of individuals who were moderately active decreases with increasing age, although this is primarily due to declines in women's physical activity as they age. Those in higher socioeconomic groups were more likely to be physically active than those with lower socioeconomic status. Residents of British Columbia were most likely to be physically active (59 percent) followed by those living in the Yukon and Alberta. The positive health impact of physical activity was also noted: Those who were active were more likely to rate their health as being very good to excellent. They also reported lower levels of stress, were less likely to report high blood pressure, and were less likely to report being overweight or obese (Statistics Canada, 2007).

In people over age 15, there has been a decrease in involvement in sports, from 45 percent in 1992 to 28 percent in 2005 (Statistics Canada, 2008a). This does not necessarily mean that Canadians are less physically active; individuals may be involved in exercise programs or physical activities such as jogging or walking. The reasons given for this decrease include an aging population, increased time pressures, careers, child rearing, and an increased interest in other leisure-time activities such as watching television and using computers. The Canadian Fitness and Lifestyle Research Institute (2009) reported that the most popular sports are, in order, hockey, soccer, golf, baseball and softball, racquet sports, basketball, volleyball, football or rugby, and curling.

It is interesting to note that in 2005, fewer Canadian children participated in sports compared to the participation rate in 1992, with boys showing the largest decline (Statistics Canada, 2008b). Parents, when asked about the potential barriers to their children's physical activity, cited, in order, cost of participation, lack of convenient facilities, child's preference for television and video games, lack of opportunities, homework, and traffic (Canadian Fitness and Lifestyle Research Institute, 2009). Epidemiological data reported by Tremblay et al. (2010) describes the increasing trend in the number of Canadian children described as overweight or obese over the past two decades. Specifically, an increase in girls from 14 percent to 25 percent and an increase from 14 percent to 31 percent in boys are reported. In response to this disturbing situation, Tremblay, Boudreau-Lariviere, and Cimon-Lambert (2012) outline physical activity recommendations for Canadian preschoolers which emphasize the importance of establishing these behaviours early in childhood as the indications are that active children tend to remain so. They conclude that such interventions have "great potential to help develop healthy PA behaviours in young children, leading to sustained health and wellness benefits throughout life" (p. 287).

In response to the need to increase physical inactivity and reduce sedentary lifestyles in Canada, a new initiative "Active Canada 20/20" has been established as a national physical activity strategy designed to coordinate recommendations in this regard through all levels of government. Nine principles outlining a population-based approach to physical activity and sedentary living have been established. These include the adoption of evidenced-based strategies, the use of an equity approach, the use of a life-stage approach, advocating for increased political commitment, and the accommodation of different needs. Of particular interest to this discussion is Principle 9: "Facilitate healthy personal choices by making the physically active choice the easy choice" (Active Canada 20/20, 2012, p. 1).

THE FIVE FORMS OF PHYSICAL ACTIVITY

There are many different types of exercise and physical activity; however, physiologically we can identify five forms of exercise. Three of them—*isometric, isotonic,* and *isokinetic*—are based on the principle of resistance, which involves placing demands on, or overloading, the muscles in order to affect both muscle strength and endurance.

Isometric exercise involves contracting a muscle group against an immovable object without movement in the body. This may seem counterintuitive, as there is no noticeable body movement; however, the contraction of the muscles improves muscle strength, although it does little for endurance. **Isotonic exercise** is the form of exercise most of us associate with weightlifting. This involves using free weights or callisthenics to place resistance on the muscle by shortening or lengthening the muscle group. Most of the exertion occurs in one direction. Over time it can be expected that such a program will improve both muscle strength and endurance. **Isokinetic exercise** is the most efficient method of developing muscle strength and endurance as it involves placing resistance that overloads a muscle group through a complete range of motion. Training of this nature requires specialized, often expensive equipment designed to vary the load placed on the muscle group according to muscle strength and position.

The two other forms of exercise are *aerobic* and *anaerobic*. Given that the word *aerobic* means "with oxygen," these can be defined in terms of the relationship between exercise and oxygen use. In **anaerobic exercise** intense effort is expended over a short period of time. The oxygen taken in is less than the oxygen required, creating a deficit that needs

isometric exercise: contracting a muscle group against an immovable object without movement in the body.

isotonic exercise: exercise that uses weights or calisthenics to place tension on a muscle through the shortening or lengthening of the muscle group.

isokinetic exercise: exercise that places tension on a muscle group through a complete range of motion.

anaerobic exercise: exercise, such as sprinting, in which intense effort is expended over a short period of time, resulting in an oxygen debt.

to be made up. A sprint to first base in a softball game or an attempt to demonstrate how fast we can still run the 100-metre dash can leave us "gasping for air." Conversely, **aerobic exercise** involves an increased consumption of oxygen over an extended period of time. The oxygen being taken in is sufficient to replace that being used. Therefore, although the exercise may be strenuous it does not result in an oxygen deficit. It is the sustained nature of aerobic exercise that produces the health benefits associated with it, as the intensity and duration of the exercise stimulates the cardiovascular, pulmonary, and muscular systems, improving the efficiency with which the body uses oxygen. Common forms of aerobic exercise include jogging, swimming, cycling, cross-country skiing, paced walking, and activities done in a fitness facility, such as "aerobics" classes or exercising on equipment like a stationary bike, a treadmill, or a stair-climber. Sports associated with high levels of aerobic fitness include soccer, cross-country skiing, marathon running, and triathlon.

aerobic exercise: exercise, such as jogging, that involves the increased consumption of oxygen over an extended period of time.

PSYCHOLOGICAL BENEFITS OF PHYSICAL ACTIVITY

The psychological benefits of physical activity have been widely documented in both the empirical and lay literature. Central to this discussion is the integration of mind and body. As Mahoney (1996) comments in a textbook on exercise and sport psychology, "The body is back and so is the mind. They are not separate realms. They never were" (p. xv).

He suggests that psychology is in the midst of a "phase transition," in which new paradigms are being established that recognize the complexity of the mind–body integration, and that "One of the areas where such integrations and elaborations are particularly evident is that of exercise and sport psychology" (p. xv). Individuals who exercise often make statements regarding their psychological well-being. We hear comments such as, "I exercise because it helps me cope with the stress of my work"; "When I run I leave the world behind"; "Exercise makes me feel good about myself." Or, conversely, "if I don't get my workout in, I get depressed." Pargman (1998) suggests that "people feel better about themselves when they believe they look better" (p. 116).

Although anecdotal evidence of the psychological benefits of exercise exists, concerns have been raised about methodological issues in the empirical evaluation of this relationship (Kircaldy & Shephard, 1990; Landers & Arent, 2001; Morgan, 1997; Pargman, 1998). One issue concerns the choice of experimental and control groups. The initial health status of the experimental group (i.e., whether they are normal, depressed, anxious, or recovering from a physical illness) will affect the impact of an exercise program and therefore the degree to which the results can be generalized. How an exercise program affects someone psychologically will be somewhat dependent on an individual's starting point.

A control group that is excluded from participation in an exercise program may not provide the appropriate comparison for a group that is assigned to an exercise condition and receives ongoing support to continue participation. Adherence to exercise programs has already been mentioned as an issue and may result in difficulties in evaluating those who remain in an exercise program as compared to those who drop out. Among those who continue with an exercise program will be individuals like Peter, who are committed to a lifestyle change that is independent of a particular form of exercise.

Physical Activity and Sense of Self

Despite these concerns, there is an increasing body of evidence to support a correlation between involvement in physical activity and improvements in psychological health. For example, it has been postulated that participation in physical activity improves one's *self-concept*. In 1981, Folkins and Syme reviewed the existing research regarding physical fitness training and improvements on psychological variables related to perceptions of the self. They concluded that physical fitness training results in improved mood, work behaviour, and self-concept and that the "personality research with the highest payoff has been that which focuses on self-concept" (p. 380). What may be most important here is the *perception* of change, which may occur quite independently of actual changes in physical fitness.

The Folkins and Syme review is discussed here as it is interesting to note that, in reviewing the literature on self-esteem and exercise 16 years later, Sonstroem (1997) came to essentially the same conclusion. Fox (2000) reviewed 36 studies published since 1972 and concluded that 78 percent of these indicated positive changes in physical self-esteem or self-concept in response to physical activity, although it is not clear what it is that makes people feel better about themselves. However, as Brannon and Feist (2000) have summarized, "It may not be necessary to know the exact variables responsible for improved self-esteem as long as increased feelings of self-worth and self-confidence are associated with an exercise program" (p. 491).

Exercise may also indirectly influence one's self-esteem. Brannon and Feist (2007) conclude that "participation in an exercise program is strongly associated with feeling good about oneself" (p. 467). Spence, McGannon, and Poon (2005) reviewed 113 studies that met their selection criteria and examined the effect of participation in physical activity on global self-esteem. They found that small but significant improvements occurred and that this effect was larger for those who experienced actual increases in physical fitness.

One of the psychological variables thought to most affect performance is **self-efficacy**, a construct that has been carefully articulated in the work of Bandura (1977, 1986, 1990, 1997) and summarized by Feltz and Lirgg (2001). Bandura defines perceived self-efficacy as "people's judgement of their capabilities to organize and execute courses of action required to attain designated types of performances. It is concerned not with the skills one has but with judgements of what one can do with whatever skills one possesses" (Bandura, 1986, p. 391).

It is important to distinguish self-efficacy, a situation-specific belief that reflects an individual's perception of his or her ability to succeed at a particular task at a specific time, from self-confidence, which reflects a global trait associated with overall performance expectations. As Bandura (1990) points out, *confidence* as a colloquial term is an idea that permeates physical activity; however, it does not indicate direction. Individuals can be quite confident that they will be unsuccessful, but self-efficacy involves the affirmation of performance capabilities. The implication is that, provided an individual has the required skills and the appropriate incentives, self-efficacy will predict actual performance. Performers in all fields are frequently told that all they need is "a little more belief" in their ability and they will realize their goals. So pervasive is this belief that it is often held out as the deciding factor in determining the outcome of one's actions. Individuals who have highly developed technical and physical skills are often believed to fall short of

self-efficacy: an individual's perception of his or her ability to succeed at a particular task at a specific time.

their goals because they are unable to use these skills in the relevant context, whereas those with limited technical and physical abilities often achieve well beyond expectations because they believe in themselves.

Most of us can relate to a time when we thought we were well prepared for an event only to find our performance deteriorating due to what we perceived to be a "loss of confidence." As Jackson and Csikszentmihalyi (1999) have observed in discussing the challenge–skills (CS) balance, "It is not the objective skills that become critical in the CS balance, but rather how one perceives one's skills in relation to the relevant challenges. It is important to realize that what you *believe* you can do will determine your actual experience more than your actual abilities" (p. 17).

There is almost a mystical quality attributed to experiencing the upper reaches of performance achievements, or what Bandura (1997) has described as "transcendent accomplishments." This sense of transcendence is often expressed in terms of overcoming physical barriers that had seemed insurmountable. One of these is the 4-minute mile. Once considered a physical impossibility, it has become commonplace following the remarkable performance of Roger Bannister and John Landy at the Commonwealth Games in Vancouver in 1954, when they became the first individuals to run the mile in under 4 minutes in the competition.

Prior to 1954, more than 50 journals contained articles predicting that it would not be possible for a human to run a mile in under 4 minutes. The next year, four more runners broke the 4-minute barrier. Steve Scott, the American miler, ran a sub 4-minute mile 136 times in his career. Obviously, the athletes who followed so quickly in breaking this barrier did not change physically or technically in this short time frame. What changed was their belief that it could be done. What had been overcome was a psychological barrier, not a physical one. Bannister, in describing the experience said, "The moment of a lifetime had come. There was no pain, only a great unity of movement and aim. The world seemed to stand still, or did not exist. The only reality was the next two hundred yards of track under my feet. The tape meant finality—perhaps extinction" (Bannister, 1955, pp. 213–214). The current world record for the mile is 3 minutes and 43.13 seconds, held by Hicham El Guerrouj, who set the record in 1999.

Researchers (e.g., Bandura, 1997; Cox, 2007; Feltz, 1988; Hardy, Jones, & Gould, 1996) have described the exercise and sport field as an excellent arena in which to study self-efficacy. It provides a microcosm of relevance and immediacy. Bandura (1990, 1997) speaks specifically to the role of self-efficacy in the context of athletic performance. Athletes develop their skills to a high level of expertise and are often asked to execute them under situations of extreme stress against individuals who are also highly skilled. Skills performed with remarkable ease in practice can become fragile under the pressure of competition due to self-doubt. Successful athletes believe in their ability to focus on the task, ignore distractions, deal with mistakes and failures, cope with fatigue and pain, and ultimately to perform to the best of their ability in the circumstances in which they find themselves. They have succeeded in what Bandura (1990) has termed the "development of resilient self-efficacy."

Bandura (1997) has identified four sources of efficacy expectations: *performance accomplishments, vicarious experience, verbal persuasion,* and *emotional arousal.* **Performance accomplishments** or enactive attainments are the most influential source of self-efficacy, as they are based on actual experiences of mastery. Success increases

performance accomplishments: actual experiences of mastery, considered to be the most influential source of self-efficacy.

self-efficacy and failure decreases it, although factors such as the perceived difficulty of the task, the effort expended, adverse external circumstances, and the temporal sequencing of events affect the strength of the relationship. For example, although early failure experiences may decrease self-efficacy, initial setbacks—if eventually overcome by effort—can strengthen one's belief that even the most difficult of obstacles can be mastered. Improved self-efficacy will incorporate occasional failures with ease and will generalize to other situations, although the degree of similarity to the original task will affect the extent of the generalization process.

Vicarious experience, which is gained through observing or imagining others perform a skill, can alert people to their own abilities and raise their sense of self-efficacy. How many times have we said to ourselves, "If they can do it, so can I." We follow the ski instructor down the hill observing every move, or we watch the tennis instructor's serve and then try to duplicate it. These models increase our sense of our own abilities and teach us better ways to do things. Conversely, observing an individual (whom we feel is competent) fail in a task may serve to decrease our own sense of ability. Although important in determining self-efficacy expectations, vicarious experiences are weaker than actual performance experiences. They may confirm our sense of inability, or they may cause us to persist despite performance failures and ultimately achieve success. We can all identify those moments when we persisted at a task despite repeated failure simply because we observed success in someone else and believed that eventually we would be able to do it. Our sense of determination is derived from our belief that, like the model, we will ultimately be successful.

Verbal persuasion refers to the commonly used strategy of attempting to persuade others or ourselves that the capability exists to achieve a desired outcome. Although considered a weaker strategy than performance accomplishments and vicarious experience, verbal persuasion can result in sustained and increased effort. However, the utility of this strategy is predicated on a sense of realism. To promote an unrealistic sense of competence in an individual who does not possess the necessary skills will likely result in a performance failure that serves to decrease self-efficacy and belief in verbal persuasion. Those involved in teaching others have to be cautious in their use of persuasion to improve performance. If it serves to remove self-doubts and allows existing skills to emerge, then it has served its purpose. However, if the results of an individual's actions serve to disconfirm your persuasive abilities, your credibility will be undermined.

The least powerful source of efficacy expectations is **emotional arousal**, or physiological state. Individuals evaluate their abilities, to a certain extent, according to their assessment of their physiological state. For example, high levels of arousal may be perceived as debilitating and predictive of failure and therefore result in a decrease in self-efficacy. The optimal level of arousal to perform a particular task will depend not only on the nature of the task but also on the causal inferences made about the arousal itself. Arousal may be interpreted positively or negatively according to the attributions we make about our physiological state. Strategies such as relaxation techniques may allow an individual to modify arousal levels in the desired direction. The high level of arousal we experience prior to engaging in a particular task might be interpreted either with anxiety and foreboding or with excitement and anticipation, depending on the attributions we make about our physiological state.

vicarious experience: experience that is gained through observing or visualizing others perform a skill, which can alert one to one's own capabilities and raise one's sense of self-efficacy.

verbal persuasion: to verbally persuade others that they have the skills to perform a particular task—that is, to talk them into it.

emotional arousal: a source of efficacy expectation in which individuals assess their emotional level and evaluate their capabilities accordingly; for example, high levels of emotion may be thought to be debilitating and predictive of failure.

There is substantial research literature supporting the framework provided by self-efficacy theory in relation to performance in both exercise and sport. Research that demonstrates improved self-efficacy as a function of participation in exercise includes that of Bozoian, Rejeski, and McAuley (1994); Michalko, McAuley, and Bane (1996); McAuley and Courneya (1992); McAuley, Schaffer, and Rudolph (1995); and Rudolph and Butki (1998). In the sport domain, self-efficacy has consistently been demonstrated to be an important discriminating factor in performance accomplishments (Feltz & Lirgg 2001; Feltz, Short, & Sullivan, 2008; George 1994; Mahoney, Gabriel, & Perkins 1987; Samson & Solmon, 2011; Weiss, Wiese, & Klint 1989). In summarizing this research, Short and Ross-Stewart suggest this is not limited to physical proficiency but "can include all aspects of performance, like reading shifting game situations, selecting effective strategies, predicting opponent's actions, using imagery, managing pressure and distractions" (2008, p. 224).

Physical Activity and Cognitive Functioning

Physical activity and exercise have also been examined in terms of their impact on information processing and cognitive functioning (Biddle & Mutrie, 2001; Etnier et al., 1997; Landers & Arent, 2001; Pargman, 1998; Tomporowski & Ellis, 1986). Does involvement in exercise have the facilitative effect on mental abilities that those who engage in exercise and sport frequently report? Does the ability to remember or discriminate improve? Based on their initial review of the existing literature, Tomporowski and Ellis (1986) concluded that the results were inconsistent, due mainly to a lack of a coherent methodology for examining the issue. They suggested that exercise, through its effect on the central nervous system, will initially improve attentional processes; however, as the intensity or duration of the exercise increases, this will be negated by the effects of increasing muscular fatigue. The implications for the assessment process are obvious. They concluded that "the dominant state determines the ability of subjects to perform tests of cognition. Thus, it may be possible for exercise to either facilitate or impair performance on the same cognitive test depending on the level of physical fitness of the subject and the point at which the subject is tested" (p. 344).

Subsequently, the meta-analysis by Etnier and colleagues (1997) further examined this relationship. They reviewed 134 relevant studies and concluded that exercise and fitness have a small yet positive impact on cognitive functioning. However, the indication is that acute exercise will have little impact on cognition, whereas chronic exercise that produces gains in fitness will improve cognition. This conclusion "would support the physiological mechanisms as explanations for the beneficial effects of exercise or fitness upon cognition" and "would suggest that the adoption of a chronic exercise program may be a useful intervention for enhancing cognitive functioning" (p. 267).

This improvement in cognitive functioning through exercise is supported in a review by Dubbert (2002). She also draws attention to the work of Kramer et al. (1999), which describes improvements in cognitive functioning in the elderly associated with regular aerobic exercise. With Canada's aging population, the positive effects of exercise in this area may have particular significance. Landers and Arent (2007), while concluding that exercise is consistently "related to better cognitive functioning" (p. 473), also indicate that "experimental and longitudinal studies demonstrate a temporal sequence leading from exercise earlier in time to better cognitive functioning at a point later in time"

(p. 473). An issue for future research in this area is the possibility of a dose–response relationship between the intensity of exercise and cognitive functioning. Chang and Etnier (2009) suggest that this is indeed the situation with resistance exercise. The implication is that it may become important to identify the optimal exercise intensity at which benefits for cognitive functioning occur. In a review of the impact that exercise can have on cognitive functioning, Cox (2012) concludes that there is support for the position that there is improvement and that "this is particularly the case in terms of information processing speed, and conditionally the case in terms of improved executive functions" (p. 411). Variables such as the individual's initial level of working memory and the mode and intensity of the exercise need to be further examined. These results, with regard to improvements in executive functioning, have been supported by research by Alves et al. (2012), who found this effect for both acute aerobic and strength exercise, and that of Chang et al. (2011) who reported a similar effect following an acute episode of aerobic exercise on planning and problem solving.

Of particular interest here, given our aging population in Canada, is the research of Boucard et al. (2012), which found a positive relationship in older adults (age 71 to 81 years) between cardiovascular fitness and cognitive aging. This is specifically related to the preservation of inhibition activities which are described as being important for instrumental activities of daily living and social functioning (p. 822).

Physical Activity and Mood

An extensive body of literature has examined the impact of exercise and physical activity on mood states, particularly anxiety and depression. This research does have methodological problems, including the use of anecdotal versus empirical evidence, the assessment of mood states, the actual effect-size found, the representativeness of the data, and the mechanisms used to explain the findings.

Despite these concerns, there is evidence that exercise is effective in reducing anxiety in some people (Hackfort & Spielberger, 1988; Landers & Arent, 2001; Landers & Petruzzello, 1994; McAuley, Mihalko, & Bane, 1996; Raglan & Morgan, 1987; Salmon, 2000). This effect applies in particular to state, as compared to trait, anxiety.

The mechanism by which physical activity produces an anxiolytic effect is not clear. Morgan, who studied the effect of exercise on mood states for many years, suggested that exercise provides a distraction or "time out" from the pressures and anxieties of daily living (Bahrke & Morgan, 1978). For many of us, this model will have considerable intuitive appeal. Our exercise time is a period of the day when we leave the world behind. We are removed from our obligations or are at least less aware of them, are often inaccessible to others, and are completely focused on the task before us. Interestingly, Miller, Bartholomew, and Springer (2005) found that the affective response is mediated by preferred modes of exercise. They report that "participants reported greater improvements in positive affect following high preference exercise modes than for low preference exercise modes" (p. 270). This suggests that exercise preference contributes significantly to exercise enjoyment and needs to be taken into account when designing individual exercise programs.

Exercise can serve as an effective distraction; however, many activities can fulfill this function if this is all that is required. Is there a moderating effect that is unique to exercise? Tate and Petruzzello (1995) have demonstrated a differential pattern of anxiety responses for those engaged in exercise compared to those in a resting control condition. Research by McAuley et al. (1996) indicates that anxiety levels increase during exercise and then decrease significantly following exercise. These authors expressed the concern that anxiety and arousal are confounded in the measurement of state anxiety.

Research by Rejeski, Hardy, and Shaw (1991) indicates that anxiety decreases in a linear fashion during exercise, whereas arousal increases during exercise and decreases noticeably following exercise. This seems a reasonable position and helps explain what appear to be confusing results. Biddle and Mutrie (2001) conclude that exercise results in small to moderate reductions in anxiety, that the effect exists for both acute and chronic exercise and both state and trait anxiety, that anxiety is reduced both during and after exercise, and that individuals with high aerobic fitness display a reduced physiological response to psychosocial stressors. However, a meta-analysis by Wipfli, Rethorst, and Landers (2008) suggests that this effect is much larger than previous studies indicate. They conclude that exercise alone is as effective in reducing anxiety as psychotherapy and pharmacology and that this "finding supports the use of exercise as one of the frontline treatments for anxiety" (p. 401).

The impact of exercise on depression has been the subject of research for some time. As with research discussed previously, methodological problems limit the conclusions that can be drawn. However, there is evidence that physical activity can decrease *non-clinical* depression (e.g., Biddle & Mutrie, 2001; Jasnowski, Holmes, & Banks, 1988; Stein & Motta, 1992). With regard to clinically depressed individuals, initial research by Greist examined the effect of running as a treatment and reported decreased levels of depression in those involved in a running program, suggesting that exercise is an effective treatment (1984).

Reviews by Martinsen (1990, 1993, 1994), Martinson and Morgan (1997), and North, McCullagh, and Tran (1990) conclude that both aerobic and anaerobic exercise are effective treatments for depression, that exercise has *not* been shown to be effective with severe depression, that fitness levels are lower for clinically depressed individuals, and that there is no evidence that exercise can prevent relapse. Biddle and Mutrie (2001) provide an excellent summary of research in this area, again making the distinction between non-clinical and clinical depression. With regard to non-clinical depression, the conclusion is that there is an antidepressant effect associated with exercise that results in moderate decreases in depression, that this effect is present for both acute and chronic exercise and for groups different in age and gender, and that lower levels of depression are related to a physically active lifestyle.

With clinical depression the results are more equivocal; however, the conclusion is that the benefits are much greater than the risks, that the physical health benefits are important, and ultimately that "physical activity and exercise should be advocated as part of the treatment for clinically defined depression" (p. 219). In their review of the literature, Landers and Arent (2007) conclude that the anxiolytic and antidepressant effects of exercise are demonstrated with consistency. They go further in suggesting that, given the U.S. Surgeon General's criteria for therapeutic efficacy, the "experimental evidence for exercise as a treatment intervention exceeds this criteria for anxiety and both minor and major unipolar depression" (p. 482).

Research by Lin, Halgin, Well, and Ockene (2008) indicates that the effects of leisure-time physical activities such as exercise are associated with lower levels of depression, particularly in women, whereas this is not the case for physical activity related to household and occupational activity. This suggests that these effects may be specific to characteristics associated with exercise such as motivation, enjoyment, and control rather than just physical activity itself.

In examining the mental health benefits of physical activity in university students, Proctor and Boan-Lenzo (2010) found that participation in athletics was associated not only with a healthier lifestyle but also with significantly lower levels of depressive symptoms than those experienced in non-athletes.

Stress is another area in which the psychological impact of exercise and physical activity has been evaluated, and indications are that physical activity may buffer the effects of stress. It has been demonstrated that "exercise plays a key role in moderating both psychological and physiological stress symptoms" (Berger & Tobar, 2007, p. 603). (This topic was considered in more detail in chapter 2, Stress and Coping.) In their review of the impact of physical activity on mental health, Landers and Arent (2001) conclude that "exercise is related to, but does not cause, desirable changes to occur in anxiety, depression, stress reactivity, positive mood, self-esteem, and cognitive functioning. The overall magnitude of the effect on these variables ranges from small to moderate, but in all cases, these effects are statistically significant" (p. 759). Alderman, Rogers, Landers, Arent, and Johnson (2006), in a meta-analytic review of the literature, found support for the position, previously described by Biddle and Mutrie (2001), that aerobically fit individuals have a reduced psychosocial stress response. The physiological implication is that they may experience lower levels of stress for a short period of time.

PHYSICAL BENEFITS OF PHYSICAL ACTIVITY

The physical benefits of physical activity can be expressed in different ways. For some, they may be manifested in a high level of fitness and the physical appearance that goes with it. For others, it may mean the absence of disease and the promotion of health and longevity. For still others, it may simply be the expression of an optimistic, positive lifestyle. Kavussanu and McAuley (1996) found that highly active individuals are significantly more optimistic and less pessimistic than inactive individuals.

Numerous studies, some of which have been enormous undertakings, have demonstrated the positive benefits of exercise. For example, the longitudinal research of Blair and colleagues (1989) examined the role of physical fitness on mortality rates in more than 10 000 men and 3000 women over an average of 8 years. Exercise appeared to reduce the risk of mortality from all causes, particularly cardiovascular disease and cancer. Some of the benefits attributed to physical activity include improved cardiovascular functioning and a reduced risk of cardiovascular disease; improved muscle strength and endurance; increased cardiorespiratory fitness; improved flexibility; improved weight control and fat metabolism; improved sleep; prevention of bone density loss; a reduction in poor health habits, such as cigarette smoking and alcohol consumption; reduced risk of injury; and increased energy. If involvement in exercise and sport can decrease mortality and increase longevity, they assume a most important status in our culture. With the increase in our aging population, the positive impact that continued physical activity can have with older adults is most relevant here. Taylor et al. (2004) report that exercise plays an important role in "improving emotional, cognitive, social and perceived physical function in older adults and alleviating physical symptoms" (p. 715). In particular, it is noted that strength training has a significant effect in improving mood and reducing the risk of falls.

A major focus for Active Canada 20/20's initiative to raise physical activity levels in Canada is that physical inactivity has been identified as the fourth leading risk factor for global mortality by the World Health Organization. Of particular concern with physical inactivity is the increasing prevalence of non-communicable diseases (Active Canada 20/20, 2012).

Since the 1950s, considerable evidence has been accumulated to demonstrate that those who are physically active are less likely to develop and die from coronary heart disease (CHD). Miller, Balady, and Fletcher (1997) state that "a sedentary lifestyle carries approximately the same risk for the development of coronary artery disease as the more traditional risk factors of cigarette smoking, hypertension, and hypercholesterolemia" (p. 220). Early research examined the presence of CHD in individuals according to their occupation and the level of physical activity required in their work (Kahn, 1963). Individuals whose work involved a high level of physical activity appeared to be at a decreased risk for CHD (Brand, Paffenbarger, Scholtz, & Kampert, 1979).

Another level of evaluation has involved the comparison of physically active and inactive individuals according to measures of energy expenditure. The most influential of these evaluative studies is the Harvard Alumni Study, carried out by Paffenbarger and colleagues. They assessed men who had graduated from Harvard University over a 50-year period according to their weekly expenditure of energy and divided them into two groups: high and low activity. They reported that men who were physically active had a 25 percent lower mortality rate from any cause and were 36 percent less likely to die from CHD (Paffenbarger, Wing, & Hyde, 1978).

The Framingham Heart Study evaluated CHD in both men and women and found that when the very active and very inactive groups were compared with regard to CHD, the risk for the latter group was approximately three times greater (Dawber, 1980). Also, exercise rehabilitation has been found to significantly decrease mortality in survivors of myocardial infarction (Haskell et al., 1994). Miller, Balady, and Fletcher (1997), after an extensive review of the literature, concluded that exercise has an important role in the prevention and rehabilitation of cardiovascular disease. Biddle and Mutrie (2001) concluded their research review by stating that "physical fitness (at least cardiovascular fitness) and habitual physical activity are both inversely related to CHD risk in adults" (p. 16).

It should be noted that the possible protective role played by physical activity with regard to illnesses such as stroke and cancer is still emerging. For example, with regard to stroke, there is evidence that physical activity provides protection, particularly for those who are middle-aged and older (Abbott, Rodriguez, Burchfiel, & Curb, 1994). The impact of physical activity in protecting against cancer appears positive, particularly for men. For example, Lee, Paffenbarger, and Hsieh (1992) reported that participants in the Harvard Alumni Study who were physically active were much less likely to develop prostate cancer than those who were inactive. An international forum on physical activity and health held in Quebec in 1995 (*Research Quarterly for Exercise and Sport*, 1995) resulted in statements of consensus, including the following: whereas a sedentary lifestyle increases the risk of atherosclerosis, hypertension, and diabetes, regular exercise decreases it; physical activity benefits the musculoskeletal system, and decreases in functional capacity with age are due, in part, to insufficient physical activity; the risk of colon cancer and perhaps breast cancer is decreased through physical activity; and physical activity for all ages is a very effective strategy for improving health. Despite these statements, Biddle and Mutrie (2001) conclude that the relationship between the benefits derived from physical activity and how it relates to disease prevention and health promotion is still not well understood.

ADHERENCE TO PHYSICAL ACTIVITY

Despite the many psychological and physical benefits attributed to physical activity, the percentage of individuals exercising on a regular basis is disturbingly low (Dishman, 2001). For those who do exercise, a significant issue is **non-adherence**, or an inability to stay with an exercise program. The most frequently cited statistic in this regard is based on the initial work of Dishman (1988), and more recently that of Estabrooks (2000), which indicate that approximately 50 percent of those involved in a physical activity program drop out within the first 6 months. This may seem counter-intuitive, as we think of ourselves as being in the midst of an exercise and sports boom. Fitness centres are everywhere, fitness equipment is readily available, and sports participation seems to be increasing, particularly through the recreational and master's sports movements. Many of us find our motivation to participate in sports through watching high definition presentations of sporting events. It is interesting to note that the most watched event in Canadian television history is the Gold medal hockey game between Canada and the United States in the 2010 Winter Olympics in Vancouver. It is reported that approximately 50 percent of the population watched all of the game and that an amazing 26.5 million people, over 80 percent of the population, watched some part of the game.

Taylor (1994) believes that the avoidance of exercise and sport is not difficult to understand, as exercise can be initially somewhat aversive and offers few immediate rewards. The environment can be unappealing, the activities are monotonous, progress is often slow, a lack of expertise may be obvious, and social comparison with experienced exercisers can be unpleasant. The first experience in an aerobics class or an exercise room can be quite threatening. With regard to sports involvement, a lack of skills development and knowledge of rules, combined with an often highly competitive environment, can be a threat to self-esteem. Ruby, Dunn, Perrrino, Gillis, and Viel (2011) suggest that we frequently make incorrect affective forecasts about what will make us happy. They suggest that the "reason why people may not engage in exercise is that they fail to fully appreciate how much they will enjoy it" (p. 67). They believe that these incorrect predictions can be easily changed to increase engagement in physical activity.

To a large extent, the positive benefits of exercise and sport emerge with time and will ultimately outweigh the initial impediments. Zifferblatt (1975) suggested some time ago that the likelihood of compliance is directly related to the visibility of the cues or reasons the individual should comply. When the reasons are vague or ambiguous, the likelihood of compliance is low, whereas if they are specific, relevant, or salient the likelihood of compliance is high. The implication is that initial experiences in exercise and sport often do not provide enough reasons to continue. They may become obvious, but it will take time.

non-adherence: failure to follow the advice of the health professional; the inability to stay with an exercise program.

To better understand the factors affecting adherence to physical activity, numerous theoretical models have been used. Many of these were introduced in chapter 1 and include the health belief model (Becker & Maiman, 1975); the theory of reasoned action (Ajzen & Fishbein, 1980); the theory of planned behaviour (Ajzen, 1985); self-efficacy theory (Bandura, 1977); the transtheoretical model (Prochaska & DiClemente, 1983); and the relapse prevention model (Marlatt & Gordon, 1980). These models were developed in the context of other behaviours, and it is still not exactly clear how relevant they are to physical activity. Important predictors of adherence include physical proximity to the exercise area, availability of time, spousal support, group size and constitution, socioeconomic status, choice of exercise, and injury (LeUnes & Nation, 2002). It seems that the issue of salience is most important here. We need to know what rewards await us as a consequence of our sustained commitment to physical activity.

In a review of exercise adherence, Buckworth and Dishman (2007) indicate that subtle differences in the terms exercise, physical activity, and lifestyle activity impact how we measure and define adherence. They conclude that the "lack of progress in increasing adoption and adherence to regular physical activity may also be a consequence of limiting interventions to motivational and educational approaches directed to individuals and small groups" (p. 526). They also suggest that the concept of adherence needs to be reframed to take into account changes in patterns of physical activity that individuals may go through in their lifetime. Within this framework, it may be unreasonable to expect stability of adherence behaviour over the life span. In this context, Williams (2008) has suggested that self-paced exercise, as compared to prescribed intensity exercise, may produce a more positive affective response which will improve exercise adherence by enhancing anticipation of subsequent exercise sessions. Schneider, Dunn, and Cooper (2009) have extended this finding in adolescents, reporting that adolescents are more likely to engage in acute regular exercise if they experience a positive affective response during the experience. Intriguingly, music has been reported to improve exercise performance and adherence in clinical populations and the elderly (Ziv & Lidor, 2011). However, it is important that in order for this to be effective the music must be chosen carefully to match the preferences of the participants (i.e., presumably it must be enjoyable). Extensive reviews of the use of music in the exercise domain and the positive impact it has have been completed by Karageorghis and Priest (2012).

It would be expected that we would continue with exercise if we perceive it to be enjoyable and it enhances our sense of self-worth, Raedeke (2007) suggests that it is important we engage in physical activity that we are skilled at and, as a result, are more likely to enjoy and find challenging. In this context, research by Ekkekakis, Backhouse, Gray, and Lind (2008) is important as it resolves a seeming conflict with regard to the utility of walking as a form of physical activity. As clearly the most popular physical activity of choice amongst adults, walking can provide moderate exercise with a high level of affective pleasure. However, concerns have been raised that walking lacks sufficient intensity to produce significant affective changes. Their research indicates that walking can indeed have a positive impact on affect in adults and that exercise need not be strenuous and exceed thresholds for intensity and duration in order to be effective in this regard. This establishes walking as legitimate exercise even in short bouts and contradicts the notion of "no pain, no gain" (p. 260).

Kirschenbaum (1998) has proposed that involvement in sport and the models that sport psychology has developed provide useful strategies for increasing adherence to physical activity. This may be important given the indications that health psychologists have achieved only modest success in this regard (Dishman & Buckworth, 1997). He uses a self-regulatory model to identify seven steps designed to improve athletic performance. He suggests that this model is similar to that used by health psychologists to increase adherence and that sport can be used as a target for exercise adherence. By focusing on the commitment many individuals have to sport, psychologists can design strategies to increase adherence to exercise. The energy expended in sport can be considerable, and the modification of existing patterns could result in even greater expenditures. Kirschenbaum proposes that "not only could we target extant interest in sport as a goal in health psychology, but we could use sport psychology interventions to maximize involvement in such sports. These interventions could help participants enjoy their sports more fully, thereby sustaining their involvement in them" (p. 17). The extraordinary commitment that many individuals display to their sport can be used to indirectly increase their levels of physical activity and produce physical and psychological health benefits.

PSYCHOLOGICAL FACTORS AFFECTING PERFORMANCE IN EXERCISE AND SPORT

Developments in the sport psychology field have implications for health psychology in general, and the choices individuals make regarding their health behaviour in particular. There are two principal areas of concern in sport psychology. One is performance enhancement as it relates to the development of psychological skills that can be used to optimize athletic performance. The second has to do with more of clinical concerns, such as injury which may compromise an athlete's performance.

Psychological skills as they can be applied to sport, physical activity, and life in general are life skills as well as sport skills, and their utility extends well beyond the domain of sport. This position is often recognized anecdotally by coaches who are aware of their impact on others, particularly young athletes, and view themselves as teachers of life skills.

Danish, Pettipas, and Hale (1993) developed a psychoeducational model for sport psychology that focuses specifically on the teaching of life skills, which they describe as "life development intervention." They suggest that sport is an effective and accessible analogy for the teaching of life skills. It is obvious that most young athletes will not go on to a career in sports; for these people, "growing up means further defining their identity, discovering other skills and interests, and, it is hoped, applying some of the valuable principles learned during sport participation to their adult pursuits. These transferable behaviours and attitudes are called *life skills*" (Danish, Nellen, & Owens, 1996, p. 211).

An area of specific concern in this life-skills program is helping young people make appropriate decisions with regard to health-enhancing, as opposed to health-compromising, behaviours. Smith (1999) has addressed the assumption that sports skills will generalize beyond the athletic environment. In an athlete-centred program, sports skills are delivered in a manner that is developmentally appropriate and where "performance excellence is pursued only in the context of the athlete's overall health and well-being" (Miller & Kerr, 2002, p. 150). Based on research integrating sport and life-skills training, Papacharisis, Goudas, Danish, and Theodorakis (2005) conclude that the "program equips young athletes

NBA MVP Steve Nash and Olympic gold medalist snowboarder Maelle Ricker are Canadians who embody health and excellence in both their professional and personal life.
AP Photo/Julie Jacobson/Canadian Press Images, Jonathan Hayward/Canadian Press Images

with knowledge and skills that are necessary for successfully coping with the complex realities of life" (p. 253). In advocating the teaching of psychological skills to young athletes, McCarthy, Jones, Harwood, and Olivier (2010) recommend that appropriate adaptations need to be made in order for them to better understand skills such as relaxation and self-talk. This will help them "to commit to sport and enhance sport performance and learn to transfer these skills to other domains of life" (p. 169).

A distinction is often made between **psychological skills** and **psychological methods** (Vealey, 1988). Concerns such as arousal or attentional control relate to psychological skills, whereas techniques such as relaxation, goal setting, and imagery are psychological methods; the latter serve to develop the former.

Others have suggested that the distinction should be made between "basic psychological skills," which can be used on their own, and "advanced psychological skills," of which the basic skills are a component (Hardy et al., 1996). In this discussion, we will focus on the basic skills, as they can be used in a psychological skills training program that can be applied both within and outside of the sport and exercise domain. For example, an edition of the *Journal of Applied Sport Psychology* focuses on excellence and the relationship between sport and business (Jones, 2002; Weinberg & McDermott, 2002); sport and the performing arts (Hays, 2002; Poczwarsdowski & Conroy, 2002); sport and acting (Martin & Cutler, 2002); and sport and police work (Le Scanff & Taugis, 2002).

These skills also have application in models of stress management that have been adapted for sport. Examples would be Kirschenbaum's (1997) self-regulatory model, Meichenbaum's (1975) stress-inoculation training, Smith's (1980) cognitive-affective stress management training, and Suinn's (1972) visuomotor behaviour-rehearsal program. It has been suggested that rather than using specific programs such as these, the

psychological skills in sport: arousal or attentional control implemented to enhance performance.

psychological methods in sport: techniques such as relaxation, goal setting, and imagery, which are used to develop psychological skills.

component skills of a psychological training program should be taught and used according to individual needs (Hardy et al., 1996).

Relaxation

The ability to relax is an important skill in coping with the pressure of athletic performance (Cox, 2002). Most individuals will acknowledge some degree of performance anxiety in anticipation of the demands of a task. **Relaxation skills** enhance one's ability to reduce anxiety to manageable levels, so that energy can be used to positively influence performance. Many of us experience "butterflies" prior to a performance, which is not a problem if we can teach them to "fly in formation." Relaxation skills assist in this process. It is also recognized that an effective performance, which is effortless and automatic, is more likely to occur in a relaxed state (Kirschenbaum, 1997; Taylor, 1996).

Many successful athletes have developed relaxation skills on their own through a process of trial and error. However, there may be limitations to their ability to relax under pressure. Relaxation is viewed as a learned skill that needs to be applicable to the performance circumstances. For example, watching television or reading a book is relaxing; however, these activities are not applicable to a performance situation. In this context, we are describing a response usually described in either physical or mental terms.

The most widely practised form of relaxation in sport is the technique of progressive muscular relaxation (PMR) pioneered by Jacobson (1938) (see chapter 2). It involves focusing attention on different muscle groups within the body (e.g., the biceps, shoulders, or stomach) and progressing systematically through the entire body. With practice, one learns to initiate what Benson (1975) has termed the "relaxation response." It is important that, as familiarity with the technique increases, the ability to relax is generalized to the relevant performance domain. It seems that PMR is most effective in coping with the somatic or physiological components of anxiety, whereas strategies such as mental rehearsal and the management of self-talk may be more appropriate to coping with cognitive anxiety. It is also recognized that proper breathing is an effective strategy for increasing levels of relaxation and successfully coping with anxiety. The deep, rhythmical breathing associated with relaxation can quickly replace the shallow, staccato breathing associated with tension and anxiety. Training in breath control can be most helpful in inducing and maintaining states of relaxation (Cox, 2007). Ultimately, as Thomas, Mellalieu, and Hanton (2009) state: "the primary goal of an applied relaxation programme is to transfer the athlete through a series of progressive stages towards an endpoint where a physically relaxed state can be rapidly attained in any given situation" (p. 137). Such an ability will have implications that extend well beyond sport: it is clearly a "life skill not a sport skill."

Self-Talk

Self-talk is a term used in sport psychology to describe one of the ways that people think (Cox, 2007). What do athletes say to themselves? It is a frequent observation that athletes talk to themselves, sometimes very negatively. Monitoring an athlete's self-talk gives us an opportunity to evaluate his or her perceptions and beliefs. We can identify cognitive distortions and irrational ways of thinking that might disrupt performance. It has been reported that patterns of self-talk can distinguish successful from unsuccessful performers (e.g., Hardy, Oliver, & Tod, 2009; Orlick & Partington, 1988; Weinberg & Gould, 2003).

Williams and Leffingwell (1996) have identified different functions that self-talk in sport, including correcting bad habits, focusing attention, modifying activation, increasing self-efficacy, and maintaining exercise behaviour. With regard to correcting bad habits, self-talk can be used to correct faulty technique. To focus attention, an athlete might say "watch the ball" or "execute." In modifying activation, the self-talk might take the form of "relax" or "let go." Self-confidence may involve changing the tendency to call oneself a "loser" to saying "yes" to oneself. Given the importance attached to productive self-talk, interventions such as those described by Hardy, Roberts, and Hardy (2009) involving diaries and monitoring strategies designed to increase awareness of self-talk and the ability to change patterns of negative self-talk are important.

With regard to exercise behaviour, Gauvin (1990) suggests that those who maintain exercise have positive and motivating self-talk in comparison to the negative self-talk of non-exercisers. Once inappropriate patterns of self-talk have been identified, the concern is to modify this behaviour in the appropriate direction. This involves a restructuring process that replaces maladaptive cognitions with more adaptive ones. It is generally recommended that the use of self-talk should emphasize positive cues rather than negative ones (Moran, 2009), although a recent review of 47 studies examining the relationship between self-talk and performance indicates that this may not necessarily be the case (Tod, Hardy, & Oliver, 2011). They conclude that positive, instructional, and motivational self-talk has a beneficial effect on performance, however, contrary to popular opinion, they did not find evidence that negative self-talk has a detrimental effect on performance.

The work of the eminent psychologist Albert Ellis (1975) in developing rational emotive behaviour therapy (REBT) is relevant here. REBT involves the modification of irrational thoughts by identifying patterns of faulty reasoning. For example, in *absolute thinking*, events are viewed in all-or-none terms, such as "I must always do well." *Overgeneralization* involves drawing global conclusions on the basis of single events—for example, "I am never going to win a match." *Catastrophization* involves viewing minor concerns as disasters—for example, "Losing this match could be the end of my career."

In REBT, irrational beliefs are actively disputed and individuals learn to substitute more rational ways of thinking. Ellis (1994) gave an invited address to Division 47, Exercise and Sport Psychology, at the 1993 American Psychological Association convention. His presentation was concerned with "The Sport of Avoiding Sports and Exercise." He believes that those who avoid exercise and sport have a low frustration tolerance that may be combined with a fear of failing. He states that "REBT helps them to discover and dispute their grandiose demands and absolutist musts" (p. 258). Ellis describes an intensive REBT program designed to help avoiders transform their inhibitions into healthy choices.

Imagery

The role of imagery in sport and exercise has been well documented (Cumming & Ramsey, 2009; Hall, 2001; Weinberg & Gould, 2003). For instance, in a frequently cited study, 99 percent of Canadian athletes who participated in the 1984 Olympic Games indicated that they had used imagery techniques to improve their performance (Orlick & Partington, 1988). Some of these athletes indicated that they had used imagery techniques for up to 3 hours in preparation for competition. A distinction should be made between *imagery* and *mental rehearsal* (Hall, 2001; Hardy et al., 1996). The former is a sensory experience that is performed in the absence of external stimuli, whereas mental rehearsal is a technique that involves the use of imagery to mentally practise a skill.

A distinction is also made between **external imagery** and **internal imagery** (Hall, 2001). In external imagery, the individual is a passive and external third-person observer of his or her actions. Internal imagery is a much more active first-person experience, in which the individual imagines being inside his or her own body, experiencing a situation as close to reality as possible.

Several explanations have been given for the mechanisms underlying the relationship between imagery and performance (Gould & Damarjian, 1996; Holmes and Collins, 2001; Hall, 2001). The psychoneuromuscular theory suggests that imagery causes the actual motor pattern to be rehearsed and therefore practised. According to symbolic learning, imagery provides the opportunity to symbolically practise an event. As one athlete said, "It felt like *déjà vu*, like I had done it before."

With regard to an imagery training program, Gould and Damarjian (1996) make several recommendations, including the following: Practice imagery on a regular basis, use all senses to enhance image vividness, use both internal and external perspectives, facilitate imagery through relaxation, use videotapes or audiotapes to enhance imagery skills, develop coping strategies through imagery, emphasize dynamic kinesthetic imagery, imagine in real time, use imagery in practice and competition (p. 48).

Driskell, Copper, and Moran (1994) carried out an initial meta-analysis of the literature and concluded that mental practice has a "positive and significant effect on performance" (p. 481), however, it is less effective than physical practice. They suggest that this makes mental practice most appropriate for difficult or dangerous training situations, for situations in which opportunities for physical practice are minimized, and simply as a strategy for supplementing normal training routines. In this regard, Williams, Cumming, and Balanos (2010) report the effective use of imagery in manipulating athletes appraisal of stress-invoking situations involving threat or challenge. They conclude that: "imagery can be used by athletes to alter their stress appraisal and produce more facilitative interpretations of responses resulting in more adaptive coping responses" (p. 356).

As Hall (2001) has indicated, we are still progressing in our understanding of imagery and how it can be used most effectively, although the indications are that "a higher competitive level is associated with greater sport specific imagery ability of varying content" (Williams & Cumming, 2011, p. 416). To this end, Murphy, Nordin, and Cumming (2008, p. 299) recommend an integrative approach, such as functional equivalence, that focuses on the imagery process and "proposes that imagery draws on the same neural network that is used in actual perception and motor control and can also activate neural circuits used in memory and emotion."

Goal Setting

Goal setting is a motivational strategy for improving performance (Burton, Naylor, & Holliday, 2001; Duda & Hall, 2001; Kingston & Wilson, 2009; Weinberg & Gould, 2003). Research on goal setting in industrial and organizational fields has been applied to the

external imagery: a technique in which an individual becomes a passive and external third-person observer of his or her own actions.

internal imagery: technique in which an individual imagines being inside his or her body, experiencing a given situation.

sports field. In particular, work done by Locke and his colleagues, beginning with his important paper in 1968, has been highly influential. The indications are that higher levels of performance are achieved through challenging goals, specific goals, and a combination of both short-term and long-term goals (Locke, 1968; Locke & Latham, 1985; Locke & Latham, 1990).

Two different goal perspectives have been identified (Duda, 1992): **ego orientation** and **task orientation**. The former is focused on success and failure, with success often coming at the expense of others. In the latter, satisfaction is derived more from the sense of competence experienced through improvement. Their focus is on effort and one's *own* performance rather than that of others. These are not independent positions, and successful performers often make use of both of them (Duda & Hall, 2001).

Three different types of goals have been described in the literature (Hardy et al., 1996; Kingston & Wilson, 2009). **Outcome goals** are concerned with the results or outcomes of events and usually involve comparisons to others. These goals might be expressed as a need to finish first in a race, where finishing second is equated with losing. **Performance goals** describe an outcome that can be achieved independently of others' performance; a novice marathoner may describe a desire to run her next race in less than 4 hours. **Process goals** focus on specific processes that a performer will be concerned with during a performance. A tennis player may indicate that during a match he plans to work on managing his self-talk.

Weinberg (1996) outlines a number of goal setting principles that are: "set specific goals, set realistic but challenging goals, set both long- and short-term goals, set goals for practice and competition, 'ink it, don't think it,' develop goal-achievement strategies, set performance goals, set individual and team goals, provide support for goals, provide for goal evaluation" (p. 11).

Sebire, Standage, and Vansteenkiste (2009) compared the impact on exercise of intrinsic goals such as health improvement, skill, and relationship development, with extrinsic goals such as image enhancement and recognition. They report that intrinsic goals were associated with increased exercise engagement, physical self-worth, and well-being while anxiety decreased (p. 202).

The role of goal setting as an effective strategy for increasing the commitment, effort and perseverance required for sustained motivation and enhanced self-efficacy has been consistently demonstrated in the sport and exercise literature (Burton & Weiss, 2008; Vidic & Burton, 2010).

ego orientation: a goal perspective that focuses on success and failure with success often coming at the expense of other people.

task orientation: a goal perspective in which individuals derive satisfaction from the sense of competence experienced as they improve; the focus is on effort and their own performance rather than that of others.

outcome goals: goals that are concerned with the results or outcomes of events and usually involve comparisons to others.

performance goals: goals that describe an outcome that can be achieved independently of others' performances.

process goals: goals that focus on specific processes that a performer will be concerned with during a performance.

Mindfulness and Acceptance-Based Interventions

Mindfulness and acceptance-based interventions, which have been developed within mainstream clinical psychology in the past 15 years, have now been applied to the field of sport and exercise psychology (Gardner & Moore, 2012). These approaches originate in meditative traditions that have been increasingly practiced in Western cultures (Kabat-Zinn, 2003). Within the clinical field there has been a questioning of the belief that psychological well-being can be enhanced through controlling internal experiences, for example, emotions, cognition, and physiological processes (Hayes, Strosahl, & Wilson, 1999). In this context, different definitions of mindfulness have been proposed. Cardaciotto, Nerbert, Forman, Moitra, and Farrow (2008) conceptualize it as "the tendency to be highly aware of one's internal and external experiences in the context of an accepting, non-judgmental stance toward those experiences" (p. 205). In the application of mindfulness and acceptance approaches to performance enhancement, Gardner and Moore (Gardner & Moore, 2006; Moore & Gardner, 2001) have raised concerns regarding the empirical and theoretical limitations of the prevailing model of psychological skills training. This model is based on cognitive-behavioural interventions as described previously, which are intended to create an ideal performance state through the self-control of internal processes. Gardner and Moore (2006) comment that: "Rather than controlling or reducing internal experiences, mindfulness and acceptance based interventions emphasize the development of a mindful, non-judging awareness of and acceptance of in-the-moment cognitive, affective, and sensory experiences" (p. 100). Through training in mindfulness techniques an attentional focus can be developed that allows for the present centered observation of both external experiences and internal processes in a non-judgmental manner. The emphasis here is on modifying the relationship with internal experiences rather than trying to change or avoid them (Gardner & Moore, 2012). Avoidance behaviours are counterproductive to long-term goals and values such as improving skills and the derived enjoyment in performance activities. In expressing concerns about traditional models of human performance, Gardner and Moore (2007) suggest that performance outcomes are affected by the extent to which the individual engages in experiential acceptance and is able to attend to the task rather than internal experiences. They state that this occurs when "attentional focus remains on the necessary aspects of the performance environment, and the performer will simply notice the cognitive, affective, and physiological arousal without the need to control, escape, or avoid it" (p. 16). Mindfulness and acceptance-based interventions have implications for behavioural choices in both the health and performance domains that will become increasingly important in psychology with the development of the theoretical and empirical foundations of the approach (Moore, 2009).

Again, the use of these psychological skills is not unique to exercise and sport; however, in the context of physical activity, sport, and exercise, they can be useful in helping us to improve our performance and to enjoy ourselves. All indications are that we are more likely to continue to engage in exercise and sport if we enjoy it.

PHYSICAL ACTIVITY AND INJURY

The final issue we will consider in this chapter is of a more clinical nature—the psychological consequences of injury during physical activity, specifically sport and exercise. Injury occurs with a high frequency in this context. Many of us will have experienced an injury while engaged in sport or exercise and could identify some of the psychological consequences of this event. We are also made very aware through the media of the injuries that regularly sideline our athletic heroes (Brown, 2014). Sometimes these are acute and sometimes they are chronic. The physical and psychological impact of these injuries is usually minimal; however, at times the impact can be very serious, extremely costly, and even career threatening (Cox, 2007; Weinberg & Gould, 2003; Williams, 2001).

An individual's reaction to an injury is a complex issue and will depend on numerous factors. These include the nature and severity of the injury, the role and importance of physical activity in the individual's life, and the response of the individual's

concussion (closed head injury): a bruising of the brain that can result in severe neurocognitive deficits, permanent disability, and even death.

support network. An injury in this context can also make us painfully aware of what we are missing. One injury that has received considerable attention recently is concussion (see Box 5-1).

When individuals experience a sports or exercise injury, they may experience a wide range of emotions, such as anger, disbelief, frustration, fear, anxiety, guilt, panic, loneliness, and depression. A number of models have been proposed to help us better understand the psychological processes associated with an athletic injury. There are essentially two approaches: those that focus on the stages of reaction and those that take a cognitive appraisal position. Stages-of-reaction approaches assume that individuals will pass through a series of stages in a set order. These approaches are frequently based on the stage model initially developed by Kübler-Ross (1969) to explain the experience of death and dying. She described five stages a dying individual goes through—denial and isolation, anger, bargaining, depression, and acceptance. In this context, the injury is considered to be similar to death and, indeed, many who suffer a debilitating injury view it this way. This model has been adapted to sport by Astle (1996) and Lynch (1988), who provide strategies for assisting those involved in the psychological rehabilitation of the injured person. The cognitive appraisal approach views an injury in the context of a stress

acceleration-deceleration injury: a type of concussion that occurs when an immobile head is hit by a moving object or a moving head hits an immobile object.

rotational injury: a type of concussion resulting from a blow to the side of the head.

second-impact syndrome: results when an athlete who has suffered a concussion returns to activity too soon and receives another blow to the head that can result in much greater trauma to the brain than that initially experienced.

post-concussion syndrome: symptoms experienced subsequent to a concussion, such as memory problems, difficulties in concentration, headaches, dizziness, and irritability.

BOX 5-1

Concussion

Athletes often describe it as "having your bell rung," while to the health professional it is known as a **closed head injury or concussion**. With disturbing frequency we read in our newspapers of the athlete whose career has been threatened by a blow to the head. After suffering a concussion during an NBA basketball game, an athlete stated, "The last thing I remember is checking into the game, then the next thing I remember is lying on the table and them asking me if I remember things. A long time elapsed between them. That's the scary part about it . . . that your mind can be altered like that" (Kingston, 1999).

Concussion is a bruising of the brain and is a serious injury. It can result in severe neurocognitive deficits, permanent disability, and even death. There is evidence that even mild concussion can result in neuropsychological impairments (Echemendia et al., 2012; Macciocchi, Barth, Alves, Rimel, & Jane, 1996). Two types of concussions are commonly described. An **acceleration-deceleration injury** occurs when an immobile head is hit by a moving object or a moving head hits an immobile object. A **rotational injury** usually results from a blow to the side of the head. A related concern in concussion is **second-impact syndrome**. This results when an individual who has suffered a concussion returns to activity too soon and receives another blow to the head, which can result in much

greater trauma to the brain than that initially experienced. **Post-concussion syndrome** is a term frequently seen in the press today. This describes a set of symptoms including memory problems and difficulties in concentration and complaints such as headaches, dizziness, and irritability.

It is important to remember that concussions can be experienced without the individual losing consciousness, and there is no visible physical evidence of concussion. The usual signs and symptoms of concussion include any period of loss of consciousness, confusion and inability to focus attention, disorientation, slurred or incoherent speech, delayed verbal and motor responses, inappropriate emotional behaviour, memory deficits, and lack of coordination. Other signs include complaints such as headaches, dizziness, ringing in the ears, nausea/vomiting, impaired vision, seeing stars, and sensitivity to light.

Concussion represents a serious problem in the sport and exercise field. With increasing public awareness of this problem, we have become more interested in understanding the nature of concussion and, most importantly, in the prevention of brain injury. Two recent Special Issues of the *Journal of Clinical Sport Psychology*, 2012, are dedicated to the topic of concussion in sport. It is interesting that of the 13 articles contained in the two volumes seven of them have Canadian authors.

and coping model (Brewer, 1994; Udry & Anderson, 2008; Williams, 2001). Individuals' emotional and behavioural responses to an injury will be determined by their personal appraisal of the event and their choice of coping strategies.

The role of the psychologist is being increasingly recognized as a crucial component in the intervention and management of injuries that occur in the context of sport and exercise (Brewer, 2001; Brown, 2005). Brewer (2010) has described a biopsychosocial model of sport injury rehabilitation that identifies psychological factors such as cognitions, emotions, and personality that impact the rehabilitation process and are important in designing psychological interventions. While acknowledging that, although there is over 30 years of work in this field, the position is taken that "inquiry on the role of psychological factors in sport injury rehabilitation outcomes is still in its formative stage" (p. 58). It is clear that despite the demonstrated effectiveness of psychological interventions they are still rarely a part of the prevention and rehabilitation of sport and exercise injury.

CHAPTER SUMMARY

- Define physical activity, exercise, and sport.

   The concept of physical activity is somewhat difficult to define; it is important to distinguish it from more formalized activities such as exercise and sport. It is important to understand the relationship of physical activity to health, particularly in Canada where geography and climate can present challenges.

- Describe the psychological benefits of physical activity.

   The psychological benefits of exercise relate to self-concept, self-esteem, and, most importantly in this review, self-efficacy. Physical activity is important, as it affects cognitive functioning and mood, particularly in relationship to anxiety, depression, and stress.

- Describe the physical benefits of physical activity.

   The physical benefits of physical activity have been demonstrated in regard to chronic illnesses such as cardiovascular disease and cancer.

- Appreciate the importance of adherence to physical activity.

   Adherence, and long-term adherence in particular, is an issue of major concern with respect to physical activity, especially as it relates to exercise. Models for improving adherence are become increasingly relevant.

- Understand some of the psychological issues involved in performance.

   Performance-enhancing factors in both sport and exercise include relaxation techniques, management of self-talk, goal setting, and imagery techniques.

- Appreciate some of the psychological concerns resulting from injury due to physical activity.

   The psychological management of injury is an increasingly important component of rehabilitation in physical activity, sport, and exercise. A major issue has become the articulation of the significance of concussion and its impact on those who experience it.

Chapter 6

Health-Compromising Behaviours

Chuck Savage/Flirt/Corbis

Learning Objectives

After studying this chapter, you will be able to:

Outline factors that contribute to smoking behaviour.

Provide explanations for why individuals drink alcohol or engage in illicit drug use.

Inform others regarding how we can help people quit their smoking, alcohol, or drug use.

Outline factors that contribute to obesity in our society.

Provide information about eating disorders.

Jennifer began to smoke in high school. She was a bright girl who enjoyed the academic side of school, but didn't always find the social side of school easy. When she began junior high school, also known as middle school, she noticed a radical shift in how her friends spent their time. Instead of playing sports and watching movies, her friends were now more interested in smoking, partying, and meeting guys. For some time, Jennifer resisted her friends' suggestions that she need not be so uptight and that she should learn to relax and start socializing at parties. However, Jennifer found that she was spending more and more time by herself and, thus, grew lonely. It seemed to her that the easiest way to fit in and regain friendships was to begin smoking. Both of Jennifer's parents smoked, so if she began too it wouldn't cause much upset in the family. So she did begin and continued to smoke even after graduating from high school.

After high school, Jennifer went in search of a job. She wanted to work as a journalist or perhaps behind the scenes at a radio or television station. She was told that the best experience she could gain would be at a small town radio or television station, where she would be expected to complete all the tasks of producing a story by herself; she'd have to find a story, write the story, and deliver the story on air.

Jennifer followed this advice. She found a job in a small town working for a local television station. In this new environment, Jennifer was able to give up smoking. Very few of the other people who worked at the television station smoked, and, of course, she no longer saw her high school friends, at least not on a regular basis. Jennifer was lucky. Unlike so many people who have a difficult time quitting, Jennifer was able to quit smoking on her own relatively easily.

Many years later, when Jennifer was going through the turmoil of a messy divorce, she began to smoke again. It all started when, after a lengthy meeting with her lawyer, she found herself craving a cigarette. After a couple of days, she gave in to this craving and bought a package of cigarettes. She smoked a single cigarette and found that this did alleviate some of her stress—she welcomed the relief. Yet, she knew smoking was unhealthy. She didn't want her children to model her behaviour and didn't want their health endangered as a result of her behaviour, so she never smoked indoors or let her children see her smoke. Fortunately, once the divorce was settled and she had obtained custody of her children, she was again able to kick the habit.

In this chapter, we will focus on specific health-compromising behaviours and the health hazards that are a product of these behaviours. Most of the behaviours we have chosen to focus on are behaviours that are voluntary in nature, at least initially. For example, we will examine the leading cause of premature death in Canada—smoking. We will also examine what is referred to as the obesity epidemic. And, in our discussion of disordered eating, we will introduce you to a disorder that has been identified relatively recently—muscle dysmorphia. To begin, we will turn our attention to the most prevalent health-compromising behaviour in our society, smoking.

SUBSTANCE ABUSE

Smoking

Age and Gender Differences in Smoking
There are few habits as potentially deadly as smoking cigarettes. Yet, almost 20 percent of the world's population does exactly

this. Specifically, about 800 million men and 200 million women smoke cigarettes (Eriksen, Mackay, & Ross, 2012). Smoking is the number one preventable cause of death and disease in Canada, accounting for more than 37 000 deaths each year (Reid, Hammond, Burkhalter, Rynard, & Ahmed, 2013). The 2011 Canadian Tobacco Use Monitoring Survey documents that 17 percent of Canadians 15 years of age or older (4.9 million people) are current smokers, of whom 13.7 percent reported smoking daily (Health Canada, 2013a). Although there was a decline in tobacco consumption over the last decade, that decline seems to have slowed with the prevalence in 2011 equally that in 2008.

People typically begin smoking during their teenage years, so the percentage of Canadians who have not started by the age of 20 is an indicator of future smoking rates. In 2011, 66 percent of males aged 20 to 24 years had never smoked, up from 36 percent in 2001, and 77.5 percent of similar aged females had never smoked, compared with 42 percent in 2001 (Health Canada, 2013a). Sadly, the highest rate of smoking occurs among those in their prime, that is, those between the ages of 20 and 35 years (Health Canada, 2013a; see Figure 6-1).

Fortunately, the number of cigarettes smoked per day has declined over the last decade (Health Canada, 2013a). On average, younger adults, those 35 and younger, smoke 12 cigarettes per day. This number increases slightly across the age groups, and those 35 years or older tend to smoke 15 or 16 cigarettes per day on average (Health Canada, 2013a). Traditionally, more males than females have smoked cigarettes. The gender gap narrowed considerably in the 1960s and 1970s and has remained relatively constant since then. It is worth mentioning that males tend to smoke more cigarettes per day than do females (15 cigarettes/day for males and 13 cigarettes/day for females; Health Canada, 2013a).

Sociocultural Differences in Smoking   Rates of smoking vary substantially by socioeconomic status: The percentage of people who smoke tends to decline with increases in income as well as in education and job prestige (Reid, Hammond, & Driezen, 2010). The amount smoked also decreases with increased level of education (Health Canada, 2013a; see Figure 6-2). People in the lowest income bracket report the highest rates of smoking (40 percent of men and 36 percent of women). A national Canadian study discovered that

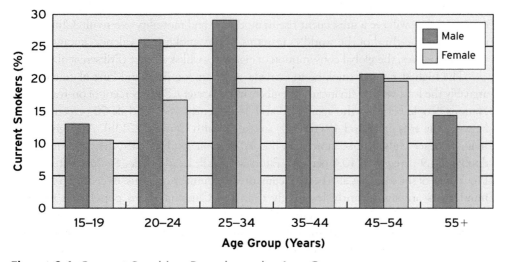

Figure 6-1 Current Smoking Prevalence by Age Group

Source: 2011 Canadian Tobacco Use Monitoring Survey (Health Canada, 2013a).

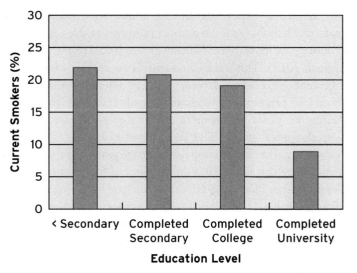

Figure 6-2 Current Smoking Prevalence by Education Level

Source: 2011 Canadian Tobacco Use Monitoring Survey, Health Canada, 2013a. Retrieved from http://www. hc-sc.gc.ca/hc-ps/tobac-tabac/research-recherche/stat/_ctums-esutc_2011/ann-eng.php#t8

a change in household income that moved an individual across the poverty line threshold was more likely to quit smoking than someone who remained in poverty (Young-Hoon, 2012). Smoking rates decrease with an increase in income, to lows of 16 and 13 percent among men and women respectively, in the highest income bracket (Reid et al., 2010). This is true within North American society and is also evidenced if we look globally.

Traditionally, it is the high-income countries who have smoked the most. However, those in high income countries have come to understand the health consequences of smoking and have implemented tobacco control policy and legislation (Eriksen et al., 2012). Cigarette consumption in Western Europe dropped by 26 percent between 1990 and 2009. In contrast, cigarette consumption in the Middle East and Africa increased by 57 percent during the same time period (Eriksen et al., 2012). As consumption rates increase in low and middle-income countries, they will see a subsequent rise in morbidity and mortality as a result. Chinese men now smoke one-third of the world's cigarettes. If the smoking prevalence among Chinese women increases, the global consumption of cigarettes will skyrocket (Eriksen et al., 2012).

The highest rates of smoking in Canada occur among Inuit and First Nations people, arguably the least well off financially members in our society. Sixty percent of on-reserve First Nations people between the ages of 18 and 34 currently smoke, while 70 percent of Inuit between the ages of 18 and 45 currently smoke (Health Canada, 2013b). Aboriginal youth living off reserve also smoke more than non-Aboriginal youth; in fact, the rate is more than double (24.9 percent to 10.4 percent; Elton-Marshall, Leatherdale, & Burkhalter, 2011). Prevalence of smoking has also been documented by immigrant status. Recent non-European immigrants are significantly less likely than the Canadian-born population to smoke (Georgiades, Boyle, Duku, & Racine, 2006). In fact, for all immigrants, the number who smoke generally increased with the length of time in Canada (Chen, Ng, & Wilkins, 1996). This leads us to conclude that there is something about our Canadian culture that promotes smoking. Unlike for the Canadian-born population, there is no clear relationship between smoking and income status for immigrants.

Why Do People Smoke? Considering that most people are aware that smoking is bad for them, that is, smoking is linked to a wide variety of negative health consequences, it is puzzling that so many people still smoke. This behaviour is even more puzzling when we realize that the first few times people smoke, they likely cough, find the taste unpleasant, and may even experience dizziness and nausea. Why would someone voluntarily engage in this behaviour? Why, after their first experience, would they want to smoke again?

Beginning to Smoke Smoking often begins during adolescence, when peer influence is strong. Numerous studies have found that adolescents are more likely to smoke if their friends smoke or if they attend a school where older students smoke (Kennedy, Tucker, Pollard, Go, & Green, 2011; Leatherdale, Cameron, Brown, Jolin, & Kroker, 2006; Leatherdale, Maske, & Kroeker, 2006). When adolescents first try smoking, they usually do so in the company of their peers and with their peers' encouragement (Milton et al., 2004). Then, once adolescents begin to smoke, this behaviour is reinforced by their peers or they select friends who are also smokers (Mercken, Candel, Willems, & de Vries, 2007).

Recall Jennifer, whom we introduced at the beginning of this chapter. Jennifer was greatly influenced by peer pressure in her decision to begin smoking. Both her parents and many of her friends smoked. In a sense, the cards were stacked against her, as she was surrounded by many situational factors associated with smoking. Researchers have documented that adolescents are more likely to smoke if they have parents or older siblings who also smoke (e.g., Gilpin, White, & Pierce, 2005; O'Loughlin, Karp, Koulis, Paradis, & DiFranza, 2009; Slomkowski, Rende, Novak, Lloyd-Richardson, & Niaura, 2005). These findings suggest that both modelling and peer pressure are likely to be important causative factors of smoking (Mercken et al., 2007).

The image of the smoker also seems to be important. A group of 11-year-olds indicated that image was a major reason for their smoking behaviour (Stanton, Mahalski, McGee, & Silva, 1993). Children between the ages of 11 and 15 years often associate smoking with being attractive to the opposite sex, with being glamorous and exciting. Another popular image of the smoker is that he or she is rebellious, tough, and mature (Dinh, Sarason, Peterson, & Onstad, 1995). There is little doubt that the media play a role in formulating an image associated with smoking.

John Pierce and colleagues (Distefan, Pierce, & Gilpin, 2004; Pierce, 2005) have conducted a series of studies in which non-smoking 12- to 15-year olds are asked to nominate their favourite movie stars. One-third of the non-smokers nominated a star who smoked onscreen. When smoking status was assessed 3 years later, the earlier "star" nomination predicted smoking behaviour. The influence was strongest for girls. Although many believe that smoking was most widespread in "classic" movies, an analysis of popular movies from the 1950s to present day revealed this is not the case. Specifically, movies in the 1950s depicted smoking incidents 10.7 times per hour. This rate slowly declined until the 1980s, when 4.9 smoking incidents per hour took place. Unfortunately, since this low rate in the early 1980s, smoking incidents in movies have increased to greater than ever before.

Witnessing cigarette smoking in popular films leads college students to view smoking as more commonplace than it actually is, and it also increases their current desire to smoke (Glantz, 2009). Glantz has boldly stated that "smoking in movies is responsible for addicting 1070 U.S. adolescents to tobacco every day, 535 of whom will die prematurely as a result" (Glantz, 2004, p. 250). Research continues to find a strong link between media exposure and smoking in many countries (e.g., Hanewinkel & Sargent, 2007; Ho, Wang, Lai, Hedley, &

Lam, 2010; Morgenstern et al., 2011). Indeed, the strong appeal of smoking presented in movies has led some academics to call for a rating of "restricted to those 18 and over" to movies with tobacco imagery in an effort to reduce youth smoking (Millett & Glantz, 2010).

Although situational factors (e.g., peer pressure) are thought to be the most important determinants in the initiation of smoking, personal characteristics also seem to be related to smoking behaviour. Characteristics such as low self-esteem and social isolation increase the tendency to imitate others' behaviour (Audrain-McGovern, Rodriguez, & Kassel, 2009; Vidrine, Anderson, Pollak, & Wetter, 2006). People who are rebellious and engage in risk-taking behaviours are more likely to smoke than are people who do not engage in such behaviours (Burt, Dinh, Peterson, & Sarason, 2000; Ryan, MacKillop, & Carpenter, 2013). Genetic mechanisms also seem to contribute to the likelihood that a person will begin and then continue to smoke (Bierut, 2011; Ling, Niu, Feng Xing, & Xu, 2004). The neurotransmitter dopamine is important in the brain's reward system and is thought to be the strongest genetic contributor to smoking initiation (Clague, Cinciripini, Blalock, Wu, & Hudmon, 2010). Sometimes teenage girls choose to smoke in an effort to control their weight (Vidrine et al., 2006). These girls would benefit from the knowledge that smoking does not help in the prevention of obesity (Zimlichman et al., 2005). To summarize, four factors tend to initiate adolescent smoking: parental modelling, peer influence, cigarette advertising, and personal characteristics. But what factors are responsible for people becoming regular smokers?

Becoming a Regular Smoker   Although the majority of people try smoking at least once in their lives, most people do not become regular smokers. For those who become habitual smokers, the habit generally develops slowly, often taking years (Chassin, Presson, Pitts, & Sherman, 2000; Stanton, Flay, Colder, & Mehta, 2004). Researchers have not discovered why some people become regular smokers while others do not. There does not seem to be a single reason why people smoke. Rather, it appears that different people smoke for different reasons.

Much of the research into this topic has stemmed from the theoretical position of Silvan Tomkins (1966, 1968). Tomkins offered four explanations as to why people who begin to smoke continue to smoke on a regular basis. Some people smoke to achieve a positive affect; a **positive-affect smoker** smokes to increase stimulation, to relax, or to gratify sensorimotor needs. In contrast, **negative-affect smokers** are people who smoke to reduce negative affect, such as anxiety, distress, fear, or guilt. You may recall that Jennifer from our opening vignette first began to smoke to reduce loneliness. Later, she began to smoke again to deal with the stress in her life resulting from divorce proceedings. Jennifer would be considered a negative-affect smoker.

Other people smoke simply out of habit. **Habitual smokers** probably initiated smoking to achieve a positive affect or to reduce a negative affect but continue to smoke without awareness of why they are doing so. These people do not derive any benefits from smoking. Finally, **addictive smokers**, those who develop a psychological dependence on smoking, are keenly aware of when they are not smoking. That is, they feel something is amiss when they are not smoking. Addictive smokers can tell you exactly when they smoked their last cigarette and when they will smoke their next one. A highly addicted smoker deems the first cigarette of the day as most important and usually waits no more than 30 minutes before "lighting up" (Health Canada, 2013b). Addicted smokers have cigarettes with them at all times and usually keep at least one extra package "stashed away" for "emergencies." Research continues to support Tomkin's theory (e.g., del Rio, Becona, & Duran, 2011; Stevens, Colwell, Smith, Robinson, & McMillan, 2005).

Because different people have different reasons for smoking, strategies to quit smoking vary in their effectiveness. For example, people who smoke for pleasure show a sharp drop in the

positive-affect smoker: a smoker who smokes to attain positive affect (e.g., increased stimulation, relaxation, or gratification of sensorimotor needs).

negative-affect smoker: a smoker who smokes to reduce negative affect, such as anxiety, distress, fear, or guilt.

habitual smokers: smokers who smoke without the awareness that they are doing so.

addictive smokers: smokers who develop a psychological dependence on smoking and are keenly aware when they are not smoking.

Flavoured Tobacco Products

With flavours such as chocolate, peach, and cherry, flavoured tobacco products are particularly enticing for youth. Those youth who are able to avoid cigarettes may still be drawn to the appeal of flavoured non-cigarette tobacco products (e.g., cigarillos, cigars, pipes, smokeless tobacco, and waterpipes). Figure 6-3 shows that 70 percent of Canadian youth in grades 6–9 and 80 percent of youth aged 15–19 years who had used any non-cigarette tobacco products in the last 30 days had used a flavoured product (Reid et al., 2013). Perhaps they choose these products because the taste of the tobacco is somewhat hidden and does not appear to be as harsh. However, don't be fooled, many of the same toxic substances appear in cigars, cigarillos, and smokeless tobacco as are present in tobacco (NCI, 2012).

Figure 6-3 Percentage of Youth Who Had Used Flavoured Tobacco Products

Source: Propel Centre for Population Health Impact, University of Waterloo. http://www.tobaccoreport.ca/2013/TobaccoUseinCanada_2013.pdf (accessed September 10, 2013).

number of cigarettes they smoke when their cigarettes have been dipped in vinegar, whereas those who smoke for other reasons (e.g., addiction) do not. In contrast, people who smoke primarily from habit show a marked reduction in the amount they smoke when asked to keep a record of cigarettes smoked, whereas this is not the case for those who smoke for pleasure.

The psychological reasons for smoking are certainly important, but heredity may also play a role. Researchers have not definitively determined the link between heredity and smoking, but three possible explanations have been put forth. First, genetic factors may underlie certain personality traits associated with smoking (e.g., rebelliousness). Second, heredity may determine the extent to which people find tobacco pleasant or unpleasant. Third, genetically based differences in reaction to nicotine influence the degree to which people exposed to nicotine become dependent on it (Bierut, 2011; Ling et al., 2004).

Once people begin smoking regularly, they become physiologically dependent on the nicotine in cigarettes, so it's important to understand how nicotine initially affects us. When a person inhales smoke from a cigarette, nicotine passes through cell membranes in the mouth and nose en route to the lungs, where alveoli absorb the nicotine and carry it to the blood. In a very short time, the blood has carried the nicotine to the brain. In the brain, nicotine triggers the release of various chemicals that activate both the central and sympathetic nervous systems, resulting in increases in heart rate and blood pressure. This entire process takes approximately 10 seconds (Health Canada, 2013b).

Health Warning Labels on Cigarette Packaging

Most smokers do not view themselves as being at increased risk for experiencing a heart attack or developing cancer because of their habit (Ayanian & Cleary, 1999). Our federal government is trying to change that. Over the decades, Canadian smokers have been exposed to more and more graphic warning labels. These warning labels attempt to change behaviour using fear appeals. Since 2012, the warning labels must cover the top 75 percent of the front and back of the principal display surface (up from 50 percent in 2000; Health Canada, 2011). There are 16 different images on these labels, many of them depicting what happens to organs after their owner has spent a lifetime smoking (e.g., a diseased mouth, a lung tumour, a brain after a stroke). The cigarette packaging also contains additional messages, including tips on quitting smoking. There are 16 additional messages inside the package.

Researchers at the University of Waterloo who form part of the International Tobacco Control Policy Evaluation Project with 18 other countries have conducted a series of research studies to evaluate the effectiveness of these images. The findings have been extremely positive. In one study (Hammond, Fong, McDonald, Cameron, & Brown, 2003), 90 percent of a sample of 600 Canadian smokers reported that they had read the warning labels. They also reported how much they thought about or discussed the messages and what their current intentions were related to quitting smoking. Three months later, when the smokers were recontacted, 23 percent had quit or had attempted to quit smoking and nearly 25 percent had reduced the amount they smoked per day. A study conducted in 2010–2011 by the same researchers found that the warning labels were having less of an impact after 10 years—a sign that it was time to change labels (ITC Project, 2012a).

Although we cannot be sure if an intention to reduce the amount smoked influenced how much smokers thought about the warning labels, those who had cognitively processed the labels to a greater degree the first time they were contacted were more likely to have quit by the time of the second contact. In other studies, people who stated that they attempted to avoid the labels were just as likely to read and think about the warnings as those who did not engage in avoidance behaviours (e.g., Hammond, Fong, McDonald, Brown, & Cameron, 2004; Hammond, McDonald, Fong, Brown, & Cameron, 2004). Very few of the smokers perceived the government-mandated warning signs as inaccurate, suggesting that the labels are a useful way to educate current smokers. Indeed, smokers from 14 of 15 countries surveyed wanted more health information presented on packages (ITC Project, 2012a). Although many smokers reported fear and disgust in response to the warning labels, those who reported greater negative emotion were more likely to quit, attempt to quit, or reduce their consumption. Additionally, former smokers who remained abstinent indicated that the warning labels helped them to do so.

The World Health Organization's Framework Convention on Tobacco Control recognizes the importance of

These graphic images and warnings are among 16 that the Canadian government has required tobacco companies to include on all cigarette packaging.
Health Canada

warning labels on cigarette packages and recommends that the labels should "be no less than 30 percent of the principal display areas" (WHO, 2005, p. 10). However, when introducing new warning labels, countries are well advised to heed recent findings that suggest warning size increases warning effectiveness and that graphic warnings may be superior to text-based warnings (Borland et al., 2009; Nimbarte, Aghazadeh, & Harvey, 2006). As of February 2012, over 45 countries have passed legislation requiring pictorial health warnings (ITC Project, 2012a).

Health Consequences of Smoking As previously mentioned, smoking is the number one preventable cause of death and disease in Canada. Research conclusively shows that smoking reduces life expectancy by several years. Ellison and his colleagues (1999) at Health Canada determined that the rate of premature death (before age 70) for lifelong smokers (both males and females) was twice that of people who had never smoked. Smoking also increases the risk of many illnesses, including cancer, cardiovascular disease, high blood pressure, high cholesterol, emphysema, pneumonia, gum disease, osteoporosis, cataracts, and sleeping problems (Health Canada, 2013b). And the more you smoke, the worse your odds become. Given this, it is not surprising that non-smokers are expected to live a higher proportion of their life without any disability (Statistics Canada, 2001).

On July 15, 2003, in an effort to protect Canada's citizens from the health hazards and economic burden of tobacco consumption and exposure to tobacco smoke, Anne McLellan, the Canadian Minister of Health at that time, signed the Framework Convention on Tobacco Control (FCTC). Member countries of the World Health Organization prepared the FCTC. Their goal was to aid in the prevention, cessation, and harm reduction of tobacco (Eriksen et al., 2012).

Smoking and Cardiovascular and Cerebrovascular Disease Together, cardiovascular disease (20.7 percent) and cerebrovascular disease (5.9 percent) were responsible for 63 376 deaths (26.6 percent) in Canada in 2009 (Statistics Canada, 2012a). In general, the risk of dying of cardiovascular disease is about twice as high for smokers as for non-smokers. The risk is particularly severe for women. The United States Department of Health and Human Services (USDHHS, 2010) states that if a woman smokes a pack or more of cigarettes a day then she will be twice as likely as a man to develop cardiovascular disease and 10 times as likely to die from chronic respiratory disease. In a large-scale study that analyzed data from 52 countries, researchers from McMaster University's Population Health Research Institute determined that the risk of myocardial infarction (heart attack) increased by 5.6 percent for every cigarette smoked (Teo et al., 2006).

Smoking is thought to contribute to cardiovascular disease in a number of ways. There is some evidence that cigarette smoking increases the level of serum cholesterol and the size of plaque within the arteries. Amazingly, the progression of atherosclerosis in smokers is estimated to increase by as much as 50 percent during a 3-year period (Howard et al., 1998). Nicotine itself may also contribute to heart disease. Nicotine has a stimulant effect on the nervous system, resulting in increases in heart rate, blood pressure, and cardiac output, combined with constriction of blood vessels. Fortunately, the risk of heart attack and stroke, like that of cancer, declines when people quit smoking (Critchley & Capewell, 2003; Teo et al., 2006).

Smoking and Cancer Cancer is the leading cause of death in Canada. In 2009, 30 percent of deaths in Canada were attributed to various forms of cancer (Statistics Canada, 2012a). Although almost 80 percent of smoking-related deaths in Canada result from lung cancer, smoking is also responsible for deaths from cancer of the lip, oral cavity, pharynx, esophagus, pancreas, larynx, urinary bladder, and kidney (Canadian Cancer Society, 2014). Female smokers may be more susceptible to lung cancer than male smokers. Kiyohara and Ohno (2010) state that researchers in the United States have documented the correspondence between the rise in lung cancer deaths and the prevalence of smoking since the 1930s. These researchers (e.g., Shopland & Burns, 1993) state that the rate of mortality from lung cancer began to rise approximately 15 to 20 years after the rate of smoking started to rise. These rates have paralleled each other since that time.

Smoking and Chronic Lower Respiratory Diseases   Chronic lower respiratory diseases include a number of respiratory and lung diseases, such as chronic bronchitis and emphysema. They accounted for 10 859 deaths (or 4.6 percent of all deaths) in Canada in 2009 (Statistics Canada, 2012a). Virtually all chronic lower respiratory diseases are experienced by smokers. In other words, these conditions are relatively rare in non-smokers. In general terms, smoking irritates and damages respiratory organs. This damage leads to reduced airflow when breathing and is particularly noticeable when trying to exhale with force.

Environmental Tobacco Smoke   We have looked at what happens to the health of people who smoke. What we have not considered is the number of people who are affected by **environmental tobacco smoke (ETS)**, also known as **second-hand smoke**. Most Canadians spend more time indoors than outdoors, and tobacco smoke is a key contaminant in indoor air quality. Breathing ETS is called **passive smoking**. Second-hand smoke is the number one risk factor for lung cancer among non-smokers and 15 percent of those who die from lung cancer are non-smokers (LCC, 2013). The Public Health Agency of Canada estimates that approximately 800 Canadian non-smokers die each year from lung cancer caused by exposure to ETS (Public Health Agency of Canada, 2002). The number of non-smokers who die from cardiovascular disease as a result of ETS is likely to be much higher, given that researchers have estimated that at least 10 times the number of non-smokers die from ETS-related cardiovascular disease than they do from ETS-related lung cancer. Pregnant women, fetuses, and young children are especially susceptible. Health consequences include complications of pregnancy and low birth weight, increased risk of sudden infant death syndrome and ear infections, reduced lung development, and increased severity of asthma and other respiratory illnesses (Kuehn, 2006).

In an effort to protect people, most provinces now have restrictions on smoking in public settings. That is, in 9 of 13 provinces and territories in Canada there is a complete smoking ban on indoor bars, restaurants, and work places. Additionally, in 8 of 13 provinces and territories and 5 municipalities, there is a ban on smoking in a car when a child is present (ITC Project, 2012b). Given the greater smoking rates among Aboriginals, it is not surprising to learn that exposure to second-hand smoke at home and in cars is almost twice that of the general population (Elton-Marshall et al., 2011). Interestingly, there are high levels of support for such bans, even by smokers; however, support does vary by ban. For instance, globally almost all individuals in all countries who are part of the ITC project support the ban of not smoking in cars when children are present. There is more variability in support for bans in countries regarding smoking in public places (ITC Project, 2012b).

Quitting Smoking   The vast majority of current smokers state that if they had to do it "over again, they would not have started smoking" (Fong et al., 2004, p. S341). In fact, each year, almost half of all smokers attempt to quit (Reid et al., 2013). Unfortunately, only about 12 percent of attempts to quit by 15- to 19-year-olds are successful. However, success rates increase with age and those 45 years and older have a success rate of 70 percent (Reid et al., 2013). Additional information that might motivate someone to quit smoking is "The majority (59 percent) of Canadians who have ever been smokers have now quit" (Reid et al., 2013, p. 53).

As previously mentioned, smoking is an **addiction**. That is, once people begin to smoke regularly, most become physically or psychologically dependent on it. Therefore, people who want to quit smoking must go through a period of **withdrawal**. Withdrawal refers to the unpleasant symptoms that people experience when they stop using a substance they have become dependent on. When people reduce or eliminate nicotine intake, they experience short-term symptoms such as a reduction in concentration, attention, and memory, combined with an increase in anxiety, irritability, and moodiness (Health Canada, 2013b; Shadel et al., 2000). The good news is that if you do quit smoking, your odds of survival steadily improve. After 15 or 20 years as a non-smoker, your odds are similar to those of people who have never smoked (Critchley & Capewell, 2003; Teo et al., 2006). Although the benefits of quitting smoking are the same for everyone, the reasons why people choose to quit vary (see Figure 6-4).

addiction: the state of being physically or psychologically dependent on a substance.

withdrawal: the unpleasant symptoms people experience when they stop using a substance to which they are addicted.

Quitting on One's Own Approximately 10 percent of individuals interviewed who had attempted to quit smoking in the past year reported being abstinent at the time of the interview (Reid et al., 2013). Most relapses occur in the first 3 months (Ockene et al., 2000). Almost half of those who attempt to quit smoking will do so on their own, without any professional help, self-help materials, or stop-smoking medications (Reid & Hammond, 2009). Why would so many smokers attempting to quit not seek help?

In Montreal (Kishchuk, Tremblay, Lapierre, Heneman, & O'Loughlin, 2004), college students expressed "uniformly negative" opinions about virtually all interventions—counselling, pharmacological aids, "Quit and Win" contests, self-help tools, media campaigns,

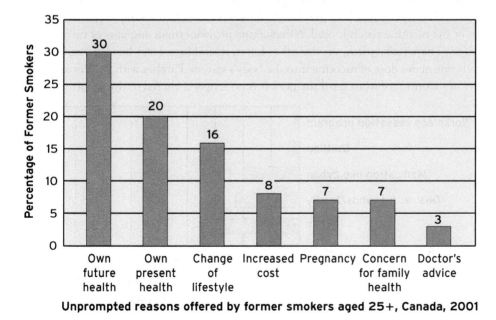

Unprompted reasons offered by former smokers aged 25+, Canada, 2001

Figure 6-4 Reasons for Quitting Smoking

Source: *Canadian Tobacco Use Monitoring Survey 2001: Quitting Smoking Among Adults,* Health Canada, 2003b. Reproduced with the permission of the Minister of Public Works and Government Services Canada, 2010.

environmental regulations, and social mobilization. These college students indicated that college life was already challenging and that they did not need more demands placed on them. To engage students, these authors suggest providing opportunities and support for exploration of, and commitment to, personal and social identities that exclude smoking, developing interventions that associate quitting with healthy outdoor environments and activities, and targeting friendship cliques with non-judgmental messages. Perhaps, however, these college students were onto something. That is, if you really want to quit, you can do so on your own.

A now classic study conducted by Stanley Schachter in 1982 suggests that it is relatively easy to quit on your own. He found that 60 percent of participants from the psychology department at Columbia University and the resident population of Amagansett, New York, were able to quit on their own. Indeed, the average time these participants could classify themselves as "former smokers" was 7 years! Schachter concluded that the low clinic success rates occurred because these were people who tried to quit on their own, but were unable to. Thus, this self-selected group has already failed at their first attempt! Taken together, this might help us understand why the number one quit method today is reducing the number of cigarettes consumed daily (Reid et al., 2013).

Quitting with Therapy   Some people who cannot quit smoking on their own do seek help from others (see Figure 6-5 for various quitting methods utilized). Most therapies include nicotine-replacement therapy, psychological interventions, or both. Therapies that combine both nicotine replacement and psychological interventions, known as multidimensional approaches, are considered most effective (Niaura & Abrams, 2002; Ranney, Melvin, Lux, McClain, & Lohr, 2006).

nicotine-replacement therapy: a stop-smoking technique that provides some form of nicotine to replace that previously obtained through smoking.

Nicotine-replacement therapy was used by 35 percent of respondents to the 2008 Tobacco Monitoring Use Survey who attempted to quit smoking (Reid & Hammond, 2009). Nicotine-replacement therapy provides some form of nicotine replacement for the nicotine that former smokers previously obtained through smoking. Typically, nicotine gum or the nicotine patch is used. *Nicotine gum* provides small amounts of nicotine when chewed. The *nicotine patch*, on the other hand, resembles a large bandage and releases a small continuous dose of nicotine into the body's system. Patches with smaller and smaller doses of nicotine are worn until the person is no longer addicted to the nicotine.

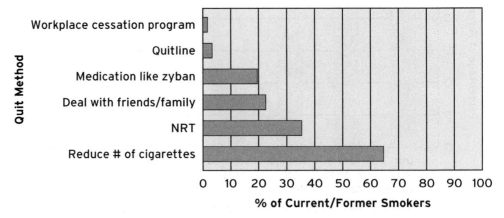

Figure 6-5 Use of Various Quitting Methods among Current and Former Smokers

Source: Propel Centre for Population Health Impact, University of Waterloo. www.tobaccoreport.ca/2013/TobaccoUseinCanada_2013.pdf (accessed September 10, 2013).

Nicotine replacement therapies such as gum, the transdermal patch, nasal spray, and lozenges increase the rate of quitting smoking by 50–70% (Stead et al., 2012). If the drug bupropion is combined with the patch, a 35-percent cessation rate is obtained (Jorenby et al., 1999). Nicotine inhalers and nicotine nasal sprays are also available. No matter what form of nicotine replacement is used, it will be more effective when used in conjunction with various psychological approaches to treatment (Niaura & Abrams, 2002).

The psychological approaches to smoking cessation generally take one of two forms—aversion therapies or self-management strategies. **Aversion therapies** involve pairing the behaviour to be eliminated, in this case smoking, with some unpleasant stimulus so that smoking will elicit negative sensations. The three most common forms of aversion therapies are electric shock, imagined aversive scenes, and rapid smoking.

Electric shock can be paired with smoking situations so that when a person smokes he or she is shocked and made uncomfortable. When *aversive scenes* are used, people are directed to think of an aversive scene that includes beginning to smoke, followed by something disgusting (e.g., you take the cigarette out of the pack and are about to light it when you suddenly vomit all over your cigarette, your hands, and the lighter. The smell is so foul that you can hardly stand it. You drop the cigarette and the lighter and, as you turn away and head toward the bathroom to clean yourself up, you begin to feel much less nauseous). The third technique, *rapid smoking,* is seldom used. Rapid smoking involves placing the smoker in a small, enclosed room where he or she inhales from a cigarette rapidly every few seconds while concentrating on the smoke, the stinging burn in the throat, and other unpleasant elements. Aversion strategies may help in the initial stages of quitting smoking, but the effects are seldom long term.

Self-management strategies are designed to help people overcome the environmental conditions that perpetuate smoking. *Self-monitoring* requires that people record each cigarette they smoke, the time of day, their location, who they are with, and their mood. Self-monitoring in itself reduces smoking, but the information obtained also aids in formulating other approaches to smoking cessation. *Stimulus control* strategies focus on removing the cues that lead a person to smoke. For example, if a person always smokes during a coffee break when sitting in the staff room, that person may want to go for a walk or have a coffee break in a different location. *Behavioural contracting* involves establishing a contract, according to which a person will be rewarded for fulfilling the contract or punished for failing to do so. These contracts often involve having the person deposit a large sum of money that he or she will lose if the contract is broken. These are only a few of the strategies that can be used to help people quit smoking.

As mentioned previously, the most common strategy used by those attempting to quit smoking over the last few years is simply to reduce the number of cigarettes smoked each day. Over 60 percent of individuals tried this approach in 2011, but this strategy was often used in combination with other strategies (Reid et al., 2013).

Alcohol Use

Alcohol Consumption   About 90 percent of Canadians (82 percent of men and 74 percent of women) have consumed alcohol in the past 12 months (Health Canada, 2013a). Women are more likely than men to be non-drinkers (13.9 percent versus 9.1 percent). Men are more likely than women to report drinking alcohol at least once a week (55.2 percent versus 32.8 percent); to exceed the low-risk guidelines than are women (30.2 percent versus 15.1 percent); to "binge" drink, that is, consume five or more drinks at

aversion therapy: therapy that includes pairing the behaviour that one is attempting to eliminate with some unpleasant stimulus so that the undesired behaviour will elicit negative sensations.

self-management strategies: strategies used to help people overcome the environmental conditions that perpetuate smoking.

a sitting (23.2 percent versus 8.8 percent); and to binge drink at least once a week (9.2 percent versus 3.3 percent; CCSA, 2014). Binge drinking is even more problematic by First Nations On-reserve where 16 percent report bingeing on a weekly basis. The largest difference is among females where 10.2 percent of First Nations females report binge drinking on a weekly basis compared to 3.3 percent in the general population (Health Canada, 2009c).

What are the low-risk guidelines? The current guidelines, put forth by the Canadian Centre on Substance Abuse (CCSA, 2014), state that men should limit their weekly alcohol intake to no more than 15 standard drinks and women to no more than 10 standard drinks. However, women should have no more than two drinks a day most days and men should have no more than three. Teens, under parental guidance, should never drink more than one to two drinks at a time, and never more than one to two times per week. A standard drink is a 5-ounce glass of wine, a 12-ounce glass of beer or cider, or 1.5 ounces of spirits. Each standard drink contains 13.6 grams of alcohol. These guidelines are put forth to "promote a culture of moderation" and to support healthy lifestyles (CCSA, 2014).

Additional demographic trends indicate that those 18 to 24 years of age and single persons were more likely to exceed the low-risk drinking guidelines than were their counterparts. Similarly, those in the highest income brackets are more likely to exceed the low-risk drinking guidelines (CCSA, 2014). This is a pattern that is in direct contrast to that found for smoking. You may remember that smoking rates decrease steadily with income level. There are, however, no alcohol-consumption differences observed according to level of education or based on living in a rural versus non-rural area. What may differ among groups is the type of alcohol consumed.

A recent trend for the consumption of alcohol include mixing energy drinks (e.g., Red Bull, Monster, Rockstar) with alcohol (Health Canada, 2010a; Malinauskas, Aeby, Overton, Carpenter-Aeby, & Barber-Heidal, 2007). A typical energy drink serving in Canada, for example, Red Bull, presented in a 250 mL can contains 80 mg of caffeine, 1000 mg of taurine, 600 mg of glucuronolactone, and several B vitamins (Rotstein et al., 2013). Various herbs and extracts may also be included such as ginseng, ginkgo biloba, and green tea extract. The carbonation of the energy drink permits a quicker absorption of alcohol while the caffeine of the energy drink may mask the drowsiness associated with alcohol leading the consumer to be less aware of their physical impairment (Rostein et al., 2013). In comparison to those who consumed alcohol alone, students who consumed alcohol mixed with energy drinks were more likely to leave a bar highly intoxicated, take advantage of someone sexually, or be taken advantage of, and either drive or ride in a vehicle when the driver was under the influence of alcohol (O'Brien, McCoy, Rhodes, Wagoner, & Wlfson, 2008; Thombs et al., 2010). It must be noted, however, that research in this area is still in its infancy and that not all research supports the notion that individuals are less aware of their impairment (e.g., Alford, Hamilton-Morris, & Verster, 2012).

ethanol (ethyl alcohol): the alcohol used in beverages.

The Effects of Alcohol   The alcohol used in beverages is called **ethanol or ethyl alcohol**. This alcohol is a depressant drug, and, like other depressant drugs (e.g., tranquillizers and painkillers) it slows down the nervous system, which may cause drowsiness, induce sleep, or relieve pain. Even the initial apparent stimulant effect actually results from depression of centres in the brain that inhibit our actions and control our behaviour. After one drink, the majority of people report feeling more relaxed. With more than one drink, a person may feel more outgoing and self-confident, but some people will become aggressive, depressed, or withdrawn. At higher doses—even below a blood-alcohol concentration of 0.05, the legal limit for driving a car in Canada—thinking, judgment, and ability to estimate distance can be impaired and reaction times increased (Canadian Centre on Substance Abuse, 2014; Tzamazis & Stough, 2000).

Excessive use of alcohol can have adverse effects on almost every system of the body, resulting in higher morbidity and shorter life expectancy (Statistics Canada, 2004a). For example, chronic alcohol abuse causes liver disease and damage to the stomach, pancreas, and intestines. Moreover, chronic drinking causes high blood pressure and depression of the immune system and is associated with coronary artery disease and cancer of the throat, larynx, mouth, esophagus, and liver (Canadian Centre on Substance Abuse, 2014; Tzamazis & Stough, 2000).

Other consequences of drinking include blackouts, hangovers, and even death. Blackouts are periods of memory loss that occur while a person is drinking heavily. Hangovers, on the other hand, occur after drinking has stopped. Hangovers are caused by mild alcohol withdrawal and may be experienced 8 to 12 hours after a bout of heavy drinking. The symptoms of a hangover include fatigue, headache, nausea, and sometimes vomiting and shakiness.

Death may occur following moderate doses of alcohol taken together with other depressant drugs, such as sleeping pills and tranquilizers, or from an overdose of alcohol as a result of excessive consumption. This kind of consumption has been associated with events such as college fraternity initiations. For example, some college students have been known to participate in the dangerous behaviour of "funnelling," putting a funnel in someone's mouth and pouring liquor into the funnel. This method of drinking can be lethal because it easily provides too much alcohol.

In addition to harming oneself, one also harms others by drinking to excess. Violence and accidents due to alcohol consumption account for approximately 6000 deaths per year in Canada. Not surprisingly, motor vehicle accidents account for a large proportion of these deaths. However, alcohol is also responsible for deaths and injuries resulting from falls, drownings, and fires; on the job accidents, absenteeism from work and illness; and crimes of violence (Canadian Centre on Substance Abuse, 2013a; Gotay et al., 2013). Alcohol may not be the underlying cause of partner violence perpetration, but it intensifies the violence (Graham, Bernards, Wilsnack, & Gmel, 2011). Excess drinking also causes harm to society, including job loss, relationship failure, disintegration of the family unit, and the contribution of deleterious drinking habits to ensuing generations. One of the most serious harms is damage to a growing fetus. **Fetal alcohol spectrum disorder (FASD),** the leading cause of mental retardation in the world, is the name used to describe the range of disabilities caused by prenatal exposure to alcohol (Murthy, Kudlur, George, & Mathew, 2009). These effects are permanent.

Although, as noted above, there are many dire negative consequences to excessive drinking, there may, in fact, be health benefits for light to moderate drinkers. Numerous studies (e.g., Gmel, Gutiahr, & Rehm, 2003; Gunzerath, Faden, Zakhari, & Warren, 2004) have reported that moderate drinking has survival advantages. Specifically, the relationship between alcohol consumption and mortality is depicted in a J-shaped curve, with the lowest mortality occurring when one to two drinks are consumed daily (Gmel et al., 2003; Gunzerath et al., 2004). These protective effects are primarily for coronary heart disease (CHD) and cerebrovascular effects (i.e., ischemic stroke; Rehm et al., 2010). The relative risk of myocardial infarction is reduced by between 25 to 50 percent for men and 20 to 40 percent for women with moderate alcohol consumption, depending on the study cited (Gunzerath et al., 2004).

Researchers believe that consuming alcohol increases levels of high-density lipoprotein (HDL), which is responsible for a decreased risk of heart attacks. The risk of ischemic stroke is

fetal alcohol spectrum disorder (FASD): the name used to describe the range of disabilities caused by prenatal exposure to alcohol; these effects are permanent.

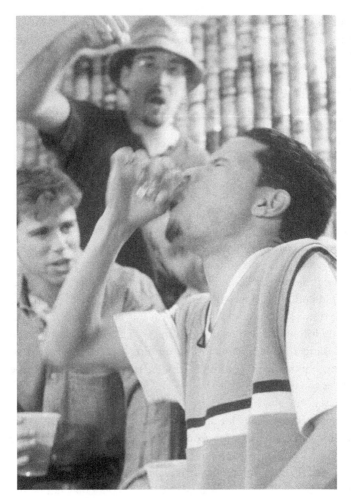

Binge drinking is the leading preventable cause of death among undergraduate students.
Chuck Savage/Flirt/Corbis

reduced for middle-aged and elderly adults, but there may be an increase in risk for young adults who are already more susceptible to hemorrhagic strokes. We should also note that women who drink moderately have an increased risk of death from other causes (e.g., breast cancer and cirrhosis). Other benefits include a lowered risk for gallstones (Walcher et al., 2010), Type 2 diabetes (Hendriks, 2007), and a possible protective factor against cognitive deficits (Lobo et al., 2010). We should point out that red wine was initially believed to have unique survival advantages; now we know that one kind of alcohol does not offer a particular advantage over another kind. Wine, beer, and liquor are all thought to produce the same advantages (Prickett et al., 2004). It is good to remember that while some researchers say the benefits outweigh the risks (e.g., Rehm, Patra, & Taylor, 2007), others suggest the benefits may be overstated (Fillmore, Kerr, & Stockwell, 2006; Nova, Baccan, Veses, Zapatera, & Marcos, 2012).

Explaining Drinking Behaviour

It has been suggested that drinking is commonplace in North America because it is so widely accepted. But perhaps drinking is well accepted because it is so commonplace. Regardless, drunkenness or problem drinking is not acceptable, and it is therefore important to explain why this behaviour occurs. The **disease model** of problem drinking maintains that alcoholism is a disease brought about by the physical properties of alcohol. Jellinek (1960), a pioneer in the field of alcoholism, described

disease model (of problem drinking): a theory suggesting that alcoholism is a disease resulting from the physical properties of alcohol.

a number of different types of alcoholism. For example, **gamma alcoholism** is loss of control once drinking begins, whereas **delta alcoholism** is the inability to abstain. This model, still common in medically focused treatment programs in North America, is closely linked to the 12-step program of treatment (Quinn, Bodenhamer-Davis, & Koch, 2004). The model is not as common in Europe, Australia, or in psychologically based treatment programs.

The **alcohol dependency syndrome model** states that at certain times and for a variety of reasons people do not exercise control over their drinking, and this leads to problem drinking (Edwards & Gross, 1976). A number of elements are said to be essential for alcohol dependency syndrome to develop, including a salience of drink-seeking behaviour (meaning that drinking begins to take priority over all other aspects of life) and an increased tolerance for alcohol. Someone with an increased tolerance for alcohol may gradually become accustomed to going about their daily routine "at blood alcohol levels that would incapacitate the non-tolerant drinker" (Edwards & Gross, 1976, p. 1059). Although this model remains popular in certain circles, it has been criticized because of its emphasis on the physical properties of alcohol and its neglect of the cognitive and social learning aspects of drinking (McMurran, 1994).

Cognitive-physiological models propose that people drink because alcohol influences cognitive functioning, allowing people to escape tension and negative self-evaluations. One of these models, the **tension reduction hypothesis**, maintains that people drink alcohol because of its tension-reducing properties. Although there is little empirical support for this theory, some research suggests that alcohol reduces participants' tension whereas others do not (Kambouropoulos, 2003). One factor that blurs our understanding of the tension reduction hypothesis is expectancy. When one expects a reduction in tension, one is more likely to experience exactly that (Pabst, Baumeister, & Kraus, 2010). Some researchers felt that the tension reduction hypothesis did not incorporate alcohol's effect on physiological responses enough, therefore, they formulated the **stress response dampening effect** which simply states that people who have been drinking do not respond as strongly psychologically or physiologically to stressors. The stress response dampening effect appears in some drinkers, but not in others. For those who did exhibit the effect, they are more likely to become problem drinkers (Sher & Levenson, 1982; Zack, Poulos, Aramakis, Khamba, & MacLeod, 2007). As you would expect, the effect is stronger at higher levels of intoxication (Donohue, Curtin, Patrick, & Lang, 2007). The **self-awareness model** suggests that drinking inhibits the use of normal, complex information-processing strategies, such as memory and information acquisition, making people less self-aware (Battista, Stewart, & Ham, 2010). Decreased self-awareness leads to decreased monitoring of behaviour, resulting in the disinhibition and decrease in self-criticism that often occurs when people are drinking. Simply stated, some people may consume alcohol to avoid self-awareness.

A third cognitive-physiological theory developed to explain drinking behaviour is called **alcohol myopia** (Steele & Josephs, 1990). Alcohol myopia refers to a drinker's decreased ability to process information outside a narrow range (myopia) (Compo et al., 2011). This effect also helps to lower inhibition of impulsive responses. Alcohol myopia is characterized by excessive behaviour (being more friendly or more aggressive, engaging in more risky sexual behaviour, etc.), the tendency to inflate self-evaluations, and *drunken relief* or a tendency to worry less and pay less attention to worries (Griffin, Umstattd, & Usdan, 2010).

The **social learning model** proposes that people drink because they experience positive reinforcement for doing so (e.g., the taste or the effects of alcohol are pleasant) or because they observe others drinking and model this behaviour. For example, you may try drinking because your friends drink, and you may continue to drink in the company of

gamma alcoholism: loss of control once drinking begins.

delta alcoholism: the inability to abstain from alcohol.

alcohol dependency syndrome model: a theory suggesting that for a variety of reasons people do not exercise control over their drinking, and this leads to problem drinking.

tension reduction hypothesis: the hypothesis that people drink alcohol because of its tension-reducing properties.

stress response dampening effect: the hypothesis suggesting that people do not respond as strongly psychologically or physiologically to stressors if they have been drinking.

self-awareness model: the theory that drinking makes people less self-aware because it inhibits the use of normal complex information-processing strategies, such as memory and information acquisition.

alcohol myopia: a drinker's decreased ability to engage in insightful cognitive processing.

social learning model: this theory, when applied to drinking behaviour, proposes that people drink because they experience positive reinforcement for doing so or because they observe others drinking and model the behaviour.

your friends. Or, once you have tried drinking you may like the taste of the beverage or you may notice a change in your behaviour that you like (e.g., you feel less shy after having a drink). Research (Freeman, Friedman, Bartholow, & Wulfert, 2010) has discovered that the mere exposure to alcohol-related contextual cues (e.g., the sight or smell of alcoholic beverages) may reduce the threshold for engaging in behaviours that would otherwise be inhibited (e.g., physical aggression and sexual risk taking).

Social learning theory can explain why people begin to drink, why they continue to drink in moderation, and why some people drink to excess. Excessive drinking may occur because of modelling (your friends are also drinking to excess) or because once you stop drinking you experience negative reinforcement in the form of a hangover or withdrawal symptoms. According to the social learning model, drinking behaviour is learned and can therefore also be unlearned. A number of treatment techniques to help people overcome excessive drinking habits rely on social learning principles.

Preventing and Treating Alcohol Abuse   Attempts to prevent alcohol abuse have taken a number of forms. Public policy and legal approaches include implementing age restrictions for individuals buying or consuming alcohol. Health promotion and education strategies incorporating social influence approaches have been useful in helping adolescents avoid drinking heavily. These may include discussions and films regarding how peers, family members, and the media influence drinking, or modelling and role-playing specific refusal skills (e.g., saying "No thank you, I don't drink") and how to deal with high-risk situations (e.g., Saltz, 2004–2005; Saltz, 2005).

The majority of people stop drinking without treatment (Cunningham, 1999). Authorities in the field of problem drinking prefer to use the term *unassisted change*. This term may be somewhat misleading, because support is likely provided to the individual by many people in an informal manner.

Those who do not obtain help when attempting to stop drinking are far more likely to relapse than those who do seek treatment (Moos & Moos, 2006). Many individuals do seek treatment, however, and the federal and provincial governments combined contribute $14 million annually to the provision of alcohol and drug treatment and rehabilitation (Health Canada, 2003b).

Twelve-step programs such as Alcoholics Anonymous (AA) are extremely popular (Kelly, Stout, Magill, & Tonigan, 2011). Yet this kind of program doesn't seem to be more effective than other formal treatments. Psychotherapy, drug therapy (e.g., disulfiram, commonly known as Antabuse), contingency management, and aversion therapy (e.g., electric shock) have all been used with limited success (Gavel-Cruz & Weinshenker, 2009; Witkiewitz & Marlatt, 2011). However, relapse is a persistent problem with all alcohol treatment approaches. Zwiak et al. (2006) have documented three distinct forms of relapse: negative affect, social pressure, and cue/craving. Women are most likely to have negative affect relapses, whereas men are most likely to relapse due to social pressure. Most often, a relapse will occur within 3 months after the end of treatment. After a year, only about one-third of those who complete a program are still abstinent.

Clinicians often adopt the *stages of change* model for guiding both treatment processes and prevention goals. You may remember this model from chapter 1. If we apply the model to drug use, we note the stages an individual goes through in deciding to use a particular substance:

Pre-contemplation	Not considering use
Contemplation	Thinking about initiating use

Preparation	Intending to use
Action	Initiating use
Maintenance	Continuing to use
Relapse	

For anyone who is not considering alcohol use or anyone who is thinking about initiating use, primary prevention is the key. If, however, an individual is currently using or continuing to use alcohol, a harm reduction strategy is appropriate. An example of a large-scale harm reduction approach was initiated in Edmonton in the 1990s. The Alberta Liquor Control Board allowed early opening hours for a retail outlet in downtown Edmonton. The purpose of the extended hours was to reduce the use of potentially lethal non-beverage alcohol (e.g., shoe polish) by skid-row alcoholics. The objective was not to reduce the consumption of alcohol, but to increase their consumption of potable or safe alcohol (Single, 2005). Whatever an individual's current state, there are specific activities and messages that can be adopted (e.g., implementation of more intensive approaches for those in the preparation, action, or maintenance stages).

Drinking and Driving We mentioned previously that drinking influences our thought processes. Unfortunately, alcohol causes people to think less negatively about drinking and driving (MacDonald, Zanna, & Fong, 1995, 1998; Ortner, MacDonald, & Olmstead, 2003). In Canada, it is illegal to drive with a blood alcohol content of more than 50 mL of alcohol per 100 mL of blood (Canada Safety Council, 2013). The good news is that drinking and driving rates have been decreasing since the 1980s. Moderate drinkers are finding alternate forms of transportation. Unfortunately, heavy drinkers seem to be immune to the anti-drinking-and-driving programs that have been implemented; this group of drivers will get behind the wheel after consuming three or more times the legal limit (CCSA, 2008).

Because judgment and decision making are impaired, it is not surprising that intoxicated individuals are often involved in traffic accidents. After two decades of steadily decreasing numbers of alcohol- and drug-impaired driving charges, the number of charges has been increasing since 2006 (CCSA, 2013). A Canadian study conducted in 2011 found that driving while intoxicated generally declines with age; however, there is a large problem with younger drivers. Indeed, young drivers are even more likely to drive after cannabis use than after consuming alcohol. Despite perceptions that drug use is less harmful to drivers, there is growing evidence that drug impairment is also a major contributor to collisions (CCSA, 2008). Twelve percent of 15- to 24-year-old drivers have driven under the influence of cannabis, a drug that compromises visual ability and reaction time and 10 percent of the same age group have driven after drinking (CCSA, 2013). A study conducted in 2009 showed that drugs, often combined with alcohol, were detected in up to 40 percent of fatally injured drivers (CCSA, 2013).

Illicit Drug Use

Compared with those who succumb to the effects of smoking cigarettes and drinking alcohol, relatively fewer people die from the effects of illegal drugs. For example, cocaine, the most lethal of the illicit drugs, kills only one person for every 1000 killed by tobacco products (Rouse, 1998). Of course, even one death from illicit drugs is too many. Illicit drugs present certain risks not found with legal drugs, regardless of pharmacological effects. People purchasing illicit drugs may be told they are buying one drug but receive another,

As of May 1, 2009, drivers in Ontario convicted of an impaired driving offence under the Criminal Code of Canada or suspended for registering a blood alcohol concentration of .05 to .08 three or more times in a 5-year period will be required to install an ignition interlock device in their vehicle. The ignition interlock device is an in-car alcohol breath screening device that prevents a vehicle from starting if it detects a blood alcohol concentration over a pre-set limit of .02 (i.e., 20 mg of alcohol per 100 mL of blood). The device is located inside the vehicle, near the driver's seat, and is connected to the engine's ignition system (Ontario, Ministry of Transportation, 2009).
Queen's Printer for Ontario

illegally manufactured drugs may be contaminated with toxic chemicals, and users never really know what drug or how much of a particular drug they are taking.

How prevalent is the use of illicit drugs? In Canada in 2009, the use of at least one of six illicit drugs (i.e., cannabis, cocaine or crack, speed, ecstasy, hallucinogens, or heroin) was 11 percent (Health Canada, 2010b). The rate of use by males (14.7 percent) was almost double than for females (7.6 percent), and the prevalence of use was more than three times higher among youth (27.3 percent) than adults (7.9 percent) (Health Canada, 2010b). Those with less education, those who lived in low-income households, and those who were single and were in younger age groups were more likely to be drug dependent. Of course, these factors do not occur in isolation. For example, young people are more likely to be single and to have comparatively low incomes. Those who were born in Canada were three times more likely than immigrants to be alcohol or drug dependent (Statistics Canada, 2004a).

Health Canada (2013a) reports that the use of illicit drugs is decreasing. In 1989, 6.5 percent of Canadians reported using cannabis during the previous year; by 2004, the figure had risen to 14.1 percent, but has decreased to 9.1 percent (Health Canada, 2013a). By 2008, almost half of all Canadians had used cannabis at least once in their lives (CCSA, 2010). Cannabis use is most prevalent in younger age groups and peaks at ages 18 and 19 (38 percent in 2004, but down to 26 percent in 2009).

The most recent survey of illicit drug use reports that in 2011 the most frequently used drug after cannabis in the previous 12 months was cocaine or crack (0.9 percent), followed by ecstasy (0.7 percent). Hallucinogens (e.g., LSD and PCP) have been used by

0.9 percent of the population, followed by speed (0.5 percent) and methamphetamine (unable to estimate due to high sampling variability) (Health Canada, 2013a). Those most likely to have tried other illicit drugs were 35- to 44-year-old adults (Statistics Canada, 2004b). The distribution was bell-shaped around this age group, with 25- to 34-year olds the next highest age range, followed by 45- to 54-year olds. We now turn our attention to the health problems associated with some of the more common illicit drugs.

Cannabis   Canadian youth are as likely to use cannabis as they are tobacco (Health Canada, 2000). Cannabis, or marijuana, is composed of the leaves, flowers, and small branches of *Cannabis sativa*, a plant that grows in almost every climate. Delta-9-tetrahydrocannabinol (THC) is the intoxicating ingredient of cannabis. Is smoking cannabis a potential health hazard? Cannabis use leads to disturbances in short-term memory, judgment, and time perception (WHO, 2006). When large doses are consumed, heart rate is increased. A rapid heart rate may lead to health hazards for people who have coronary problems. Long-term use is a risk factor for a diagnosis of schizophrenia and the development of psychotic symptoms. This is biologically plausible given that the cannabinoid system interacts with the dopamine neurotransmitter systems and psychotic disorders involve disturbances in these systems (Degenhardt & Hall, 2006; Fernandez-Espejo, Viveros, Nunez, Elllenbroek, & de Fonseca, 2009).

As well, smoking cannabis leads to many of the same respiratory problems as smoking tobacco, as both contain many of the same carcinogens. However, those who smoke cannabis are exposed to unfiltered smoke, larger puffs, deeper inhalation, and breath-holding, suggesting that negative respiratory effects may occur sooner than when smoking filtered cigarettes (CCSA, 2010).

Cannabis has been used in medical situations because of its physiological effects. It has been used as an appetite stimulant for AIDS patients and has been used medically to treat glaucoma, to relieve pain, and to prevent the vomiting and nausea associated with chemotherapy (Ware, Doyle, Woods, Lynch, & Clark, 2003; WHO, 2006).

Why do people use cannabis in spite of the aforementioned side effects? They do so to experience euphoria, a sense of well-being, relaxation, and heightened sexual responsiveness. The psychological effects of cannabis seem to depend, in part, on the setting and on personal expectation. It is not surprising that those who attain these psychological effects are usually experienced cannabis smokers who expect to attain them.

Hallucinogens   MDMA (3,4-methylenedioxymethylamphetamine), most often referred to as "ecstasy", is a derivative of methamphetamine, but people use it for its mild hallucinogenic qualities. Typically, MDMA causes feelings of tranquility and empathy for others resulting from the rapid release of the neurotransmitter serotonin. The effects of MDMA usually last up to 8 hours. Other **hallucinogens** such as LSD (lysergic acid diethylamide, commonly referred to as "acid") and PCP (phencyclidine), and psilocybin wield more complex effects on neurotransmitters (Halberstadt & Geyer, 2011). These drugs dramatically affect perception, emotions, and mental processes. As the name suggests, they can cause hallucinations. Hallucinations not only can elicit feelings of euphoria, but can also cause one to feel threatened. This fear, anxiety, or panic can cause the user to behave quite violently. More often, however, users report a sense of well-being and heightened tactile sensations and emotions. The effects of LSD last up to 12 hours, while the effects of PCP may last as long as several days when taken in a single dose. However, the effects of high doses of PCP have been known in some cases to last from 10 days to 2 weeks (Tzamazis & Stough, 2000). *Salvia divinorum* is becoming popular with youth and

hallucinogens: drugs that dramatically affect perception, emotions, and mental processes; can cause hallucinations.

its prevalence was examined for the first time in 2009. Approximately 1.6 percent of Canadians over the age of 15 had tried salvia, but 7.3 percent of youth had tried this legal hallucinogen (Health Canada, 2009a).

Short-term physiological reactions to hallucinogens include increased blood pressure, heart rate, and temperature; dilated pupils; impaired motor skills and coordination; dizziness; and nausea. Larger doses can cause convulsions, coma, and death. Persistent speech problems, memory loss, severe depression and anxiety, and social withdrawal have also been noted following prolonged use.

Cocaine

stimulant: a drug that increases alertness, decreases appetite and the need for sleep, and may produce intense feelings of euphoria and a strong sense of well-being.

Cocaine   Cocaine is a **stimulant** drug, extracted from the coca plant indigenous to the Andes Mountains in South America. Cocaine is most often snorted through the nasal passages, but is also smoked and "freebased"—that is, injected intravenously. Cocaine provides a sense of well-being, heightened attention, and a powerful euphoria. This effect lasts approximately 15 to 30 minutes. When the effects wear off, the user is often left with a feeling of fatigue, sluggishness, and a strong desire to "use" again. Increased doses do not make the euphoria last longer and can endanger the cardiovascular system.

Studies exploring long-term cocaine use among young adults have found mixed results regarding the relationship between heavy use of cocaine and various cardiovascular risk factors (Health Canada, 2009b). Using cocaine causes blood vessels to constrict, heart rate to increase, and blood pressure to speed up suddenly. It can also trigger cardiac arrhythmia. These factors may cause a stroke or myocardial infarction. Physiological withdrawal symptoms do not accompany cessation of cocaine use, but psychological dependence does seem to occur.

Prescription Drug Misuse   Illicit use of pharmaceuticals is a growing problem in Canada (CCSA, 2013). Commonly abused prescription medication includes opioid pain relievers (e.g., fentanyl, Percodan, Demerol, Oxycodone, and OxyNEO), stimulants (e.g., Ritalin, Concerta, Adderall, and Dexedrine), and tranquilizers and sedatives (e.g., benzodiazepine, Valium, Ativan, and Xanax). At least 7 percent of Canadian youth used prescription medication in the past year for the sole purpose of getting high according to a 2008–2009 study (CCSA, 2013).

Of particular concern is the misuse of prescription opioids. Prescription opioid-related deaths doubled in just over 10 years in Ontario, from 13.7 deaths per million people in 1991 to 27.2 deaths per million in 2004 (CCSA, 2013). The College of Physicians and Surgeons of Ontario recently called the misuse of prescription opioids a "public health crisis" (as cited in Kotalik, 2012). Similarly, some First Nations communities found addiction problems to be so severe that they declared a "state of crisis" (Meadows, 2009). In the journal *Canadian Family Physician*, Kotalik (2012) stresses that physicians are obliged to relieve pain, but that this obligation must be balanced with the responsibility not to create opportunities for drug trafficking and the addiction of their own patient and the addiction of others. Canada is the second largest consumer of prescription opioids. Indeed, North America consumes almost 80 percent of the world's opioids (CCSA, 2013).

Preventing and Treating Illicit Drug Use   Programs aimed at preventing teenage drug abuse are similar to those aimed at preventing smoking. Children and adolescents can be educated through the schools and mass media about the deleterious effects of drug abuse. These educational programs (e.g., DrugsNot4Me) are based on social influence and life skills training methods that teach children and adolescents how to resist starting to use drugs (Fraguela, Martin, & Trinanes, 2003; Government of Canada, 2013; Lloyd, Joyce, Hurry, & Ashton, 2000). A second preventive technique that is common in all Western countries is the use of laws to limit the legal access to drugs. Unfortunately, this approach may produce other social problems (e.g., a large criminal enterprise). Finally, encouraging parents to monitor their children has been found to reduce the likelihood that children will try drugs (Lloyd et al., 2000).

Treatment programs for drug abuse are similar to those for alcohol abuse. In fact, it's not uncommon for formal treatment centres to treat both forms of abuse. The most promising treatment approaches include both behavioural and cognitive methods, such as self-management techniques (Dutra et al., 2008; Margolis & Zweben, 2011). Unfortunately, as with the treatment of alcohol and smoking, there is a high rate of relapse, and the first 6 months after treatment are critical. Many drug treatment programs now include follow-up or "booster" sessions to help people remain abstinent.

The use of drugs and alcohol directly results in numerous health consequences, including indirect health consequences. For instance, individuals who are intoxicated are more likely to engage in risky behaviours, such as unsafe sexual practices (e.g., MacDonald, Fong, Zanna, & Martineau, 2000).

UNSAFE SEXUAL BEHAVIOURS

The negative effects of unsafe sexual behaviours are numerous. In addition to unplanned pregnancies, unsafe sexual behaviours can lead to serious health consequences such as sexually transmitted diseases (STDs), infertility, and HIV infection. Results from a 2005 Ipsos Reid Canada study of 14- to 17-year olds found that 27 percent of teens were sexually active with an average of 2.5 lifetime partners. The last time these teens had sex 76 percent had used a condom (Frappier et al., 2008). That's up from 50 percent reported by the Canadian Youth, Sexual Health and HIV/AIDS Study conducted in 2002 (Health Canada, 2002).

Somewhat more disappointing results are found with American youth. In a nationwide U.S. survey of high school students, 34.2 percent were currently sexually active and 38.9 percent of currently sexually active students had not used a condom during their last sexual intercourse (Eaton et al., 2010).

Approximately 340 million incident cases of sexually transmissible infections occur worldwide each year (Warner, Gallo, & Macaluso, 2012). Given this, why do people not use condoms when engaging in intercourse? A national survey of grade 9 and 11 students attempted to gain insight into this question (Health Canada, 2002). The students reported not using condoms because they did not expect to have sex, they already used some other method of birth control, they had too much alcohol/drugs, they did not want to spoil the moment, they did not like to or know how to use a condom, they did not have enough money to buy condoms, they had difficulty discussing condom use with their partner, they did not want to show distrust of their partner, or they felt they had a faithful (safe) partner.

Research conducted with gay and bisexual males residing in Ontario finds that anxiety, both in terms of social anxiety and stressful life events, is a contributing factor to unsafe sex (Calzavara et al., 2012; Hart & Heimberg, 2005). Another factor cited in the previous studies for the failure to use condoms was insufficient knowledge of HIV/STDs (e.g., Boroditsky, Fisher, & Sand, 1995; Calzavara, Bullock, Myers, Marshall, & Cockerill, 1999). Trevor Hart, now at Ryerson University, and his colleagues report that recent immigrants to Canada are less knowledgeable about HIV than non-immigrants, but engage in a similar amount of risky sexual behaviour as non-immigrants (Zhuk, Hart, & James, 2006).

We know that individuals who are intoxicated are more likely to engage in unsafe sexual practices (e.g., Griffin et al., 2010; MacDonald et al., 2000). This is, at least in part, due to the effect that alcohol has on decision making. People also state that they make poor decisions in the "heat of the moment." A recent study has examined the effect of sexual arousal on judgment and decision making. Ariely and Loewenstein (2006) had male college students indicate their willingness to engage in unsafe sex when sexually aroused (arousal was induced by self-stimulation). Participants were also asked how appealing they found a wide range of sexual stimuli and activities, and they were asked about their willingness to engage in morally questionable behaviour in order to obtain sexual gratification.

Ariely and Loewenstein report that sexual arousal acts as an amplifier of sorts. That is, a far wider range of activities was deemed sexually appealing when the participants were sexually aroused. In addition, the motivation to engage in sex decreased the relative importance of other considerations, including protecting oneself or one's partner against unwanted pregnancy or STD.

A variety of theoretical approaches have been used in an attempt to understand sexual and reproductive health behaviours using a decision-making framework (see Fisher & Fisher, 1998, for a review of these theories). Some of these theories have been developed outside the domain of sexual and reproductive health and applied within it—for example, the health belief model (Rosenstock, Strecher, & Becker, 1994), the theory of reasoned action (Fishbein & Ajzen, 1975), the theory of planned behaviour (Ajzen, 1991), and the stages of change model (Prochaska & Velicer, 1997). You may remember reading about these theories in chapter 1. Other theories have been developed and applied specifically within the area of sexuality and reproductive health, including the sexual behaviour sequence model (Byrne, 1977), the AIDS risk reduction model (Catania, Kegeles, & Coates, 1990), and the information-motivation-behavioural skills model (Fisher & Fisher, 1998).

information-motivation-behavioural skills model: a theory maintaining that there are a number of steps one must go through to successfully achieve safe-sex practices.

The **information-motivation-behavioural skills model** (Fisher & Fisher, 1998; Fisher, Fisher, & Shuper, 2009) maintains that there are a number of steps individuals must go through before they will engage in safe-sex practices. First, they must recognize and accept that they are sexually active. Second, they must create a "sexual and reproductive health agenda." In other words, individuals must be motivated to engage in safe-sex practices to prevent pregnancy and infection. Third, individuals must be capable of engaging in behaviours that fulfill this agenda. For example, they must be able to negotiate cooperation in contraceptive and condom use with a partner. If cooperation is not forthcoming, the individual must be able to exit the situation.

This model also acknowledges that it is frequently necessary to engage in public behaviour regarding sexual and reproductive health (e.g., condom purchasing, HIV testing). To maintain safe sexual practices over time, individuals must have this behaviour reinforced. Finally, individuals must be able to adjust sexual and reproductive health behaviour scripts appropriately as their needs change over time. For example, it may be appropriate to shift from condom use to non-use in a monogamous relationship after a window period, after mutual STD and HIV antibody testing, and after reaching an agreement about how to continue mutual monogamy and how violations of this agreement will be handled.

OBESITY

Obesity has been recognized by the World Health Organization as one of the top 10 global health problems. It is predicted that obesity could have as great an impact on health as smoking (Kelner & Helmuth, 2003; Statistics Canada, 2002). Woldwide obesity has nearly doubled since 1980 (WHO, 2013). Currently, 65 percent of the world's population live in countries where more people die from obesity than from being underweight (WHO, 2013). In fact, more than 10 percent of the world's population is obese (WHO, 2013). The Canadian Health Measures Survey indicates that, in 2009, 24 percent of our adult population were obese (Shields, Carroll, & Ogden, 2011). This compares to 34 percent of the population in the United States. In both countries, the number of obese adults is increasing rapidly. Since 1986, for example, the adult obesity rate has increased 10 percent. Since 1986, the increase was highest among men aged 60 to 74 and among women aged 20 to 39 (Shields et al., 2011). The rates for youngsters are also increasing dramatically. The prevalence of obesity in children has tripled since 1981 (Janssen, 2013). In Canada, 13 percent of those aged 6 to 11 and 10 percent of those aged 12 to 17 were classified as obese (Roberts, Shields, de Groh, Aziz, & Gilbert, 2012). This equates to 7 million obese adults and 600 000 obese school-aged children in Canada (Janssen, 2013). The highest levels of obesity occur in the Maritimes and the northern Territories, while the lowest occur in British Columbia. Figure 6-6 provides a map indicating the prevalence of obesity among all Canadians by province.

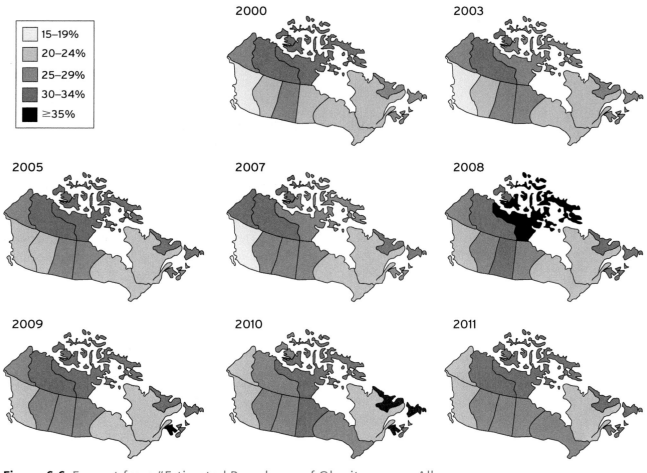

Figure 6-6 Excerpt from "Estimated Prevalence of Obesity among All Canadians by Province, 2000-2012"

Source: Gotay, C., Katzmarzyk, P., Janssen, I., Dawson, M., Aminoltejari, K., & Bartley, N. (2013). Updating the Canadian obesity maps: An epidemic in progress. *Canadian Journal of Public Health, 104* (1). Retrieved from cancerprevent.ca/sites/cancerprevent.ca/files/documents/Obesity-in-Canadian-adults_2000-2012-new.pdf.

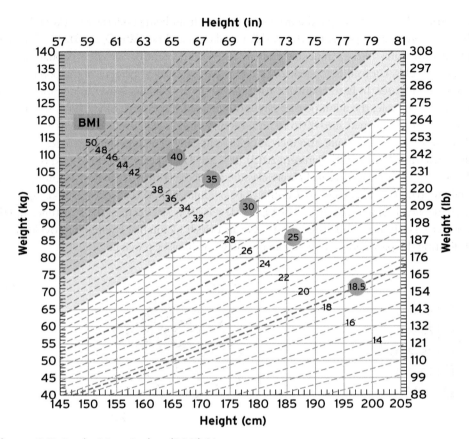

Figure 6-7 Body Mass Index (BMI) Nomogram

Source: Health Canada (2014). *Canadian guidelines for body weight classification in adults.* Reproduced with the permission of the Minister of Public Works and Government Services Canada.

What exactly is obesity? **Obesity** refers to an excess of body fat that may impair health (WHO, 2013). The most commonly used measure of obesity is the **body mass index (BMI)**. Obesity is defined as a BMI of 30.0 or greater (Health Canada, 2014; WHO, 2013). To determine your BMI, refer to Figure 6-7. To ascertain the health risk associated with your BMI, refer to Table 6-1.

Table 6-1 Health Risk Classification According to Body Mass Index (BMI)

BMI	Classification	Risk of Developing Health Problems
<18.5	Underweight	Increased
18.5–24.9	Normal weight	Least
25.0–29.9	Overweight	Increased
30.0–34.9	Obese class I	High
35.0–39.9	Obese class II	Very high
>40.0	Obese class III(Morbid obesity)	Extremely high

Source: Health Canada (2014). *Canadian guidelines for body weight classification in adults.* Reproduced with the permission of the Minister of Public Works and Government Services Canada.

Keep in mind that, although the BMI estimates total body fat, it may not be accurate for selected populations (e.g., the elderly, certain ethnic groups, and persons with large muscle mass). For example, Arnold Schwarzenegger's BMI index might suggest that he is obese. However, we know better and we would suggest that he is fit rather than fat. More complex methods (e.g., densitometry) are available to professionals who require a more accurate measurement of body fat.

Generally speaking, as one's BMI increases so does one's risk of early mortality. A large prospective study following more than 1 million adults in the United States for 14 years documented that participants with a BMI of 40 or above had a relative risk of death two to six times that of their thinner counterparts with a BMI of 24 (Calle, Thun, Petrelli, Rodriguez, & Heath, 1999). Other studies report similar findings (Flegal, Kit, Orpana, & Graubard, 2013; Katzmarzyk, Craig, & Bouchard, 2001). For example, Katzmarzyk and colleagues (2001) found that the relative risk of mortality in obese class I adults increased by 25 percent and in class II and III obese adults by 196 percent in a national Canadian sample. However, we must point out that the relationship between body weight (BMI) and increased risk of death is actually J- or U-shaped. That is, those who are underweight have a slightly increased risk of mortality compared to those classified as normal weight (e.g., Fontaine, Redden, Wang, Westfall, & Allison, 2003). In essence, the relative risk of death is highest among the thinnest and the heaviest individuals in our society.

Obesity helps create a burden that is economic and emotional as well as physical. The physical ailments associated with obesity that contribute most to premature death are hypertension, type 2 (adult onset) diabetes, cardiovascular disease, lung disease, various forms of cancer, and gallbladder disease (Janssen, 2013). Obesity also predisposes people to arthritis, gout, sleep apnea, deep vein thrombosis, complications in pregnancy, and complications following surgery (Janssen, 2013).

The economic burden of obesity in Canada for the year 2006 accounted for $3.9 billion in direct health care costs (e.g., hospitalizations, medications, physician and emergency room visits) and $3.2 billion in indirect costs (e.g., costs related to disability and lost productivity due to illness or premature (Janssen, 2013). Personal costs are also prevalent. One prospective study documented that overweight adolescents were less likely to marry, had lower household incomes, and completed significantly fewer months of high school (despite equal grades) than their non-overweight counterparts (Gortmaker, Must, Perrin, Sobol, & Dietz, 1993). Prejudice and discrimination when seeking college admissions, employment, health care, or a place to live are also consequences experienced by those who are overweight (Puhl & Heuer, 2009; Wadden, Womble, Stunkard, & Anderson, 2002).

Despite these obstacles, some studies report that there is no evidence of an effect of being overweight on self-esteem in the general population (Wadden et al., 2002). Overall, however, the research points to a bidirectional link between being overweight and depression. A review of research to date indicates that obese people have a 55 percent increased risk of becoming depressed, whereas depressed people have a 58 percent increased risk of becoming obese (Luppino et al., 2010). This trend occurs in both men and women (Luppino et al., 2010).

The statement "genes load the gun, the environment pulls the trigger" (Bray, as cited in Wadden, Brownell, & Foster, 2002, p. 512) summarizes the contributions of genetics and the environment to obesity. Genes are partly responsible for variance in BMI (Price, 2002). Genes also contribute to individual differences in basal metabolic rate (people with naturally lower basal metabolic rates burn fewer calories), in amount of weight gained after overeating, and in body fat distribution (Wadden et al., 2002).

Some individuals are simply born with a genetic predisposition to obesity, and our current cultural environment contributes to its exhibition.

Biological Factors That Contribute to Obesity

Heredity   Twin studies, adoption studies, and family studies indicate that genes contribute to the development of obesity. The strength of the heritability of obesity is akin to the strength of heritability of height (Friedman, 2003). Maes, Neale, and Eaves (1997) reviewed the literature on the familial resemblance of BMI. Based on data from more than 25 000 twin pairs and 50 000 biological and adoptive family members, the following correlations were computed: 0.74 for monozygotic twins, 0.32 for dizygotic twins, 0.25 for siblings, 0.19 for parent–offspring pairs, and 0.06 for adoptive relatives. These figures provide convincing evidence that there is substantial heritability for obesity. Maes and colleagues conclude that genes account for approximately 67 percent of individual differences in BMI. The results of other studies corroborate these conclusions (e.g., Bulik, Sullivan, & Kendler, 2003).

Hormones and the Brain   The biological system that regulates our food intake and energy expenditure is extraordinarily complex and not well understood. Consider that over a period of 10 years, an average individual consumes approximately 10 million calories. Typically, a person will experience only a slight change of weight in that 10 years. For such a slight weight variation, food consumption must be within 0.17 percent of energy expenditure over the entire decade (Friedman, 2003). Achieving this balance is quite an accomplishment; it is highly unlikely that a nutritionist counting calories could be so precise in matching food consumption with energy expenditure.

set-point theory: the idea that the body contains a set-point that works like a thermostat; when a person gains weight, biological control mechanisms diminish caloric intake; when a person loses weight, similar mechanisms increase hunger levels until the weight returns to its ideal or target level.

leptin: hormone that responds to weight loss by increasing hunger levels until the person's weight returns to its ideal or target level.

How does our body maintain such a constant weight? The **set-point theory** proposes that the body contains a set-point that works like a thermostat regulating heat in a home. When one gains weight, powerful biological control mechanisms diminish caloric intake. When one loses weight, similar mechanisms respond by increasing hunger levels until the person's weight returns to its ideal or target level. In 1994, a key element of this homeostatic system was discovered—the hormone **leptin** (Zhang et al., 1994). Leptin reports to the neurons of the hypothalamus (a key regulatory centre in the brain) whether there are sufficient fat stores in the body or whether additional energy is needed. Leptin is produced by fat cells; therefore, when fat stores increase, the body's level of leptin increases. This, in turn, suppresses the neurons that stimulate hunger and activates those that reduce food intake. When there is a decrease in body fat the reverse occurs—leptin levels decrease, resulting in stimulation of appetite and a reduction of energy expenditure (Friedman, 2000, 2003).

If this homeostatic system can maintain weight within a relatively narrow range, why are some individuals obese and others are not? There appear to be individual differences in sensitivity to leptin. It may be that obese individuals are simply less sensitive to leptin or that they are leptin-resistant (Friedman, 2003). This would explain why obese people tend to have more leptin in their bodies. They must produce more of the hormone to compensate for their lack of sensitivity (Nakamura et al., 2000). In very rare conditions, individuals may lack the hormone leptin completely (see Case 6-1).

The hormone ghrelin is also involved in hunger. Ghrelin is produced by cells in the stomach wall. The primary function of ghrelin is to tell the brain to stimulate appetite; thus, it seems to be involved in the short-term regulation of food intake (Benso, Casanueva, Ghigo, & Granata, 2013). The neuropeptide, galanin, is now being studied to determine its role in obesity (Barson, Morganstern, & Leibowitz, 2010).

Psychosocial Factors That Contribute to Obesity

Hunger and eating behaviour are not controlled solely by biological factors. In fact, our biology is now almost maladaptive in our environment of food abundance and sedentariness (Hebebrand & Hinney, 2009). Currently, social norms and values serve to reinforce behaviours that promote obesity (Herman & Polivy, 2005). We associate food with celebrations, rewards, and social occasions. Therefore, it is not surprising that we turn to food when anxious or depressed (Thoburn & Hammond-Meyer, 2004).

Stress and Eating   Stress affects people differently, and consequently it also affects people's eating behaviours differently (O'Connor, Jones, & Conner, 2011). Approximately half the population will eat more when feeling stress, and the other half will eat less (Ogden, 2010; Willenbring, Levine, & Morley, 1986). People of average weight who are not preoccupied with food often ignore or misinterpret physiological cues to hunger and therefore eat less. In contrast, stress can cause dieters to lose control, causing disinhibition or counterregulation and, consequently, overeating (e.g., Heatherton, Herman, & Polivy, 1992; Polivy, 1996).

Stress may also influence the food choices people make. Individuals experiencing daily hassles, ranging from a job interview or public talk to being late for a meeting or having an argument, report that their eating habits are compromised (O'Connor, Jones, Conner, McMillan, & Ferguson, 2008). There is a tendency for people experiencing stress to increase their fat consumption and reduce their consumption of fruits and vegetables. As well, snacking increases in times of stress (O'Connor & O'Connor, 2004).

Sociocultural Factors That Contribute to Obesity

When we look through a broader lens, there is also clear evidence that our eating and activity habits are influenced by the people around us. When people move from a less developed country to a more modern country where food, particularly rich food, is plentiful, they tend to gain weight. For most immigrants to Canada, "the probability of being overweight or (for women) obese is lower on arrival than for comparable native-born Canadians, but increases gradually with additional years in their new country" (McDonald & Kennedy, 2005, p. 2479). The more likely a group is to acculturate, or take on characteristically Canadian ways of living, the narrower the new immigrants' health advantage with respect to comparable native-born Canadians. Chinese Canadian communities are the most geographically

CASE 6-1 HORMONES CONTRIBUTE TO REGULATION OF BODY WEIGHT

Two young English girls have become famous as a result of their obesity. The older, 9-year-old cousin had legs so large she could barely walk. The younger cousin could consume more than 1100 calories at a single meal. That's half of what the average adult will eat in a day! The girls were found to lack the weight-regulating hormone leptin. In order to treat their obesity, the girls were given leptin injections. After only a few such injections their calorie consumption decreased by a dramatic 84 percent. Their new appetites were now similar to those of other children of their age. The outcome is amazing. Both girls are now at body weights considered normal for their size and are enjoying normal lives (Farooqui et al., 2002; Friedman, 2003).

concentrated and least likely to acculturate. It follows then that immigrants of Chinese ethnicity exhibit little change in weight with increasing years in Canada.

On a more immediate level, we are influenced by our parents' eating behaviours (Keski-Rahkonen et al., 2005). Parents may influence their children's eating behaviours by encouraging them to overeat. Or, on a more positive note, parental presence at mealtime may lead to better food choices and less likelihood of adolescents skipping breakfast (Videon & Manning, 2003). The affluence of your family will also contribute to your weight, or it will if you are a female. In general, the more affluent a woman is, the less likely she is to be obese. For men, those in low- to middle-income households were the least likely to be obese (Statistics Canada, 2005c).

Environmental and Hunger Cues   Most of us live a lifestyle that is laden with time pressures. We are exposed to an environment bursting with highly advertised, highly accessible foods (e.g., fast-food restaurants, buffet restaurants, food franchises in school cafeterias) (Cawley, 2011; Hill, Wyatt, Reed, & Peters, 2003). Is it any wonder that we respond to these cues by eating more prepackaged and fast foods? The way we respond to cues in our environment led Schachter (1971) to propose the **internality–externality hypothesis**. This hypothesis asserts that, in people of normal weight, feelings of hunger and satiety come from within in the form of internal stimuli (e.g., hunger pangs or feelings of fullness).

In contrast, obese people are more likely to respond to external stimuli (e.g., time of day, smell, or sight of food) in determining their level of hunger. Although highly influential, there has not been consistent support for this hypothesis. For example, Rodin (1981) discovered that internal sensitivity is not a characteristic unique to normal-weight persons. Likewise, externality can lead to overeating in everyone, regardless of weight category. Remick, Polivy, and Pliner (2009) suggest that there may be an evolutionary explanation for these findings. To further understand the relationship between external stimuli and eating behaviour, Herman and Polivy have focused much of their research on this topic (see Focus on Canadian Research 6-2).

Another external stimulus that influences eating behaviour is the presence of others. There are three psychological explanations regarding the effects of the presence of others on food intake (Herman, Roth, & Polivy, 2003). Briefly, the **social facilitation approach** suggests that when people eat in groups, they tend to eat more than when alone. The **modelling or matching effect** states that people tend to eat as much or as little as do those in their presence (Herman, Koenig-Nobert, Peterson, & Polivy, 2005). The **impression management approach** states that when people believe they are being observed or evaluated, they will suppress eating (Herman et al., 2003).

Prevention and Treatment of Obesity

Clearly, prevention is the best way to attack the current obesity epidemic. Pi-Sunyer (2003) reports that education at two levels is essential. On one level, we must educate the public. Campaigns like those for smoking should be launched. Also because we know that people consume more energy than they expend, Hill et al. (2003) advocate that only a small reduction in net energy input will prevent further increases in obesity rates.

Based on the average weight gain in the U.S. population of 1.8 to 2.0 pounds per year, Hill determined that on average people have an energy gap of 100 kcal a day. To reduce this energy gap, we should either reduce our caloric intake by 100 kcal or find a way to expend more energy. Adding 2000 to 2500 extra steps throughout the day would burn

---

internality–externality hypothesis: assertion that in people of normal weight, feelings of hunger and satiety come from within, in the form of internal stimuli (e.g., hunger pangs or feelings of fullness), whereas obese people are more likely to determine their level of hunger in response to external stimuli (e.g., time of day, smell, or sight of food).

social facilitation approach: this approach states that people tend to eat more when in the presence of others.

modelling or matching effect: people tend to eat the same amount as those in their presence.

impression management approach: when people believe they are being observed they will eat less than when they believe no one is watching.

Eating Behaviour: Can You Restrain Yourself?

Peter Herman and Janet Polivy, both of the University of Toronto, have spent more than 30 years studying eating behaviour. In 1975, Herman and Mack proposed the **restraint theory** of eating behaviour. According to their theory, external sensitivity is linked to *restrained eating* (or strict dieting), rather than to body weight. When one is preoccupied with body-weight norms, food consumption will swing between restrained eating and overindulging.

In a typical study (e.g., Herman & Polivy, 1980), participants are classified as either high or low on restraint based on their responses to questions, such as "How often are you dieting?" and "Do you give too much time and thought to food?" Initially, the participants are given food to consume, for example, a milkshake. Subsequently, participants take part in a "taste test," and they are allowed to "taste" as much food (e.g., ice cream) as they like from the selection that is offered. The researchers are interested only in the amount of food consumed, and each plate of cookies or dish of ice cream is measured after the participant is finished "tasting." The restrained eaters, who frequently think about food and are more likely to be dieting, consume more food than do the *unrestrained eaters* (those who are not trying to limit their food intake).

Subsequent studies have determined that restrained eaters are more sensitive to and reactive to food cues than are unrestrained eaters. Consequently, their appetites increase in response to these cues, and they will consume more food than if not exposed to such cues. Both cognitive and olfactory cues produce increased intake of food by restrained eaters compared to unrestrained eaters. In 2008, Herman and Polivy proposed the sensory-normative distinction theory, which states that sensory cues have a powerful effect on obese and/or restrained eaters, whereas normative cues (e.g., portion size) affect everyone (i.e., everyone eats more when the portion of food they are presented is large).

Variations on this research have discovered that restrained participants' own hunger ratings can be affected by fictitious hunger reports, but their actual food consumption remains unaltered (Herman, Fitzgerald, & Polivy, 2003). Another variation determined that restrained eaters who were led to believe that they weighed 5 pounds more than they actually did consumed more food during a subsequent "taste test" than did those who were provided with their true weight or a weight that was 5 pounds lighter than their actual weight. The authors contend that lowered self-worth and a worsening of mood experienced by those who were led to believe they were heavier than they really were led them to abandon their dietary control and overindulge (McFarlane, Polivy, & Herman, 1998).

Herman and Polivy's research also highlights the dynamic connection between dieting and overeating. One of their studies investigated the effect of anticipated food deprivation on food consumption in restrained and unrestrained eaters. Participants completed a taste test immediately after being assigned to either a diet condition (in which they expected to diet for a week) or a control condition (no diet). Unrestrained eaters consumed the same amount of food no matter what condition they had been assigned to. In contrast, restrained eaters had greater food intake when assigned to the diet condition than when assigned to the control condition. These and similar findings indicate that restricting one's eating or dieting to lose weight may have unanticipated deleterious effects (e.g., eating binges and preoccupation with food and eating). In a recent article, Polivy and Herman (2006) provide an evolutionary explanation for why restraint is a maladaptive strategy to lose weight. To oversimplify, we have evolved to abandon our self-control when foods are abundant or when there is no immediate shortage of food. They conclude that to avoid obesity, one should choose to eat foods in moderation, pay attention to satiety cues, and avoid overeating. In essence, a healthful, balanced diet is the best approach to "dieting."

100 calories for most people. Alternatively, eating 15 percent less a day by reducing portion sizes should accomplish the same goal.

Childhood obesity has become increasingly prevalent over the past 30 years. Moreover, if obesity begins in childhood then obesity in adulthood is likely to be more severe; therefore, we should take extra steps to ensure that we are giving the best possible start for our children. A recent Canadian study discovered that exclusive breastfeeding for

restraint theory: an explanation for eating behaviour claiming that external sensitivity is linked to restrained eating (or strict dieting), rather than to body weight, and that overeating is more likely in people who restrain their eating.

6 months, an adequate number of hours of sleep each night, and being physically active all contribute to a reduced likelihood of obesity for children (Shi, de Groh, & Morrison, 2013). Of course, we must also encourage children to make healthy food choices and to exert energy (Ball & McCargar, 2003). Programs that do exactly this are currently being implemented (e.g., the Action Schools! BC–Healthy Eating Program in British Columbia; Living Schools in Ontario, and others). On another level, Pi-Sunyer (2003) states that more health care professionals should become equipped to educate and treat obese people.

Health care professionals should also advise their patients that getting more sleep might also help them lose or maintain their current weight. Not getting enough good quality sleep either because of not allowing oneself the time for a full night sleep or because of insomnia, anxiety, shift work, or late-night screen time is problematic (McNeil, Doucet, & Chaput, 2013). Sleep restriction is leading to increased food intake, but does not generally alter total energy expenditure, nor resting energy expenditure (McNeil et al., 2013). A number of explanations have been put forth for why this occurs. For example, staying up late is thought to lead to greater cortisol levels, which may alter insulin sensitivity resulting in greater hunger sensations (Chaput, Despres, Bouchard, & Tremblay, 2011; Chaput & Tremblay, 2007). There is some support for the prediction that restricted sleep results in increases in ghrelin, which stimulates eating, and decreases in leptin, which acts as a satiation signal has only been partially supported (e.g., Knutson & van Cauter, 2008; Nedeltcheva et al., 2009; Schmid et al., 2009). Another possibility is that sleep deprivation may lead to the motivation to eat when you are not hungry. This might also explain why our food choices change if we are tired. That is, when tired, people use an excessive amount of seasoning, consume less vegetables, and make fattier food choices (Bosy-Westphal et al., 2008; Brondel, Rober, Nougues, Touyarou, & Davenne, 2010). The result of lack of sleep tends to be more weight gain and more of that weight gets concentrated around your mid-section.

For many, education about prevention of obesity comes too late, and treatment is required. Historically, dieting has been the most common approach to losing weight. At any given time, nearly 40 percent of women and 25 percent of men in the United States are trying to lose weight (Kruger, Galuska, Serdula, & Jones, 2004). Some individuals are motivated to lose weight because it reduces health risks, whereas others are motivated to lose weight to improve appearance (Polivy & Herman, 2006). The majority of people who try to lose weight do so on their own rather than following preset guidelines. Approximately 20 percent of people follow healthy guidelines that restrict their caloric intake and supplement their balanced diet with exercise (Powell, Calvin, & Calvin, 2007). Weight loss is usually successful following this approach.

Generally, when people do lose weight by dieting, they are not able to keep the weight off. Paradoxically, the more people try to control their weight, the more their weight increases in the long run (Polivy & Herman, 2006). Frequently people will lose the same 10 pounds over and over again. This repeated cycle of weight loss and gain is referred to as yo-yo dieting. Unfortunately, frequent dieting has a negative impact on psychological well-being and is often accompanied by compromised psychological functioning in the form of impaired concentration, food preoccupation, and binge eating (McFarlane, Polivy, & McCabe, 1999). The best approach to losing weight is to do so gradually and to make permanent lifestyle changes that can be maintained.

Pharmacological Treatment of Obesity   Both prescription and over-the-counter drugs are often used to reduce appetite and restrict food consumption (Bray & Tartaglia, 2000). Stimulants, such as amphetamines, have provided short-term weight loss. Stimulants result in weight loss because they increase metabolism and reduce appetite. However, to remain effective, ever-increasing doses must be consumed, which may result in physical dependence, a health hazard worse than obesity. Most currently available obesity drugs are not very effective and have negative side effects. For example, the drug phentermine, an appetite suppressant, can lead to an 8 to 10 percent weight loss; however, this loss usually plateaus in 3 to 6 months. Perhaps that is good as this will dissuade individuals from taking the drug for longer periods. Indeed, because of the side effects, including increased heart rate, increased blood pressure, overstimulation of the central nervous system, dryness of mouth, etc., phentermine is not recommended for long-term use (Yznovski & Yanovski, 2014).

The drug orlistat is available by prescription. This "diet" medication works differently than most in that it decreases dietary fat absorption, but it is accompanied by adverse effects, including fatty, oily stools, and oily leakage from the rectum. As well, there is concern that orlistat may decrease absorption of the fat soluble vitamins A, D, E, and K (Powell et al., 2007; Powers & Bruty, 2009). Yet, only 15 to 30 percent of patients achieve greater than 5 percent weight loss after a year (Powell, Apovian, & Aronne, 2011). New pharmacological agents are under development, and it is expected that the new approach will involve combination therapies and not a single anti-obesity drug (Powell et al., 2011).

Leptin, a hormone discussed earlier, is currently being tested in both animal and clinical trials; however, initial trials have been disappointing (Gura, 2003; Wadden et al., 2002). Investigators expect that additional research on the genetics of body weight regulation will provide new drug targets (Gura, 2003). However, the physiology of weight control is complex and "most researchers doubt that a pharmaceutical 'silver bullet' will be found that will allow us all to achieve healthy weights" (Komaroff, 2003).

Behavioural Treatment of Obesity   Behavioural treatments described previously in the context of smoking cessation have also been applied to reducing obesity. Behavioural treatment of obesity is at least as effective as pharmacological treatment (Wadden et al., 2002). Typically, individuals will take part in a program that lasts approximately 20 weeks. The program will likely include one or more of the following strategies (e.g., Stewart, Reilly, & Hughes, 2009):

- stimulus-control procedures that identify and modify external cues to eating (e.g., confining food intake to a particular place and time, such as in the dining room at mealtime)

- self-monitoring and record keeping of the type and quantity of food eaten each day; this provides awareness of the foods that are eaten and the situations in which one eats

- self-control techniques to control the amount eaten or to slow the act of eating (e.g., dieters can be instructed to place the proper proportion of food on their plate at one time, and once all of the food is on the plate to eat by putting down their forks after each bite)

- social support to help control stress that may arise (e.g., having a dieting "buddy," joining a program such as Weight Watchers, or enlisting the help of a friend or family member)

- contingency contracts, also known as behavioural contracts, that consist of rewards for achieving goals (or punishments for not reaching a goal); the contracts may be self-monitored or another person may be enlisted to monitor the behaviour and reward or punish accordingly

A behavioural treatment program usually leads to a loss of 8.5 to 9.0 kg, or approximately 9 percent of initial body weight (e.g., Wing, 2002). Regrettably, without further treatment (at least monthly), those who lost weight using behaviour therapies are likely to regain approximately one-third of the weight lost in the subsequent year (Powell et al., 2007).

Surgical Treatment of Obesity   Surgical interventions are a radical way to control extreme obesity (BMI > 40). In the 1960s, Drs. Mason and Ito developed a procedure called **gastric bypass** that is still widely used today. In this procedure, a small pouch is created at the bottom of the esophagus to limit food intake. Food that enters the pouch bypasses the stomach and part of the intestine. Those who undergo this procedure can expect to lose approximately 30 percent of their initial weight during the first 18 months. Approximately 25 percent of the weight loss will be maintained (Wadden et al., 2002).

Gastric banding, a far more common procedure, is a minimally invasive surgical procedure, involves placing a band around the stomach so that a person feels full after consuming only a small amount of food (Nickel et al., 2005). Positive changes in health-related quality of life have been noted after gastric band surgery. These changes are most dramatic in the first year after surgery, but are still evident 3 years later (Nickel et al., 2005).

Although drastic, these procedures do result in dramatic weight loss (Moldovan & David, 2011). Consequently, health risks for a number of ailments linked to obesity are reduced, for example, for diabetes, hypertension, and cardiovascular disease. However, there are risks involved, and patients must alter their eating behaviours and take nutritional supplements for the rest of their lives (Tucker, Szomstein, & Rosenthal, 2007).

EATING DISORDERS

In Case 6-2, Julia's behaviour is indicative of an eating disorder known as **bulimia nervosa**. Bulimia nervosa involves recurrent episodes of binge eating followed by purging. The purging strategies used most frequently are vomiting and laxative use. According to the DSM-V (American Psychiatric Association, 2013), to be classified as having this disorder, an individual must engage in at least four of these episodes in a month for a period of 3 months. As well, the individuals must view their weight and shape as a major contributor to their self-worth. This disorder can result in numerous medical problems, such as anemia, inflammation of the digestive tract, heart arrhythmias resulting from electrolyte imbalances (which may cause sudden death), and irreversible erosion of dental enamel

gastric bypass: radical surgical intervention to control extreme obesity; a small pouch is created at the bottom of the esophagus to limit food intake.

gastric banding: a minimally invasive surgical procedure that involves placing a band around the stomach so that a person feels full after consuming only a small amount of food.

bulimia nervosa: An eating disorder that involves recurrent episodes of binge eating followed by purging.

CASE 6-2   BULIMIA NERVOSA IN TEENAGERS

Julia is an attractive girl of normal weight who has always been concerned with her appearance. If you ever want to know what clothes are trendy, take a look at what Julia is wearing. She can even tell you what colours of lipstick and fingernail polish are "in" this month. How does she know this? She reads magazines such as *Elle* and *Cosmopolitan* religiously. Her friends are also very "up to date," and in junior high school they jointly began to engage in a behaviour they felt was "fashionable." As a group, the girls would go into the washroom and throw up. Julia says she was not all that concerned with losing weight, but she didn't want to gain any either. In fact, the purging began more because it seemed to be a "cool" thing to do rather than because of concerns Julia might have had about her own weight. Unfortunately, the purging changed from a group activity to something she did frequently on her own. It soon became a habit for Julia to vomit after eating—a very unhealthy habit.

(Brown & Mehler, 2011; Mehler, 2011; Polivy, Herman, & Boivin, 2005). Although some bulimics are overweight, most, like Julia, are of normal weight. Despite the fact that the behaviour may begin as a group activity, bulimics are typically aware that their behaviour is not normal and they are ashamed of it. Because of this, they usually try to hide their behaviour from others. In addition to reporting negative aspects of the disorder, such as shame and preoccupation with weight or shape, patients with bulimia nervosa also describe positive aspects of the disorder. These positive aspects include being able to eat and not get fat and as a way to combat boredom (Serpell & Treasure, 2002).

The binge portion of the bulimic episode is often impulsive, and bulimics are likely to engage in other impulsive and reckless behaviours as well (Fischer, Smith, & Anderson, 2003; Peterson & Fischer, 2012). For example, kleptomania is more common among bulimics than among the general population, although the items stolen are usually associated with the bulimic's binging and purging (such as food or laxatives). Bulimics are also more likely than the general population to engage in spending sprees or sexual promiscuity because of their impulsive nature (e.g., Matsunaga, Kiriike, Iwasaki, Miyata, & Matsui, 2000).

The number of patients diagnosed with eating disorders is increasing (Polivy & Herman, 2002). Although eating disorders are most common among adolescents and adults, even children suffer from eating disorders. Seventy percent of children with eating disorders are female. In the adolescent and adult eating-disorder population, 90 to 95 percent of those with eating disorders are female (Behar, 2006).

How prevalent are eating disorders? More than 500 000 Canadians reported suffering from an eating disorder in 2005 (Canadian Mental Health Association, 2014). A study conducted by the Douglas Mental Health Institute at McGill University found that nearly 15 percent of women sampled reported some type of eating disturbance (Gauvin, Steiger, & Brodeur, 2008). Approximately 13 percent of women will be affected by eating disorders in their lifetime (Stice, Marti, & Rohde, 2013). Although reports vary greatly, prevalence rates for bulimia nervosa typically range from 1 to 2.5 percent and for anorexia nervosa the range is from 0.3 to 1 percent (Hoek, 2006; Stice et al., 2013). There are reports that the number of patients with bulimia nervosa and binge eating disorder (BED) outnumbers the number with anorexia nervosa by at least two to one (Stice et al., 2013).

Anorexia nervosa is an eating disorder characterized by a dramatic reduction in food intake and extreme weight loss. According to the DSM-V (American Psychiatric Association, 2013), the diagnostic criteria for anorexia nervosa are maintaining a body weight at less than 85 percent of normal weight for one's age and gender, a focus on one's weight when determining self-worth, and an intense fear of weight gain of more than 75 percent of the time in the last 3 months. Anorexics are very fearful of gaining weight and consequently will refuse food and may engage in excessive exercise. Yet anorexics are extremely preoccupied with food and may spend a lot of their time cooking for others or engaging in other pursuits that revolve around food. The self-starvation in anorexia will lead to low blood pressure, heart damage or cardiac arrhythmias, and eventually death. At the point of near starvation, the person will lose the hair on his or her head, and fine hair growth (lanugo) will appear on the face and body. Anorexics are also at increased risk of osteoporosis (Mehler, 2003).

Anorexia occurs most often in Caucasian adolescent females from the upper social classes and in those who dance, model, or are competitive in sports (Behar, 2006; Polivy et al., 2005; Ravaldi, Vannacci, & Zucchi, 2003). Yet anorexia is increasingly being seen in people of colour, those who are less affluent, patients who are very young, and males, particularly same-sex attracted males (Boisvert & Harrell, 2009; Story, French, Resnick, & Blum, 1995).

anorexia nervosa: an eating disorder characterized by a dramatic reduction in food intake and extreme weight loss due to an extreme fear of gaining weight.

binge eating disorder (BED): compulsive overeating or bingeing; unlike bulimia nervosa, BED uses no compensatory measure or purge to counteract the binge.

Binge eating disorder (BED) is compulsive overeating or bingeing. To be classified as binge eating disorder, a person's binge will be characterized by at least three of the following: must eat rapidly, eat to uncomfortably full, eat large amounts when not hungry, eat alone because of embarrassment, feel disgusted, depressed or guilty after overeating (American Psychiatric Association, 2013). Unlike with bulimia nervosa, with BED there is no compensatory measure or purge to counteract the binge (American Psychiatric Association, 2013). Recurrent binge eating is reported to be as common in men as in women, as common in persons of colour as Caucasians, and is evenly distributed throughout adulthood (Striegel-Moore & Bulik, 2007; Wilson, Grilo, & Vitousek, 2007). Obesity is frequently a co-occuring problem, and the typical patient often suffers from additional serious psychiatric disorders (e.g., major depressive disorder, anxiety disorder, alcohol use disorder, or personality disorder; Skinner, Haines, Austin, & Field, 2012; Wilson et al., 2007).

Biological, Cultural, and Psychological Contributors to Eating Disorders

Biological, cultural, and psychological factors may all be possible contributors to eating disorders. See Box 6-1 for more contributors to our eating behaviour. Twin studies have documented that both twins are more likely to suffer from eating disorders if the twins are identical rather than fraternal (Klump, McGue, & Iacono, 2000). A large study that included 31 406 Swedish twins reported a heritability estimate of 56 percent for anorexia nervosa (Bulik et al., 2006). Other studies have reported heritability estimates between 48 and 76 percent (Striegel-Moore &

Box 6-1

Mindless Eating

We often are not aware of exactly how much we are eating. Brian Wansink, a professor of marketing and nutritional science, has dedicated his career to understanding the environmental factors that influence food consumption. Package size, plate shape, food variety, accessibility of food, and even lighting can influence food consumption more than most people realize (Wansink, 2006).

Wansink (2004) demonstrates that atmospherics influence our food consumption. For example, dimmed or soft lighting leads people to be more comfortable in their environment and less inhibited. Consequently, these people consume more food. The smell of food can lead us to eat when we weren't planning on it (e.g., think of the smell of coffee brewing in the morning or of the delightful smells one encounters at a local fair or amusement park), whereas unpleasant odours tend to decrease our consumption (e.g., burnt toast or sour milk).

The variety of food available also alters consumption. That is, providing an assortment of food causes people to eat more (Kahn & Wansink, 2004). In fact, the subtle

difference in an assortment of 300 M&M's candies in 10 different colours rather than 7 colours leads to the consumption of 43 percent more candies.

Another environmental factor that contributes to our consumption rates is portion size. Food packaging and portion sizes have steadily increased over the past three decades. Given this, it is not surprising that people are eating more. Studies indicate that people will help themselves to more food and consume more food when given a large plate rather than a small plate. Yet they argue that they have not eaten any more. Smaller snack portions, on the other hand, do lead people to feel satisfied despite eating less and it doesn't matter what the snack is, that is, chocolate, potato chips, etc. (van Kleef, Shimizu, & Wansink, 2013). People are often surprised at how much they consume. Wansink provides suggestions for altering one's personal environment to help curb "mindless eating" in his book of the same name (2006). In a more recent publication, he discussed how one can go about "Turning mindless eating into healthy eating" (Wansink, 2013).

Bulik, 2007). Similarly, heritability estimates for bulimia nervosa range from 50 percent to 83 percent and those for BED are approximately 40 percent (Striegel-Moore & Bulik, 2007).

Researchers at McGill University report that there is "a region on Chromosome 1 that differentiates people with and without anorexia. The abnormality on this chromosome is linked to personality traits like compulsivity and anxiety" (Douglas Mental Health Institute, 2012) that are common in those with anorexia and bulimia. Neuroendocrine factors, which might or might not be genetic in origin, may contribute to eating disorders (Polivy & Herman, 2002).

In North American society, there is pressure on individuals to be thin and stay youthful. This expectation is learned at a very young age. When children reach puberty and naturally gain weight, many become distressed. Often adolescents will try to control their weight by dieting. Unfortunately, this strategy is sometimes carried too far, and this is when many eating disorders begin (Walsh, 2013). Eating disorders are more likely to occur in individuals from families in which eating disorders, psychopathology, alcoholism, or sexual abuse exist or have taken place (Polivy & Herman, 2002). The media are also partly to blame for this pressure. Researchers (Groesz, Levine, & Murnen, 2002) have documented that females who have greater exposure to media containing a high concentration of body images show more charac-teristics of eating disorders than do females with less exposure to these media. Media images seem to have less impact on body dissatisfaction among African Americans than Caucasians (DeBraganza & Hausenblas, 2011). However, it remains unclear why most women exposed to thin media messages do not develop eating disorders (Polivy & Herman, 2004).

Psychological factors associated with eating disorders include issues of control, low self-esteem, extreme sensitivity to others' feelings, perfectionism, maturity fears, and distorted body image. Indeed, in this population, decreased body weight is associated with increased self-esteem (Brockmeyer et al., 2012). Hilde Bruch (1973, 1978, 1982, 2001), who spent more than 40 years studying eating disorders, reported that anorexics typically are troubled female adolescents who feel incapable of changing their lives. These young women are from families that do not encourage autonomy and are per-ceived by the adolescent as overdemanding. More recent research corroborates this view and implies that insecure attachment is common in eating-disordered populations (Ward, Ramsay, & Treasure, 2000; Ward, Ramsay, Turnbull, Benedettini, & Treasure, 2000). To exert some control in their lives, they exert control over the thing closest to them—their bodies. Many individuals who suffer from eating disorders do not perceive their bodies accurately, a condition referred to as **body dysmorphic disorder** (Kaplan, Rossell, Enticott, & Castle, 2013). Women, in general, see themselves as one-fourth larger than they really are (Thompson, 1986). Men may also see themselves as larger than they really are, but they do so to a lesser degree, and, unlike women, many of these men may want to be larger (Geist, Heinmaa, Katzman, & Stephens, 1999; see Box 6-2). Both anorexics and bulimics tend to overestimate their body size to a greater extent than does the general population.

body dysmorphic disorder: condition in which individuals who suffer from eating disorders do not perceive their bodies accurately.

Treatment for Eating Disorders

Instruction and clinical experiences offered to Canadian psychiatry residents for the treat-ment of eating disorders is deemed insufficient (Williams & Leichner, 2006). Yet success-ful treatment for eating disorders is literally a matter of life and death. This is particularly true for anorexics, because there is such a high mortality rate within this population. Estimates vary but often indicate that between 5 and 10 percent of all anorexics die from

Box 6-2

Muscle Dysmorphia: The Body Dysmorphic Disorder Especially for Men

For men, the fear of being and looking like a "97-pound weakling" is not new, as a look through the ads in old comic books will attest. Yet today more than ever, many men fear that they are too small and skinny. In the words of Roberto Olivardia, "They feel like Clark Kent and long to be Superman" (2001, p. 254).

While conducting research on anabolic steroids, Olivardia and his supervisor, Harrison Pope, met several large and muscular bodybuilders who confided that they felt small and frail (Pope, 2001). Sometimes these people were referred to as experiencing "reverse anorexia" or "bigorexia," but the term most often used today is **muscle dysmorphia** (Olivardia, 2001). There is some debate as to whether muscle dysmorphia should be classified in the American Psychiatric Association's Diagnostic and Statistical Manual as a subcategory of body dysmorphic disorder or a subcategory of obsessive compulsive disorder, or whether it and anorexia nervosa should be in a category on their own (Nieuwoudt, Zhou, Coutts, & Booker, 2012). However, most people agree on the criteria for making a diagnosis of muscle dysmorphia (Olivardia, 2001, p. 255): (1) a preoccupation with the idea that one's body is not sufficiently lean and muscular; (2) clinically significant distress or impairment in social, occupational, or other areas of functioning; and (3) a primary focus on being too small or inadequately muscular.

Due to their preoccupation with their bodies, individuals with muscle dysmorphia look at their bodies in the mirror many times a day. The need to look in the mirror becomes so strong that "one young man got into several car accidents because he compulsively checked a large hand-held mirror while driving to ensure that he wasn't getting smaller" (Olivardia, 2001, p. 255). Obviously, a preoccupation such as this can be detrimental. Many men with muscle dysmorphia are so obsessed with working out that they lose their jobs. Lawyers, doctors, and businessmen relinquish their careers so that they can spend more time working out (Olivardia, Pope, & Hudson, 2000; Pope, 2001). A few specific examples include a lawyer who was fired because he often took 3- to 4-hour lunch breaks to fit in his workout, a student who missed a final exam because the time conflicted with his workout, and a man

G.I. Joe has become more muscle-bound over the last three decades. The latest doll, G.I. Joe Extreme, has a body that is unattainable by even the largest bodybuilders. Is the current North American cultural ideal of the male body so large and muscular that it represents an unattainable standard?
HASBRO/KRT/Newscom

who missed the birth of his child so that he could lift weights (Olivardia, 2001).

Some individuals with muscle dysmorphia react by hiding their bodies. These individuals are so ashamed of their bodies that they avoid situations where their bodies will be exposed to others. Many even refuse to take off their shirts at the beach (Pope, 2001). Unfortunately, those with muscle dysmorphia report anabolic-androgenic steroid use to increase their muscle mass (Pope et al., 2005; Rohman, 2009).

What causes muscle dysmorphia? Biological, psychological, and sociocultural explanations have all been put forth (Kanayama & Pope, 2011; Olivardia, 2001). There may be an underlying biological or genetic predisposition toward muscle dysmorphia. Those with muscle dysmorphia have higher rates of mood and anxiety disorders than those without muscle dysmorphia (Cafri, Olivardia, & Thompson,

Box 6-2

(Continued)

2008). Also, low self-esteem and masculinity issues are typical in men with muscle dysmorphia. Achieving a body that is respected and admired by others may be a response to these psychological issues.

The explanation that has received the most attention, however, is sociocultural in nature. That is, boys and men are now experiencing appearance-related societal pressures similar to those that women have experienced for decades. The ideal male body in our culture is becoming increasingly more muscular. A look at either centrefold models in *Playgirl* magazine (Leit, Pope, & Gray, 2000) or male action toys such as G.I. Joe (Pope, Olivardia, Gruber, & Borowiecki, 1999) confirms this. Todd Morrison

(Morrison & Halton, 2009), at the University of Saskatchewan, analyzed popular action movies and concluded that there has been a trend in both increased leanness and muscularity over the last several decades. However, in addition to experiencing more aggressive actions, the more muscular characters were also more likely to be romantically involved and experience more positive outcomes than their less muscular counterparts. We also know that when exposed to muscular images, men will perceive a greater discrepancy between their own muscularity and the level of muscularity that they consider ideal (Leit, Gray, & Pope, 2002). Thus, it is likely that there are a number of factors contributing to muscle dysmorphia.

their disorder—the majority from suicide (Birmingham, Su, Hlynsky, Goldner, & Gao, 2005; Preti, Rocchi, Sisti, Camboni, & Miotto, 2011; Wilson et al., 2007).

Not surprisingly, anorexics are very difficult to treat because they believe that the only aspects of their environment they can control are their own bodies. As long as they refuse to eat, they maintain control. As starvation continues, anorexics eventually reach the point of exhaustion and possible physical collapse, so the first goal of treatment is to medically stabilize the patient and increase his or her weight.

Weight restoration is a step in the treatment process but is not a cure. Anorexics need to change both their body image *and* their eating habits. Cognitive behaviour therapy attempts to eradicate the irrational beliefs of patients while maintaining a warm and accepting attitude. For example, anorexics are encouraged to avoid absolutist thoughts like, "If I put on one pound, I'll go on to gain one hundred." Similarly, they are educated about nutritional facts. Superstitious beliefs such as "laxatives prevent the absorption of calories" are dispelled. Patients are also encouraged to recognize that others do not have the same high standards for their behaviour than they do.

Cognitive behaviour therapy is often used in conjunction with pharmacotherapy, particularly antidepressants or selective serotonin reuptake inhibitors (SSRIs; Flament, Bissada, & Spettigue, 2012; Powers & Bruty, 2009). Most commonly, fluoxetine is used. Some studies report that when cognitive behavioural therapy (CBT) and fluoxetine are used in combination, secondary outcomes, namely improvements in self-esteem, are produced in addition to weight gains (Stein et al., 2001). Yet other studies show that fluoxetine is not superior to either a placebo or CBT alone (Powers & Bruty, 2009; Walsh et al., 2006). Other pharmacotherapy treatments include second-generational antipsychotics. These can be useful during the initial weight restoration phase of anorexia when clients have particularly severe obsessions, anxiety, or near delusional thinking (Powers & Bruty, 2009).

Pharmacotherapy as a sole treatment is not recommended as this results in a higher dropout rate than when used in conjunction with CBT (Halmi et al., 2005; Stein et al., 2001).

muscle dysmorphia: condition characterized by a belief that one's body is not sufficiently lean and muscular; clinically significant distress or impairment in social, occupational, or other areas of functioning; and a primary focus on being too small or inadequately muscular.

CBT appears most useful in preventing relapse (Pike, Walsh, Vitousek, Wilson, & Bauer, 2003). Family therapy is often included in the treatment process. It has been found that family participation positively influences the results of therapy, both in terms of weight gain and the reduction of cognitive distortions (Cardi & Treasure, 2010; Fisher, Hetrick, & Rushford, 2010; Gardner & Wilkinson, 2011; Hay, 2013; Smith & Cook-Cottone, 2011).

An extreme approach to the treatment of anorexia is now being explored. Researchers (Lipsman et al., 2013) at the University of Toronto treated six patients with **deep brain stimulation**. Electrodes were placed in the subcallosal cingulate region of the patients' brains. Half of the patients had gained weight 9 months post-surgery. Additionally, improvements in mood and quality of life were reported. This study was considered a pilot study, but it does show promising results.

Bulimia is much easier to treat than anorexia, because bulimics are aware that their eating habits are not normal. As a result, they are motivated to change these behaviours. The most successful approach for treating bulimia is CBT (Hay, 2013; Spielmans et al., 2013). Typically, therapy begins by patients being instructed to monitor their eating habits. An individualized treatment program is then developed to help break down patterns of behaviour that maintain disordered eating. The program will include reinforcement, relaxation training, and cognitive restructuring.

Specific techniques might include increasing the regularity of meals, eating a greater variety of foods, delaying the impulse to purge for as long as possible, and eating foods in new settings not previously associated with binges. The CBT techniques implemented should address the pathological concerns bulimics have about their weight and eating in addition to increasing perceptions of self-esteem. CBT may be combined with pharmacotherapy. The antidepressants fluoxetine (Prozac) is used in managing bulimia as it has been determined that it decreases the frequency of binges. However, drugs do not treat the cause of the problem and there is a lack of evidence supporting their long-term efficacy (Wilson et al., 2007). As such, they should be used to treat bulimia only in conjunction with other forms of therapy.

Psychological treatments are found to be most effective in treating BED, although pharmacotherapy is also utilized. Psychological treatments including CBT and interpersonal psychotherapy are useful in reducing bingeing over both the short and the long term. Pharmacological therapy is more prone to relapse on the part of the BED patient (Spielmans et al., 2013; Stein et al., 2001).

Unfortunately, as many as half of previously treated eating-disorder sufferers will continue to have eating problems. The difficulty in treating eating disorders effectively, coupled with their increasing prevalence, suggests that researchers should focus more on ways to prevent eating disorders rather than focusing almost exclusively on treating them after they have developed (Austin, 2013; Becker, Smith, & Ciao, 2006; Taylor, Bryson, & Luce, 2006).

deep brain stimulation: a surgical procedure that involves implanting an electrode that delivers electrical signals to the brain.

CHAPTER SUMMARY

■ Outline factors that contribute to smoking behaviour.

This chapter focused on health-compromising behaviours. Almost one in five individuals over the age of 15 in Canada smokes. Smoking is a preventable cause of death accounting for approximately 37 000 deaths each year. As socioeconomic levels increase, smoking levels tend to decrease. The highest rates of smoking occur among Inuit and

First Nations people. People often begin to smoke because of parental modelling, peer influence, advertising, or because of personality characteristics (e.g., rebelliousness). Those who become regular smokers tend to do so to increase positive affect and decrease negative affect, and then smoking may become habitual and addictive.

Smoking leads to cardiovascular and cerebrovascular disease, cancer, and chronic obstructive pulmonary disease. Those who do not smoke but breathe in the second-hand smoke of others are also at increased risk for these illnesses. The federal government has attempted to prevent smoking by banning advertising and by including warning labels on tobacco products. More than half of those who begin to smoke attempt to quit at some later date. Quitting attempts take many forms, including reducing the number of cigarettes smoked and using nicotine replacement therapy. Aversion therapies and self-management therapies may also be useful.

■ Provide explanations for why individuals drink alcohol or engage in illicit drug use.

More than 75 percent of Canadians have consumed alcohol in the last 12 months. Excessive use of alcohol can have adverse effects on almost every system of the body. Moderate consumption of alcohol may have protective health benefits, primarily by reducing the risk of cardiovascular and coronary heart disease. A number of theories have been put forth to attempt to explain drinking behaviour, including the disease model, the alcohol dependency syndrome model, the tension reduction hypothesis, the self-awareness model, the social learning model, and alcohol myopia theory.

■ Inform others regarding how we can help people quit their smoking, alcohol, or drug use.

Attempts to limit drinking include implementing age restrictions for buying or consuming alcohol, anti-drinking, and anti-drinking-and-driving campaigns. Treatments include 12-step programs, psychotherapy, drug therapy, aversion therapy, and multimodal therapies. Canada's Drug Strategy adopts the stages of change model for guiding both treatment processes and prevention goals.

More than 10 percent of the Canadian population admitted to using illicit drugs in the year preceding the survey. Cannabis is the most frequently used illicit drug. Treatment programs are similar to those used for alcohol abuse.

Many youths engage in unsafe sexual behaviours that can lead to serious health consequences. A variety of theoretical approaches have been used in an attempt to understand sexual and reproductive health behaviours using a decision-making framework, for example, information-motivation-behavioural skills model.

■ Outline factors that contribute to obesity in our society.

Obesity is becoming a significant health problem in Canada. Heredity, hormones, stress, and sociocultural and environmental factors all contribute to obesity. Treatment can be behavioural, pharmacological, or surgical.

■ Provide information about eating disorders.

Eating disorders such as anorexia nervosa and bulimia nervosa are more common in women than men. Muscle dysmorphia, another body dysmorphic disorder, is more common in men. Treating eating disorders is very difficult, especially for anorexia and muscle dysmorphia, because the individuals don't admit to having a problem. Pharmacotherapy, cognitive behavioural therapy, and family therapy are all used with limited success.

Chapter 7
Chronic and Life-Threatening Illnesses

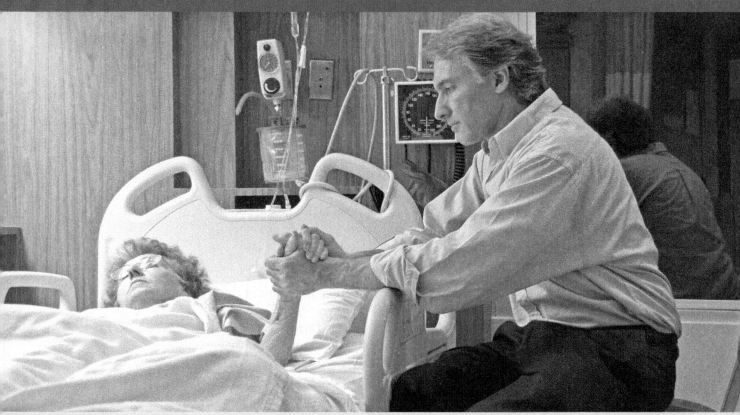

Claudio Rossol/Shutterstock

Learning Objectives

After studying this chapter, you will be able to:

1. present statistics related to serious and chronic illness, including prevalence and mortality rates.

2. describe common psychological challenges associated with specific serious and chronic illnesses, including cancer, diabetes, heart disease, and HIV/AIDS.

3. explain ways in which professionals, family members, friends, and fellow patients can help people cope with these psychological challenges.

4. define quality of life and explain its importance in the treatment of serious illness.

5. list and describe the elements of death and dying, as identified by Elisabeth Kübler-Ross.

6. list the steps involved in helping someone cope with bereavement.

At first, Mario attributed his fatigue to a lack of sleep. However, his fatigue persisted, even on days when he had slept well the night before. And then there was the light-headedness, especially when he hadn't eaten for a while. Once, it got so bad that Mario actually felt disoriented.

After a trip to his doctor and some blood tests, Mario found out that he had Type II diabetes. He was discouraged by the diagnosis. It sounded so serious. He had heard of people dying or going blind from diabetes. Just as discouraging was the fact that he was going to have to make significant and permanent changes to his life. This was because diabetes is a chronic condition. It doesn't go away or get better. Instead, people with chronic conditions must learn to cope with them on a daily basis.

Mario was going to have to change his diet and closely monitor it. He was going to have to lose weight, too. These major changes were going to be particularly difficult for Mario to make because, for the first time in his life, he was feeling very depressed and fearful. Fortunately, his wife and friends were supportive, and there were some excellent information sessions put on by the hospital, so Mario did not have to feel alone in facing the daily challenges brought on by diabetes.

In this chapter, we will look at the psychology of **chronic conditions**, those that people live with for life, and *serious conditions* that are life-threatening and often accompanied by severe symptoms. For most of us, illness is **acute**, which means it is episodic in nature, having a defined beginning and end. But chronically ill people might not view their illness in episodic terms, and this can make coping difficult (Gathchel & Oordt, 2003). It is not surprising that health psychology has dedicated a great deal of research effort to understanding chronic conditions, which are often accompanied by emotional distress.

Mario's reaction to his diagnosis of diabetes is not uncommon. Many people feel anger, depression, and fear when they learn they must cope with serious or chronic illnesses. Moreover, in most cases these emotional reactions are not conducive to successful coping. Table 7-1 presents four different ways in which chronically ill patients may respond psychologically to physical symptoms. A chronically ill person may well experience a range of symptom patterns, resulting in a confusing mix of psychological responses.

In this chapter, we'll look closely at a number of conditions that are either chronic, serious, or both. We'll also look at the factors affecting people's abilities to cope with these conditions and how people can be helped to cope better. You may remember that, in chapter 1, we

chronic condition: a condition that doesn't go away or get better.

acute illness: an illness with a defined beginning and end.

Table 7-1 The Range of Symptom-Related Experience for People with Chronic Illness

Symptoms that are	Produce
constant	discouragement and fear
lessened or in remission	hope
unpredictably erratic	anger and frustration
relentlessly progressive	exhaustion and a sense of being overwhelmed

Source: Goodheart, C.D., & Lansing, M.H. (1997). *Treating people with chronic disease: A psychological guide.* Washington, DC: American Psychological Association. Reprinted with permission.

made the point that major causes of death have changed since the beginning of the twentieth century. While viruses and bacteria were the main killers in 1900, diseases of lifestyle and environment—cancer and cardiovascular diseases—are now the main culprits. In this chapter, we are going to look closely at what it is like to have these and other diseases.

CANCER

oncology: the study and treatment of cancer.

sites of cancer: types of cancer as defined by the location of the tumour.

Cancer is not one disease, but many. The experience of a patient with one form of cancer can differ radically from that of another patient with a different form. The study of and treatment of cancer is called **oncology**. Oncologists often specialize in a particular *site* where cancer occurs in the body. This specialization is further indication of the differences between types of cancer, or **sites of cancer**, as oncologists would refer to them. For example, one group of oncologists might specialize in cancers of the genitourinary system. These oncologists would treat prostate cancer. Others may focus on the central nervous system. The site at which the cancer occurs and the symptoms associated with it are significant factors in determining a person's psychological reactions to a diagnosis of cancer.

metastasized: spread (frequently used to denote the spread of cancer).

What all forms of cancer share is the uncontrolled growth of abnormal cells. General cell growth is, of course, common throughout the body. This growth is controlled as cells wear out and are replaced. Cancer cells are different. They grow in an uncontrolled manner and destroy normal cells in the process. When these abnormal cells form a mass, it is called a tumour. This tumour may be localized, or cells may spread to other parts of the body. When this happens, the cancer is said to have **metastasized**, or spread. Metastasized cancer is considerably harder to treat, since the treatment cannot be localized. Early detection of tumours reduces the likelihood that the cancer will have metastasized and thus increases chances of survival. In Case 7-1, Anna hopes that her physician detected the lump early, before the cancer had a chance to spread.

Some Statistics

It is estimated that 40 percent of all Canadian women and 45 percent of men will develop cancer at some point in their lives. Approximately one in four Canadians will die from cancer: An estimated 186 4000 cases of cancer and 75 700 deaths occurred in Canada

CASE 7-1 AN UNWELCOME DIAGNOSIS

Anna's life changed the day her physician discovered a lump in her breast during a routine examination. Then came the mammogram, the biopsy, and the result she had feared. She had a malignant tumour in her breast. Just the day before, she had been most concerned about her workload, her children's over-enthusiastic soccer coach, and her husband's reluctance to paint the kitchen. Suddenly, all of that seemed to pale in comparison to the questions that now had to be answered. Had the cancer spread? Could all the cancer be removed with a lumpectomy, or would she require a mastectomy? How could she cope with that? What would her husband think? There would be more tests and more procedures. She remembered a colleague at work who had died from breast cancer. Was Anna going to die? She could not answer any of these questions. All she knew for sure was that she had never been so afraid in her life.

in 2012 (Canadian Cancer Society, 2013). These numbers do not include cases of non-melanoma skin cancer. The leading cause of cancer death is lung cancer. Colorectal cancer is the second leading cause for men and third leading cause for women. Males generally have higher rates of cancer than women do. With the exception of lung cancer, rates of all other cancers in women have dropped by 20 percent since 1979. Also, mortality rates due to prostate cancer are dropping, and survival periods for most cancers are increasing, so the news isn't all bad. For all cancers combined, the incidence rate has been stable since 1979. However, incidence rates vary from one cancer to another, with some increasing and some decreasing (Marrett, De, Airia, & Dryer, 2008). The Canadian Cancer Society has an informative website for those seeking more information at www.cancer.ca.

Illness Burden for Cancer

Whatever the site of the tumour, a diagnosis of cancer can have a profound effect. Some people will view it as a death sentence, others as the ultimate challenge of their lives. Many will go through strong denial in the early stages in an attempt to cope with trauma that is unprecedented in their experience. Even after receiving her diagnosis, Anna may deny that she has cancer.

Patients must cope with aggressive treatments that bring on side effects that are worse than the symptoms of many other diseases. They must face the real possibility that their lives will be shortened, and they must also face the possible stigma associated with serious illness. Friends and colleagues aren't always adept at providing support for the cancer patient. Their own fear and lack of familiarity with cancer can get in the way. There is evidence, though, that the stigma of cancer is diminishing and that people have become more adept at lending support to friends and family members with the disease (Bloom & Kessler, 1994). This might not apply as clearly to lung cancer, however, since its association with cigarette smoking increases the sense of "victim blaming," even when patients have never smoked (Chapple, Ziebland, & McPherson, 2004).

The nature of cancer patients' illness burden has been described in many ways. Some have talked about being "at the mercy of the body, the consciousness, the illness, the treatment and the death" (Rydahl-Hansen, 2005, p. 217). Others have focused on cognitive interventions (Strasser, Walker, & Bruera, 2005) and coping strategies (Surtees, Wainwright, Luben, Khaw, & Day, 2006) that reduce this sense of being at pain's "mercy," and thus reduce burden while helping prolong life. Still others have categorized cancer burden into three general areas—physical, psychological, and social (Kuuppelomäki & Lauri, 1998). About 44 percent of illness burden relates to psychological factors.

Adolescents with cancer report cancer-related limitations as long as 2 years after they have been treated. Such limitations include being unable to play contact sports or, for one teen who had been diagnosed with a brain tumour 14 years earlier, experiencing fear every time he had a headache. A large U.S. study discovered that adult survivors of childhood cancer continued to experience burdens of the illness. These included greater limitations to one's work and life due to general poor health (Dowling et al., 2010).

Physical Problems

According to research in which cancer patients were asked to complete questionnaires about their illness burden, approximately 60 percent of cancer burden is related to physical factors (Kuuppelomäki & Lauri, 1998). These factors break down further into two subcategories—

illness-caused and treatment-caused. The most common physical complaints are fatigue, pain (Ferrell, Smith, Cullinane, & Melancon, 2003), and the side effects of chemotherapy.

Pain management is a major challenge for patients and for those providing treatment. One source of frustration in this regard is that cancer pain tends to be under-treated (Aiello-Laws, Reynolds, Deizer, Peterson, & Bakitas, 2009). It has been estimated that more than 90 percent of cancer pain can be controlled by current treatments; however, these treatments are underused (American Pain Society, 2005). Why is this? Three types of explanations have been suggested: issues related to the health care system, issues related to health care practitioners, and issues related to patients and their families (Jacox, Carr, & Payne, 1994).

For example, patients' fears about building up a tolerance to analgesic medication and, to a lesser extent, becoming addicted to it keep them from seeking adequate pain-relieving treatment (Letizia, Creech, Norton, Shanahan, & Hedges, 2004). Yet most of these fears are unfounded. Other patient-related barriers to taking analgesics for their cancer pain include forgetfulness, the belief that the pain should be tolerated, and concerns regarding side effects. For these and a host of other reasons, patients may be unwilling to report mild or moderate pain, making it difficult for practitioners to prescribe adequate medication (Thomason et al., 1998). (See chapter 8 for more on pain management.) We will discuss fatigue when we look at cancer treatment.

Psychological Distress

There are many different psychological reactions to the cancer experience. The most common and the most distressing for patients and their families are fear and depression. Depression is particularly prevalent at the initial diagnosis (Ferrell et al., 2003), when or if the cancer metastasizes, and when patients are in poor physical condition. Breast cancer patients' most common concerns during the early stages of their illness include issues of body integrity, fear of radiation therapy, cancer relapse, and death (Monti, Mago, & Kunkel, 2005; Wu, Freeman, Greer, Freeman, & Goodwin, 2001). For some patients, fear and depression become chronic, even if cancer treatment is proceeding successfully. These patients may fear recurrence or that the cancer will metastasize (Bishop & Warr, 2003). They may fear the side effects of the treatment and the changes to their self-image (Pruzinsky, Levine, Persing, Barth, & Obrecht, 2006).

Depression is a common form of psychological distress for cancer patients, and current estimates suggest that from 10 to 58 percent of patients experience depression, depending upon the form of cancer (Massie, 2004). For example, depression is diagnosed at a higher rate for pancreatic cancer, a disease that tends to have a poor prognosis (Zabora, Brintzenhofeszoc, Curbow, Hooker, & Piantadosi, 2001). Depression results in poorer quality of life, less compliance with medical treatment, longer hospital stays, and higher mortality rates (DiMatteo, Lepper, & Croghan, 2001; Sarna et al., 2002; Wenzel et al., 2002). You may recall from chapter 3 on psychoneuroimmunology that there are hypothesized links between psychological states and disease progression in cancer. These links continue to be investigated (Edelman, 2005), and research has found associations between psychological distress (stress and depression) and immunocompromise in the form of decreased natural killer cell activity and other immune cell functioning (Reiche & Nunes, 2005). Depressed patients also report greater pain intensity (Sist, Florio, Miner, Lema, & Zevon, 1998).

To compound the problem, a patient's depression is positively correlated with family caregivers' depression (Kurtz, Kurtz, Given, & Given, 1995), and depression persists even for some long-term survivors (McCorkle, Tang, Greenwald, Holcombe, & Lavery, 2006; Steinbach et al., 2006). Depression among survivors has become an important issue because there are now so many more of them. The number of people alive today after having had a cancer diagnosis at some time in their lives has more than tripled in the past 30 years (Hewitt & Rowland, 2002).

Analysis of cancer-related depression has shown that it is linked to **intrusive cognitions**. These are unwanted thoughts, often visual in nature, that are related to memories the patient has about cancer. They usually involve illness and death, often that of a friend, relative, or someone in a movie. One study discovered that 48 percent of anxious cancer patients experienced intrusive thoughts (Whitaker, Watson, & Brewin, 2009). These intrusive cognitions result in poor coping because they produce an anxious preoccupation with cancer, as well as a sense of helplessness and hopelessness (Whitaker, Brewin, & Watson, 2008).

> **intrusive cognitions:** unwanted thoughts, often visual in nature, related to the patient's ideas about cancer and death.

Brewin and colleagues studied 65 cancer patients who were either severely or mildly depressed, comparing them to a group of 65 non-depressed cancer patients. Thirty-two percent of mildly depressed patients and 43 percent of severely depressed patients reported intrusive memories, even though most of the participants had received their diagnoses years before. Only 11 percent of the non-depressed patients reported such memories (Brewin, Watson, McCarthy, Hyman, & Dayson, 1998).

The extent to which a person with cancer experiences depression and anxiety may be related to the person's coping style. For example, he or she may cope by focusing on ways to reduce the emotional impact of the disease. This is called **emotion-focused coping**. Alternatively, the person might engage in **problem-focused coping**. In this case, the person might seek information about the disease, closely follow treatment recommendations, and actively address the stressors associated with cancer and its treatment. One tendency in emotion-focused coping is to avoid thinking about possible stressors because to address them would be upsetting.

> **emotion-focused coping:** coping by focusing on ways to reduce the emotional impact of a disease without trying to cure it.
>
> **problem-focused coping:** coping by actively addressing the stressors associated with a disease, such as cancer, and its treatment.

There has been a long-standing belief that problem-focused coping is superior to emotion-focused coping (Coyne & Racioppo, 2000). One assumption behind this belief is that problem-focused coping has been viewed as an *approach-oriented* strategy, in which problems are faced and dealt with. On the other hand, emotion-focused strategies have been seen as being *avoidance-oriented* (Table 7-2). However, it has been pointed out that it is possible to adopt an approach orientation to emotion-focused coping (Austenfeld & Stanton, 2004). In this orientation, patients address their emotions, vent them, and deal with them. Thus, **emotional-approach coping**, in which patients face their emotional responses and deal with them effectively, could be quite adaptive (Austenfeld & Stanton, 2004).

> **emotional-approach coping:** coping by facing emotional responses to a disease and dealing effectively with those responses.

Table 7-2 A Comparison of Emotion-Focused and Problem-Focused Coping

	Emotion-focused coping	Problem-focused coping
Main objective	to reduce the experience of unpleasant emotions associated with the situation	to learn about the situation in order to affect factors that are causing the problem
Coping style	avoidant	active
Typical behaviours	avoid thinking about the situation	seeking information, following recommendations, and analyzing factors involved

Although problem-focused coping may be associated with an enhanced sense of control over an illness, this control, and a related sense of responsibility, can be associated with state anxiety (Cousson-Gélie, Irachabal, Bruchon-Schweitzer, Dihuydy, & Lakdja, 2005). At these times, patients might engage in self-blame, believing they should be able to control something that, in fact, they cannot. Self-blame has been shown to predict psychological distress in newly diagnosed breast cancer patients 7 to 12 months after diagnosis (Bennett, Compas, Beckjord, & Glinder, 2005).

In addition to the distinction between problem- and emotion-focused coping, other approaches have also been categorized according to fighting spirit, helplessness/hopelessness, denial, and avoidance (Petticrew, Bell, & Hunter, 2002). For example, prostate cancer patients who attended support groups were more likely than non-attendees to have adopted a coping style that was low in hopelessness and high in fighting spirit (McGovern, Heyman, & Resnick, 2002). In another study, patients who were considered to have adapted poorly to their cancer diagnosis showed low fighting spirit and high helplessness/hopelessness (Montgomery, Pocock, Titley, & Lloyd, 2003).

In summary, the cancer experience causes emotional responses and, in turn, is affected by those responses. People's psychosocial resources and the ways they think about their condition certainly affect coping. For example, optimism (David, Ruttenberg, & Bovberg, 2006) and having a sense of purpose in life (Pinquart & Frohlich, 2009) are positively associated with coping, and style of coping has implications for well-being.

Cancer Treatment

Cancer is most often treated through surgery, radiation therapy, chemotherapy, hormone therapy, or some combination of these. Anna, from Case 7-1, may have surgery to remove her tumour and possibly part or all of her breast. She may also have radiation therapy before surgery to shrink the tumour and chemotherapy after surgery to treat any cancer that may have spread.

Hormone therapy is used for cancers such as prostate and some breast cancers. When tumour growth is stimulated by the presence of certain hormones, the therapy reduces the existence of these tumour-stimulating hormones.

Prostate cancer patients on hormone therapy can experience persistent fatigue. Moreover, their sex drive can be severely diminished, and they may start developing female secondary sex characteristics, such as breast enlargement. Other forms of treatment also come with common side effects that can make coping difficult (Roesch et al., 2005).

Pain management is an important component recovery from surgery and this is particularly true for cancer patients recovering from surgery, but other psychological issues exist. One is the anxiety associated with the outcome of the surgery. Were all the cancerous cells removed? Was there evidence that the cancer had metastasized? How much normal tissue had to be removed? Will this affect normal functioning after the patient has recovered from the surgery?

Cancer surgery that requires the removal of a considerable amount of normal tissue is called **radical surgery**. Radical surgery has the potential to change not only normal functioning but also appearance. Thus, another important issue in cancer surgery is **disfigurement**. Cancers of the head and neck, for example, may require surgery that changes facial shape (Pruzinsky et al., 2006). Throat cancer surgery may require the removal of the larynx, which is responsible for making speech sounds. Following this surgery, patients often require the use of a prosthetic speech device that dramatically changes the sound of their voice.

radical surgery: cancer surgery that requires the removal of a considerable amount of normal tissue.

disfigurement: a potential physical result of cancer surgery that can have serious psychological consequences.

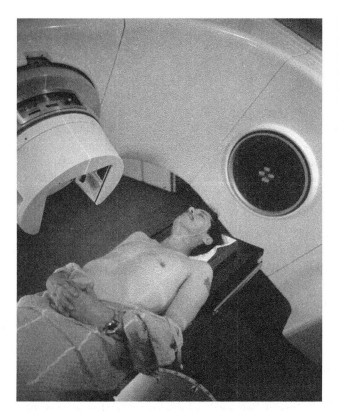

Machines like this radiation therapy machine deliver precise dosages of radiation designed to shrink tumours.
K.Glaser & Associates/Custom Medical Stock

Colorectal cancer is one of the four most common cancers in Canada, afflicting 23 200 Canadians in 2012 (Colon Cancer Canada, http://coloncancercanada.ca/statistics-2012/, accessed April 19, 2013). If surgery is required to remove part of the colon, a patient may require a prosthetic replacement of the lower colon. This requires that the patients wear a colostomy bag to collect waste materials, and they may also lose control of the bowel. Patients undergoing radical mastectomy, in which part or all of a breast is removed, can experience depression and disruptions in sexual activity. One study has shown that this depression is unaffected by whether or not breast reconstruction occurs immediately after mastectomy (Holly, Kennedy, Taylor, & Beedie, 2003). However, patients tend to cope better following the much less radical lumpectomy surgery (Moyer, 1997).

Surgery, then, comes with considerable psychological and physical costs. Opting against surgery, however, creates the real risk of having the tumour grow and spread. For young patients, decisions regarding surgery are usually easier to make than for elderly patients, who might suffer more from the surgery than the cancer and who don't have as many years left to lose as the younger patient.

Radiation therapy is used to shrink tumours. It can be used prior to or following surgery, or may be used on its own. Radiation therapy is usually administered on an outpatient basis, though patients' experiences with radiation therapy will differ significantly depending on the site of their cancer. A person may have just a few treatments or as many as 30 or more over the course of several weeks, as is the case with many prostate cancer patients.

Patients with head and neck tumours may have to undergo preliminary dental work before their radiation treatments can begin. They must also be fitted with a mask that will hold their heads in precisely the same position each time they come in for a treatment.

radiation therapy: a form of cancer treatment in which radiation is used to shrink or destroy tumours.

Patients with tumours in abdominal regions may be fitted with a body mould that they are placed in before treatments to ensure accuracy. They may also be tattooed with small cross-hair target marks to help the radiation technologists line up the beams that position the treatment. Side effects from radiation therapy depend on the extent to which the radiation hits neighbouring cells and organs.

Surgery and radiation therapy are treatments intended to deal with specific sites as precisely as possible. In cases in which it is suspected that the cancer has metastasized, or to help prevent it from doing so, **chemotherapy** is used in addition to surgery and/or radiation therapy. It is called an **adjuvant therapy** when used in conjunction with other therapies in this way. Rather than attacking specific sites, the powerful drugs used in chemotherapy are distributed throughout the body (with the exception of the brain in some circumstances).

As with radiation therapy, the side effects of chemotherapy are caused by unavoidable harm being done to healthy cells. These side effects include fatigue, nausea, hair loss, erosion of oral, and gastrointestinal mucosa, which can result in pain and diarrhea, and increased susceptibility to infection (Stuber, 1995). The number of side effects and their intensity vary depending upon the drug and the dosage. Fatigue is reported in up to 70 percent of chemotherapy and radiation patients (Dimeo, Stieglitz, Novelli-Fischer, Fetscher, & Keul, 1999) and, for many patients, is more problematic than pain (Curt et al., 2000). In some cases, fatigue is severe enough that the dosages have to be limited. It has been found, however, that exercise in the form of pedalling a stationary bike (in the supine position) (Dimeo, 2001, 2002) or moderately intensive walking (Mock et al., 2005) can significantly reduce fatigue in chemotherapy treatment.

Interestingly, of all the side effects associated with chemotherapy, 47 to 58 percent of breast cancer patients identified hair loss (called *alopecia*) as being the most difficult to deal with (Tierney, Taylor, & Closs, 1992). Both men and women find it difficult to cope with treatment-related hair loss (Hilton, Hunt, Emslie, Salinas, & Ziebland, 2008). In fact, the thought of hair loss might affect patients' willingness to pursue treatment that could be life-saving (Fawzy, Secher, Evans, & Giuliano, 1995). There are a number of understandable psychological reasons for this, many which relate to patients' sense of identity and many which have been shown to apply more to women than to men.

Hair is a distinctive, defining characteristic for us. We look markedly different without it. At the same time, hair loss signals a new identity—that of a cancer patient. Patients differ in how comfortable they are with this new identity. They may find that distinctive hats, scarves, and wigs help them re-establish a sense of uniqueness and normality. One of our students who had gone through chemotherapy chose not to cut his hair for years after it grew back. Others may pursue a program such as *Look Good . . . Feel Better* (see lgfb.ca).

The nausea and vomiting many patients experience as side effects of chemotherapy have received considerable study. Most chemotherapy treatments are administered in clinics on an outpatient basis or in physicians' offices. The patient then returns home to cope with the side effects. Patients might experience nausea and vomiting on the same day of the treatment, or after a delay of 2 to 5 days. Physicians and nurses have been shown to underestimate the frequency of delayed nausea and vomiting, which may occur in 50 to 60 percent of cancer patients (Grunberg et al., 2004).

It is not uncommon for patients to begin feeling nauseated *before* they receive their treatment. This is called **anticipatory nausea**, and it is explained in terms of classical conditioning (Jacobson et al., 1995) and also in terms of patients' expectations (Coiagluri et al., 2008; Montgomery & Bovbjerg, 2003). The setting in which the treatment is

chemotherapy: treatment used in addition to surgery and/or radiation therapy when it is suspected that cancer has metastasized, or to help prevent it from doing so.

adjuvant therapy: therapy used in conjunction with other therapy.

anticipatory nausea: nausea that is felt before a chemotherapy treatment begins, explained in terms of classical conditioning.

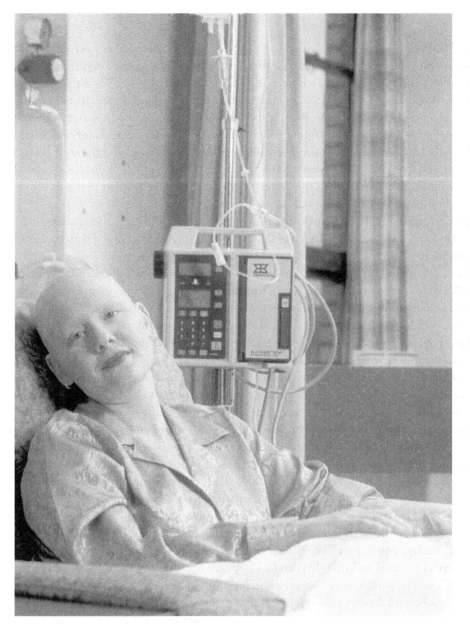

Hair loss can change the identity of patients undergoing chemotherapy. Some patients cover up with distinctive scarves and hats. Others display their new-found baldness comfortably.

Kevin Laubacher/Taxi/Getty Images

administered, the medical staff involved, and the smells of the room all become potential conditioned stimuli that bring on nausea in anticipation of the treatment. And to make matters worse, it is possible that immune suppression may be another conditioned response that accompanies anticipatory nausea.

When patients are given chemotherapy, they are also often given medication intended to reduce nausea and vomiting, called **antiemetic medication**. This can be administered before and after chemotherapy and radiation treatments. Studies have shown it to be effective for some patients (e.g., Dando & Perry, 2004; de Wit et al., 2004) but certainly not all (Hickok et al., 2003). Whether antiemetic medication is used may depend on the nature of the cancer and whether or not it could interfere with the effectiveness of the treatment (Muustedt et al., 1999).

antiemetic medication: medication intended to reduce nausea and vomiting.

Helping People Cope with Cancer

Social Support   It is clear that cancer provides many challenges to a person's capacity to cope. It is also important to realize that virtually every cancer patient has a family and a collection of close friends who are also affected by the disease. With this in mind, those treating cancer patients adopt comprehensive **family-oriented care**. In essence, the family becomes the patient. The lives of spouses and children can be changed dramatically when a family member is diagnosed with cancer. At the same time, family and friends will be called upon to provide much needed support for that person, and the strain on the family can be overwhelming (Sherwood et al., 2006). The family's ability to cope with cancer will be directly related to the extent to which they have learned in the past to be flexible in stressful situations (Goodheart & Lansing, 1997).

Modern medicine has sophisticated treatments for malignancies. It can also provide medication for depression and anxiety. However, when it comes to coping with cancer on a long-term basis, there is no substitute for a strong social support network (e.g., Holland & Holahan, 2003; Hoskins, Baker, Sherman, & Bohlander, 1996). We discuss social support a number of times in this book. We mention it here because of its importance as a mechanism for helping cancer patients and their families cope with serious illness. We know that social support is beneficial, but just how does it work? Those attempting to answer this question have taken a close look at the *social* nature of social support. What is it about some interactions that are so helpful and supportive?

We all know that sometimes it is enough to just "be there" as a sounding board for someone's concerns or to alleviate loneliness. Support can also be provided by helping with practical problems, such as providing a ride to an appointment, doing some cooking, or taking out the garbage. Some forms of support, especially some forms of emotional support, require that people *communicate* with one another. This has been called **help-intended communication** (Goodman & Dooley, 1976) and is defined as communication that attempts to alleviate emotional distress (Goldsmith, 2004). The interesting thing about help-intended communication is that, despite its good intentions, it doesn't always work. In fact, sometimes it can be perceived by the person with cancer as being *un*helpful (Dunkel-Schetter, 1984).

To identify some of the differences between helpful and unhelpful communication, Pistrang, Barker, and Rutter (1997) analyzed conversations between recently diagnosed breast cancer patients and their husbands. They audiotaped the conversations and played them back for the participants to get their impressions of what had been helpful and what had been unhelpful. Many women felt that a husband's attempts to lighten the conversation were unhelpful because they suggested that he didn't empathize with what she was going through. Similarly, attempts to "look on the bright side" may be seen as unhelpful because they fail to acknowledge legitimate fears and concerns.

While microanalyses such as these can provide valuable insights into the interactive aspects of social support, they can also be somewhat daunting for those trying to provide this support. When we become preoccupied with "saying the right thing," we may become paralyzed and thus entirely unhelpful. The general conclusion to draw from work like that of Pistrang and colleagues is that support providers should acknowledge the person's concerns and fears as being legitimate while trying to help the person find effective ways of dealing with them. We can do this without dwelling on the intricacies of every word we say.

The fact that a patient's husband might think he is being helpful while she thinks he is being unhelpful indicates that perceptions are very important when it comes to social

family-oriented care: in comprehensive cancer care, the family becomes the patient because for virtually every cancer patient there is a family and a collection of close friends who are also affected by the disease.

help-intended communication: communication that includes support, especially emotional support.

support. In fact, it may be that our beliefs about the *availability* of our support are as important as the actual support we receive (Komproe et al., 1997). The reassurance we get from knowing that support is out there if we need it has been shown to reduce depression and encourage cancer patients to actually seek support. This, in turn, reduces feelings of helplessness. This is reminiscent of what Vancouver residents say when asked how they can appreciate the city's mountains, which are so often obscured by cloud. They say, "It's important just knowing that they are there." When it comes to our social support networks, just knowing that they are there is very important.

Many patients also benefit from having a **navigator**. This person, often a nurse, community health worker, or social worker, can help people such as Anna from Case 7-1 negotiate the sometimes complicated world of cancer treatment (Doll et al., 2005). The navigator can also help Anna prepare for her appointments in terms of knowledge and expectations (Doll et al., 2003). Research on the value of navigators for cancer patients is mixed, however, in terms of treatment outcomes and survival, and more research is called for in this important area (Wells et al., 2008).

navigator: often a nurse, community health worker, or social worker who helps patients diagnosed with serious illnesses find their way through the sometimes complicated world of hospitals and treatment.

Empathy is an important element of support. Family and friends can provide some, but to truly empathize, two people must draw on similar experiences. For cancer patients, this means interacting with other patients in more formally organized support groups or being paired with volunteers who have had similar cancer experiences. For example, a well-timed visit from a volunteer can help breast cancer patients feel less isolated and more optimistic about the future (Dunn, Steginga, Occhipinti, & Wilson, 1999).

Community agencies and cancer centres coordinate such groups. In addition to providing empathy, these support groups can be good sources of information as new patients meet with others who have learned through experience how best to cope with various aspects of the disease. Studies have shown that support groups are of considerable benefit for prostate cancer patients. They help men feel more informed about the illness and more involved in the treatment (Gregoire, Kalogeropoulos, & Corcos, 1997; Kaps, 1994), and they provide opportunities to talk with other patients about difficult issues (Poole et al., 2001). In short, support groups provide good opportunities for problem-focused coping.

Having said this, it isn't necessarily true that support groups are good for all patients. Support groups often emphasize education, and so they suit people who cope best by being informed. These people are called *monitors*. By contrast, some patients cope best by blocking out information. These people are called *blunters* (Miller, 1980). It is very possible that blunters would have to change their coping style to benefit from support groups.

Social comparison processes may help explain why some people benefit from support groups while others do not (Bogart & Helgeson, 2000; Simoni, Franks, Lehavot, & Yard, 2011). When we engage in **social comparison**, we look to the opinions and experiences of others to determine what is right and wrong, normal or abnormal. We use this information to help guide us in our decision making (Festinger, 1954). This process is akin to the subjective norm component of the theory of reasoned action (Fishbein & Ajzen, 1975), which we discussed in chapter 1. When we engage in social comparison, we can compare *upward*, by looking at people who are better off than us, or we can compare *downward*, by looking at people who are worse off.

social comparison: monitoring the opinions and experiences of others to determine what is right and wrong, normal and abnormal; also subsequent use of this information to help with decision making.

In support groups, upward comparisons are made with group members who are seen to be coping better than the person doing the comparing, and downward comparisons are made with those seen to be doing worse. Patients who view upward comparisons as evidence that they can get better or downward comparisons as reminders that they should be thankful because they could be worse off would be more likely to attend a support group. On the other hand, people who find upward comparisons discouraging because they feel worse off by comparison and downward comparisons depressing because they see themselves eventually declining to that state would not be likely to attend. For example, a person recently diagnosed with a brain tumour may attend a support group and meet people whose cancer has advanced to the point where they are terminally ill. The person could be thankful that her disease isn't that bad, or she could be frightened by the prospect that her disease will progress the same way. The majority of people attending support groups make downward comparisons and feel better for having done so (Bogart & Helgeson, 2000). At the same time, research suggests that support groups should include people at similar stages of cancer to reduce the risks of maladaptive upward and downward comparisons (Vilhauer, 2011).

While cancer is undeniably distressing and can even lead to post-traumatic stress disorder (PTSD) (Kangas, Henry, & Bryant, 2002), it is not uncommon for cancer survivors to report positive outcomes from their cancer experience (Cordova, Cunningham, Carlson, & Andrykowski, 2001). These positive experiences fit in the category of **post-traumatic growth** (Tedeschi & Calhoun, 1995), which is often attributed to **benefit finding** (Katz, Flasher, Cacciapaglia, & Nelson, 2001; Lee & Poole, 2005), a term that refers to what might be called finding the "silver lining in the cloud." Growth can also stem from changing or affirming one's sense of spirituality (Gall & Cornblat, 2002), developing a greater appreciation of life, seeing new possibilities, and recognizing personal strength (Tedeschi & Calhoun, 1995).

post-traumatic growth: positive psychological or lifestyle outcome resulting from an experience with a life-threatening illness.

benefit finding: attitude or technique often referred to as finding the "silver lining in the cloud," which appears to aid in post-traumatic growth.

Psychotropic Medication and Psychotherapy   For many cancer patients, the depression and fear they experience can be adequately managed with the help of social support, whether from family, friends, or a support group. Support networks may be readily available for the patient or may be created with the help of the hospital, community, or social worker. For some patients, however, more intensive intervention is needed. These people may need to work with a clinical psychologist, counselling psychologist, or psychiatrist.

Psychiatrists might prescribe antidepressant medication such as fluoxetine (Prozac), which has been shown to be effective in treating depression in people with advanced cancer (Bailey et al., 2005). However, it is possible that complications may arise from taking antidepressant medication in conjunction with other cancer-related treatments, and so drug interactions have to be taken into consideration when antidepressants are prescribed (Franco-Bronson, 1996).

Because of the concerns associated with the use of medication and because psychotherapy has been shown to be effective as a means of helping cancer patients (Jacobsen & Hann, 1998), psychotherapeutic interventions are not uncommon. Psychotherapy in these settings may focus on thoughts and behaviours (cognitive-behavioural approaches), and it may provide opportunities for the patient to express emotions and address anxieties (supportive expressive therapy) (Schneiderman, Antoni, Saab, & Ironson, 2001).

Goodheart and Lansing (1997) have outlined a series of steps to follow when developing a psychotherapeutic treatment strategy for working with people who are chronically ill. These steps apply very well to cancer patients and their families. The first step is to *obtain sufficient medical information*. Some of this can be obtained from the patient. This may be difficult or burdensome for the patient, however, so the therapist must be able to communicate well with medical staff. Second, the therapist must *assess the person's psychological status and response to the illness*. In so doing, the therapist must weigh the demands of the illness against the coping resources of the patient. Also, the therapist must develop a sense of the person's psychological state before the illness. Third, the therapist must *integrate a theoretical orientation.* To probe the person's feelings and unstated anxieties, the therapist might adopt a psychodynamic orientation. To address functional quality-of-life issues, a behavioural orientation might be adopted. The key is to offer a range of interventions and then to match the intervention with the patient's most pressing needs.

Clinical psychologists, psychiatrists, and counsellors often work with people in groups. These therapeutic groups differ from support groups in that they are guided by a professional trained in psychotherapy, with the emphasis shifting somewhat from the provision of information to strategies to alleviate depression and anxiety. Therapy of this nature has been shown to reduce the physical and emotional distress associated with radiation therapy (Forester, Kornfeld, Fleiss, & Thompson, 1993). Indeed, research reviews on the outcomes of group psychotherapy for cancer patients have identified considerable evidence that such therapy helps coping (Classen et al., 2001; Goodwin et al., 2001), though the effects of psychotherapy on survival rates remain contested (Coyne, Thombs, Stefanek, & Palmer, 2009; Kraemer, Kuchler, & Spiegel, 2009). Others argue that, while we might not have evidence of a direct effect of psychotherapy on the biology of cancer (via the immune system), treatment outcomes may nevertheless be positively affected by behavioural mechanisms, such as improved adherence to treatments, improved diets, and increased physical activity (see Kissane, 2009, for a review).

Consistent with the notion of family-oriented care, psychotherapy is also often provided for families of the person with cancer. European research has shown that patients' relatives reported higher levels of anxiety and depression than the patients did (Schmid-Büchi, Halfens, Dassen, & van den Borne, 2011). The roles of family members change when one of them is diagnosed with cancer. Household responsibilities must be shared, as one or more members become the principal caregiver. There can also be financial difficulties if the person with cancer must take an extended leave from work. Family members may need help managing the psychological burdens associated with taking on various caregiving roles and, in some cases, being a "midwife to death" (Brown & Stetz, 1999). In these cases, grief counselling may also focus on the entire family.

Given the prevalence of cancer and the myriad coping challenges associated with the disease, it is clear that health psychologists can make significant contributions to the quality of life of cancer patients and to the coping abilities of the patients' families.

DIABETES

Approximately 2.4 million people in Canada have diabetes, and the disease is more common among males (Public Health Agency of Canada, 2011a). People with diabetes have mortality rates at least twice as high as those without. Diabetes occurs when the pancreas produces too little insulin, which is needed to help the body use sugar for energy. People with **insulin-dependent diabetes (Type I)** produce very little or no insulin. According to Health Canada, about 10 percent of all diabetics are Type I. People with **non-insulin-dependent diabetes (Type II)** do produce insulin, but they either don't produce enough or they can't use their insulin effectively. There is a third type, called **gestational diabetes**, which is a temporary condition affecting 2 to 4 percent of all pregnant women.

Type I diabetes is more prevalent among people of Aboriginal, African, and Latin-American decent, and among people who have a history of diabetes in their families. Type II diabetes is more common among people over the age of 45, especially if they are obese. While diabetes becomes more prevalent with age, over half of Canadians diagnosed

insulin-dependent diabetes (Type I): a condition in which a person produces very little or no insulin and as a result is required to take insulin on a daily basis, usually by way of self-administered injection.

non-insulin-dependent diabetes (Type II): a condition in which a person does not produce enough insulin or is not able to use insulin effectively.

gestational diabetes: a temporary condition affecting two to four percent of all pregnant women.

with diabetes are between 25 and 64 years of age (Public Health Agency of Canada, 2011a). For people with Type I diabetes, symptoms usually come on quite quickly and are severe, including frequent urination, unusual thirst, extreme hunger, unusual weight loss, and extreme fatigue. People with Type II diabetes might also experience frequent infections, and cuts and bruises that take a long time to heal.

People with Type I diabetes must monitor their blood sugar levels very carefully and take insulin, usually by self-administered injection, on a daily basis. While the vast majority of Type I patients monitor their blood glucose levels, a large study in Germany found that only 41 percent do so as often as they should (Haupt et al., 1996). Also, adherence to prescribed Type II diabetes medications ranges between 62 and 64 percent (Cramer, 2004). Research with children has found that their adherence to monitoring regimens varies considerably and is related to dynamics within the family. Not surprisingly, children with supportive parents who do not use nagging tend to control their diabetes better (Lewin et al., 2006). People with Type II diabetes do not have to take insulin; however, they must also monitor their blood sugar and maintain a well-controlled diet.

Diabetes and Psychological Distress

As is the case with most chronic illnesses, fear and depression are two of the most common psychological problems for people with diabetes.

Fear and Diabetes   Diabetic patients' fears tend to focus on the possible long-term consequences of the disease. These include amputation, cardiovascular disease, kidney failure (nephropathy), neurological problems, blindness (retinopathy), and stroke (Hendricks & Hendricks, 1998). These fears cause problems because they tend to get in the way of disease management for the patient and because stress-related hormones can interfere with insulin action (Wysocki, 2006). Consistent with the health belief model, diabetic patients who become fearful may doubt the efficacy of the management program in the face of these potentially terrible consequences.

People with Type I diabetes have other fears as well. They might fear self-injection or self-testing (Mollema, Snoek, Ader, Heine, & van der Ploeg, 2001). They might also have concerns when their blood sugar levels get out of balance. This condition, called **hypoglycemia**, brings on adverse physical symptoms, such as fatigue. Hypoglycemia can also be accompanied by disorientation, confusion, and negative mood. In extreme cases, hypoglycemia can lead to seizure or loss of consciousness.

hypoglycemia: low blood sugar.

The disorientation and negative mood states that sometimes accompany hypoglycemia can have upsetting social consequences. For example, a spouse, partner, or friend will often notice that a person is becoming hypoglycemic before the person notices it himself or herself. When the other person points this out, the suggestion might be met with anger and confusion (Ritholz & Jacobson, 1998). After the person gets his or her blood sugar stabilized, he or she may be discouraged by his or her inability to take quick action to remedy the condition and feel guilty about blowing up at someone who was only trying to help.

Type I diabetes often occurs in childhood. When it does, parents become very involved in disease management. Because of this, the parents' fears are just as relevant as those of the child. These fears include long-term complications, early death, and severe insulin reactions (Drozda, Allen, Standiford, Turner, & McCain, 1997). For example, parents of children who have had a diabetes-related seizure or loss of consciousness are significantly more afraid of hypoglycemia than are parents of diabetic children who have not suffered in this way (Marrero, Guare, Vandagriff, & Finebert, 1997). Parents must also find ways to help their children cope with daily routines that are usually much more structured than those of other children. These structures, and the symptoms of diabetes, can make diabetic children feel different from their healthy peers (Drozda et al., 1997). Family-oriented interventions have shown promise in supporting those dealing with the challenges of controlling diabetes by, for example, reducing the need for trips to hospital emergency departments (Ellis et al., 2005). (For an excellent review of the literature on families managing pediatric diabetes, see Lewin et al., 2006).

Depression and Diabetes   Depression and discouragement are frequent psychological consequences of diabetes. Depression is twice as prevalent among diabetics as among non-diabetics, and it is estimated to affect 18 to 28 percent of people with diabetes (Anderson, Freedland, Clouse, & Lustman, 2001; Chyun et al., 2006). Diabetics often have trouble talking to others about hypoglycemia and the emotions associated with it. As a result, they may feel isolated or unsupported. Moreover, as we have already mentioned, they may have a difficult time accepting help when it comes during a hypoglycemic episode. It is not surprising, then, that depression is significantly related to a diabetic's quality of life (Chyun et al., 2006).

To complicate matters, depression and blood sugar are linked bidirectionally. Low blood sugar worsens depression and, in turn, depression reduces the likelihood that people with diabetes will monitor their blood glucose levels regularly (Hood, Rausch, & Dolan, 2011). Not surprisingly, depression is also worse for people who suffer diabetes-related complications, such as cardiovascular problems, and it increases the risk for such complications (Lloyd, Mathews, Wing, & Orchard, 1992; Lustman, Freedland, Griffith, & Clouse, 1998). For these reasons, it is very important to treat depression in order to break the cycle of depression and worsening symptomology.

Focus on Canadian Research 7-1

Diabetes among Canada's Aboriginal Population

Fifty years ago, diabetes was virtually unheard of among Canada's Aboriginal peoples. Today, the prevalence of Type II diabetes in this population is three to five times the national average. Diabetes is more prevalent for First Nations people living on reserves than for those living elsewhere, pointing to risk factors such as diet. The diets of Canada's First Nations people have been influenced significantly by non-Aboriginal trends. Fast foods and high-sugar products, such as pop and candy bars, are replacing more traditional foods in the diets of First Nations people. The result has been this high rate, and earlier onset, of diabetes. This trend is compounded by later detection; by the time the disease is diagnosed, it is more severe than it would be in other populations (Public Health Agency of Canada, 2011b). All of this has resulted in the conclusion that diabetes has reached epidemic proportions among our Aboriginal peoples.

What can be done to address this problem? To find answers, Grams and colleagues (1996) held focus-group sessions with the Haida Gwaii living on the Queen Charlotte Islands, where 17 percent of the adults in one village suffered from diabetes. Through these discussions, it was discovered that the Haida found diabetes to be a very upsetting condition. They feared death and suffered grief from the loss of the things they loved to do and the things they loved to eat. They had a strong desire to regain personal control. The researchers concluded that attempts to help the Haida manage diabetes must not be dictatorial or prescriptive in nature. Rather, they must respect the way the Haida's feelings about the disease are manifest and work to give them a sense of control over their symptoms and valued aspects of their lives that suffer because of diabetes.

Helping People Cope with Diabetes

There are at least two major goals of programs designed to help diabetics. The first is to ensure cooperation with the disease-management regimen. The second is to treat psychological distress. As you can probably tell, these two goals are closely related. Psychological distress decreases cooperation with the disease-management regimen. Also, poor management results in worse symptoms and complications, which in turn bring on more distress.

One way to break this cycle is through cognitive behaviour therapy (CBT). It is important to explore this option, because antidepressant medication can have unwanted side effects for diabetics. Fortunately, research indicates that CBT can reduce depression significantly (Jacobson & Weinger, 1998) and, in adolescents, help improve glycemic control (Winkley, Landau, Eisler, & Ismail, 2006). Lustman, Griffith, and colleagues (1998) randomly assigned diabetic patients to either a CBT group or a control condition. They discovered that 85 percent of the CBT group showed relief from depression compared to only 27 percent of the control patients. It was also encouraging to note that, at follow-up, 70 percent of the CBT group were still not depressed, compared to 34 percent of the controls. A systematic review of the literature in this area, however, has shown that this reduction in depression does not always translate into better glycemic control by patients (Wang, Tsai, Chou, & Chen, 2008).

Educational and support groups are also provided for people with diabetes. This support is usually offered as part of a hospital education program that patients attend on a regular basis to learn more about the disease and its management, as well as to have their blood glucose and other indicators measured. At these sessions, patients can do much more than learn about nutrition and exercise. They also meet other patients, many of whom are coping well with their diabetes. This provides them with important information regarding efficacy—namely, that diabetes can be controlled. Patients also get "inside information" on disease control and emotional coping that can only come from other patients.

Family and friends of people with diabetes can help by being aware of the emotional side of the disease. The fears regarding long-term consequences are real. And when someone is experiencing hypoglycemia, it is important to remember that mood changes and disorientation might make him or her appear unreceptive to help. This does not mean that help shouldn't be offered.

DISEASES OF THE CARDIOVASCULAR SYSTEM

myocardial infarction (MI): heart attack caused by lack of blood flow to the heart.

coronary artery bypass graft (CABG, or bypass surgery): a procedure in which healthy arteries from other parts of the body, often the legs, are grafted into the coronary artery system to bypass blocked arteries.

angioplasty: a procedure in which a bubble-like device is inserted into the artery at the point of the blockage, thus expanding the artery and allowing for better blood flow.

In Canada, cardiovascular disease death rates have declined by 40 percent in the last 10 years. Still, every 7 minutes someone in Canada dies from stroke or heart disease (Statistics Canada, 2012b). When health psychologists work with and study people with heart and cardiovascular disease, they typically focus on three types of conditions.

The first is heart attack, or **myocardial infarction (MI)** as it is known medically. Of particular interest are people who have had their *first* MI. The medical and psychological challenge for these people is to reduce the likelihood that they will have a second MI, which far fewer people survive. A second group consists of people who have had a **coronary artery bypass graft (CABG)**. This is commonly called bypass surgery, a procedure in which healthy arteries from other parts of the body, often the legs, are grafted into the coronary artery system to, as the term implies, bypass blocked arteries. The third group consists of people who have had **angioplasty**. In this procedure, a bubble-like device is inserted into the artery at the point of the blockage, thus expanding the artery and allowing for better blood flow. In a similar procedure, a cylindrical piece of metal called a stent is inserted to support the walls of the vessel. Other procedures, such as excimer laser coronary angioplasty, make use of laser technology (Karaca, Ilkay, Akbulut, & Yavuzkir, 2003; Topaz et al., 2003). Bypass surgery and angioplasty are used to treat a condition called **myocardial ischemia**, in which there is a lack of blood flow to the heart muscle.

myocardial ischemia: a lack of blood flow to the heart muscle.

Taken collectively, these conditions associated with MI and CABG represent coronary heart disease (CHD). Many of the risk factors for CHD are related to health psychology. Prominent among predisposing factors are those related to psychological distress, including depression, anxiety, social isolation, low perceived emotional support, hostility, and work-related stress (Hemingway & Marmot, 1999; Rozanski, Blumenthal, & Kaplan, 1999).

Cardiovascular Disease and Psychological Distress

Patients with cardiovascular disease often experience accompanying psychological distress. This not only affects their quality of life when they have the disease, but also puts them at greater risk for developing CHD in the first place (Wulsin & Singal, 2003).

One common form of psychological distress accompanying cardiovascular disease is anxiety. Trait anxiety results in poorer quality of life for cardiac patients (Engebretson et al., 1999). A heart attack can be a frightening experience, so it is not surprising to find that some patients live in fear of having another one. As a result, these patients become crippled by their cardiac history; they curtail their activity levels far more than their disease status requires. This phenomenon, called **cardiac invalidism** (Riegel, Dracup, & Glaser, 1998), creates two major problems for the patient. First, the patient stops engaging in some of the things that enhance his or her quality of life, such as tennis, golf, or sexual activity. Second, the patient lapses into a sedentary lifestyle that is not conducive to good cardiovascular health.

cardiac invalidism: anxiety regarding a subsequent heart attack causes patients to curtail their activity levels far more than required by their actual disease status.

Anxiety is particularly strong for people who experience cardiac arrest, in which their heart actually stops beating and they must be resuscitated. In the first few weeks after cardiac arrest, phobic anxiety and panic symptoms are not uncommon (Ladwig & Dammann, 1997). An additional problem with these reactions is that panic symptoms often mimic heart problems or heart attack. This, in turn, fuels the sense of panic and a vicious cycle begins that further compromises the person's cardiac health. Fortunately, this anxiety stabilizes for most patients in time, though many experience intrusive thoughts about the event and try to avoid anything that might remind them of their resuscitation (Ladwig et al., 1999).

Perhaps the most common form of psychological distress associated with cardiovascular and heart disease is depression (Blane, Hughes, & McElnay, 2006). In fact, the incidence of major depression is three to four times greater for coronary artery disease patients than it is for the general population (Sheps & Rozanski, 2005). In addition, depression is a risk factor for the development of cardiovascular disease (Ward, Tueth, & Sheps, 2003; Wulsin & Singal, 2003) and for mortality after disease has been diagnosed, even for minor depression (Bush et al., 2002).

Five-year follow-up studies have shown that people with major depression are more likely to be hospitalized for cardiac problems than are patients with minor depression (Sullivan, LaCroix, Spertus, Hecht, & Russo, 2003). As well, depression predicts major adverse cardiac events (Frasure-Smith & Lespérance, 2008) and mortality after a diagnosis of cardiac disease (Frasure-Smith & Lespérance, 2003). Given these findings, it appears that there is a bidirectional relationship between depression and cardiovascular disease. It becomes imperative, therefore, to treat the depression and break this dangerous cycle.

There is evidence to suggest that this depression might be more problematic for women, especially those who are older (Naqvi, Naqvi, & Merz, 2005). It has been estimated that women are twice as likely as men to suffer post-MI depression (Frasure-Smith, Lesperance, & Talajic, 1993). One study found that 23 percent of female cardiac patients, including those with problems other than heart attack, were depressed.

Depression is particularly problematic for older cardiac patients. Patients over the age of 65 who are depressed are more than twice as likely to report difficulties with activities of daily living (ADL) (Steffens et al., 1999). Again, the consequences of depression appear to be somewhat more severe for women in this age group.

Regarding the physiological mechanisms by which depression increases risk of mortality for cardiac patients, research is examining the autonomic nervous system (Carney, Freedland, & Veith, 2005) and the immune system (Kop & Gottdiener, 2005), especially in terms of inflammation (Surtees et al., 2008; Taylor et al., 2006). (See chapter 3.)

Helping People Cope with Cardiovascular Disease

In addition to the support of family and friends, cardiac patients can benefit from rehabilitation programs and, where appropriate, psychotherapy. Modern rehabilitation programs for people recovering from heart attack, bypass surgery, or angioplasty are holistic in nature. That is to say, they address all aspects of the participant's life, from diet to exercise to psychological well-being (Lett, Davidson, & Blumenthal, 2005). (See the story of Peter in chapter 5). Rehabilitation programs for people who have had one myocardial infarction have been shown to reduce mortality by 47 percent 1 year post-MI (Frasure-Smith & Prince, 1985) and improve psychological status in terms of reduced negative affect and state anxiety (Engebretson et al., 1999).

Rehabilitation programs may differ somewhat from location to location, but most share certain elements in common. Participants have their physical condition monitored. They are provided with education regarding their medication and the reduction of risk factors. They are also put on programs intended to reduce those risk factors, focusing on diet, exercise, and stress reduction. One such program, which featured three 75-minute sessions per week over 12 weeks, reduced levels of anxiety, depression, and confusion while increasing the participants' sense of vigour. This was particularly true for participants with high trait anxiety, which is a risk factor for further morbidity and poor quality of life (Engebretson et al., 1999). Another program tailored specifically to women yielded lower depression, anxiety, and hostility and increased exercise capacity and quality of life for the participants (Lavie, Milani, Cassidy, & Gilliland, 1999). For a listing of programs across Canada, visit http://www.cardiachealth.ca/index.php?o=locate-rehab-centre (accessed April 26, 2013.)

Another important psychological factor to address in therapy with cardiac patients is anger. Anger is a risk factor for CHD, especially when expressed as hostility; one episode of intensely expressed anger can trigger a fatal heart attack for people with severe CHD. Therapy intended to reduce anger features a number of components. Participants are taught to monitor their emotions, so they can identify times when anger is a problem (Davidson, Gidron, Mostofsky, & Trudeau, 2007; Mayne & Ambrose, 1999). They are also taught relaxation skills. In terms of their thinking, participants go through what is called **cognitive reappraisal and restructuring**. In this, they learn to think differently about the things that tend to make them angry. For example, they may have been blaming other drivers for traffic jams or may mistakenly assume that people who frustrate them do so intentionally.

cognitive reappraisal and restructuring: therapy sometimes used with cardiac patients, in which they learn to think differently about the things that make them angry, and to make behavioural changes such as learning to control their breathing.

Is Feeling Down Bad for the Heart?

Since the mid-1980s, Nancy Frasure-Smith and her colleagues at McGill University have led the investigation into the relationship between cardiovascular disease and depression. One of their studies (Frasure-Smith & Lesperance, 2003) followed patients for 5 years after they'd had a myocardial infarction. Frasure-Smith and her team administered a collection of self-report measures to assess such things as depression, anxiety, anger, and perceived social support soon after the participants had their heart attacks. The researchers then kept track of mortality statistics over the 5-year period. The participants were 896 patients taken from 10 hospitals in the Montreal area. The purpose of the study was to determine the extent to which each of those psychological states helped predict mortality after heart attack.

They found that 155 people died during the 5-year period. Of those deaths, 121 were cardiac-related. After taking factors such as sex and age into account, Frasure-Smith and colleagues then used correlation methods to determine which psychological factors best predicted mortality.

A number of psychological measures correlated significantly with mortality. These included depression and anxiety, as well as a more general measure of psychological distress (the General Health Questionnaire). Anger, stress, and social support were not significant predictors of mortality. Of all the measures, depression was the best single predictor of mortality.

Participants also spend time on behavioural change, in which they learn to control their voice tone, breathing, and so on.

With the proven benefits of holistic cardiac rehabilitation programs you might think that such programs are well attended, but they are not. In Canada, fewer than 20 percent of patients with coronary artery disease participate in such programs (Gravely-Witte et al., 2010; Suskin et al., 2003). Researchers at the University of Alberta have suggested that psychological factors affect these attendance rates. Such factors as self-efficacy, motivation, and social support may all be predictive of program completion (King & Teo, 1998). Again, this suggestion is consistent with the health belief model and the theory of reasoned action discussed in chapter 1. These theories predict that attendance would be higher for people who thought the program would work and who knew others who had either attended successfully or who encouraged them to do so.

For some patients, rehabilitation programs are not enough to help them overcome depression, and so medications are prescribed. For example, sertraline has shown promise for safe use as an anti-depressant soon after acute MI (Carney & Jaffe, 2002).

HIV AND AIDS

Acquired immune deficiency syndrome (AIDS) was first reported in Canada in 1982. As of 2008, an estimated 65 000 people in Canada were living with HIV infection (Public Health Agency of Canada, 2010a). The number of people diagnosed as positive for the **human immunodeficiency virus (HIV)** began to decline in 1995; however, this number began to increase again in 2000 and has more recently levelled off (see Figure 7-1). Prolonged HIV infection results in AIDS and the number of people who die from AIDS continues to drop each year.

There are some groups that are at greater risk than others for contracting AIDS. These include men who have sex with men, injection drug users, those who receive blood and blood products, and the Aboriginal population (see Box 7-1).

acquired immune deficiency syndrome (AIDS): a disease caused by the human immunodeficiency virus (HIV); after infection, the body's compromised immune system makes it susceptible to a host of other infections.

human immunodeficiency virus (HIV): a virus that gradually breaks down the body's immune system, making it susceptible to a host of other infections, eventually resulting in AIDS.

Figure 7-1 Reported Number of People Testing HIV Positive in Canada, 1995–2005

Source: *HIV and AIDS in Canada. Surveillance Report to December 31, 2005.* Figure 1: Number of positive HIV test reports by year of test (all ages), Surveillance and Risk Assessment Division, Centre for Infectious Disease Prevention and Control. Source: Public Health Agency of Canada, 2006. Reproduced with the permission of the Minister of Public Works and Government Services Canada, 2010.

The profile of just who has AIDS has changed significantly over the decades. The proportion of newly diagnosed cases of AIDS has dropped significantly among men who have sex with men—from 75 percent of cases diagnosed between 1985 and 1994 to 37 percent in 2005. However, among injection drug users, the rate has increased from 9 percent of diagnosed cases to 30 percent (Health Canada, 2002). Also, the female proportion of those with AIDS has increased sharply, from 6.6 percent in 1996 to 21.7 percent in 2005 (PHAC, 2006).

Box 7-1

AIDS and Canada's Aboriginal Population

In 1993, 2 percent of everyone infected with AIDS were known to be Aboriginal persons. By 1999, that proportion had grown to 10 percent (*HIV/AIDS among Aboriginal Persons in Canada: A Continuing Concern*, 2003). The proportion dropped during 2000 and 2001, but it climbed in 2002 to reach over 14 percent. Among these growing numbers, young people and women are disproportionately represented (*HIV/AIDS among Aboriginal Persons in Canada: A Continuing Concern*, 2003). In 2003, more than 60 percent of Aboriginal peoples testing HIV positive were injection drug users, making it the most common mode of transmission for this group (PHAC, 2011c).

AIDS develops at an earlier age within Canada's Aboriginal population. Over 30 percent of the Aboriginal people who are HIV positive are under the age of 30, compared to 20 percent for non-Aboriginal people.

Twenty-three percent of Aboriginal persons living with AIDS (PLWA) are female, compared to just 8 percent of the non-Aboriginal PLWA population. Females represented almost half of HIV diagnoses between 1998 and 2008, compared to 22 percent in the non-Aboriginal population. AIDS and HIV, therefore, are growing problems for Aboriginal peoples (Public Health Agency of Canada, 2010a).

HIV is a so-called slow virus, with a long time delay between initial infection and the surfacing of serious symptoms. During this time period, CD4+ cells, which have receptors for the virus, cease to function and eventually die. Thus, the immune system is gradually compromised.

The symptoms of AIDS include persistent fever; swelling of the lymph glands on the neck and under the arms; frequent fatigue; diarrhea; sweating during sleep; and yeast infections in the vagina, ears, and tongue. Since these symptoms aren't unique to HIV, a person with concerns should see a physician.

HIV gradually breaks down the body's immune system, making it susceptible to a host of other infections, including neoplasms such as non-Hodgkin's lymphoma and Kaposi's sarcoma. HIV can be transmitted through unprotected vaginal or anal sex, through the sharing of needles, or during pregnancy or childbirth, when a mother can transmit HIV to her child.

HIV/AIDS and Psychological Distress

HIV and AIDS are different from most other chronic and serious illnesses in a number of ways. First, though modern medicine has made encouraging strides in prolonging the lives of persons living with HIV and AIDS, there is still no cure for AIDS. In addition to a set of symptoms that can be difficult to endure, people living with AIDS often experience stigmatization (Joachim & Acorn, 2000; Rintamaki & Brashers, 2005). Their self-esteem and well-being suffer as they internalize this stigma (Lee, Kochman, & Sikkema, 2002).

Unlike many other serious illnesses, AIDS is contagious; in addition to which there are many myths about contagion. AIDS patients may feel personal responsibility or guilt regarding their illness. Additionally, many people with AIDS have lost people from their social network to the very disease they are trying to cope with. For all these reasons, people with HIV and AIDS must deal with a host of unique psychological challenges (Kelly, 1998). Generally, psychological distress is worsened if there is a lack of acceptance by family members; isolation is exacerbated if the patient does not attend a support group or know other people with HIV (Lee et al., 2002; Schmitz & Crystal, 2000). It is not surprising to find that over 54 percent of people living with HIV and AIDS in Canada experience depression (Williams et al., 2005).

Anxiety is a common problem for persons living with AIDS (Phillips & Morrow, 1998), even in the current era of life-prolonging therapies (Mkanta, Mejia, & Duncan, 2010). This anxiety stems from uncertainty about the future, the losses that are experienced, the social stigma, the prejudice that the offspring of people living with AIDS must endure, and the disease process itself (Phillips & Morrow, 1998). An HIV-positive diagnosis can be traumatic enough to elicit symptoms of PTSD, which is often related to major depression (Springer, Chen, & Altice, 2009). One study discovered that 30 percent of HIV-positive gay and bisexual men showed symptoms of PTSD, and the onset of these symptoms in one-third of the infected men began 6 months or more after their HIV-positive diagnosis (Kelly et al., 1998). PTSD symptoms were more prevalent for men who had a history of PTSD prior to their HIV diagnosis.

Helping People Cope with HIV and AIDS

When providing psychotherapy for people who are HIV positive, a number of clinical issues must be considered (Smiley, 2004). Unlike other diseases, it can be difficult for

HIV/AIDS patients to disclose their disease status to others. Telling someone you are HIV positive just isn't the same as telling that person you have a blocked artery. To compound things, persons living with AIDS have higher rates of bereavement and may have been caregivers themselves, especially if they are gay men or intravenous drug users (IDU). For these reasons, persons living with AIDS must often re-establish their social support systems. They must also make and maintain major changes in terms of risk-related behaviour and adhere to medical regimens that can be complex and extensive.

Psychotherapy issues for persons living with AIDS have changed somewhat over the past few years due to advances in medicine that prolong life expectancies (Fox & Gourlay, 2000; Gushue & Brazaitis, 2003). **Highly active antiretroviral treatment (HAART)** (Gray, Chretien, Vallat-Decouvelaere, & Scaravilli, 2003) and **protease inhibitor** drug combinations are significantly prolonging the lives of persons living with AIDS. International research with leadership from Simon Fraser University has found that these therapies are increasing life expectancies for people with AIDS by 13 years (Hogg et al., 2008). People living with HIV now live more than 10 years before developing AIDS (BC Centre for Disease Control, 2013), and those diagnosed with HIV/AIDS live an average of 24 years after diagnosis, provided they receive the best care (Schackman, Finkelstein, Neukermans, Lewis, & Eldred, 2005). The psychotherapeutic issues are changing accordingly. Not surprisingly, psychological status is often related to disease-related milestones, such as the first notification of seropositive status, first symptoms, and first sign of AIDS-defining illness (Kelly, 1998).

Therapy for people dealing with these and other factors is often conducted in groups, which has proven effective (Smiley, 2004). The therapist must take into account the makeup of the group, given that AIDS affects many different types of people. For example, a group consisting exclusively of gay men is quite different from one in which there are gay men, IDU, and heterosexual women.

Groups may adopt a cognitive focus in which they help participants put a stop to intrusive thoughts or address irrational beliefs that lead to depression and anxiety. Groups can also take on a behavioural focus, looking at ways to cope with problems at home and at work, strategies for regaining social support, and ways to relax and manage stress. In general, psychological interventions for persons living with AIDS improve psychological status, and there is some evidence that therapy improves endocrine levels and immune system functioning (Schneiderman et al., 2001).

Those providing care to people living with AIDS are in need of considerable support. When AIDS patients are from the gay community, it is not uncommon for their caregivers to be from that same community. These caregivers may well have seen many of their friends and loved ones die. They may fear HIV infection themselves or know that they are, in fact, seropositive.

A Final Word about Our Discussion of HIV and AIDS

It is important to note that our discussion of HIV and AIDS has been from a decidedly North American perspective. AIDS, however, is a worldwide disease that is experienced very differently depending upon geopolitical and socioeconomic contexts. For example, survival rates based on "best" or "optimal" care may be relevant in parts of the world where such care is available but of little relevance in places where it is not. To develop an international perspective on HIV/AIDS, see Volume 17, Issue 3-4, of the *Journal of*

highly active antiretroviral treatment (HAART): a treatment for AIDS that has been shown to significantly increase life expectancy.

protease inhibitor: medication that can significantly prolong the lives of people living with AIDS.

Human Behavior in the Social Environment, published in 2008. In that issue, you will find articles describing the AIDS experience of people in many countries.

OTHER CHRONIC CONDITIONS

Cancer, cardiovascular disease, diabetes, and AIDS are four of the most commonly studied chronic conditions in health psychology. There are, of course, other chronic conditions that are equally pressing for the people experiencing them. Included in this list would be Parkinson's disease and arthritis. More generally, many people live with physical and mental disabilities. Each of these conditions carries its own set of coping challenges.

For example, major depression occurs in 20 to 40 percent of all people with Parkinson's disease (Lieberman, 2006). This causes further problems in terms of memory, language, and motor performance. Not surprisingly, depression can also be a problem for people coping with the chronic pain of arthritis (Mangelli, Gribbin, Buchi, Allard, & Sensky, 2002), a disease that affects about 1 percent of the population and between 5 and 7 percent of those over the age of 65. One study found that 36 percent of patients with arthritis (average age, 57 years) had scores indicative of clinical depression, which is above the norm for the general population (Walsh, Blanchard, Kremer, & Blanchard, 1999). As is the case with depression and most chronic conditions, the depression and disease symptoms tend to worsen together. Also, depression is related to feelings of isolation and self-blame and is worse for people who feel a lack of control over their illness (Murphy, Dickens, Creed, & Bernstein, 1999).

Additionally, many people cope with permanent physical disabilities that may impair their movement or sensory capacities. One of the main obstacles for people with disabilities is the attitudes of people *without* disabilities. These attitudes, which may range from pity to understanding to impatience, are often formed in childhood and might be based on stereotypes rather than first-hand experience (Bracegirdle, 1995; Dovidio, Pagotto, & Hebl, 2011; Harper, 1999).

The quality of life of people living with disabilities depends, in part, on their belief that they are engaged in meaningful activities. Another important factor is their sense of social integration, which is, of course, related to the extent to which they are accepted by others (Viemeroe & Krause, 1998). When trying to understand the psychological factors associated with coping with a disability, it is important to consider when the person became disabled. People who have recently become disabled may still be struggling with changes in their sense of self and re-evaluating their identity (Iwai, 1996; Mpofu & Houston, 1998).

Psychotherapy for people with physical disabilities has yielded encouraging results, although many psychotherapists neither see clients from this population nor specialize in the unique needs of people with physical disabilities (Hurley, Tomasulo, & Pfadt, 1998), which can include an accurate assessment of the person's physical capabilities and an understanding of the person's beliefs regarding his or her disability. Also, as is the case with many chronic conditions, there are caregivers to consider, who may be burdened by their responsibilities (Dumont, St. Onge, Fougeyrollas, & Renaud, 1998).

QUALITY OF LIFE

In this chapter on chronic and serious illness, we have made repeated reference to a patient's "quality of life." Just what does this mean? When we refer to **quality of life** in the context of serious and chronic illness, we are talking about the extent to which symptoms

quality of life: the extent to which symptoms and treatment affect a person's physical, social, cognitive, and emotional functioning.

and treatment affect a person's physical, social, cognitive, and emotional functioning. Furthermore, we are interested in how the patient *prioritizes* and *values* these functions, so that we can develop a more complete understanding of the impact the condition and treatment are having on the patient's life.

It may seem obvious that quality of life would be a primary concern in the treatment of people with serious and/or chronic illness. However, this has not always been the case. This is because treatments that might alleviate some of the medical symptoms of the disease can have very negative effects on other aspects of a patient's life. If the treatment plan is focused solely on biological factors, such as tumour size, it is easy to lose sight of the price the patient is paying for that treatment in a more holistic sense.

At least two issues become important when quality of life is made a priority as a treatment outcome. First, those providing treatment must be sensitive to the *tradeoff* between duration of life and quality of life. Second, the patient must be an integral member of the decision-making team, because quality of life is a *subjective* phenomenon (Gathchel & Oordt, 2003).

The Tradeoff between Duration and Quality of Life

The efficacy of treating a serious illness is often defined by the extent to which the treatment prolongs the life of the patient. For example, a person with throat cancer may have surgery that will prolong his life by 5 years. Without the surgery, he might live 1 year. Thus, the treatment is deemed reasonably efficacious because it has the potential to prolong the person's life by 4 years. Of course, after the surgery, which will very possibly involve the removal of the patient's larynx, a prosthetic device will be needed in order to talk. The patient's voice will not resemble his own and will sound somewhat mechanical. Also, there will be high levels of postoperative pain. In this case, the tradeoff is clear—5 years with an artificial voice and pain versus 1 year with his own voice and much less pain. The fact that the two options are clear does not make the decision an easy one, however.

The point of the example, of course, is that this decision must be based primarily on quality of life. If the person is an opera singer who cannot stand the thought of having a mechanized voice, then his quality of life would be compromised so severely by the surgery that it ceases to be a viable option. On the other hand, if the patient has a granddaughter who is getting married in 18 months and the patient dearly wants to be at the wedding, surgery is a good option because his quality of life is defined in terms of the wedding rather than his voice.

Figure 7-2 presents a graphic representation of what practitioners and patients must consider (Albertsen, 1998). In Figure 7-2a, the decision is quite straightforward. The therapeutic gain from the treatment is realized immediately from the time of treatment, as indicated by the distance between the treatment and no treatment lines at the start of the graph. Also, this gain is maintained for 7 years, and the duration of life is equivalent with or without treatment. This would be analogous to the types of treatment gains typically found in coronary bypass surgery or angioplasty for older patients. The decision in Figure 7-2b is more difficult. Without treatment, the patient could live a high-quality life for approximately 3 years. With treatment, she would live at least twice as long but at a much lower quality of life. It is not until those lines cross, at about 3.5 years, that any therapeutic gain is realized by the treatment. This graph is representative of the kinds of decisions some cancer patients must make.

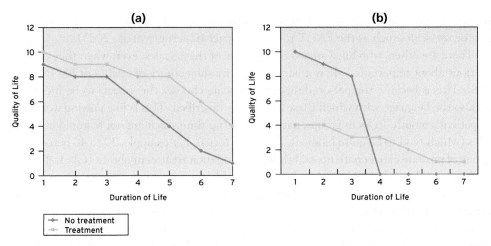

Figure 7-2 Treatment and Quality of Life

Figure 7.2a Treatment enhances quality of life
Figure 7.2b Treatment prolongs life but does not improve quality of life

Source: Based on Albertsen, P. "A competing risk analysis of outcomes associated with men treated conservatively for clinically localized prostate cancer." Paper presented at the Cancer Care: Quality of Life and Outcomes Symposium, Chicago, Illinois (Nov. 13–14,1998). Adapted by permission.

Quality of Life as a Subjective Phenomenon

Quality of life must be measured **phenomenologically**—that is, by asking the patient directly to report on the phenomenon. In this respect, quality of life is like freedom. If someone says she is free, then she has freedom, regardless of whether she lives in an oppressive regime or on a deserted island. To illustrate this, consider the following conversation between a physician and her patient:

phenomenologically: according to a person's own report on the phenomenon.

Patient:	If I have this operation, will I be able to play competitive tennis again?
Physician:	No. It will give you at least 5 more years of life, but your mobility will be restricted so that tennis would be very difficult.
Patient:	Then I don't want the operation.
Physician:	Because of tennis?
Patient:	Yes.
Physician:	But it's only a game!

For the physician, the notion that someone would rather not live than live without tennis is unthinkable, as it may be for you. However, what the physician thinks or what you and I think is irrelevant, because this is a quality-of-life decision, which is by definition subjective.

Most of the quality-of-life questionnaires in use today acknowledge the subjectivity of the phenomenon when they ask respondents to indicate not only if they are able to perform a given function, but also how *important* the function is to the respondents. A good example is the Functional Assessment of Cancer Therapy (FACT) scales (Brucker, Yost, Cashy, Webster, & Cella, 2005; Cella et al., 1993). After completing each subscale, which assesses such things as emotional well-being, respondents are asked how important emotional well-being is to them. Research measuring the effects of psychotherapy and exercise use scales such as the FACT to assess impact (Courneya et al., 2003).

There are others who have argued that the use of these scales, even when they do ask questions about importance, do not account for the subjectivity of quality of life (Clark, 1998). This is because the person designing the scale chooses the aspects to be included and also the language with which these aspects are described. This is like putting words in the patient's mouth. In focus groups, patients bring up things that are not featured in most scales (which tend to be quite biomedical in their focus). For example, 30 to 40 percent of a group of prostate cancer patients said they regretted their treatment choice (Clark, 1998), which is something that isn't explored in quality-of-life questionnaires as a rule.

Another consideration when measuring quality of life is whether the assessment is **multidimensional** or **global**. The scales we have been discussing have been multidimensional in that they assess different aspects of quality of life, such the ability to function physically, emotionally, and socially. A global approach would require just one question—for example, "How would you rate your quality of life today?" (Gough, Furnival, Schilder, & Grove, 1983). Generally, multidimensional approaches are favoured because they allow for an assessment of how an illness is affecting specific areas of a patient's life.

multidimensional measures of quality of life: assessment that includes specific aspects of quality of life, such as physical, emotional, and social.

global measures of quality of life: a general or overall assessment of quality of life without focusing on specific aspects.

DEATH AND DYING

Any attempt to help people cope with chronic and serious illnesses must address the prospect of premature death. In some cases, this prospect is very real.

Patients' Reactions to Death

Our thinking about death and the process of dying has been influenced greatly by the foundational work of psychiatrist Elisabeth Kübler-Ross (Kübler-Ross, 1969). Through her work, we moved from the belief that dying people did not want to know or talk about their death to the realization that they *did* want to talk about their impending death (see Table 7-3). Another important contribution was her theory identifying a series of

Table 7-3 Reactions to Impending Death

Reaction	Description
Denial	Refusing to acknowledge the potential seriousness of a diagnosis or condition, perhaps to the point of making long-range plans in spite of a poor prognosis.
Anger	Often in response to feelings of unfairness, anger can be directed at health care professionals, family, or others.
Bargaining	"Buying more time" by taking on altruistic projects or striving to make self-improvements.
Depression	Can be associated with giving up, or feelings of helplessness and hopelessness.
Acceptance	Being at peace with one's situation and possibly viewing death as a relief.

Source: Kübler-Ross, (1969). *On Death and Dying*. New York: MacMillian.

reactions a person might experience when facing his or her own death. When her theory was first published, it was presented as a stage theory, which is to say that the reactions were postulated to occur in a particular sequence (Kübler-Ross, 1969). Now, it is believed that the reactions she identified may be common to many patients, but that not all patients experience all reactions, nor do they do so in a particular order.

The first reaction identified by Kübler-Ross is **denial**. Denial is a defence mechanism we call upon when we are confronted with novel and severe trauma. The news that one is about to die certainly fits in that category. When people receive this news, they may think the physician is not being serious, or that some mistake has been made. They may make long-range commitments, ignoring the fact that their prognosis indicates they will not be alive to keep them.

Anger is a reaction that often follows denial. Patients might get angry at the medical system for being "incompetent" and for "all its fancy equipment and pills" being unable to prevent the patient from dying. They might get mad at the unfairness of it all. The anger may spread to family and friends. The dying person may become angry with them for not being helpful enough or trying to be too helpful, regardless of what they are actually doing. This can be difficult for family and friends to understand. Patients may also respond by **bargaining**, trying to do things that will buy more time. Perhaps they will volunteer for research or make strong commitments in terms of religiosity or spirituality. (This is not to say that all expressions of spirituality should be viewed as attempts at bargaining.)

We have discussed depression quite extensively in this chapter, so it will come as no surprise to learn that Kübler-Ross identifies **depression** as a common reaction to dying. While understandable, depression is still problematic because it often means the person gives up, thus unduly hastening death.

Finally, there is **acceptance**. If and when patients reach this point, they are likely to be at peace. Perhaps they view death as a relief. In fact, the patient might be considerably more peaceful than the family members and friends who are preparing for bereavement. Acceptance is emotionally very different from depression. Acceptance tends to come later than depression in the dying process and is not accompanied by a sense of despondency.

Group therapy for people with serious illnesses must confront participants' feelings regarding death. If not, some of these people may die without the very important sense of reassurance that allows them to die peacefully (or, as people who work in palliative care might say, successfully). When patients do talk about death, a number of issues emerge (Hickman, Tilden, & Tolle, 2004). Patients are often concerned about loss of body functioning, being dependent on others, and being a burden, and they fear losing their decision-making capacity at a time when they feel they must make important decisions. In addition, existential and spiritual issues can be very important.

Given these issues and concerns, what are the most important assurances therapists can give to those who are seriously ill? Certainly, global assurances, such as "Everything will be just fine," won't be very helpful. Molyn Leszcz and Pamela Goodwin, from the University of Toronto and Mount Sinai Hospital, respectively, have identified some key assurances that can be offered (Leszcz & Goodwin, 1998). These include assurance that the person will not die lonely or alone, that the person's wishes will be respected, and that every effort will be made to minimize physical suffering. Of course, wishes must be clearly communicated in order to be respected, and this can occur only if the group doesn't collude to avoid discussions about death, fearing that discussing death will somehow bring it on (Leszcz & Goodwin, 1998).

denial: a coping strategy in which people deny that distressing events exist or that negative emotions are being felt.

anger: a reaction that often follows denial when people are confronted with novel and severe trauma, as identified by Kübler-Ross.

bargaining: a response, identified by Kübler-Ross, that may occur when a person is confronted with novel and severe trauma; includes trying to do things that will buy more time.

depression: a common mental disorder of varying severity and impact that features depressed mood, loss of interest or pleasure, feelings of guilt or low self-worth, disturbed sleep or appetite, low energy, and poor concentration.

acceptance: the final stage of Kübler-Ross's theory of death and dying, in which someone achieves a peaceful acceptance of their own death.

Bereavement and Grief

It is also important to consider the family, friends, and loved ones who are left to cope with the patient's death. They are coping with **bereavement**, which is the loss of someone close to them. **Grief** is a common psychological response to bereavement. Vancouver palliative care physician David Kuhl has described grief as the feeling that accompanies the realization one will never again have something that one wants very much (Kuhl, 2003). The bereaved are clearly an at-risk population (Walsh-Burke, 2000). They suffer higher death rates and suicide rates than the rest of the population. They also have a higher incidence of depression and substance abuse, and they have more medical problems.

There are a number of possible approaches that can be taken in grief therapy (Clements, DeRanieri, Vigil, & Benasutti, 2004). The therapist may pick one or a combination of them, depending on the needs of the participants and the preferences of the therapist. For example, there is the approach that acknowledges "the six *R*s of mourning," which include recognizing the loss, reacting to the separation, recollecting and re-experiencing the relationship with the deceased, relinquishing old attachments, and readjusting to the new world without the deceased person in it (Rando, 1996, cited in Clements et al., 2004).

CHAPTER SUMMARY

- Present statistics related to serious and chronic illness, including prevalence and mortality rates.

  Approximately one in four Canadians will die from cancer. An estimated 186 400 cases of cancer and 75 700 deaths occurred in Canada in 2009. These numbers do not include cases of non-melanoma skin cancer. It is also estimated that 40 percent of all Canadian women and 45 percent of men will develop cancer at some point in their lives.

  Approximately 2.4 million people in Canada have diabetes, and the disease is more common among males (Public Health Agency of Canada, 2011a). Every 7 minutes in Canada, someone dies with cardiovascular disease as the underlying cause.

  As of 2008, more than 65 000 people were living with HIV infection in Canada. Some groups are at greater risk than others for contracting AIDS. These include men who have sex with men, injection drug users, those who receive blood and blood products, and Canada's Aboriginal population.

- Describe common psychological challenges associated with specific serious and chronic illnesses, including cancer, diabetes, heart disease, and HIV/AIDS.

  Serious and chronic illnesses, such as cancer, diabetes, heart disease, and HIV/AIDS, create psychological challenges. The most common psychological challenges associated with all these conditions are depression, anxiety, and fear. All of these reactions can have detrimental effects on the patient, not only in terms of coping ability, but also on disease progression. Thus, there is the danger that problems will become cyclical, with the reactions worsening as the condition is, in turn, worsened by the reactions.

- Explain ways in which professionals, family members, friends, and fellow patients can help people cope with these psychological challenges.

  Professionals, family members, friends, and fellow patients can help people cope with these psychological challenges. Social support is very important for people coping with serious illness. This support can be emotional, practical, or informational in nature. Psychotherapy can also be helpful, usually in the form of cognitive behaviour therapy, which focuses on the ways people think about their condition (or learn to stop thinking about their condition), and the behaviours associated with successful coping, such as following medical regimens and continuing with activities that enhance daily life. Fellow patients can provide empathy and "inside information" that can only come from people who have first-hand experience with the condition.

- Define quality of life and explain its importance in the treatment of serious illness.

  Quality of life is an important consideration in the treatment of serious illness. It refers to the extent to which symptoms and treatment affect a person's physical, social, cognitive, and emotional functioning.

- List and describe the elements of death and dying, as identified by Elisabeth Kübler-Ross.

  Elisabeth Kübler-Ross identified the following stages that typically accompany a terminal diagnosis: denial, anger, bargaining, depression, and acceptance. When in denial, the patient might believe that the diagnosis or prognosis is wrong. Anger might be expressed toward caregivers and loved ones. Bargaining can refer to the hope that if the person does certain good things, or generally tries to be a better person, then he or she will live longer. Acceptance comes when the person is finally at peace with coming death.

- List the steps involved in helping someone cope with bereavement.

  Helping someone cope with bereavement can involve the following steps: (1) recognizing the loss, (2) reacting to the separation, (3) recollecting and (4) re-experiencing the relationship with the deceased, (5) relinquishing old attachments, and (6) readjusting to the new world without the deceased person in it.

Chapter 8

Pain

Learning Objectives

After studying this chapter, you will be able to:

1. explain the benefits of experiencing pain.
2. describe theories that attempt to explain the phenomenon of pain.
3. identify factors that contribute to the experience of and expression of pain.
4. provide examples of how pain is assessed.
5. list and explain a variety of pain control techniques.

At 22 years of age, Jake was a happy-go-lucky, athletic apprentice chef in an exclusive restaurant. He loved his job and took it very seriously. One day when the master chef was away, two boxes of chickens were delivered. Jake cut up the chickens and packaged them for the freezer. Not long after, he became very ill. Jake was finally diagnosed as having been infected with salmonella, caused by a bacterium that is usually present on raw chicken meat. Jake was quarantined in the hospital, where he spent 10 days and lost 30 pounds.

Upon his discharge from the hospital, Jake rapidly resumed his old activities—he went back to work and immediately returned to playing soccer. However, 6 weeks later, a host of new symptoms appeared: joint pain, urethritis (inflammation of the urethra), and conjunctivitis (inflammation of the eye). This triad of symptoms is indicative of Reiter's syndrome. Reiter's syndrome occurs in 2 to 3 percent of patients exposed to bacteria known to promote it (including that which produces salmonella). In North America, 30 in every 100 000 individuals will experience this syndrome at some point in their lives; the incidence rate is five times higher for males than for females. Although most people recover from this illness in 6 months, in some it "grumbles on" for a year or more, and a small minority develop unremitting and potentially disabling arthritis. Unfortunately, Jake was one of the unlucky ones. His physician told him his pain would increase over time and that he would eventually lose mobility—not an easy prognosis for anyone to accept and especially not for an active person at such a young age.

With his eternal optimism, Jake continued to embrace life. He made a career change and found a job where he would be interacting with others all day—he became a bus driver. This job was the perfect fit for Jake, because he loved people and almost everyone he came in contact with became an instant friend.

In the beginning, Jake rarely exhibited any pain. He married and had two children. As the years passed, however, his pain increased, causing him to take more and more painkillers. The pain became more and more excruciating, until he was consuming 14 Tylenol 3 a day (far exceeding the recommended dosage). Then, 13 years after the initial diagnosis, he just couldn't keep it together any longer.

Jake became extremely depressed and began to experience anxiety attacks. He was off work for a few months, then returned to his jovial self. He returned to work, but after driving a bus for only 3 weeks he had to go on leave again. Emotionally, he was sinking deeper and deeper. He became suicidal and began abusing his medication, taking far more than the physician had prescribed. Secretly, he also began abusing alcohol. Jake was checked into a hospital where he would receive psychiatric help.

After a number of weeks in the hospital, Jake was discharged and seemed to be in better spirits. Unfortunately, he will have to live with physical pain for the rest of his life. He has tried, in his words, "every pain management technique available." In addition to pharmacological treatment, he has tried acupuncture, guided imagery, meditation, physical exercises, and massage therapy. He recently returned from a 10-day stay at a pain clinic. Jake said that the pain management techniques at the clinic ranged from group hugs to a few very painful procedures where he screamed louder than he had ever screamed before. Jake states that the most beneficial aspect of this visit was that he learned that he really wasn't "so bad off." Many of the other patients were currently experiencing more pain than he was, and the ordeals that they had gone through were heartrending. Currently, Jake continues to be in good spirits; he participates in aqua therapy and visits a massage therapist. He knows that he will be taking medication for the rest of his life, and very recently his physician told him he may have to give up the idea of ever driving a bus again.

The chronic (or long-term) pain that Jake experiences as a result of Reiter's syndrome has affected him in many ways. It has affected him emotionally. Jake can no longer work in the job he loves and is currently living on disability payments, a situation that is hard on his self-esteem. It is not surprising that depression and anxiety are often experienced by people with chronic pain. His social life has changed considerably, and for more than a year he didn't want to see even his closest friends. Obviously, the pain has affected him physically as well. Jake can no longer play soccer with his teammates. He only hopes that he will still be able to kick the soccer ball around with his children when they are old enough. It is true that pain of any kind usually leads people to change their activity level. As this chapter explains, such pain behaviours are an important component of the pain experience.

THE SIGNIFICANCE OF PAIN

After reading about Jake, the idea of a life without pain might sound rather appealing. You would feel no pain when falling down, when stubbing your toe, or when slamming your finger in the car door. Headaches would not exist. You would feel no pain while exercising, and giving birth might even be considered a pleasant experience. But before you conclude that life would be wonderful with no pain, consider the case of Miss C., a young Canadian woman who was a student at McGill University (Melzack & Wall, 1996). Miss C.'s father, a physician, suggested to his colleagues in Montreal that they should examine her. Miss C. was highly intelligent and seemed normal in every way except that she had never felt pain. As a child, she had bitten off the tip of her tongue while chewing food and had suffered third-degree burns on her legs after kneeling on a hot radiator to look out a window. In fact, Miss C. could not remember ever sneezing or coughing, and she had neither the gag reflex nor the corneal reflex that protects the eyes.

The physicians who examined Miss C. subjected her to tests that would have felt like torture to a normal person. They administered electric shocks to different parts of her body and immersed her limbs in hot water at temperatures that usually produce reports of burning pain. They immersed her limbs in cold water for prolonged periods and pinched tendons. She felt no pain. In addition, her heart rate, blood pressure, and respiration remained normal throughout the tests.

As a result of her inability to experience pain, Miss C. had severe medical problems, including pathological changes in her knees, hip, and spine. Melzack and Wall (1996) explain that insensitivity to pain can lead people to remain in one position too long, causing inflammation of the joints. Even worse, the failure to feel pain leads one to neglect injuries; as a result, healing is impeded. Injured tissue can easily become infected. These infections are very difficult to treat, particularly if they extend to the bone.

Miss C. died when she was only 29 years old of massive infections that could not be brought under control. Miss C.'s insensitivity to pain directly contributed to the infections that killed her.

Rare disease makes girl unable to feel pain: Genetic disorder deprives kindergarten student Ashlyn Blocker of natural alarms.
Stephen Morton/AP Images

Thus, there are benefits to experiencing pain. Pain is known to serve at least three functions. First, the pain that occurs before serious injury, such as when we step on or pick up hot, sharp, or otherwise potentially damaging objects, has real survival value. It causes us to immediately withdraw, which prevents further injury. Second, the pains that prevent further injury serve as the basis of learning to avoid injurious objects or situations that may occur at a later time. Third, pains due to damaged joints, abdominal infections, diseases, or serious injuries set limits on activity and enforce inactivity and rest, which are often essential for the body's natural recuperative and disease-fighting mechanisms to ensure recovery and survival.

PAIN PERCEPTION

When a person comes in contact with injurious stimuli, signals of tissue damage follow a particular route from **afferent (sensory) neurons** of the peripheral nervous system to the spinal cord and then to the brain. The afferent nerve endings that respond to pain stimuli are called **nociceptors**. When activated, these nerve endings generate impulses that travel to the central nervous system. The afferent peripheral fibres that transmit pain impulses are **A-delta fibres** and **C-fibres**. A-delta fibres are associated with sharp, distinct pain. The A-delta fibres are small, myelinated fibres that transmit impulses very quickly. In contrast, C-fibres transmit impulses more slowly because they are unmyelinated. The C-fibres, which comprise over 60 percent of all sensory afferents, are involved when pain is diffuse, dull, or aching (Melzack & Wall, 1996).

The afferent fibres group together after leaving the periphery, and this grouping forms a nerve. The nerves then enter the dorsal horns of the spinal cord; these contain several layers, or laminae, each of which receives incoming messages from afferent neurons. The cells in the first two layers form the *substantia gelatinosa*, and it is here where sensory input information is thought to be modulated. Sensory aspects of pain are strongly influenced by activity in A-delta fibres, which send messages through the thalamus on their way to the brain's cerebral cortex. Here the A-delta fibres signal sharp pain. The motivational and affective elements of pain appear to be more heavily determined by the C-fibres, which send pain messages to the brain stem and lower portions of the forebrain.

afferent (sensory) neurons: nerve cells that conduct impulses from a sense organ to the central nervous system, or from lower to higher levels in the spinal cord and brain.

nociceptors: the afferent nerve endings that respond to pain stimuli.

A-delta fibres: the afferent peripheral fibres that are associated with transmitting sharp, distinct pain.

C-fibres: the afferent peripheral fibres that are associated with transmitting diffuse, dull, or aching pain.

THEORIES OF PAIN

Gate Control Theory

In 1965, Melzack and Wall proposed the **gate control theory** of pain. This theory improved on earlier theories of pain by recognizing the contribution of psychological factors to our perception of pain (Melzack & Katz, 2004). According to the gate control theory, pain is not a sensation that is transmitted directly from the peripheral nerve endings to the brain. Instead, the theory emphasizes that sensations are modified as they are conducted to the brain by way of the spinal cord. They are also influenced by downward pathways from the brain that interpret the experience. Melzack and Wall propose that there is a structure in the dorsal horns of the spinal column, a gatelike mechanism that is able to control the flow of pain stimulation to the brain.

According to the gate control theory, information enters the dorsal horns of the spinal cord by way of primary afferent neurons. This information passes through the *substantia gelatinosa*, where the information is modulated by stimulation from the periphery as well as by feedback from the fibres descending from the brain. This then affects the activity of the transmission cells, causing them to either conduct (excitatory influence) or not conduct (inhibitory influence) pain sensations to the brain.

The gate control theory proposes that the experience of pain is affected by the balance of activity in the small and large nerve fibres. This activity determines the patterning and intensity of stimulation. Activity in the small A-delta and C-fibres causes prolonged stimulation in the spinal cord. This type of activity promotes sensitivity and opens the gate, which produces pain. In contrast, activity in the large A-beta fibres tends to close the gate.

The gate may be closed by activity in the spinal cord and also by messages descending from the brain. A specialized system of large-diameter, rapidly conducting fibres, called the **central control trigger**, activates selective cognitive processes that then influence, by way of descending fibres, the opening and closing of the gate. The experience of pain is thus influenced by past experience, attention, and other cognitive activities through the central control trigger. Consequently, affective reactions such as anxiety, depression, fear, or focusing on an injury can exacerbate the experience of pain by affecting the central control trigger, thus opening the gate. Intense involvement in other activities, or relaxation, or positive experiences can mute the pain experience by causing the gate to close.

Consider observations made by Beecher (1959) during World War II. An injury or wound sustained by a civilian produces pain (the gate is open). However, a soldier with the equivalent injury does not experience the same amount of pain, because the soldier is distracted by the environment (the gate is closed). Suppressing the pain of injuries allows individuals to defend themselves during attack and to escape from further harm. Evidence in support of this observation can be seen in the amount of analgesic requested by patients from each group. A civilian patient will ask for significantly more analgesic than will a soldier who sustained the same injury (Watkins & Maier, 2000).

This theory also explains how injuries can go virtually unnoticed. If sensory input is sent into a heavily activated nervous system, the stimulation may not be perceived as pain. A hockey player may fracture a rib during a game but not notice the acute pain because of excitement and concentration on the game. It isn't until after the game is over that the player notices the pain. At this time, the nervous system is functioning at a different level of activation, and the gate is more easily opened.

The gate control theory was arguably the leading theory of pain for over 25 years. And, in fact, the conceptual components of the theory have stood the test of time (Melzack & Katz, 2004; Moayedi & Davis, 2013). The theory continues to spur research and generate interest in the psychological and perceptual factors involved in pain. However, the gate control theory is not able to explain several chronic pain problems, such as **phantom limb pain** (see Box 8-1).

phantom limb pain: the experience of pain in an absent body part.

Neuromatrix Theory

Melzack (2001) has proposed an extension to the gate control theory—the **neuromatrix theory**. This theory places a greater emphasis on the brain's role in pain perception. According to this theory, a genetically determined neuromatrix or network of brain neurons "distributed throughout many areas of the brain, comprises a widespread network of neurons that generates patterns, processes information that flows through it, and ultimately produces the pattern that is felt as a whole body" (Melzack & Katz, 2004, p. 23). The neuromatrix-generated patterns are called *neurosignature patterns*. These patterns may be generated from sensory inputs; however, they may also be innately produced, such as in the case of phantom limb pain. The neurosignature patterns are responsible for producing a multidimensional experience of pain. Indeed, neuroimaging techniques imply that brain function involves networks and various networks have been implicated in the experience of pain (Moayedi & Davis, 2013). Like the gate control theory, the neuromatrix theory maintains that pain perception is part of a complex process that is affected by sensory input, activity of the nervous system, and past experiences and expectations.

neuromatrix theory: an extension of the gate control theory, with greater emphasis placed on the brain's role in pain perception.

NEUROCHEMICAL BASIS OF PAIN AND PAIN INHIBITION

The gate control theory of pain asserts that the brain can control the amount of pain an individual experiences by transmitting messages down the spinal cord to block the transmission of pain signals (Melzack & Wall, 1965, 1996). There is evidence that supports this view. David Reynolds (1969) conducted a now-classic study in which he implanted an electrode in the midbrain portion of a number of rats' brain stems. The exact location of the electrode varied from one rat to the next. Then, he made sure that the rats could feel pain by applying a clamp to their tails. Not surprisingly, each rat responded by demonstrating pain.

Several days later, Reynolds tested whether stimulation through the electrode would block pain. At the same time the rats were electrically stimulated, he again applied the clamp. Those rats with electrodes in the area of the midbrain known as the **periaqueductal gray area** did not exhibit pain. Those rats that did not experience pain in response to having their tails clamped later had abdominal surgery performed on them while the periaqueductal grey area of their brains was being electrically stimulated. Again, the rats did not feel any pain. This phenomenon has been termed **stimulation-produced analgesia (SPA)**. Reynolds' findings encouraged researchers to look for the neurochemical basis of pain. Subsequently, *endogenous opioids* were identified.

Endogenous opioids are naturally occurring opiate-like substances, produced in the brain, spinal cord, and glands, that regulate pain. They appear to relieve pain by slowing or blocking the transmission of nerve impulses—much like exogenous opioids such as

periaqueductal gray area: an area of the midbrain that is involved in pain reception.

stimulation-produced analgesia (SPA): freedom from pain as a result of electrical stimulation.

endogenous opioids: opiate-like substances produced within the body that regulate pain.

Box 8-1

Phantom Limb Pain

CMSP/Custom Medical Stock

In 1866, the first account of phantom limbs was published. It appeared not in a scientific journal—as one might expect—but in the *Atlantic Monthly,* as an anonymously written short story. In "The Case of George Dedlow," the main character loses an arm to amputation during the Civil War. At one point, he awakens in the hospital after, unbeknownst to him, both his legs have also been amputated.

> [I was] suddenly aware of a sharp cramp in my left leg. I tried to get at it . . . with my single arm, but, finding myself too weak, hailed an attendant. "Just rub my left calf . . . if you please."

> "Calf? . . . You ain't got non, pardner. It's took off." (cited in Woodhouse, 2005)

The author happened to be Wier Mitchell, the foremost American neurologist at the time. Historians have proposed that Mitchell chose to publish this account in the *Atlantic Monthly* anonymously because he was unsure how his colleagues would respond to the concept of phantom limb pain. He feared that they would not believe that amputated arms and legs could be felt by their previous owners.

In fact, the phenomenon of phantom limbs is common to those who have undergone amputation. The limb is very vivid to the amputee, who can usually tell you the precise position of the phantom. A phantom limb behaves very much like a normal limb. Usually, a phantom arm hangs straight down at the side when the person sits or stands but moves in perfect coordination with other limbs during walking. Similarly, a

phantom leg bends like a normal leg would when its owner sits; it stretches out when the individual lies down; it becomes upright during standing (Melzack, 1992).

Occasionally, the amputee becomes convinced the limb is stuck in an unusual position. Melzack (1992) noted that one man believed his phantom arm extended straight out from the shoulder, at a right angle to the body. Consequently, whenever the man walked through a doorway he would turn sideways so that his arm would not hit the wall. Another man slept only on his front or side because his phantom arm was bent behind him and got in the way when he tried to rest on his back.

The most extraordinary feature of phantom limbs is their reality to the amputee. The phantom limb may seem so real that the amputee might try standing up on a phantom foot or answering a phone with a phantom hand. A phantom limb can experience many sensations, including warmth, cold, and pressure. A phantom limb can feel wet (as when an artificial arm is seen entering into a lake during a swan dive). It can also feel itchy, which can be very annoying. Fortunately, scratching the apparent site of discomfort can sometimes actually relieve the distress. It may sometimes seem that the phantom limb is sweaty, prickly, or even being tickled (Melzack, 1992).

Of course, the sensation in phantom limbs that causes the most distress to the sufferer is pain. Researchers (Ephraim, Wegener, MacKenzie, Dillingham, & Pezzin, 2005; Richardson, Glenn, Nurmikko, & Horgan, 2006) have found that approximately 80 percent of amputees had phantom limb pain in the months and years following surgery. A national study deemed that the majority of amputees are "bothered" by the phantom (Ephraim et al., 2005). Yet general practitioners seem to underestimate both the prevalence and the severity of phantom limb pain (Whyte & Niven, 2004; Woodhouse, 2005). Unfortunately, this type of pain seems to be resistant to treatment (Hunter, Katz, & Davis, 2005).

Originally, it was believed that one must first possess and then lose a limb and the corresponding nerves to experience phantom pain. Certainly, there is good evidence indicating that cortical reorganization takes place following amputation, a possible cause of phantom limb pain (e.g., Flor, Nikolajsen, & Staehelin Jensen, 2006; Grusser et al., 2001; Karl, Muhlnickel, Kurth, & Flor, 2004). However, there is now considerable evidence of phantoms in people born without limbs and in those who experienced limb amputation in very early childhood (e.g., Melzack, Israel, Lacroix, & Schultz, 1997; Woodhouse, 2005).

heroin and morphine (Julien, Advokat, & Comaty, 2011). Researchers have identified three main groups of these endogenous opioids: beta-endorphin, proenkephalin, and pro-dynorphin (Akil et al., 1998; Julien et al., 2011).

The system of endogenous opioids and their function in the body is very complex. Researchers do not have a full understanding of the mechanisms by which they work. However, it is apparent that having internal pain-relieving chemicals serves as an adaptive function. It may be that because pain and emotions are closely linked, studies have found that psychological stress can trigger endogenous opioid activity (Turk, 2001). There is also evidence that intense physical exercise can trigger the release of beta-endorphin, resulting in natural, short-term pain suppression and subjective feelings of physical well-being. The release of endogenous opioids may help to explain how injured athletes in competition and soldiers on the battlefield continue to function after being injured, with little or no perception of pain.

ACUTE VERSUS CHRONIC PAIN

Medical professionals make an important distinction between two main kinds of clinical pain—acute and chronic. Case 8-1 presents these two different types of pain in the examples of Riley and Michelle's individual experiences. Riley is suffering from **acute pain**. Acute pain seems to serve to warn of impending tissue damage or the need for convalescent rest. A toothache, the discomforts of childbirth, a broken limb, and postoperative pain are all forms of acute pain. Acute pain is by definition temporary (Turk & Winter, 2006). The physiological responses to acute pain seem partly proportional to the stimulus intensity. Acute pain can cause considerable anxiety and distress. Fortunately, painkillers can often ease the discomfort, and as the injury begins to heal, the anxiety subsides.

acute pain: pain that lasts less than six months and serves to warn of impending tissue damage or the need for convalescent rest.

CASE 8-1 ACUTE VERSUS CHRONIC PAIN

Riley is 28 years old and is just finishing his residency in anesthesiology. Recently, Riley received an invitation to his high school reunion. Riley had enjoyed high school and, in particular, his participation in school sports. He played volleyball and basketball, but the sport he enjoyed most was football. He decided that returning to his hometown for his high school reunion would be just the break he needed from life at the hospital.

The first night of the reunion weekend Riley met up with many of his former buddies and they reminisced about their football success. They really had been one of the greatest teams in the high school's history. In fact, six of the team members had gone on to play football in university, and four others had turned professional. The guys decided to get together for a scrimmage before the weekend was out.

On Sunday morning, 16 members of the former team gathered for a scrimmage. The guys played hard and even the spectators were impressed with the quick moves the players exhibited. After the game, the guys vowed to get together every year on the last weekend of August for a scrimmage.

Riley flew home on Sunday night. When he tried to rise from his seat at the conclusion of the flight, he experienced a sharp pain in his back. Slowly and carefully, he eased himself into a standing position. He had obviously overdone it at the scrimmage earlier that day. Riley knew he was going to be extremely stiff the next day. He decided that a walk before bed might help ward off some of the stiffness.

Compare Riley's experience of pain to that experienced by Michelle.

Michelle has been a professional pairs figure skater for almost 20 years. She and her partner have decided they will call it quits at the end of the current season. One factor that played a part in this decision is Michelle's pain. For the past few years, Michelle has found it increasingly difficult to land the jumps and throws that she and her partner practise over and over on a daily basis. After landing each throw and after landing each jump, Michelle experiences a sharp, searing pain in her knees. After each practice session, Michelle must ice her knees to help alleviate the pain, swelling, and tenderness. Not only does Michelle have a hard time landing her jumps, but she has also noticed that she is having some difficulty simply walking. It is likely that Michelle will be diagnosed with osteoarthritis. Although Michelle is going to miss skating, she hopes that a less physically demanding schedule will ease some of the pain she has been experiencing.

chronic pain: pain lasting for longer than 6 months.

But sometimes the pain lingers on. When it lasts longer than 3 to 6 months, pain is considered **chronic**. Specifically, chronic pain continues beyond the period of healing and "disrupts sleep and normal living, ceases to serve a protective function, and instead degrades health and functional capability" (American Pain Society, 2013). Michelle, like Jake in the chapter-opening vignette, is experiencing chronic pain. The prevalence of chronic pain varies widely across countries (e.g., 9.7 percent in Colombia to 42.2 percent in Ukraine; Demyttenaere et al., 2007) suggesting that there is a cultural component to the experience of pain. In Canada, estimates of those suffering from chronic pain are most recently estimated to be 18.9 percent among adults aged 18 years and older (Schopflocher, Taenzer, & Jovey, 2011). The largest causes of chronic pain were deemed to be arthritic, back and spine, and pain due to trauma. The rate of chronic pain reported in Canada is identical to the overall mean reported using the identical survey questions and methodology in a large-scale European study of 16 countries (Breivik, Collette, Ventafridda, Cohen, & Gallacher, 2006). The prevalence of pain in children is estimated at 15–30 percent (Stanford, Chambers, Biesanz, & Chen, 2008) and that number increases as one ages (Hadjistavropoulos, Gibson, & Fine, 2011). Additionally, the prevalence of pain is higher among the Aboriginal population in Canada than the rest of the population (Ramage-Morin & Gilmour, 2010) and in those with lower socioeconomic status (King et al., 2011; Ramage-Morin & Gilmour, 2010). In terms of dollars, what does this mean? It is estimated that the annual cost of chronic pain in Canada is at least $56–60 billion dollars (Canadian Pain Society, 2014).

chronic recurrent pain: intermittent intense episodes of acute pain followed by relief.

chronic intractable benign pain: continuous pain that varies in intensity.

chronic progressive pain: continuous pain that gradually intensifies as a person's condition worsens.

Chronic pain can be intermittent or constant, mild, or severe. It varies a great deal depending upon its type (Turk & Winter, 2006). **Chronic recurrent pain** does not become progressively worse. It is characterized by intense episodes of acute pain followed by relief. For example, a person who suffers from migraine headaches may have excruciating headaches lasting from hours to days, but then may have several pain-free weeks or months. By comparison, the person who has **chronic intractable benign pain** has pain all the time, with varying intensity. People who suffer from lower back pain generally experience their pain continually and find that they can do little to reduce it. Finally, **chronic progressive pain** involves continuous discomfort that gradually intensifies as the condition worsens. It is typically associated with malignancies or degenerative disorders, such as cancer and advancing arthritis.

In many types of chronic pain, the disease process is primarily responsible for the pain experienced. However, psychosocial factors may also play a role. Although tissue damage may result in the initial acute pain that the person experiences, subsequently, psychosocial factors may play a more prominent role. To clarify this process, we must distinguish between respondent and operant pain. **Respondent pain** refers to pain that occurs in response to noxious stimulation or tissue damage. In contrast, **operant pain** is pain that is reinforced by the person's environment.

Typically, people in pain will alter their behaviour in an attempt to reduce the pain. For example, a person may limp, guard a painful arm, avoid exercise, or even stay in bed to avoid pain. When such **pain behaviours** either reduce the pain or prevent it from getting worse, the tendency to continue the behaviour is reinforced. As the pain behaviours appear successful at preventing or reducing the pain, the person will continue to engage in these behaviours for fear that the pain will return if they are discontinued. Consequently, these behaviours are particularly resistant to change (Fordyce, 1976; Hadjistavropoulos & de C. Williams, 2004).

The verbal and behavioural expressions of pain also have a powerful effect on other people. When individuals complain of pain, display pain on their face, or exhibit an abnormal gait or posture, they may receive attention, concern, and even assistance from those witnessing these behaviours—this can further reinforce pain behaviour. Researchers have discovered that chronic pain sufferers who report higher levels of satisfaction with social support also exhibit higher levels of pain-related behaviours. Positive attention provided by supportive spouses in response to the expression of pain may build intimacy (Cano & de C. Williams, 2010), but it may also inadvertently maintain or increase an individual's expression of pain and the experience of disability (Patterson, 2005).

One of the most common complaints described by those with chronic pain is the resulting sleep disturbance (American Pain Society, 2013; Breivik et al., 2006; Brennan & Lieberman, 2009; Kelly, Blake, Power, O'Keeffe, & Fullen, 2011). A large majority (79 percent) of those experiencing moderate or severe chronic pain complain about the difficulties

respondent pain: pain that occurs in response to noxious stimulation or tissue damage.

operant pain: pain that is reinforced by a person's environment.

pain behaviours: alterations in behaviour by a person experiencing pain to either reduce the pain or prevent it from getting worse.

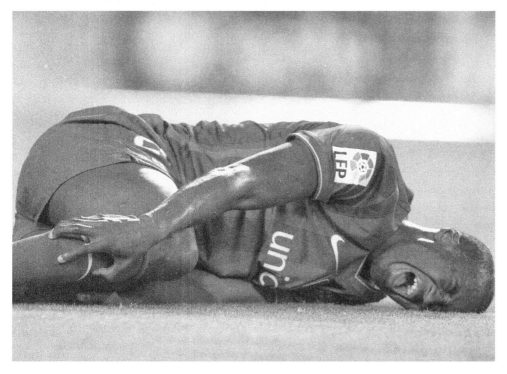

An individual's experience of pain is often obvious to others.
Maxisport/Shutterstock

they have in falling asleep. As well, these individuals are frequently awakened as a result of the pain. In the morning, they wake up exhausted. They are tired and drained of energy, not merely from lack of sleep but also because the continuous pain wears them down. It is not surprising that these chronic pain sufferers also find themselves irritated by little things and trivial comments of those around them. These people recognize that they are snapping at their friends and family for insufficient reasons, yet they cannot seem to stop. This situation often leads those with chronic pain to withdraw from their families and friends.

The chronic pain sufferer who withdraws from family and friends experiences little social or recreational life. In addition, 59 percent of those with moderate or severe chronic pain have had to leave their jobs (American Pain Society, 2013). As a result, people's standard of living is reduced and an added strain is put on the family. In addition, both personal and career goals may be set aside because the sufferer's life is beginning to revolve around pain (Breivik et al., 2006). Ironically, if compensation is received for the pain experience because it resulted from an injury on the job or perhaps in an automobile accident, this may exacerbate the perceived severity of pain and distress (Turk & Okifuji, 1996). Indeed, when the compensation system for traffic injuries in Saskatchewan changed to a no-fault system, which resulted in no payments for pain and suffering, the result was a decreased incidence and improved prognosis of whiplash injury (Cassidy et al., 2000).

All of the previously mentioned behaviours resulting from the experience of pain have an impact on one's emotional state. Many chronic pain sufferers are irritable, and many report being listless, unable to cope, and depressed. In fact, people who suffer from chronic pain share many of the same symptoms as people who suffer from depression. Merskey (1986) reports that in almost all published studies of psychiatric and psychological test findings, chronic pain patients report mild but significant depression. Furthermore, approximately 50 percent of hospitalized patients with depression report pain as a major symptom.

These are daunting statistics, especially considering that depression is known to exacerbate pain and pain-related behaviours (Corbière, Sullivan, Stanish, & Adams, 2007; Tennen, Affleck, & Zautra, 2006). Fortunately, once pain is controlled there is a significant improvement in individuals' abilities and moods.

PSYCHOSOCIAL FACTORS AND PAIN
Gender Differences

Clinical research has documented that women are more likely than men to experience a variety of recurrent pain. Recurrent pain can result from many ailments, including migraine and other headaches as well as musculoskeletal, back, and abdominal injury (Schopflocher, Taenzer, & Jovey, 2011). In most studies, women report more severe levels of pain, more frequent pain, and pain of longer duration than men (Bingefors & Isacson, 2004).

Researchers agree that there are gender differences in the perception of and response to pain (see Bartley & Fillingim, 2013, or Keogh, 2009, for reviews). The extent of these differences is under debate. Anita Unruh (1996) from Dalhousie University has identified three key issues surrounding gender differences and pain: (1) the manner in which women and men perceive and respond to pain, (2) the psychosocial and biological factors that may influence gender variations in pain experience, and (3) the response of the health care system to the pain presented by women and men.

Laboratory research has documented how men and women differ in their pain responses (Keogh, Bond, Hanmer, & Tilson, 2005; Sullivan, Tripp, & Santor, 2000). For example, Lowery, Fillingim, and Wright (2003) reported that women have a lower pain threshold and lower pain tolerance than men have. To determine a participant's pain threshold, researchers will inflict pain on the participant by one of a number of methods. A commonly used method is known as a "cold-pressor task." This entails participants submerging their hand in cold water until they experience pain. They indicate to the researcher, usually by pushing a button, when this point is reached. At this time, participants are said to have reached their **pain threshold**.

Researchers are sometimes interested in identifying participants' *pain tolerance* levels rather than their pain threshold. The **pain tolerance level** is either the duration of time a person is willing to endure a stimulus beyond the point where it began to hurt, or the intensity of the stimulus a person will endure beyond that point. When the participants "can't stand it" any longer, they have reached their level of pain tolerance. Once the participants have indicated that they have reached their limit, they can remove their hand from the noxious stimuli. Laboratory studies investigating gender differences in pain threshold and pain tolerance generally suggest that women demonstrate a greater sensitivity to pain than men do (Keogh, 2006; Bartley & Fillingim, 2013). Any inconsistencies in results are generally deemed due to the variety of noxious stimuli and measurement tools used by investigators (e.g., Giles & Walker, 2000; Hashmi & Davis, 2010; Keogh, 2006).

Another approach, taken by researchers at the University of Western Ontario (Rollman, Abdel-Shaheed, Gillespie, & Jones, 2004), indicates that individuals who have experienced greater pain in the past show lower pain tolerance. Given that women frequently have experienced high pain levels and demonstrate lower pain tolerance, we might consider whether these two factors are related.

Critics argue that apparent gender differences in response to pain are actually due to differences in reporting pain (e.g., Robinson, Wise, Gagnon, Fillingim, & Price, 2004). Some researchers (Robinson et al., 2001; Myers, Riley, & Robinson, 2003) believe that female participants in lab studies give a more unbiased report of their pain than do male participants. Men feel there is a social cost to admitting publicly that something hurts. Men are taught to "tough out" pain, and so in the lab they endure more discomfort. In contrast, women feel little pressure to endure unnecessary pain and therefore have no trouble admitting when something hurts.

It is plausible that societal beliefs about gender differences in response to pain are a product of different societal gender-role expectations (Robinson et al., 2004). Unruh (1996) points out that when we experience pain, we engage in a process of cognitive appraisal. That is, we determine what this experience means to us. To determine the meaning of an event, we ask ourselves the following questions: "What does it mean?" "In what way does it affect me?" "Should I be concerned?" and "Is any action required on my part?"

Although psychosocial factors may influence pain perception, underlying biological differences in pain mechanisms may also predispose women to feel more pain. For example, there are known gender differences in brain chemistry, metabolism, physical structures, and hormones that may influence the biological mechanisms of pain transmission, pain sensitivity, and pain perception (Bartley & Fillingim, 2013; Keogh, 2006). Wisenfeld notes that, after puberty, females are more sensitive to acutely painful stimuli than are males. Furthermore, pain sensitivity may vary depending on the stage a woman is at in her menstrual cycle; however, the

pain threshold: the point at which the intensity of a stimulus is perceived as painful.

pain tolerance: duration of time or intensity at which a person is willing to endure a stimulus beyond the point where it began to hurt.

evidence is mixed (Bartley & Fillingim, 2013; Wisenfeld, 2005). Pain sensitivity also appears heightened in women using estrogen replacement therapy (Fillingim & Edwards, 2001).

Both biological and psychosocial factors related to the experience and reporting of pain by men and women may lead to differences in the way men and women are treated by the health care system. For example, psychosocial factors, such as catastrophizing, may be responsible for women describing their pain in more detail and with more expressive and social language than do men. (See Focus on Canadian Research 8-1 for a more detailed discussion of catastrophizing.) As a result of these descriptions, women are more likely to receive a psychogenic interpretation of their pain by their physicians, particularly when the pain is not directly related to tissue damage. Unruh (1996) claims that these interpretations may "cause women to receive more attention for psychological aspects of pain but inadequate pain relief" (p. 159).

Women are also perceived by physicians and nurses as dramatizing or exaggerating their pain. As a result, they are provided less analgesia than are men (e.g., Chen et al., 2008; Hoffmann & Tarzian, 2001; Weisse, Sorum, Sanders, & Syat, 2001). Men, on the other hand, are thought to minimize their pain and its consequences. This attitude may lead men to seek medical attention only when the pain characteristics have become more

Focus on Canadian Research 8-1

Catastrophizing

A group of Canadian researchers, led by Michael Sullivan at the University of Montreal, has been conducting research on pain catastrophizing for almost two decades. Pain catastrophizing involves a "negative emotional and cognitive response to pain involving elements of magnification, helplessness and pessimism" (Edwards, Haythornthwaite, Sullivan, & Filingim, 2004, p. 336). In other words, people who spend considerable time ruminating about aspects of the pain experience become fearful of pain and adopt a form of helplessness. Specifically, they fear any movement that might be painful, and they also fear (re)injury; consequently, they engage in avoidance behaviour. Disuse, depression, and disability ensue, fostering the development of chronic pain problems.

The general conclusion that those who score high on the Pain Catastrophizing Scale experience greater pain intensity has been demonstrated numerous times (Bishop & Warr, 2003; Sullivan, Bishop, & Pivik, 1995; Sullivan et al., 2001). For example, Pavlin, Sullivan, and colleagues (2005) asked a sample of patients who were to undergo anterior cruciate ligament repair to complete this scale presurgery. After surgery in the postanesthetic care unit, as well as 1, 2, and 7 days after surgery, patients rated their pain on a scale of 0–10. Results indicated that those who scored higher on the Pain Catastrophizing Scale experienced greater pain postoperatively.

The relationship between catastrophizing and pain perception in a special subset of the population—that of ballet dancers—is not as clear. When examining the relationship between pain perception and catastrophizing in ballet dancers, Paparizos, Tripp, Sullivan, and Rubenstein (2005) noted that the relationship isn't simply that greater catastrophizing leads to a greater perception of pain. Ballet dancers, like athletes competing in competitive sports, are continually at risk for pain and injury. It seems that more experienced and highly skilled ballet dancers catastrophize less than ballet dancers who are less experienced and less skilled. Perhaps this trend is due to the rigorous training that a dancer must endure. Or, perhaps those who would have scored high on catastrophizing left dance earlier in their dance careers.

The literature germane to catastrophizing continues to grow. Recently, researchers have reported that high pain catastrophizers communicate pain more effectively when an observer is present (Gauthier, Thibault, & Sullivan, 2011; Sullivan, Adams, & Sullivan, 2004), high pain catastrophizers report using fewer cognitive coping strategies (Sullivan et al., 2004), they perceive more intense pain in others than do low pain catastrophizers (Sullivan, Martel, Tripp, Savard, & Crombez, 2006), and that their perceptions of others' pain are more accurate (Martel, Thibault, Roy, Catchlove, & Sullivan, 2008). Further research exploring the concept of catastrophizing will continue to contribute to our understanding of the experience of pain.

extreme, which may result in the pain being more difficult to treat. It is also true that men seem to implement fewer coping strategies than women in response to pain.

Cultural Differences

Pain is something that people all around the world experience, and ethnic differences in response to painful stimuli are believed to exist (see Rahim-Williams, Riley, Williams, & Fillingim, 2012, for a review). For example, a Canadian study discovered that Chinese students reported higher levels of pain when undergoing the cold-pressor task than European Canadians (Hsieh, Tripp, Ji, & Sullivan, 2010). Both U.S. and European studies have indicated that non-Hispanic whites show a greater tolerance to painful stimuli than do African Americans, and Asian Americans reportedly have the lowest pain tolerance (Campbell, Edwards, & Fillingim, 2005; Rahim-Williams et al., 2007; Sheffield, Biles, Orom, Maixner, & Sheps, 2000; Watson, Latif & Rowboth, 2005). Cultural background and social context will affect each person's experience, expression, and treatment of pain.

These differences may result from the meaning each culture attaches to pain and from stereotypes associated with various cultural experiences. Consider, for example, members of certain African cultural groups who walk on burning coals and pierce their bodies with spikes yet show no outward appearance of pain. Similarly, in North America, body piercing and tattooing are commonplace in certain age and social groups. In both instances, stoicism is expected, and expressions of pain might be ridiculed. In comparison, some Mediterranean peoples encourage the open expression of pain (Straub, 2007).

Researchers at Queen's University (Hsieh, Tripp, & Li, 2011) studied cultural differences in response to pain experimentally. That is, they monitored Euro-Canadian and Chinese participants' responses to pain when in the presence of an experimenter from their own culture (ethnic concordance) or from the other culture (ethnic discordance). Consistent with previous results, the Chinese participants were found to report higher ratings of pain in response to the cold-pressor task than the Euro-Canadians no matter who was present. What did differ based on ethnic concordance (i.e., the participant and researcher from the same culture) was the nonverbal behaviours the Chinese participants exhibited. When in the presence of a Chinese researcher and tested using the Chinese language, the Chinese participants depicted higher nonverbal pain behaviour than did the Chinese participants in the presence of Euro-Canadian researchers.

In a clinical setting, we see that cultural differences exist even if we focus on pain derived from one specific cause, such as cancer. For example, Europeans and North Americans consider pain to be a common experience for cancer patients, and pain experts state that pain is undertreated (Ferrell et al., 2001; Streltzer, 1997). In contrast, experts from Asian countries do not consider cancer pain to be as much of a problem. These different attitudes lead to differences in treatment—approximately 70 percent of patients in Europe receive opiates for cancer pain. In contrast, only about 4 percent of Asian cancer patients receive this medication. It is possible that these variations may be due more to physicians' beliefs than to patients' pain. Support for this idea is provided by a number of American studies that report that racial and ethnic minority groups often receive different diagnoses and less favourable care than do white Americans (Bonham, 2001; Rathmore et al., 2000).

Rollman (2004) aptly summarizes his review of ethnocultural variations in pain by stating that "it is misleading and potentially detrimental to generalize to all members of one group" (p. 174). In fact, there is stronger evidence of individual differences within ethnic groups than of differences between ethnic groups (Straub, 2007). In sum, health care practitioners should focus on the person before them rather than the ethnic group to which the person belongs (Korol & Craig, 2001).

THE MEASUREMENT OF PAIN

Pain is a challenge to assess because people have difficulty describing pain objectively. If you have cut your arm, you can point to the wound. Or, if you are concerned that you might have broken a bone, this can be determined by radiography. Pain lacks these objective referents. Yet assessing pain is very important in determining treatment for patients and evaluating the effectiveness of different pain-reducing methods. As a result, clinicians and researchers have developed many techniques for measuring the pain that an individual feels. These techniques include psychophysiological measures, behavioural assessment, and self-reports. Each technique has certain advantages and certain limitations.

Psychophysiological Measures

Pain has both sensory and emotional components that can produce changes in the autonomic nervous system as well as other physiological conditions. The physiological changes resulting from the pain experience can be assessed using psychophysiological measures.

electromyograph (EMG): an instrument that assesses pain by measuring electrical activity in muscles.

One psychophysiological measure researchers use for assessing pain is an **electromyograph (EMG)**. This measures the electrical activity in muscles, which reflects the level of muscle tension. Because muscle tension is associated with certain pain states, such as headaches and low back pain, we would expect that EMG recordings would be different for people experiencing pain and those not experiencing it (Levine & Levy, 2006). Measures of **autonomic activity**, such as heart rate, respiration rate, blood pressure, hand surface temperature, and skin conductance, assess generalized arousal, which may provide an emotional indicator of pain. Another instrument that measures pain is the **electroencephalograph (EEG)**. The EEG measures electrical activity in the brain. When a person's sensory system detects a stimulus, such as pressure on one's heel, the signal to the brain produces **evoked potentials** or a change in EEG voltage. The evoked potentials increase with the intensity of stimuli and decrease when people take analgesics.

autonomic activity: physiological processes that cannot be consciously controlled, such as heart rate, respiration rate, blood pressure, hand surface temperature, and skin conductance.

electroencephalograph (EEG): an instrument that assesses pain by measuring electrical activity in the brain.

evoked potentials: electrical responses produced by stimuli.

Even though psychophysiological measures objectively assess bodily changes that occur in response to pain, these bodily changes may also occur in response to other factors (e.g., attention, diet, and stress). Therefore, whenever possible, psychophysiological measures should be used in conjunction with other approaches in assessing pain.

Behavioural Assessment

Other measures of pain have focused on *pain behaviours*. Pain behaviours are behaviours exhibited when a person is in discomfort. They include nonverbal expressions (e.g., facial and vocal cues), distortions in movement and posture, irritability, and restrictions or avoidance of activity. Analyses of pain behaviours provide a basis for assessing how pain has disrupted the life of patients. Procedures have been developed for assessing specific pain behaviours in both daily activities and structured clinical settings.

Assessment of Pain Behaviour in Day-to-Day Activities   In assessing day-to-day activities, researchers and clinicians might be interested in the amount of time sufferers spend in bed, for example, or how many complaints they express. Do they bend over very carefully or not at all? Do they seek help in moving, walking, or climbing stairs? Do they walk with a limp? Family members or significant others in patients' lives are often the best people to make these assessments. If these people are willing to help, they can be trained to make careful observations and keep accurate records. Fordyce (1976) documents a procedure for doing this, which has been refined by Turk (Turk, Meichenbaum, & Genest, 1983).

Assessment of Pain Behaviour in Clinical Settings   Undertreatment of pain is a serious concern (Hadjistavropoulos, 2004; Herr, 2011). Laboratory studies indicate that in general, health care professionals underestimate patients' pain (Prkachin, Solomon, & Ross, 2007). We might infer, then, that undertreatment of pain is due to the health care professionals' inaccuracy in assessing pain in the clinical setting. We must consider, however, that in a controlled laboratory environment, researchers limit the pain behaviours that are available to those making judgments. To further elucidate this point, consider the following study. Kappesser, Williams, and Prkachin (2006) asked health care professionals to make their judgments of pain by viewing only the patients' faces. When they did so, their judgments underestimated the amount of pain experienced by the patient. However, when the patients' actual verbal description of their pain accompanied the facial expression, the judgment was more accurate.

In clinical settings, health care practitioners might include a measure of patients' pain behaviour to aid in their assessment. For example, in hospitals nurses may use the UAB Pain Behavior Scale (Richards, Nepomuceno, Riles, & Suer, 1982) during routine care of patients. When using this scale, the nurse has the patient perform several activities and rates 10 pain behaviours (e.g., mobility, medication use) on a three-point scale: "none," "occasional," and "frequent." These ratings are assigned numerical values and summed for a total score. A number of studies have focused on assessing discomfort in patients (Keefe, Williams, & Smith, 2001; Tsai, 2011). These studies suggest that behavioural assessments of pain can be made relatively easily and reliably.

Self-Reports of Pain

The third and most obvious approach to pain measurement is to ask people to describe their pain, either in their own words or by filling out a rating scale or questionnaire. These are the most common types of pain assessment and are considered to be the gold standard (Tsai, 2011). In treating a patient's pain, health care practitioners ask where the pain is, what it feels like, how strong it is, and when it tends to occur.

Interviews   Interviews about pain can provide valuable information. In addition to a description of pain, such interviews can determine the history of the pain problem. The history would include when the patient first experienced the pain, how the pain developed, and the techniques the patient used for controlling it. Factors seeming to trigger or exacerbate the pain can be discussed. The patient's emotional adjustment and whether or how the patient's lifestyle has been altered can also be explored. The information obtained in these interviews can be supplemented with information provided by significant others in the patient's life (Turk, Monarch, & Williams, 2004).

Rating Scales   Rating scales are one of the simplest and most direct measures of pain. Therefore, it is not surprising that rating scales are the most frequently used measures of pain (Jensen & Karoly, 2001). These scales are usually used to measure pain intensity. Sometimes, one can use a numerical rating scale where patients are simply asked to respond verbally to the following statement: "On a scale from one to ten, with ten being the most excruciating pain possible, and one being the lowest level of pain detectable, how much pain are you currently experiencing?" Or, the health care practitioner may ask the patient to respond to this statement on a scale of one to one hundred. In either of these cases, the basic question is really the same. However, the form of the scale can vary (see Figure 8-1).

The numerical rating scale is often used orally; however, it can also be provided as a **box scale** where of phrases "no pain" and "worst pain imaginable" are added as numerical equivalents. Patients are shown a series of numbers in boxes and must choose the number that best indicates the degree of pain they are experiencing. A second rating scale is the **verbal descriptor scale**, in which patients are asked to describe their pain by choosing the phrase that most closely resembles the pain they are experiencing. The **visual analog scale (VAS)** is similar to the box scale in that the left end of the scale is anchored by the phrase "no pain" and the right by a phrase such as "worst pain imaginable." With this scale, however, people rate their pain by marking a point on the line provided. Some research suggests that the VAS is deemed superior to scales using either word descriptors of pain (Rosier, Iadarola, & Coghill, 2002); however, other studies show no difference or show that greater compliance occurs with numerical rating scales (Hjermstad et al., 2010).

Rating scales are quick and easy to use, allowing people to rate their pain frequently. Averaging ratings across time gives a more accurate picture of the amount of pain a person generally experiences than does a single rating. Turk, Meichenbaum, and Genest (1983) describe how this method can be used to identify patterns of pain in chronic pain patients. Multiple ratings provide a record to determine if the patient's pain is generally improving or getting worse. In addition, they allow patterns in the timing of severe pain to be recognized. For example, it may be that severe pain occurs most often first thing in the morning

box scale: a scale on which people rate and report their pain by choosing the number that best indicates the degree of pain that they are experiencing from a series of numbers in boxes ranging from "no pain" to "worst pain imaginable."

verbal descriptor scale: a rating scale on which people are asked to describe their pain by choosing the phrase that most closely resembles the pain that they are experiencing.

visual analog scale (VAS): a rating scale on which people report their pain by marking a point on a line anchored by the phrase "no pain" and by a phrase such as "worst pain imaginable."

Visual Analog Scale:
Mark a point on the line to show how strong your pain is.

no pain   worst pain imaginable

Box Scale:
Rate the level of your pain by circling one number on the scale, where 0 means "no pain" and 10 means "worst pain imaginable."

1	2	3	4	5	6	7	8	9	10

Verbal Rating Scale:
Circle the phrase that best describes your pain.

Not Painful   Slightly Painful   Moderately Painful   Very Painful   Extremely Painful

Figure 8-1   Rating Scales for Pain Management

or later in the day. Or, it may be that on certain days the patient's pain is more severe. If these patterns can be identified, the patient may be able to alter his or her schedule or environment to accommodate or eradicate at least the most severe pain.

Pain Questionnaires Pain questionnaires were developed to address the realization that pain is not one-dimensional. That is, the experience of pain is much more than a feeling of discomfort that can be described in terms of its intensity. Melzack asserts that describing pain on a single dimension is like "specifying the visual world only in terms of light flux without regard to pattern, color, texture, and the many other dimensions of visual experience" (1975, p. 278). In an effort to measure the multidimensional nature of pain, Melzack (1975) developed the McGill Pain Questionnaire (MPQ).

The MPQ (see Figure 8-2) offers patients the opportunity to describe their pain on three broad dimensions—sensory, affective, and evaluative. *Sensory* qualities of pain include its temporal, spatial, pressure, and thermal properties; *affective* qualities include fear, tension, and autonomic properties; *evaluative* qualities are the subjective overall intensity of the pain experience.

The MPQ has four parts. Part 1 consists of front and back drawings of the human body. Patients are asked to indicate on these drawings the areas where they feel pain. Part 2 consists of a list of 78 descriptive words, separated into a total of 20 subclasses. Patients are instructed to select a word from each subclass that most accurately characterizes their pain. The words are ordered in increasing intensity (e.g., *hot, burning, scalding,* and *searing*). Each word in each class has an assigned value based on the degree of pain it represents. In the previous example, *searing* would contribute the largest number of points, and *hot* would contribute the lowest number. These points are summed across the 20 subclasses, and the total score is called the "pain-rating index." This index is the most commonly used part of the questionnaire. Part 3 of the MPQ asks how patients' pain has changed with time. Part 4 contains a series of verbal descriptor scales. One of these scales inquires about the amount of pain the patient is experiencing at the present time. This scale provides a separate score called the Present Pain Intensity (PPI) score.

There are many advantages to the MPQ over previous instruments for measuring pain. The MPQ's largest contribution is its measurement of more than one dimension of pain. Also, patients suffering from similar pain syndromes often identify the same patterns of words from the MPQ to characterize their pain, just as those with different pain syndromes (e.g., cancer, arthritis, headaches, or phantom limb pain) identify different words to characterize their pain (Melzack & Wall, 1996). Yet there are drawbacks to the MPQ. For instance, because a fairly strong vocabulary is required to complete the questionnaire, the MPQ is not useful for assessing pain in young children or in people who do not have a strong grasp of the English language.

The MPQ is the most commonly used pain questionnaire. It has been used to assess pain in both clinical populations and in laboratory research (e.g., Gagliese & Katz, 2003; Sullivan, Lynch, & Clark, 2005). A short form of the MPQ is also available (Melzack, 1987).

However, the MPQ is not the only pain questionnaire available. The West Haven–Yale Multidimensional Pain Inventory (MPI) assesses many aspects of psychological and physical functioning and can provide a comprehensive assessment of the lives of pain patients (Kerns, Turk, & Rudy, 1985). The MPI comprises 52 items divided into three sections. The first section measures (1) pain severity, (2) pain's interference with patients' lives, (3) patients' dissatisfaction with their present functioning, (4) patients' view of the

Part 1	Where Is Your Pain?

Please mark on the drawing below, the areas where you feel pain. Put E if external, or I if internal, near the areas which you mark. Put EI if both external and internal.

Part 2	What Does Your Pain Feel Like?		
1 Flickering Quivering Pulsing Throbbing Beating Pounding	2 Jumping Flashing Shooting	3 Pricking Boring Drilling Stabbing	4 Sharp Cutting Lacerating
5 Pinching Pressing Gnawing Camping Crushing	6 Tugging Pulling Wrenching	7 Hot Burning Scalding Searing	8 Tingling Itchy Smarting Stinging
9 Dull Sore Hurting Aching Heavy	10 Tender Taut Rasping Splitting	11 Tiring Exhausting	12 Sickening Suffocating
13 Fearful Frightful Terrifying	14 Punishing Grueling Cruel Vicious Killing	15 Wretched Blinding	16 Annoying Troublesome Miserable Intense Unbearable
17 Spreading Radiating Penetrating Piercing	18 Tight Numb Drawing Squeezing Tearing	19 Cool Cold Freezing	20 Nagging Nauseating Agonizing Dreadful Torturing

Part 3	How Does Your Pain Change with Time?

1. Which word or words would you use to describe the pattern of your pain?

1	2	3
Continuous Steady Constant	Rhythmic Periodic Intermittent	Brief Momentary Transient

2. What kind of things relieve your pain?

3. What kind of things increase your pain?

Part 4	How Strong Is Your Pain?

People agree that the following 5 words represent pain of increasing intensity. They are:

1	2	3	4	5
Mild	Discomforting	Distressing	Horrible	Excruciating

To answer each question below, write the number of the most appropriate word in the space beside the question.

1. Which word describes your pain right now? _____
2. Which word describes it at its worst? _____
3. Which word describes it when it is least? _____
4. Which word describes the worst toothache you ever had? _____
5. Which word describes the worst headache you ever had? _____
6. Which word describes the worst stomach-ache you ever had? _____

Figure 8-2 The McGill Pain Questionnaire

Source: Copyright © R. Melzack, 1984. Reprinted with permission.

support they receive from others, (5) patients' perceived life control, and (6) patients' negative mood states. The second section measures patients' perceptions of the responses of significant others. The final section identifies how frequently patients engage in each of 30 different daily activities. The MPI is not without its problems, however, and long-term predictions of a patient's category of coping with pain have not been accurate (Broderick, Junghaenel, & Turk, 2004).

Many pain questionnaires have been developed for both general and specific uses and some for use with particular populations. For instance, the Dalhousie Everyday Pain Scale (von Baeyer, Baskerville, & McGrath, 1998) was developed for use with children; the Parents' Postoperative Pain Measure was designed to assist parents in the at-home assessment of their children's pain (Finley, Chambers, McGrath, & Walsh, 1999). Other questionnaires have been developed for use with specific pain syndromes, for example, the Chronic Pain Coping Inventory (Jensen, Turner, Romano, & Strom, 1995). The MPQ, as previously mentioned, is by far the most common instrument used by clinical practitioners and researchers. In fact, it has been translated and adapted for use in 20 languages, including Arabic, Chinese, Japanese, German, Italian, and Spanish (Melzack & Katz, 2001).

Assessing Pain in Infants and Children

Assessing pain in infants and children is often more challenging than assessing pain in adults. Obviously, infants cannot complete self-report questionnaires. Similarly, young children have difficulty expressing their experience of pain because of their limited language abilities and their level of cognitive development. Therefore, pain assessments conducted on these populations cannot follow the standard questionnaire format used with adults (McGrath & Gillespie, 2001).

At one time, it was believed that very young infants were insensitive to pain (Gibson & Chambers, 2004). Currently, experts believe that infants are capable of feeling pain from the moment they are born (Stevens & Franck, 2001). If we cannot ask newborns whether they are in pain, or how much pain they are in, what should we do? A sample of 72 neonatal intensive care unit (NICU) nurses were asked which indicators they used to interpret the experience of pain in the infants entrusted to their care (Howard & Thurber, 1998). The 10 pain indicators used by the NICU nurses, listed in decreasing order of frequency, were fussiness, restlessness, grimacing, crying, increasing heart rate, increasing respirations, wiggling, rapid state changes, wrinkling of forehead, and clenching of fist.

Canadian researchers (e.g., Hadjistavropoulos, Craig, Grunau, & Johnston, 1994; Hadjistavropoulos, Craig, Grunau, & Whitfield, 1997) have documented the relative importance of each of the cues available when judging infant pain. They have discovered that while cry characteristics seem to command attention, cues provided through infant facial activity are weighted more heavily in adults' judgments of newborn pain. These facial characteristics include a brow bulge, eyes squeezed shut, a taut tongue, and a deepened nasolabial furrow (the line or wrinkle that runs down from either side of the nose to the outer corners of the mouth). Facial characteristics also appear to convey more information to judges than does the infant's bodily activity.

Measurement of facial characteristics has been incorporated in the Neonatal Facial Coding System (NFCS). The NFCS was developed by Grunau and Craig (1987) to provide a detailed, anatomically based, and objective description of newborns' reactions to potentially painful stimuli. This instrument was developed primarily for use by researchers. It requires the researcher to assign a value of "1" or "0" to each facial action (brow bulge, eye squeeze, nasolabial furrow, open lips, vertical stretch mouth, horizontal stretch mouth, lip purse, taut tongue, and chin quiver). The scoring is completed by microanalyzing videotaped recordings of the infant. A similar system entitled the Child Facial Coding System (CFCS) was developed for use with preschool children (Chambers, Cassidy, McGrath, Gilbert, & Craig, 1996). As mentioned, these systems were created primarily for use in research settings, although some have attempted to use them in clinical settings (Prkachin, Hughes, Schultz, Joy, & Hunt, 2002).

There are, however, a number of instruments that are available to assess pain in children in clinical settings (McGrath, Latimer, Finley, & Chambers, 2009; Stevens, 2001). Children's behaviour can be observed and their pain rated by using scales such as the Dalhousie Everyday Pain Scale (von Baeyer et al., 1998). Self-report measures may also be used with children. However, these measures provide considerably less detail to the health professional than do self-report measures used with adults, in part because of the descriptors young children use to describe their pain. Elizabeth Job, a graduate student at the University of British Columbia, interviewed 106 children between the ages of 3 and 6 years. She discovered that the word *pain* didn't appear in the children's vocabularies until they were old enough to attend kindergarten. Instead, children tend to use words such as *ouch, ow,* and *hurt* to describe their pain (Job, 2003). Preschool children may be asked to indicate the degree of their "hurt" by choosing from a scale of facial expressions (e.g., Faces Pain Scale Revised, Hicks, von Baeyer, Spafford, van Korlaar, & Goodenough, 2001; www.painsourcebook.ca). The Oucher scale displays six photographs of a child's face, showing increasing levels of discomfort. Pain questionnaires have also been developed for use with children. The Children's Comprehensive Pain Questionnaire (McGrath, 1987) is just one example of a pain questionnaire designed for use with children.

Assessing Pain in Older Adults

Interest in and research on pain in older adults are relatively recent. When comparing the usefulness of the numeric rating scale (NRS), the verbal descriptor scale (VDS), the visual analog scale (VAS), and the MPQ to assess pain intensity in surgical patients, Gagliese and her colleagues (Gagliese, Weizblit, Ellis, & Chan, 2005) discovered that the NRS was best. Specifically, the NRS had lower error rates and greater validity than the other scales. The VDS also fared well; however, the use of the VAS led to high error rates and numerous incomplete or unscorable responses. Previous reports acknowledge that the failure rate of older adults on the VAS is as high as 30 percent (Gagliese & Melzack, 1997). Evidence suggests that the MPQ, with its emphasis on adjectival descriptors of pain, is a useful measurement tool for this age group; however, Gagliese (Gagliese & Melzack, 1997; Gagliese et al., 2005) deems the NRS superior.

Pain assessment strategies with this population have proved challenging (Herr, 2011). For example, a protocol was developed to simulate the movements of older adults' activities of daily living. However, many of the individuals were not able to complete the protocol because it triggered severe pain (Weiner, Peiper, McConnell, Martinez, & Keefe, 1996). Using a different approach, a study was conducted to identify the accuracy of judgments of older adults' facial expressions of pain. Although this study resulted in higher pain ratings ascribed to older than to younger patients, it was unclear if the higher pain ratings were due to objective changes in facial expression, to preconceived notions held by the judges that older adults experience more pain, or if a combination of these factors was responsible for the results (Matheson, 1997).

Pain assessment in cognitively impaired persons and those with communication disabilities presents additional challenges (Hadjistavropoulos, LaChapelle, MacLeod, Snider, & Craig, 2000; Hadjistavropoulos, von Baeyer, & Craig, 2001; Prkachin, 2007; Tsai, 2011). The Pain Assessment Checklist for Seniors with Limited Ability to Communicate (PACSLAC) was developed in response to this need (Fuchs-Lacelle & Hadjistavropoulos, 2004). Using PACSLAC to assess and manage the pain of individuals with dementia has resulted in improved pain management practices (Fuchs-Lacelle, Hadjistavropoulos, & Lix, 2008).

PAIN CONTROL TECHNIQUES

In addition to the many consequences of pain already mentioned, there is a consequence even more severe: death. Uncontrolled pain compromises immune function, promotes tumour growth, and can compromise healing—all factors that can lead to an early death (Lynch & Watson, 2006). Given the negative impact that pain has on the life of the sufferer, the World Health Organization has declared that "pain relief should be a human right" (WHO, 2004). There are a number of pain control techniques available for those seeking pain relief, but we must recognize that they are met with varying degrees of success.

Pharmacological Control of Pain

The traditional and most common method of controlling pain is through pain-relieving medications. **Peripherally acting analgesics**, also known as non-narcotic analgesics, are probably the most frequently used analgesics (Julien et al., 2011; Melzack & Wall, 1996). Included in this group are such common pain relievers as acetylsalicylic acid (e.g., Aspirin), acetaminophen (e.g., Tylenol), and ibuprofen (e.g., Advil). These drugs work by reducing inflammation at the site of tissue damage and inhibiting the synthesis of neurochemicals in the peripheral nervous system that facilitate the transmission of pain impulses. Peripherally acting analgesics provide substantial pain relief for a wide variety of pain conditions, especially arthritis and other conditions involving inflammation (Julien et al., 2011). Although peripherally acting analgesics are generally available over the counter, they do have side effects and may interact with other drugs. Used in recommended amounts, however, they are generally safe and are effective when dealing with mild to moderate pain.

peripherally acting analgesics: non-narcotic medications that decrease pain by reducing inflammation at the site of tissue damage; they also inhibit the synthesis of neurochemicals in the peripheral nervous system that facilitate the transmission of pain impulses.

Centrally acting analgesics are pain-killing medications called **narcotics**. Narcotics work by binding to opiate receptors in the central nervous system (Julien et al., 2011). These drugs are either derived directly from the opium poppy (e.g., codeine and morphine) or synthetically reproduced but based on opium molecules (e.g., heroin, methadone, oxycodone and the brand-name drugs Percocet, and Oxycontin). These drugs operate on the central nervous system by imitating the effects of the body's endogenous pain relief system. Specifically, the molecules in these drugs bind to receptors for endorphins and enkephalins in the brain and spinal cord, blocking the transmission of pain signals. They are considered the most potent pain relievers available. They are frequently used to alleviate labour pain, postoperative pain, and chronic progressive pain experienced by some terminal cancer patients.

centrally acting analgesics: pain-killing medications that operate on the central nervous system by imitating the effects of the body's endogenous pain relief system.

narcotics: pain-killing drugs that work by binding to opiate receptors in the central nervous system.

Although narcotics are extremely useful for relieving pain, they also have disadvantages. Narcotics are known to be psychoactive; they depress respiration; they have tremendous potential to produce tolerance, so that higher and higher doses are needed to achieve the same effect; and they can be addictive (Aronoff, 2000; Julien et al., 2011).

There is considerable controversy about the likelihood of a patient becoming addicted to narcotics. Some researchers argue that this is a very real possibility, whereas others believe that this issue has been blown out of proportion (Aronoff, 2000; Dillard & Hirchman, 2002; Passik & Weinreb, 2000). You'll recall in chapter 6 our discussion of the abuse of prescription pain relievers such as oxycodone. Research suggests that when allowed to self-administer narcotics, patients recovering from surgery use less medication than would have been given by hospital staff. For further discussion of this topic, refer to the section on patient-controlled analgesia in chapter 9.

Local anaesthetics, such as novocaine and lidocaine, make up a third category of chemicals for relieving pain. These medications can be applied topically but are much more effective when injected at the site where the pain originates. You would likely have received a local anaesthetic from your dentist before he or she began drilling or pulling a tooth. Likewise, you may have received a local anaesthetic before receiving sutures. Local anaesthetics work by blocking nerve cells from generating pain impulses (Winters, 1985). Although they work well to block impulses in pain fibres, they also block impulses in motor neurons. Consequently, you will have little or no control over your mouth, tongue, lips, and cheeks for several hours after a dental procedure if you received a local anaesthetic prior to it.

Other drugs affect pain indirectly. For example, **sedatives,** such as barbiturates, and **tranquillizers,** such as diazepam (Valium), are depressants; that is, they depress bodily functions by decreasing the transmission of impulses throughout the central nervous system (Julien et al., 2011). These drugs probably do not directly affect pain but rather reduce patient anxiety and help the patient to sleep (thereby escaping the pain for a while and resting so as to better tolerate the pain when awake). **Antidepressants** also help patients who are in pain by reducing the depression that frequently accompanies pain (Bair et al., 2004). In addition, it is believed that they affect pain-related neurotransmitters.

There has been a dramatic increase in research on drug combinations that enhance pain reduction (Dalal & Melzack, 1998). This research involves (1) drugs that have not traditionally been viewed as analgesics, such as antidepressants and sedatives; (2) drugs that have been viewed as effective analgesics in their own right, such as opioids and some anti-inflammatory drugs; and (3) combinations of both types, such as opioids and antidepressants. Combining drugs in the treatment of pain increases analgesia, either as a result of their interaction or as a result of their additive effects. For instance, opioid analgesia is enhanced when combined with the administration of amphetamines. Furthermore, a combination of drugs may reduce their side effects because the amount of each drug administered is reduced, or because of the way the two drugs interact. For example, the general cognitive decline and drowsiness caused by opioids can be counteracted by introducing amphetamines.

Surgical Control of Pain

Surgical treatment of pain is the most extreme form of treatment available to pain patients. Surgery is considered only as a last resort, after all other treatment options have been exhausted (Cullinane, Chu, & Mamelak, 2002; Dillard & Hirchman, 2002). Surgical techniques include those that attempt to interrupt the transmission of pain from the periphery to the spinal cord, as well as those that disrupt the flow of pain sensations from the spinal cord to the brain. However, not all patients experience relief from their pain following surgery and, for those who do, relief may be temporary. We now know that the nervous system has regenerative abilities that enable pain impulses to reach the brain along a variety of neural pathways. As a result, surgical techniques that were once relatively common are now rarely performed.

Transcutaneous Electrical Nerve Stimulation

Transcutaneous electrical nerve stimulation (TENS) involves placing an electrode on the surface of the skin close to where the patient feels pain and applying electrical stimulation. This stimulation affects all nerves within approximately 4 centimetres of the skin's surface. Although stimulation is usually applied for approximately 20 minutes, the duration of pain relief reportedly lasts several hours and occasionally lasts for days or weeks., However, the clinical effectiveness of TENS is controversial (Sluka & Walsh, 2003). Researchers from New Zealand tested the effectiveness of TENS for pain relief in labour. Their conclusion was that "it probably does little good and they do not advocate its widespread introduction" (Thomas, Tyle, Webster, & Neilson, 2008, p. 182).

On the other hand, positive results can also be found. The effectiveness of TENS in reducing acute muscular and postoperative pain in the majority of patients is well documented (Bjordal, Johnson, & Ljunggreen, 2003). In a moving example, Chapman (1984) describes a 9-year-old boy who began receiving TENS while still unconscious from surgery. When the surgeon left the room, the boy spoke casually with the others in the room. When asked whether there was anything he feared, he began to cry and confessed his terror of the expected operation that would remove his kidney. His surprised nurse tried to reassure him that the surgery had already been done, and that there was nothing to worry about. He refused to believe her. "But don't you remember?" she contended, "that's why they put you to sleep this morning—so they could do the operation." The little boy looked very threatened. "It's not true!" he shouted. "It's not true!" When asked why it couldn't be true, he asserted confidently, "Because I haven't got any bandages." He was asked to feel

transcutaneous electrical nerve stimulation (TENS): a pain control technique that involves placing an electrode on the surface of the skin and applying electrical stimulation.

Transcutaneous electrical nerve stimulation (TENS) machines are easy to use and can help to relieve pain. Portable TENS machines allow individuals to engage in daily activities while their nerves are being stimulated.
Blue Planet Photography

his belly. When he did, an expression of astonishment came over his face. At that moment, he declared he felt pain, and he began to cry. As a recent review article concluded, the usefulness of TENS is largely dependent on the intensity, frequency, and the site of stimulation (Claydon, Chesterton, Barlas, & Sim, 2011).

Acupuncture

acupuncture: an ancient Chinese pain control technique that involves the insertion of fine needles to create stimulation to the peripheral nerves.

Acupuncture is an ancient Chinese pain control technique that has been in continuous practice for at least 2000 years (Turk & Winter, 2006). Basically, the procedure involves the insertion of fine needles (made of steel, gold, or other metals) through specific points in the skin then twirling or electrically charging them to create stimulation to the peripheral nerves. The effects of acupuncture are not immediate, and the needles must be stimulated for approximately 20 minutes to produce analgesia. For some analgesia can last for hours after the stimulation has ended.

The practice of acupuncture is part of a complex theory of medicine in which all diseases and pains are believed to be due to disharmony between *yin* (spirit) and *yang* (blood). In China, where this philosophy is more widely accepted, 5 to 10 percent of surgical operations are conducted with the use of acupuncture as the only form of analgesia. The patients must volunteer for the procedure, and the surgeries using acupuncture analgesia are relatively straightforward, with little likelihood of complications. In Western countries, acupuncture is rarely used for surgery; it is seen instead as a treatment for less intense pain.

Laboratory studies have shown that acupuncture produces only mild analgesia in most people. Traditionally, it was believed that exact points on the body, outlined on acupuncture charts, must be stimulated to have the desired effect. For example, certain points on the nose and ear were associated with the small intestine, whereas other points were associated with the kidneys heart, or abdomen. It is now believed that the degree of pain relief experienced is dependent on the intensity of the stimulation, rather than on the exact point of stimulation.

While proponents assert that there are many situations in which acupuncture may be useful as an adjunct treatment or possibly an acceptable alternative to traditional treatments (e.g., cancer pain, headache, myofascial pain, osteoarthritis, low back pain, neck pain) (Carlsson & Sjölund, 2001; Haake et al., 2007; Lu, Lu, & Kleinman, 2001; Weidong & Rosenthal, 2013), there is mounting evidence that acupuncture may not be effective in reducing pain independently of the psychological impact. Relatively recent reviews (Ernst, Lee, & Choi, 2011; Hall, 2011; Madsen, Gotzsche, & Hrobjartsson, 2009; Standaert et al., 2011) of randomized clinical trials with acupuncture question its effectiveness.

Physical Therapy

physical therapy: therapy involved in the rehabilitation of muscle, bone, joint, or the results of nerve disease.

Physical therapy involves a variety of treatment approaches to help patients who suffer from both acute and chronic pain. Patients usually work with a physical therapist to prepare an individualized treatment program. The program should provide daily or weekly goals that allow for gradual but steady progress. It should also progress rapidly enough to ensure the patient experiences a feeling of accomplishment but slowly enough to prevent overexertion or re-injury.

In order to restore their range of motion, patients who have undergone surgery or experienced injury should exercise regularly. Exercise also benefits arthritis patients because it helps maintain joint flexibility and prevents joints from deteriorating

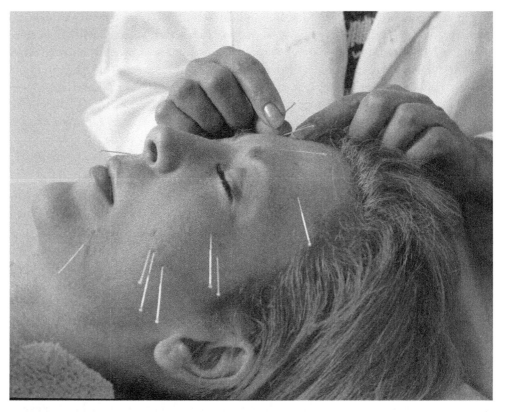

Stimulation of the peripheral nerves by acupuncture needles may provide varying degrees of pain relief.
Vinicius Tupinamba/Shutterstock

(Levy et al., 2012; Minor & Sanford, 1993). In addition, exercising is extremely beneficial for low back pain patients who need to maintain flexibility and develop strength in key muscles to provide support for their spines (Hayden, van Tulder, & Tomlinson, 2005; Moffett et al., 1999). As part of an exercise program, patients are typically also taught body mechanics and proper posture to prevent further injuries.

Massage

Several years ago, a massage was considered a luxury. Today, massage therapy is one of the pain management techniques that Canadian physicians are keen to learn more about. A large-scale, primarily European survey revealed that the most common non-drug treatment for pain is massage (Breivik et al., 2006). Massage therapy is used to ease muscle pain and other pains, including that resulting from cancer. The procedure consists of systematic stroking and kneading of the body. The two main types of massage therapy are Swedish massage and Shiatsu massage. **Swedish massage** is a set routine of basic strokes to work the body and includes slow, gentle stroking movements, known as *effleurage*, to warm and relax tissue and to stimulate blood circulation. A deeper massage is also conducted with movements such as friction, percussion, and *petrissage* (massage in which the muscles are kneaded and pressed). **Shiatsu massage** is based on the belief that there is a flow of energy through the body and that at times energy blockages develop. Consistent with this belief, energy blockages are released through the strong and sustained pressure of the massage at specific points on the body.

Swedish massage: slow, gentle stroking movements to warm and relax tissue and stimulate blood circulation.

Shiatsu massage: sustained massage pressure on specific points of the body; according to the beliefs of practitioners, Shiatsu massage releases blockages in the flow of energy through the body.

Both laboratory and clinical research indicates that massage is effective in reducing pain (Breivik et al., 2006; Frey Law et al., 2008). Research conducted with 32 hospital staff at a large teaching hospital investigated the usefulness of Swedish massage (Katz, Wowk, Culp, & Wakeling, 1999). Participants received either a series of eight 15-minute, on-site massage treatments or eight sessions of seated rest. Those in the massage group experienced significant reductions in pain and tension levels compared to the control group that received seated rest. This pain and tension relief persisted for up to a day or longer following the massage. An added benefit experienced by those who received the massage treatments was a lift in overall mood.

Relaxation

Many of the same relaxation strategies that are used to cope with stress (see chapter 2) are effective treatments for both acute and chronic pain. Relaxation is often used in conjunction with other pain management strategies and is thought to be an essential part of both biofeedback and hypnotic treatment. The rationale for relaxation training is straightforward: Continual muscle contraction is considered both a cause and an effect of pain. Researchers have found that muscle tension results in lactic acid buildup in muscles and also decreases blood flow to muscles. Both factors can significantly increase people's experience of pain.

As discussed in chapter 2, relaxation can be accomplished by many different techniques, including **progressive muscle relaxation** and meditation. Researchers (e.g., Carlson & Hoyle, 1993; Jacobs, 2001) report that progressive muscle relaxation is generally helpful in coping with stress-related disorders, such as migraine and tension headache, depression, hypertension, and low back pain. However, the actual effect size varies substantially from study to study, in part because of variation in the experimental procedures. Relaxation training was most effective when patients had participated in a sufficient number of training sessions, when they had been trained individually rather than in a group, when the patients used audiotapes to supplement their training, and when the patients had enough time to master the technique.

But how long do the effects of relaxation treatment for pain last? Edward Blanchard and colleagues addressed this issue in a 5-year follow-up investigation of chronic headache patients (Blanchard, Andrasik, Guarnieri, Neff, & Rodichok, 1987; Blanchard, Appelbaum, Guarnieri, Morrill, & Dentinger, 1987). These patients had all experienced an average of 18 years of headache, either muscle contraction (tension-type) headache or "vascular" headache, which includes both migraine and combined (migraine plus tension-type) headaches. These patients completed training for progressive muscle relaxation in 10 sessions over 8 weeks. Those patients whose headache pain had not improved by at least 60 percent were offered additional treatment in the form of biofeedback. The treatment effects endured over time. That is, 5 years after the initial treatment, patients reported headache pain at levels similar to those reported immediately after taking part in the treatment. The headache pain did not return to pretreatment levels. Other research has supported this conclusion, with patients experiencing durable relief from both relaxation and biofeedback for at least 2 years (Blanchard, 1987, 2000).

Meditation is another form of relaxation. *Meditative relaxation*, developed by Herbert Benson and colleagues (e.g., Benson, Beary, & Carol, 1974), is derived from various religious meditative practices but has no religious connotations. With Bensonian relaxation,

progressive muscle relaxation: a technique in which a person achieves relaxation by flexing and gradually relaxing muscle groups.

meditation: a form of relaxation in which one attempts to focus attention fully on a single thought or image.

the patient attempts to focus attention fully on a single thought or image. Often a very simple syllable, such as "ohm" or "one," is repeated slowly over and over again with each breath. This process usually takes place in a quiet environment where the participant sits with eyes closed and muscles relaxed for a period of approximately 20 minutes.

Mindfulness meditation is a related strategy for achieving relaxation. This type of meditation has its roots in Buddhist practice. Participants engaged in mindfulness meditation do not try to ignore unpleasant thoughts or sensations. Instead, they are instructed to focus on any thoughts or sensations as they occur but to view these thoughts in a non-judgmental manner. As Kabat-Zinn (1993) explains, "Observing without judging, moment by moment, helps you see what is on your mind without editing or censoring it, without intellectualizing it or getting lost in your own incessant thinking" (p. 263). Brain imaging studies tell us that the right hemisphere of the brain becomes less active and the left more active during mindfulness meditation. With increased activation in the left hemisphere, a corresponding increase in positive affect is experienced (Davidson et al., 2003). A meta-analysis of mindfulness meditation studies indicates its effectiveness for stress- and pain-related problems and for those who are simply looking for a way to manage the everyday stresses in their lives (Grossman, Niemann, Schmidt, & Walach, 2004).

Guided imagery can be considered a form of relaxation and can also be classified as a technique that relies on distraction. With guided imagery, the participant is told to envision a calm, peaceful, and pleasant image. The image should be relatively unchanging, and participants are told to focus all of their attention on the image.

guided imagery: a form of relaxation that relies on distraction, in which the participant is told to imagine a calm, peaceful, and pleasant image.

Guided imagery is a technique suggested to pregnant mothers for use in childbirth. Women in labour are told to choose a focal point, either real or imagined, that they can concentrate on when giving birth. The focal point may be the image of waves washing onto the beach, for example, or a picture of a loved one.

Children are also encouraged to use guided imagery when undergoing cancer treatment. One child described skiing down a mountain as fast as he could. He commented on the warmth of the sunshine but insisted that focusing on the speed with which he skied in and out of the gates was how he became most "absorbed" in his image.

When used to manage pain, guided imagery is most often used in conjunction with other pain-control techniques. Thus, the unique contribution of guided imagery is difficult to establish. Studies conducted on guided imagery suggest that it is superior to biofeedback in treating headaches (Evans & Penzien, 2003; Ilacqua, 1994), aids cancer patients in coping with the pain of treatments (Battino, 2000), reduces postoperative pain and length of hospital stays for child surgical patients (Huth, Broome, & Good, 2004) and older adults (Antall & Kresevic, 2004), and is especially useful for reducing musculoskeletal pain (Posadzki & Ernst, 2011).

Distraction

Like guided imagery, **distraction** involves focusing attention on something other than the sensation of pain. As we mentioned earlier, athletes, soldiers, and others who are "caught up" in what they are doing may not immediately notice when they have injured themselves. Although we sometimes engage in distraction unknowingly, it is also possible to consciously apply the technique of distraction to help control the experience of pain. We can distract ourselves by focusing on a completely different activity, such as listening to

distraction: a pain management technique in which the patient focuses attention on something other than the sensation of pain.

music, singing a song, playing a video game, doing arithmetic problems, or reading a book. Researchers at Dalhousie University note that when 5-year-olds are watching a program on television during immunization, they experience lower levels of pain than when faced with a blank TV screen (Cassidy et al., 2002). Canadian researchers conclude that infants and young children display less pain-related distress during immunization when parents, clinicains, or the children themselves use distraction during the procedure (Taddio et al., 2010). Researchers at Washington University (e.g., Hoffman et al., 2006) have discovered a new way to help burn patients manage their pain—virtual reality pain control. This method of pain management relies on distraction to diminish severe pain (see Box 8-2 for more details).

Box 8-2

Virtual Snowmen Alleviate Pain of Burn Victims

A can of gasoline placed too close to a campfire exploded, leaving 17-year-old Mark Powers with deep flash burns to 33 percent of his body. Mark was hospitalized in a regional burn centre, where he would receive skin grafting on his neck, chest, back, and stomach. The opioid painkillers that helped to alleviate his pain while he lay motionless in his hospital bed failed to relieve the excruciating pain Mark experienced when having his wounds cleaned. To help Mark and other burn victims control the severe pain experienced during wound care, psychologists David Patterson of the University of Washington's Harborview Burn Center and Hunter Hoffman of the university's Human Interface Technology Laboratory created a new psychological pain-control technique—virtual reality analgesia (Hoffman, 2004; Hoffman et al., 2006; Patterson, Hoffman, Weichman, Jensen, & Shara, 2004).

Virtual reality analgesia relies on distraction to help reduce perceived pain intensity and unpleasantness. As we have discussed in this chapter, pain is not entirely determined by sensory input. Instead, as the gate control theory of pain suggests, the same pain signal can be viewed as more or less painful depending on what one is thinking about or attending to. We have a finite amount of attention that can be divided between tasks, so if we are immersed in a 3-D computer-generated environment, less attention is directed to the real world (Patterson et al., 2004) and consequently, less pain is experienced. In fact, the greater "presence" the virtual environment has for us, the less pain we experience (Hoffman et al., 2006).

SnowWorld was one of the first virtual reality software programs designed for the treatment of pain. To use this program, patients are outfitted with a virtual reality helmet that positions two miniature LCD screens in front of the viewer's eyes. These screens present patients with a view of the computer-generated world and prevent patients from seeing what is going on in the real world. As patients look around the virtual world, what they see changes. For example, as they look up, they will see an image of a virtual sky, and when they look down the image will change to an icy river and river canyon walls (Hoffman et al., 2006). Using a joystick, patients are able to shoot snowballs at snowmen, robots, and penguins. When hit, snowmen become puffs and penguins turn upside down, and these victories are accompanied by appropriate sound effects. The environment portrayed in SnowWorld is purposely cool and icy, a direct contrast to the "hot" unpleasant memories that most burn victims hold.

Patients participating in virtual reality treatments have been shown to have 50 percent less pain than patients in a no-distraction control condition (Hoffman, Patterson, et al., 2004). Treatment results using the virtual reality helmets are far superior to using distractive techniques in the form of Nintendo games, and the better the quality of the image presented on the screen, the better the analgesic effects (Hoffman, Sharar, et al., 2004). These researchers continue to develop new attention-grabbing virtual environments (e.g., ChocolateWorld), and they are optimistic that virtual reality analgesia will prove valuable for treating other patient populations in pain (e.g., for those undergoing cancer procedures, childbirth, dental work, and physiotherapy).

Box 8-2

(Continued)

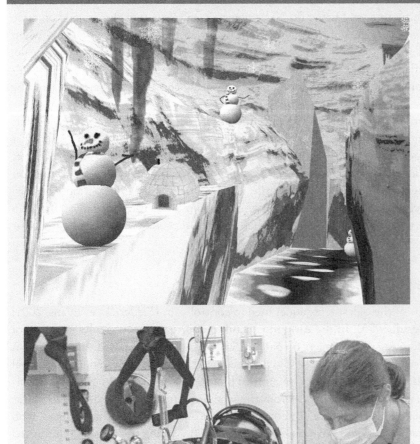

Virtual snowmen help burn victims control pain psychologically.
Hoffman/University of Washington

A burn patient uses a water-friendly fibre-optic virtual reality helmet.
University of Washington

Distraction can also involve reinterpreting the event that is resulting in pain. Bandura (1991) provides a description from an 8-year-old boy who is re-interpreting a painful event: "As soon as I get in the dentist's chair, I pretend he's the enemy and I'm a secret agent, and he's torturing me to get secrets, and if I make one sound, I'm telling him secret information, so I never do." The boy goes on to say that this is good practice because he is going to be a secret agent when he grows up. There may be times when this technique works too well. On one occasion, the boy got quite absorbed in his role; when the dentist asked the boy to rinse his mouth, the boy snarled and said, "I won't tell you a damned thing." The dentist and apparently even the boy were surprised by this outburst.

Distraction techniques are particularly useful for reducing acute pain, such as that experienced during some medical and dental procedures. However, that doesn't mean that individuals experiencing chronic pain don't use distraction to cope with their discomfort (Santavirta et al., 2001). People who experience chronic pain are likely to use distraction most often when they anticipate a sharp rise in pain. For example, distraction would be particularly useful when a person suffering from chronic lower back pain must endure a bumpy car ride to the physician's office or when an arthritic patient needs to climb a flight of stairs.

Hypnosis

hypnosis: an altered state of consciousness.

Hypnosis is one of the oldest techniques used to control pain (Fredericks & Evans, 2001; Hilgard & Hilgard, 1975). In the early nineteenth century, sensational tales appeared of physicians performing major surgery on patients who had been hypnotized. In 1829, it was reported that a French surgeon, Dr. Cloquet, removed a malignant tumour and several enlarged glands from a 64-year-old woman who had been hypnotized. In order to accomplish this feat, an incision was made from the woman's armpit to the inner side of her breast—in other words, the incision went halfway across her chest. Yet the woman, who had not received any drugs, conversed with the physician during the surgery and showed no signs of experiencing pain (Kroger, 1957, cited in Chaves & Barber, 1976).

Hypnosis is often considered an altered state of consciousness that involves several components. First, a state of *relaxation* is necessary so that a hypnotic trance can be induced. Second, *distraction* or diversion of attention from the pain experience is established (this step is also referred to as "narrowing of attention"). Next, the practitioner *suggests* to the patient that the pain is diminishing. In this step, the practitioner may suggest that the pain is being replaced by a more pleasant sensation, such as warmth (Barber, 1986; Orne & Dinges, 1989).

The hypnotic procedure can take a number of forms. Consider Dylan, a 26-year-old who is currently experiencing extreme pain in his left arm, resulting from a fall he experienced while snowboarding.

Scenario One: Dylan's practitioner first induces hypnosis and then suggests, "The arm is going to begin to feel numb, with a pins-and-needles sensation as though it has received novocaine, and it will go entirely to sleep." After a period of giving such suggestions, the practitioner adds, "This numbness is now so complete that there will be no pain sensation whatsoever, though you just might be able to feel my touch."

These suggestions rely upon Dylan's imagining sensations he has had in the past—numbness, pins and needles, and the feeling that novocaine has been injected and that the arm has gone to sleep. If Dylan can imagine these sensations well enough to actually experience them, he will also gain control over the pain sensation in his arm.

Scenario Two: Dylan's practitioner first induces hypnosis and then suggests, "Your arm will begin to float up, bending at the elbow." After this is repeated a few times, the practitioner grasps Dylan's arm and adds, "You now see your arm floating down, slowly, and gently your arm is cradled in your lap."

This procedure, first described by Erickson (1967), is an indirect way of suggesting away pain. Dylan's arm no longer seems to belong to him. Consequently, he no longer feels pain in his arm.

Scenario Three: Dylan's practitioner first induces hypnosis and then suggests, "Collect your pain in your left hand. As you do so, slowly make a fist. Squeeze your fist tighter as you continue to capture the pain." After a number of these suggestions, the practitioner adds, "You have gathered all of the pain in your hand. Now throw it away."

This technique relies on the experience of focusing on the left hand and providing the sensation of muscular tension and pressure to facilitate the response to suggestion. This tension and pressure lead Dylan to believe he is in fact holding something (i.e., the pain), and therefore there can no longer be any pain left in his body. The practitioner might also have Dylan relive an experience he had before experiencing pain in his arm, thereby indirectly eliminating the pain.

Unfortunately, hypnosis does not work for everyone. For people who are highly responsive to suggestion, hypnosis can be very helpful in pain relief. However, researchers are not entirely sure whether hypnosis actually blocks pain or simply interferes with the reporting of it. Under hypnotic suggestion, people tend not to show behavioural signs of pain, such as grimacing or tensing their muscles. As well, hypnotized people report verbally that they feel no discomfort (Hilgard & Hilgard, 1975). They may recognize that they are in pain, but they indicate that the pain is not affecting them or does not matter to them. Under hypnosis, people still show the classic physiological reactions to pain, such as changes in respiration, and increased heart rate and blood pressure (Orne, 1980; Patterson & Jensen, 2003); however, there are measurable changes in brain activity during hypnosis (e.g., in the somatosensory cortex and limbic system; Patterson & Jensen, 2003).

Researchers have yet to achieve a complete understanding of the mechanism responsible for the success of hypnosis. Consequently, modern physicians have been reluctant to adopt it in clinical practice. However, there is now considerable documentation demonstrating the effectiveness of hypnosis for patients undergoing surgery, childbirth, and dental procedures as well as for those receiving treatment for burns, low back pain, cancer pain, and headaches (Abdeshi et al., 2013; Harandi, Esfandani, & Shakibaei, 2004; Lewis, 2013; Patterson, 2004; Walker, 2004). For example, in a classic study, Spiegel and Bloom (1983) randomly assigned 54 women with metastatic breast cancer to three groups. Group one members met weekly for 90 minutes and comprised a support group. During the session, the women underwent hypnosis for approximately 5 to 10 minutes. The women assigned to group two also had a 90-minute weekly support group meeting but did not undergo hypnosis. The third group received only the usual medical treatment. One year later, the women in groups one and two reported significantly less pain compared to group three, with group one reporting the least pain. In fact, group three, the control group, actually reported an increase in pain and suffering a year after the experiment commenced. Many studies have reported an added benefit of using hypnosis in the treatment of pain—patients who receive hypnosis report less anxiety than do patients who receive other forms of pain treatment (Lewis, 2013; Liossi & Hatira, 2003).

Multidisciplinary Pain Management Programs

Pain clinics and pain management programs have been developed to aid the chronic pain patient. Our review of existing pain treatments illustrates that no single method of treatment is completely effective. Furthermore, the success of each method of treatment varies considerably from one patient to the next. Therefore, a treatment approach that combines several treatment methods is likely to succeed for the largest percentage of patients and provide the greatest pain relief for each individual. Given that multidisciplinary interventions consistently prove more effective than a single treatment approach, the good news is that almost all patients are currently receiving several forms of treatment for their pain. Typically, the treatment involves a non-pharmacological treatment in addition to medication (Fedoroff, Blackwell & Speed, 2014; Moulin, Clark, Speechley, & Morley-Forster, 2002).

The concept of having special institutions to provide multidisciplinary treatment for pain originated with John Bonica. He founded the first pain clinic at the University of Washington Medical School in 1960. There are now thousands of pain clinics across North America, although the structure, methods, and quality of pain clinics vary widely. Many pain clinics are private institutions, whereas others are affiliated with medical schools, universities, or hospitals. Accessing publicly funded programs in Canada can be challenging. The average wait time in Canada was documented to be 6 months in 2007 (Peng et al., 2007). Some clinics provide inpatient care, while others provide treatment on an outpatient basis. Often the program will include the interdisciplinary efforts of physicians, psychologists or psychiatrists, physical therapists, and occupational therapists (Peng et al., 2008; Singh, 2005; Turk & Winter, 2006). However, there are countless experts who can be included or consulted in any particular program (e.g., neurologists, rheumatologists, orthopaedic surgeons, acupuncturists, and massage therapists).

Initially, patients are assessed to determine the qualitative nature of their pain. This assessment typically involves documenting the location, sensory qualities, severity, and duration of the patient's pain, as well as its onset and history. Determining the patient's current emotional and mental state, the degree to which family and work lives have been interrupted, and how the patient has coped with the pain in the past is also part of the initial assessment. This assessment allows for the program to be customized to match the needs of the patient (Gatchel, 2005; Turk & Stacey, 2000). Goals for each patient are established, and the program is constructed to help the patient attain those goals.

The goals and objectives of different pain management programs may vary. However, they typically include reducing the patient's experience of pain, improving physical and lifestyle functioning, improving social support and family life, decreasing reliance on medications, and reducing the patient's need to use health care services (Fedoroff et al., 2014; Turk & Winter, 2006). The programs generally include specific treatment components for attaining each goal. For example, most programs include patient education to provide patients with a more complete understanding of the nature of their condition. Patients may take part in discussions about nutrition, medications, depression resulting from pain, how to combat sleep disturbances, stress management, and assertiveness or social skills. Usually patients are also educated about various methods of pain control. For instance, relaxation training and exercise are regular components of pain clinic programs. Guided imagery, acupuncture, massage, and other pain-reducing strategies may also be included. Familial and vocational counselling are also incorporated in many pain management programs.

How effective are multidisciplinary pain management programs? Numerous studies have documented that chronic pain sufferers who receive treatment at multidisciplinary pain centres report much less subsequent pain and a greater quality of life than individuals who receive standard pain treatment (Fedoroff et al., 2014; Scascighini, Toma, Dober-Spielmann, & Sprott, 2008).

Consider the evaluation of the pain management program at the Miller-Dwan Hospital Pain Control Center in Minnesota (Cinciripini & Floreen, 1982). Participants taking part in the program at the time of evaluation were men and women who had suffered intractable pain from known injuries or diseases (e.g., arthritis) for at least 1 year. At the time, all of the participants were unable to work because of the disabling pain they were experiencing. The participants took part in the program on an inpatient basis for 4 weeks, with weekends off. In this program, patients participated as part of a group.

All patients took part in the full program, which included a medication-reduction procedure, physical therapy, relaxation and biofeedback training, self-monitoring, behavioural contracting, cognitive-behavioural group therapy, and family involvement and training. The patients' behaviour and functioning were assessed at the start of the program, at the end of the program, and at 6 and 12 months following program completion. Upon completing the program, patients' activity levels had increased and their pain experiences, pain behaviours, and medication use had sharply decreased. Amazingly, 90 percent of the patients were no longer taking analgesic medication. Follow-up assessments revealed that participants continued to be physically active and that approximately half of them were employed. The participants' pain continued to decrease. The average pain rating reported by participants before treatment was 4.6 on a 10-point scale; at the time of program completion it was 2.2, and after 1 year it was 1.2. This program can certainly be regarded as successful.

Not all chronic pain patients benefit from the treatment provided at a pain clinic, but most do. You may recall that Jake, whom we introduced at the beginning of this chapter, had recently returned from a 10-day stay at a pain clinic. Jake was a prime candidate for this kind of treatment because his pain had not been relieved even after trying "every pain management technique available." Jake was skeptical about the benefits he might receive at the clinic, and certainly some of the pain management techniques worked better than others for him. For example, he felt that the acupuncturist caused more pain than he relieved. Fortunately, not all of the treatments were perceived in this way. Jake thought that many of the exercises he learned from the physical therapist, for example, were quite helpful. Jake derived other benefits from his stay as well. He now possesses more coping skills and social support than he did when he entered the program. In addition, over the course of his stay, he dramatically reduced the amount of medication he was taking.

Multidisciplinary pain management programs represent a truly biopsychosocial approach to pain management. They can provide medical, psychological, physical, and occupational therapy. They can also improve chronic pain sufferers' psychological and physical functioning and reduce their pain, pain behaviour, and drug use.

CHAPTER SUMMARY

- Explain the benefits of experiencing pain.

    Pain is beneficial because it helps to prevent serious injury, teaches us to avoid injurious behaviours, and forces us to limit our activity, thereby aiding in recuperation.

- Describe theories that attempt to explain the phenomenon of pain.

    The gate control theory of pain emphasizes that both physiological and psychological factors contribute to the experience of pain. The neuromatrix theory of pain extends the gate control theory and suggests a greater role of the brain in pain perception.

- Identify factors that contribute to the experience of and expression of pain.

    Most research indicates that women have a lower pain threshold and lower pain tolerance than men. Cutural differences have been reported in both the experience and expression of pain; however, the strongest evidence indicates that there is more difference between individuals within each ethnic group than there is between ethnic groups.

- Provide examples of how pain is assessed.

    Pain is assessed using (1) psychophysiological techniques such as an EMG or EEG, (2) behavioural measures, and (3) self-report. Various questionnaires (e.g., the McGill Pain Questionnaire) and rating scales (e.g., the Visual Analog Scale) are available to assist with the measurement of pain in both research and clinical settings.

- List and explain a variety of pain control techniques.

    A wide array of pain control techniques is available to the pain sufferer. Pain control techniques include pharmacological and surgical control, TENS, acupuncture, physical therapy, massage, relaxation strategies, distraction, biofeedback, hypnosis, and virtual reality programs. Multidisciplinary pain management programs use a combination of these techniques.

Chapter 9

The World of Health Care:
Places, Procedures, and People

VILevi/Fotolia

Learning Objectives

After studying this chapter, you will be able to:

1. describe key factors that influence our perception and interpretation of symptoms.

2. apply a stage model to understand why people delay in seeking medical care.

3. explain specific ways in which the procedures and rules within a hospital affect patients' sense of control and their ability to cope with being in hospital.

4. define "invasiveness" and place various medical procedures on a continuum of invasiveness, using this definition.

5. describe ways in which the nature of care and preparation for medical procedures can help patients cope.

6. describe psychological challenges associated with specific hospital departments (emergency, surgery, intensive care, discharge, and palliative care) and the coping and care needed to manage these challenges.

7. identify the major sources of stress and satisfaction for physicians.

8. describe the important role nurses play in patient care.

9. identify the major sources of stress in nursing.

10. understand the challenges associated with work in physical and occupational therapy.

As soon as Nora heard her elderly father's breathing, she knew he needed immediate attention. Edgar had been dealing with a cold for a few days, but the 86-year-old was now dealing with something considerably worse. His breathing had deteriorated rapidly in 24 hours, and he was experiencing periods of disorientation.

At the emergency department of their large urban hospital, Nora and her father encountered their first hospital staff member, someone on the other side of a glass panel. The nurse asked a few questions and then Edgar was whisked away through swinging double doors, and Nora was left to provide further information for the admissions clerk.

Nora then entered through those same doors, albeit considerably more tentatively. To her surprise, no one paid any attention to her. Doctors and nurses were scurrying about amid machines and whiteboards with names written on them, dealing with what looked like about 20 patients all at once—everything from a soccer injury to an overdose. She found her father on a bed in a recess surrounded by curtains. Edgar was afraid. His disorientation had worsened. He asked Nora who all the people were and what was to become of him. Nora didn't have the heart to tell him that she didn't know. She was beginning to share her father's disorientation.

SEEKING MEDICAL CARE

How do we decide when to seek medical advice? Clearly, Nora knew she should seek medical care for her father. But most people don't seek medical advice every time a "symptom" arises. After all, someone's breathing sounds peculiar almost every time they "catch" a cold. People have difficulty deciphering and even noticing some symptoms. People often don't notice even highly visible external symptoms, such as a mole-like lesion that may be melanoma (Miles & Meehan, 1995). It is, therefore, not surprising to learn that people also have difficulty accurately assessing their internal states. For example, people's estimates of their own heart rate are not well correlated with physiological indices (Pennebaker, 2000). These differences partly account for the considerable variability in individuals' decisions to seek medical advice.

Perceiving Symptoms

Certainly, there are individual differences in the perception of symptoms. Have you ever noticed how some people seem to keep going no matter what, whereas others seem to adopt the role of patient the instant they are faced with a minor ailment? Some of these individual differences are constant over time. That is, individuals who pay a lot of attention to their internal states are consistently more likely than others to notice a symptom (Brink, Karlson, & Hallberg, 2002; Jurgens, 2006).

Other personal factors, including current mood, personality traits, and stress level, influence people's response to symptoms. We have all experienced being in such a good mood that we didn't notice our normally aggravating aches and pains, as well as being in such a bad mood that we noticed every discomfort, no matter how minor. Research backs up these experiential observations. People in a good mood report fewer symptoms and fewer illness-related thoughts. In contrast, people in a bad mood report more symptoms, are less likely to believe that any behaviours they engage in will relieve symptoms, and assume they are more vulnerable to future illness (Gendolla, Abele, Andrei, Spurk, & Richter, 2005; Leventhal, Hansell, Diefenbach, Leventhal, & Glass, 1996; Salovey, Rothman, Detweiler, & Steward, 2000).

Stress is a personal factor that tends to elevate symptom reporting (Dorner, Stronegger, Rebhandl, Rieder, & Freidl, 2010). Stressful periods in people's lives can precipitate or aggravate the experience of symptoms. And people who have experienced a great deal of stress are more vulnerable to illness. People who believe they are more likely to contract an illness will also attend more closely to their bodies. This inward focus of attention may lead them to interpret stress-related physiological changes, such as accelerated heart rate or breathing, as symptoms of illness (Cameron, Leventhal, & Leventhal, 1995). However, those experiencing tremendous stress are more likely to seek health care than those under less stress, even with equal symptoms (Martin & Brantley, 2004).

In addition to personal factors, gender contributes to the perception of symptoms. However, the research into which gender is most sensitive to internal bodily signals is equivocal. Some studies report that women are more sensitive to their internal state (Brannon & Feist, 2007), while others report that men are more sensitive (Pennebaker, 2000). We know that women seek health care more frequently than do men, but they may delay longer in seeking that care (Galdas, Cheater, & Marshall, 2005; Goldberg, Gurwitz, & Gore, 1999). Interestingly, men attribute minor symptoms to major problems more readily than women do (Martin et al., 2004).

There are also age differences in the reporting of symptoms and willingness to seek care. Elderly people frequently complain of physical symptoms that prompt them to seek medical intervention. There is evidence to suggest that older people perceive normal age-related bodily changes as illness (Gott, Rogstad, Riley, & Ahmed-Jushuf, 1999; Haug, Musil, Warner, & Morris, 1997). Other researchers have suggested that the tendency for symptoms to increase as one ages may be partially due to the decreased cognitive performance that some adults experience as they age (Frisoni, Fedi, Geroldi, & Trabucchi, 1999). In other words, mild cognitive impairment is associated with the perception of poorer body functioning. These studies suggest that older adults may over-report their symptoms.

However, studies of cancer patients have discovered that older adults were less likely than younger adults to notice cancer symptoms—perhaps, in part, because they perceived less personal risk of developing the disease than did younger adults (Bish, Ramirez, Burgess, & Hunter, 2005). One study (Ryan & Zerwic, 2003) found that older people with symptoms of acute myocardial infarction misattributed these symptoms to the pains of old age. Other studies report that older men delay seeking help for symptoms that might be viewed as embarrassing, such as those indicative of sexually transmitted disease

(Gott et al., 1999; Pitts, Wooliscroft, Cannon, Johnson, & Singh, 2000). Thus, the role of age differences in the recognition of symptoms is quite complex.

One of the most important factors in the interpretation of symptoms is the environment. When people are in environments that lack stimulation, they are more likely to pay attention to their internal states. Pennebaker (2000) relate many findings that are consistent with this view. He has observed, for example, that "individuals are more likely to notice itching or tickling sensations in their throats and emit coughs during boring parts of movies than during interesting portions" (p. 191). Similarly, environments that are isolated or that discourage interpersonal communication allow people time to ponder their bodily sensations—that is, in places where talking is discouraged (e.g., libraries) or where there is a great deal of noise (e.g., factories) (Pennebaker, 2000). This does not necessarily mean that these people are more accurate in their interpretation of sensations; in fact, they may overestimate changes in their physiological functions, such as heart rate and nasal congestion. In contrast, when the environment is exciting or demands a great deal of attention or concentration, people are less likely to notice internal symptoms (Pennebaker, 2000).

In summary, symptom recognition depends on several factors. The perception of symptoms is influenced by individual differences in body awareness as well as transitory situational factors. When attention is directed inward, symptoms are more likely to be recognized. When attention is directed outward, by physical activity or a distracting environment, symptoms are less likely to be noticed. Gender differences, age differences, personality differences, and current mood influence symptom recognition.

Interpreting Symptoms

Once a symptom is perceived, it must then be interpreted. How a symptom is interpreted is influenced by a number of factors, including prior experience with the symptom. If, for example, your mother or your sister has had her appendix removed, you are more likely to consider appendicitis whenever you experience pain in your lower abdomen. Other people, who do not share this family history, would likely consider other causes for the pain before considering appendicitis.

Cultural factors can affect how quickly someone recognizes symptoms and reports them. An important consideration in assessing reported symptoms is learning, because in a very real sense we learn how to experience symptoms. It is, therefore, likely that people in different cultures receive different "lessons" about the experience of symptoms. For example, in Western culture men have traditionally been socialized to avoid complaining about emotional and physical symptoms of discomfort, as this is seen as a sign of weakness. Not surprisingly, men are less likely than women to report such symptoms (Nicholas, 2000). At a very young age, children are taught both directly and by example which symptoms are important and which are trivial. A parent's concern over a fever and seeming lack of concern over a superficial cut provide a child with powerful cues about which symptoms to attend to and which to ignore.

Our families contribute to our interpretation of symptoms in other ways, as well. We often consult our family and friends for help in interpreting the meaning of a symptom. These advisers form a lay referral system, an informal network of non-practitioners who offer their own interpretations long before any medical treatment is sought (Skevington, 2004; Suls, Martin, & Leventhal, 1997). People in the lay referral system provide advice when someone mentions the symptoms, requests an opinion, or even if he or she simply looks sick. The advice provided by the lay referral network varies in its usefulness. Sometimes it is very helpful. For example, a study conducted at the Children's Hospital in Montreal determined that mothers who consulted their lay referral system about their child's symptoms were less likely to take their children to the emergency department unnecessarily. Although much of the advice provided by the lay referral network is helpful, lay persons are also far more likely than health professionals to recommend actions that worsen the condition or result in a delay seeking appropriate and needed treatment.

Seeking Help from the Health Care System

It isn't simply the case that people visit their physician when they have experienced one or more symptoms. Studies of illness behaviour indicate that when a person seeks help is a function of the specific nature of the symptoms experienced as well as of the person's social and personal needs.

Perhaps the most obvious determinant of when a person seeks help is the type of symptoms experienced. Symptoms that are new, unexpected, painful, disruptive, highly visible, or that affect highly valued parts of the body are interpreted as more serious and are more likely to lead someone to seek medical care (Meechan, Collins, & Petrie, 2003; Skevington, 2004; Turk & Melzack, 2001). If the symptoms are recognizable from past experience and are believed to be unimportant or explainable, such as muscle aches after an athletic competition, they will probably be ignored. Emergency situations are, at times, ambiguous (Brink et al., 2002). Most heart attack victims, for example, are initially confused by their symptoms and attribute them instead to a wide array of causes, including gas pain, ulcers, gallbladder disease, or even the common cold. Even after they have correctly attributed the symptoms to a serious condition, such as a heart attack, people will waste a substantial amount of time before taking direct action to receive treatment.

Delaying Medical Care

What is responsible for such delay? In attempting to answer this question, researchers have developed a model to outline different stages of delay. They refer to patient delay as the period between an individual's first awareness of a symptom and treatment of that symptom. As illustrated in Figure 9-1, total patient delay occurs in a sequence of stages (Andersen, Cacioppo, & Roberts, 1995): (1) appraisal delay, the time it takes for a person to decide that a symptom is a sign of illness; (2) illness delay, the time between recognizing one is ill and deciding to seek medical care; (3) behavioural delay, the time that elapses between the decision to seek medical care and acting on this decision by making an appointment; and (4) medical delay (scheduling and treatment), the interval between making an appointment and first receiving medical care.

Much of the recent research investigating delay behaviours has focused on cancer patients. Studying this population's delay behaviour is appropriate because, as previously mentioned, delays in treatment for cancer have a significant influence on survival rates (Ramirez et al., 1999; Richards, Westcombe, Love, Littlejohns, & Ramirez, 1999). A review of the literature estimates that 20 to 30 percent of women with breast cancer symptoms delay seeking medical advice for 3 months or more (Bish et al., 2005). Both prospective and retrospective research reveals that appraisal delay accounts for the majority of the total delay time.

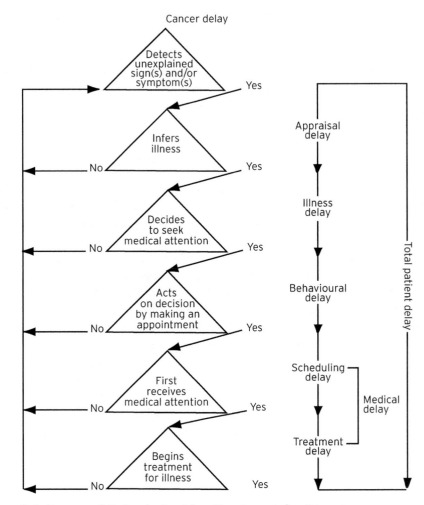

Figure 9-1 Stages of Delay in Seeking Treatment for Symptoms

Source: Andersen, B.L., Cacioppo, J.T., & Roberts, D.C. (1995). Delay in seeking a cancer diagnosis: Delay stages and psychophysiological comparison processes. *British Journal of Social Psychology*, 34, 33–52. Reproduced with permission from the British Journal of Social Psychology, © The British Psychological Society.

Both high and low levels of fear are associated with longer delays in reporting breast cancer symptoms. Fear, for these women, may include fear of doctors and hospitals, cancer, embarrassment, chemotherapy, disfigurement, pain, loss of femininity, and loss of control. And such fears will lead to delays in reporting symptoms in order to avoid having to deal with these issues (e.g., Burgess & Ramirez, 2006). Those with very little fear are likely to delay seeking medical advice because they feel it is unnecessary. On the other hand, when researchers focus on trust, they find that those who are trustful of others are less likely to delay seeking care (Dracup, 2009).

Social influences may also affect delay behaviour (Skevington, 2004). Many women believe that if they are diagnosed with breast cancer, their male partner will abandon them (Facione & Giancarlo, 1998). And while a number of studies reveal that marital status is unrelated to delays by patients (Macleod, Mitchell, Burgess, Macdonald, & Ramirez, 2009), there is support for the hypothesis that the role responsibilities of married women with children influence delay behaviour (Facione, Miaskowski, Dodd, & Paul, 2002). Women report that devoting time and attention to the needs of others, making domestic arrangements prior to the biopsy, arranging for child care, and dealing with work-related demands all receive priority over discovered breast cancer symptoms.

Another factor that has been considered in delay behaviour is the age of the patient. Age appears to contribute to delay in breast cancer patients, but not in patients with other forms of cancer (Macleod et al., 2009). Furthermore, a review of studies with acute myocardial infarction patients (i.e., heart attack victims) showed that women and older patients tend to delay seeking medical care longer (Nguyen, Saczynski, Gore, & Goldberg, 2010).

In summary, there are a number of factors that contribute to patient delay, including characteristics of the symptom, age, gender, societal role obligations, and psychological attributes such as fear.

THE HOSPITAL

Imagine being asked to spend a week in a place you have never been before. In this place, most of the people dress quite differently from you. They speak your language, but they also speak another language to one another. It is a language that you cannot comprehend. They will speak this language even when you are with them and they are talking about you. In fact, these people have very different rules of social interaction. They will ask you personal questions and expect detailed answers, even though they have just met you. They will wake you in the middle of the night. They will prevent you from getting out of your bed when you want to and will make you get up when you want to stay in bed.

And there are rituals. Many people must first provide a small amount of their blood to the inhabitants before they start their stay. These people may have incisions made in their bodies, sometimes removing body parts. When it is time to leave, the people may be made to exit in a chair with wheels, even though they would rather walk.

Does this sound like the sort of place you would like to visit? Does it sound somewhat alien? The place we are describing is, of course, a hospital. When viewed as a distinct culture, with its own set of interaction patterns, rules, and rituals, it is easy to see why hospital stays can be quite disorienting and stressful.

Almost 2.1 million Canadians were hospitalized in acute care facilities between April of 2010 and February of 2011 (CIHI, 2012b). This actually is a smaller number than in earlier years, but the length of stay is increasing. Why would the number of people spending time in hospital go down while length of stay increases? The answer can be found in the changing nature of hospital treatment and health care funding.

For example, you might be surprised to learn that only one-quarter of all hospitalizations today involve surgery, and these do not account for the longest hospital stays. More than 40 percent of hospitalizations are categorized as "medical," including digestive disorders, respiratory diseases, heart diseases, and diabetes. Surgical patients stay in hospital an average of 5.4 days, whereas medical patients average 8.9 days per stay (CIHI, 2005c).

While some hospital stays can be difficult and lengthy, others are brief. In fact, some people are **outpatients,** which means that they will not be staying overnight. Neither will **day care patients**, who might be having a procedure such as laser surgery to remove cataracts from their eyes. Or they might be having tubes inserted in their ears to treat recurring infections. Day care patients might be put under general anaesthetic, and so

outpatient: a person who goes to the hospital for a procedure or test but does not stay overnight.

day care patient: a person who goes to the hospital for a procedure or test that is more involved than, for example, routine radiography, but does not stay overnight.

they tend to be admitted early in the day and discharged by late afternoon. These patients usually need to be accompanied by someone who can be sure they get home safely and comfortably after the procedure. These patients will also get one of those identification wristbands that are a common part of hospital stays.

Still other patients enter the hospital by way of the emergency room and be treated and released from there in the same day. Others may be admitted through emergency and end up staying overnight or longer. Indeed, some may be unconscious when admitted and need to have their circumstances explained to them when they regain consciousness in some other part of the hospital. Clearly, this is a very different experience from that of day care patients or others who have had their procedure booked for a long period of time and have gone through the anticipation. Some will have gone through this waiting period only to be told just before their scheduled admission day that their procedure has been postponed. Sometimes the consequences of waiting are minor, amounting to frustration and inconvenience. But sometimes they are dire. In Canada in 2004, 242 people died while waiting for organ transplants. Keep in mind that approximately 1800 patients receive solid organ transplants in Canada in a year (CIHI, 2005c), a figure that has risen by 22 percent in the past 10 years.

Each of these admission patterns can have a different effect on the patient's psychological response to being in hospital. For some, it is a sign that something traumatic and frightening is going on. For others, there is a sense of relief that the waiting is over and something constructive is going to be done. Whatever the pattern of admission, it must be emphasized that the admission procedure often constitutes a patient's first encounter with the hospital. As such, it carries all the weight we would expect of a first impression in shaping the patient's perceptions of the hospital experience.

Studies dating back to the mid-1990s captured well the loss of control that often accompanies a hospital stay. Spencer and colleagues (1995) documented the case of a 30-year-old man who suffered a spinal cord injury and had to spend 116 days rehabilitating in hospital. You can imagine the challenges associated with learning to adapt to the disability incurred by a spinal cord injury. Interestingly, the investigators discovered through daily interviews with the patient that adaptation to his long-term hospital stay was almost as challenging. In fact, the injury and the hospital had a similar effect on the patient. Each took away some of the control he once had over his life. Adaptation to both hospital and injury meant regaining as much of that control as possible.

A Hospital Patient's Loss of Control

A study conducted in the Netherlands clearly showed that patients feel they relinquish control to others during hospital stays (Halfens, 1995). Seventy-two people were asked to complete the Health Locus of Control Scale, which measures their sense of internal control, external control (luck, fate, and circumstance), and control by powerful others, such as hospital staff. Participants completed the scale three times: 9 days before admission, during their stay, and 7 days after being discharged from the hospital. Figure 9-1 shows the significant increase in people's scores on the powerful-other subscale during their hospital stay.

More recently, a survey of women's hospital experiences identified three factors that were closely connected to their satisfaction with the experience (Polimeni & Moore, 2002). These were respect through communication, maintenance of dignity, and day-to-day control. The more these elements were compromised, the greater the level of dissatisfaction experienced. While most women reported being satisfied with their hospital experience, many still made reference to their perceived powerlessness. For many surgical patients, hospital stays are improved when adequate information is provided about their surgery and their recovery, as well as general information about their upcoming stay and the sensations that will be part of it (Krupat, Fancey, & Cleary, 2000). The stronger a patient's need for control, the more he or she will value the information received.

When hospitalized, the new patient enters what Erving Goffman (1961) calls a **total institution**. In other words, the hospital takes control of virtually every aspect of a patient's life. Patients are expected to adapt to the hospital's schedule, to eat and sleep at specified times, perhaps to receive visitors only during designated hours, to conform to hospital procedures, and to make their bodies available for examination when requested.

Generally speaking, people want to share the decision-making control with their physician. In one Canadian hospital, 49 percent of patients preferred this shared approach when the medical condition involved chest pain, whereas only 1 percent wanted totally autonomous decision-making control, and 50 percent wanted to give total control to the physician. Patients' preferences were linked to the trust they had in the physician—the more trust they felt, the more control they wanted the physician to have (Kraetschmer, Sharpe, Urowitz, & Deber, 2004).

Being involved in this decision-making process could lead to better outcomes for patients. A study analyzing decision-making control for patients with chronic kidney disease found better outcomes (lower death rates and higher transplantation rates) for those patients who led their decision-making process compared to those whose decisions were led by the medical team (Stack & Martin, 2005).

Practitioners' impressions of patients can also be affected by the patients' behavioural responses to a loss of control. Attempts to regain control can be misunderstood as attempts to be "difficult." One example of such a patient was a 74-year-old man who had had his gallbladder removed and had postoperative psychological and medical complications. He "was labelled a problem patient by the surgeon, resident, intern, and day staff nurse" (Lorber, 1975, p. 218).

Patients who led the decision-making process regarding treatment for their kidney disease had lower death rates and higher transplant rates. (Death rates and transplant per 1000 patient-years living at risk.)

The behaviours of the "bad patient" are viewed as a form of **reactance** (Brehm, 1966), which is a response to an unacceptable challenge to one's freedom. This challenge may arouse anger. Thus, the so-called problem patient's complaints and demands for additional attention may be angry attempts by the patient to re-establish at least a small measure of personal freedom. The person in this case was 74 years old. Generally, however, patients who are younger, better educated, or accustomed to being able to control their environment are more likely to respond with reactance (Taylor, 1979).

The concept of learned helplessness has also been applied to hospital settings to explain why **empowering care** yields independence and **disempowering care** yields dependence (Faulkner, 2001). It is Faulkner's contention that disempowering care results in learned helplessness, whereas empowering care results in learned mastery. He has demonstrated this in a study with hospitalized older adults (mean age 79 years). At mealtimes, patients were either given considerable aid (i.e., over-assisted) or told they were in control. This simple difference improved independence at mealtimes.

total Institution: An institution that takes responsibility for the total care and control of its inhabitants.

reactance: behaving counter to recommendations in response to feeling that one has lost personal control over health behaviours; the non-compliant behaviours and attitudes of patients who perceive hospital rules and regimens to be unacceptable challenges to their freedom.

empowering care: patient care that yields independence and results in learned mastery.

disempowering care: patient care that yields dependence and results in learned helplessness.

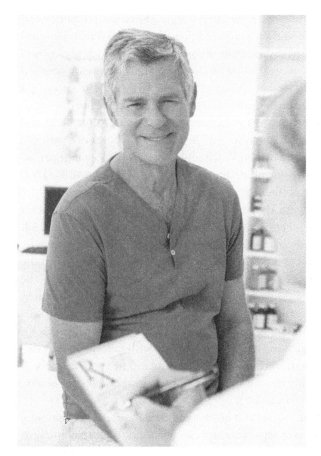

Patients who lead the decision-making process regarding treatment have better health outcomes for such conditions as kidney disease.
Fotolia

We have already mentioned the link between the provision of information and control, but this crucial link deserves a closer look. Krupat and colleagues make the point that, about 40 years ago, many people facing surgery were poorly informed about their upcoming procedure. Some did not even know which organ was going to be the focus of the surgery. In response to this problem, a number of programs have been developed to train practitioners in the skills of information giving. A comprehensive study of patients from over 60 hospitals assessed the extent to which this provision of information affected patients' perceptions of their hospital stays. It was found that the provision of general information was the single best predictor of patients' satisfaction. This was also significantly correlated with patients' sense of control. These relationships were unaffected by other patient factors, such as age or desire for information (Krupat et al., 2000).

Numerous studies have reported the benefits of providing information to patients in preparation for surgery. However, unlike those in the Krupat et al. study, not all people have been shown to respond well to the provision of information. For example, some people, known as **monitors**, welcome information and seek it out, whereas others, called **blunters**, avoid it. These concepts are well-demonstrated in a classic study by Suzanne Miller and Charles Mangan (1983), which showed how individual differences may affect responses to information about medical procedures. In this study, women about to undergo a diagnostic procedure for cervical cancer were divided into monitors and blunters based on their preference for information in a variety of naturalistic stress situations.

monitors: patients who welcome information and seek it out.
blunters: patients who avoid information.

Half the monitors and half the blunters were randomly assigned to either a high- or low-information condition. Patients in the high-information group were given a 20-minute verbal and visual preparatory communication detailing the procedure they were about to undergo. The other half of the monitors and blunters also spent 20 minutes with the research assistant but were given only minimal information about the upcoming procedure; the rest of the time was spent providing information on general nutrition. Measures of the patients' distress were taken in the form of pulse rates at three times: before receiving the information, after receiving the information but before the examination, and after the examination. Patients who showed the least physiological stress in response to the exam were those who were given the amount of information that fit their preferences. In other words, monitors given a large amount of information showed low physiological stress and blunters given little information showed low physiological stress. Monitors who were given little information and blunters given a large amount predictably showed much greater stress (See Table 9-1).

Stress is lower when the amount of information presented to a patient matches the patient's preferences for more or less information (Miller & Mangan, 1983).

We would expect that, in preparation for potentially stressful events, such as hospital procedures, monitors, and blunters would adopt different approaches. In terms of advice for practitioners, though, there is more to this story. Some practitioners and researchers argue that an informed patient simply copes better, and so all patients should receive information in their preparation for a hospital stay. Others have called this homogeneous approach to hospital preparation the **uniformity myth** (Kiesler, 1966; Miró, Turk, & Rudy, 1991).

Preparation for surgery in particular has also received considerable attention. Information provision, or *psychoeducation*, as it is sometimes called, includes the provision of information about surgical processes and potential outcomes as well as about the patient's role in managing pre- and postoperative pain. Like the preparation for hospital stays, it would be a mistake to adopt a "one-size-fits-all" all approach to the provision of such information.

Good psychological preparation for surgery involves more than information provision, however. It includes other elements that should benefit all patients, regardless of their psychological state or characteristics. Brent Van Dorsten (2006) provides a number of helpful categories for such preparation. For example, pre-surgical treatment expectations need to be addressed. In the case of surgery intended to lower chronic pain, patients can have unrealistically high expectations of the surgery's effect. Pre-operative preparation can help patients and practitioners come to a mutually agreed upon definition of "treatment success."

Practitioners must also consider how to manage and assess patients' emotions by helping patients develop self-monitoring skills related to emotion, pain, and other symptoms. These skills help the patient recognize warning signs, as well as indications that they are getting better. Finally, there is relaxation training, which can have a positive effect on many of the other targets for pre-operative preparation.

uniformity myth: belief that all patients should receive the same amount of information in their preparation for a hospital stay regardless of their personal styles of coping with stress.

Table 9-1 Stress May Depend upon the Goodness of Fit between the Amount of Information and Preference for Information

	Amount of Information	
	Low	High
Monitors	Higher stress	Lower stress
Blunters	Lower stress	Higher stress

Whereas the Miller and Mangan study (1983) reminds us that health care providers should match the amount of information they provide with an individual's coping style, research has shown that *all* patients, regardless of their coping style, benefit from relaxation training prior to surgery (Miró & Rosa, 1999). Perhaps this is because monitors tend to experience greater stress and anxiety generally, as they scan for information and ruminate over the problem at hand (Ben-Zur, 2002; Miller, 1996). Thus, monitors benefit from the relaxation itself and blunters from the distraction it provides.

What can we conclude from all of this regarding preparation for surgery? All patients appear to benefit from relaxation training. Of course, all patients need a certain amount of information as well, or else they will risk being confused and disoriented by their hospital stay. Ideally, the exact amount of information provided would be matched with coping style, provided a practitioner was privy to that knowledge.

There are other ways of improving psychological control in patients. For example, researchers in Hamilton, Ontario, increased patients' perceptions of control by giving them the option of walking to the operating room rather than being transported on a stretcher (Porteous & Tyndall, 1994). During the study, 111 of 160 patients chose to walk to the operating room. Only two of these patients were not satisfied with their choice. The reasons given by these patients included becoming uncomfortable waiting and believing that he or she "would have felt more pampered on a stretcher" (Porteous & Tyndall, 1994, p. 23). However, the majority of patients were satisfied with their decision, stating that as a result they "felt better, less like a sick person . . . more in control" (Porteous & Tyndall, 1994, p. 23). These examples suggest ways that hospitals can increase patients' perceptions of control with solutions that are fairly easy to implement.

Depersonalization   Loss of control is only one of the complaints patients have about hospitals. They also report experiencing **depersonalization** or **dehumanization**. Depersonalizing environments take away people's sense of individuality, making them feel more like objects than people. (You may have felt a bit like this at school when asked for your student number rather than your name.)

Depersonalization can result from many encounters in the hospital setting. For example, if you need to undergo even a fairly simple medical procedure it is likely that you will be required to follow a set procedure or routine and that the medical staff will also follow a routine. A pregnant woman may be required to undergo a glucose tolerance test to ensure that she has not developed gestational diabetes. Before this test begins, someone will explain to the woman that she must drink a very sweet "cocktail" and then remain in the hospital or lab for a number of hours so that her blood sugar can be monitored at various points. To aid the technologist and ensure all pertinent information is shared with the patient, it is likely that the technologist will run through a "spiel" (which he or she obviously has repeated many times), never seeming to pause for a breath. Although all the facts may be relayed to the patient during this interaction, it is unlikely that the patient will be able to retain all this information. The technician's routine is an example of an impersonal interaction.

Patients may also experience depersonalization when they are required to wear a hospital gown, when they are referred to by ailment rather than by name, and when their privacy is not respected, all of which do occur. However, hospitals are improving. Today, many hospitals encourage their patients to bring their own pyjamas and other personal effects. As well, patients are made as comfortable as possible in their environment.

depersonalization: the taking away of one's sense of individuality.

dehumanization: the tendency to see people as objects or body parts rather than human beings.

Patient-Centred Care: An Ideal in the Hospital

In Zussman's words, hospital patients are more than just "the human backdrop for dramatic enactments of professional socialization" (Zussman, 1993, p. 173). Yet, in the traditional biomedical approach, the needs of health care professionals can become paramount (Ponte et al., 2003). Contrast this with **patient-centred care** in which patients and families become active members of the treatment team (Ponte et al., 2003).

There are, of course, limits to how far we can go in dedicating resources to patients' psychosocial needs. In a San Francisco–area hospital, model units were created that featured homelike environments, art, and music. The nurses were specially trained to promote greater patient involvement in decision making, to provide more personalized care, and to increase the health education provided to patients. Not surprisingly, patients who were randomly assigned to these patient-centred units reported greater satisfaction with their stays (Martin et al., 1998). Administrators of Canadian hospitals must strike a balance between dedicating such extensive resources to patients' psychosocial needs and providing environments that address patients' fundamental biomedical needs.

patient-centred approach: approach in which patients and families become active members of the treatment team.

SPENDING TIME IN HOSPITAL

We now shift our focus to those people who spend at least one night in hospital. In 2004–2005, there were 2.2 million hospital admissions in Canada (CIHI, 2005c).

The Emergency Department

As you may have ascertained from our opening vignette, the emergency department of a hospital deserves the attention of health psychologists. It is, after all, a common point of entry for many patients. In Canada, 53 percent of all hospital admissions take place through the emergency department, and the people admitted this way tend to stay longer than those who have pre-arranged admissions (CIHI, 2005c). However, most people visiting an emergency department are not admitted to the hospital. In fact, one study found that 29 percent of patients presenting at emergency were discharged without a specific treatment or investigative procedure (Cooke, Arora, & Mason, 2003). Surprisingly, of these discharged patients, 15 percent had arrived by ambulance.

The second reason a hospital's emergency department deserves the attention of health psychologists is that patients often come to emergency in a state of distress or even disorientation, depending on the nature of their problem. Their treatment needs are pressing, and they are in a setting where it is likely that many other people have equally pressing treatment needs. The way hospital staff members interact with these people from their first encounter in admission is very important.

In order to meet the various psychological needs of emergency patients, the emergency department must, at the very least, have sufficient staff and organization to provide expert attention as soon as possible after the patient has entered the hospital. An important early step in emergency medicine is **triage** (Concheiro, Diaz, Luaces, Pou, & Garcia, 2001), which is the sorting and classifying of patients to determine priority of need and proper location and means of treatment. The admission and other staff must also have the interpersonal skills needed to communicate a sense of caring. Asking questions while

triage: the sorting and classifying of patients to determine priority of need and proper location and means of treatment.

fixing one's gaze on a computer screen doesn't establish real communication. Neither does stoicism. Often all that is required is someone who will pay immediate attention to the patient-to-be, by indicating that a doctor or nurse will be with him or her as soon as possible. Patients and their families appreciate knowing if there is going to be a wait and why.

Recovering from Surgery

For a number of reasons, postoperative recovery can be a difficult time psychologically. In addition to having to cope with the unfamiliar surroundings of the hospital, postoperative patients must manage varying degrees of incapacitation, unfamiliar bodily sensations, actions that may be painful or uncomfortable (like forced deep breathing and coughing), and uncertainty about the expected rate of recovery.

We have seen that one way to help many patients through the postoperative period is by helping them develop accurate expectations regarding the surgical experience and postoperative recovery and pain experience. When applied to the postoperative period, this psychoeducational care includes the provision of information regarding self-care practices, further procedures, and typical patterns of recovery (Devine, 2003; Lenz & Perkins, 2000).

A number of challenges arise when providing pain medication for postoperative patients. One challenge is to ascertain correct dosage. Undermedication will discourage the patient and be ineffective. Overmedication may be harmful when strong drugs, such as opioids, are used. Another challenge is the psychological issue of control we discussed earlier in the chapter. Patients may not like being dependent on other people to relieve their pain. In asking for pain medication, patients might feel that they are being weak or "whiny." Finally, they might not want to give the impression that their recovery is not going well and thereby risk lengthening their stay in hospital (Taylor, Hall, & Salmon, 1996).

To deal with these challenges, in the 1980s hospitals introduced **patient-controlled analgesia (PCA)**. As the term suggests, PCA puts the control of analgesic administration in the hands of the patient (Alon, Jaquenod, & Schaeppi, 2003). This can be done a number of ways, from intravenous administration to oral tablet. One common way is to give the patient a device that, when pressed, releases a certain dosage of the prescribed analgesic intravenously. The device allows practitioners to set the dosage as well as the **lock-out interval**, which is the time period between allowable dosages.

What happens when the responsibility for analgesic administration is passed to the patient? In general, studies have had encouraging outcomes. For example, women who had undergone gynecological tumour surgery required lower dosages of analgesics postoperatively when using PCA (Standl et al., 2003). Colon surgery patients who were in the PCA group used less sedation and analgesia and enjoyed faster recovery times than did the group whose medication was administered by staff (Roseveare et al., 1998). Similarly, bone marrow transplant patients reported lower pain intensity and used less medication when in the PCA group (Zucker et al., 1998). A study of cardiac surgery patients found that the PCA group reported less pain postoperatively but that they used more medication than the nurse-administered group did (Boldt, Thaler, Lehmann, Papsdorf, & Isgro, 1998). All of these studies were prospective in design, with randomized assignment to group.

Another study included a third group of patients who were in a patient-controlled condition but received a placebo rather than an analgesic (Stainer, Grond, & Maier, 1999). A placebo is a substance that does not contain active medication but might bring

patient-controlled analgesia (PCA): analgesic administration that is independently controlled by the patient.

lock-out interval: the time period between allowable dosages, when patient-controlled analgesia is used. A device is set by a practitioner to control this period.

about desired effects for psychological reasons, such as the patient's belief that it will work. Patients in this "patient-controlled placebo" group administered twice the amount of medication as patients receiving opioid analgesic.

PCA restores some sense of control for the patient and results in effective pain management in the majority of cases. It is not surprising, therefore, to find that PCA is commonly used in Canadian hospitals. The research is inconsistent, however, about whether the PCA approach results in more analgesic use than do staff-administered approaches. The differences between studies may be due to differences in the nature of the surgery featured in each. Also, it is possible that there are some patients who are not well suited to PCA. For example, researchers at Simon Fraser University, York University, and elsewhere have found that patients with a more passive or avoidant preoperative coping strategy tend to self-administer more analgesic when using PCA than do people with more active coping strategies (Cohen, Fouladi, & Katz, 2005). Also, other York researchers have found that older patients tend to administer less analgesic medication than younger patients do (Gagliese, Weizblit, Ellis, & Chan, 2005).

While PCA does tend to reduce opiate consumption and increase patient satisfaction, errors can occur. To minimize these, practitioners are advised to have the patient be the only person to use the device. Well-meaning family members can unintentionally overdose the patient. Also, because education on the use of the device is important, PCA should be offered only to patients who are alert enough to follow the instructions. These cautions combine with other safety issues, such as adequate monitoring of the patient and careful checking that the right medications are used and that the device is properly programmed (Cohen & Smetzer, 2005).

The Intensive Care Unit

Nowhere in the hospital is modern technology more prominent than in the intensive care unit (ICU). It is the unit in which life-support machinery is used and where patients are closely monitored by a staff where the nurse-to-patient ratio is the lowest in the hospital. The ICUs of hospitals are growing rapidly in terms of the number of beds dedicated to them. Yet they still cannot meet the need in Canada and elsewhere (Stelfox et al., 2012). For these reasons, and because the ICU is a place where emotional consequences can persist for up to a year after discharge (Rattray, Johnston, & Wildsmith, 2005), and that emotional distress can of course be significant for family members as well (Wartella, Auerbach, & Ward, 2009), the ICU is an important area of study for health psychologists.

Interviews with patients after they have been in ICU have yielded some very interesting data regarding their experiences. Pallavicini-Gonzalez and colleagues (1995) discovered that patients in ICU go through three distinct stages. First, there is what the authors call the **incommunication stage**. In this stage, patients are either unconscious or barely conscious. Their memories of the experience are poor, but the memories they do have are somewhat strange. The equipment is imposing and the passage of time is unclear. The second stage is called the **readaptation stage**. At this point, patients become aware of their struggles to recover. It is during this stage that patients recognize their dependence on the machines, especially the ventilator, which helps them breathe. The equipment provides some reassurance, and patients perceive the staff as helpful. The final stage is the **reflection stage**, when patients try to piece together the details of the experience, wanting to know what happened to them.

incommunication stage: a period in ICU during which a patient is either unconscious or barely conscious.

readaptation stage: a period in ICU when a patient can sense a struggle to recover and recognizes his or her dependence on machines.

reflection stage: a period during which a patient who was in ICU tries to piece together his or her recent experience.

A modern ICU, in which technology abounds.

The Image Bank/Getty Images

relocation stress (translocation stress): the stress caused by being separated from those things that were keeping patients alive—the one-on-one care and the technology.

Not all patients experience these stages, and some are moved out of ICU before they get through all three stages, which might explain why some patients have no recollection at all of their time in the unit. In fact, Russell (1999) discovered that 34 percent of the 298 patients he interviewed had no memory of being in ICU, 42 percent had some memory of it, and 24 percent reported having clear memories of their ICU experience.

Upon discharge from ICU, patients can experience **relocation stress** (Beard, 2005), sometimes called translocation stress (Strahan & Brown, 2004). This is the stress caused by being separated from those things that were keeping patients alive—the one-on-one care and the technology.

Consistent with the readaptive stage identified by Pallavicini-Gonzalez, Russell's participants remembered the close surveillance of technology and staff providing them with a sense of safety. Interestingly, though, they reported that the staff provided a feeling of safety more than the machines did. In fact, 76 percent of the participants had either a vague memory of the technology or no memory of it at all. Of those who did remember it, some found it reassuring, while others were frightened by it because of a lack of knowledge regarding what the machines were for. Many of these machines monitor vital physiological processes and can be set to sound an alarm if levels drop below or rise above a certain level. Not surprisingly, patients found these alarm sounds to be quite frightening when they did not know what they signalled. Much of this fear can be alleviated if nursing staff provide basic explanations of the machines' functions.

Indeed, the data from Russell's interviews suggests strongly that *communication* is a key factor in determining a patient's psychological reaction to ICU. However, there are a number of reasons why communication is sometimes poor in ICU. For instance, it has been found that nurses sometimes deliberately minimize communication with the patient in order to minimize their own anxiety (Leathart, 1994). Not talking to patients makes it easier to *dehumanize* them. Health practitioners may do this, not because they are uncaring but because it is easier emotionally to think of an ICU patient as "the acute MI in bed three" rather than as Mr. Chen, who has six grandchildren and may die.

Communication is also inhibited by the fact that patients in ICU tend to be unresponsive (Turncock, 1991). Some, of course, are unconscious. If they are conscious, they may have tubes inserted in their throats. Nevertheless, communication is still important. Just because a patient can't respond does not mean he or she can't *hear*. This is illustrated most graphically by the recollection of one of Russell's interviewees:

> I remember hearing a voice saying "His blood pressure's dropping, it's 60, 57, 55." Another voice saying, "Tell me when it is 50 and we can all knock off." I still think of that sometimes. (p. 789)

Overheard remarks like these carry a great deal of psychological weight for patients. Russell discovered that these remarks were remembered 6 months later and, as the quote suggests, may be remembered forever. These remarks were cited by Russell's participants as a major source of upset. Another patient recalled hearing one staff person telling another that they might as well pull the plug. It is doubtful that the staff member would have made that remark had he or she known the patient could hear.

When staff members do talk to patients, they tend to focus on procedure—what is going to be done—rather than on the patient's condition and progress (Baker & Melby, 1996). Information regarding progress may be very important for patients who have entered the readaptation stage and are aware of the struggle that faces them.

Russell also asked participants if they would want to go into ICU again if they were seriously ill or injured. Eighty percent said they would, 10 percent said they would leave that decision to the doctor, and 10 percent said they would not want to be a patient in ICU again, even if their condition warranted it. Studies report that between 14 and 27 percent of people experience post-traumatic stress disorder after their ICU experience (Cuthbertson, Hull, Strachan, & Scott, 2004). Russell also discovered that some patients need to revisit the ICU after their recovery to put the experience behind them. These revisits can be good for staff morale, too. Unfortunately, they can be difficult to schedule in a unit in which trauma is an everyday experience.

From the work of Russell and others, we can conclude that the psychological impact of ICU can be strong and lasting. Many patients credit the technology and staff with saving their lives, although recurring thoughts, dreams, nightmares (Minton & Carryer, 2005), or hallucinations (Magarey & McCutcheon, 2005) about the experience are not uncommon. As is the case throughout a hospital, communication is central to reducing the distress of being in ICU. Staff must assume that patients can hear them, and they must provide feedback regarding the patient's condition and progress.

This feedback must also be provided for the families of the patients, who, in the spirit of family-centred care, are essential to the patient's treatment. Family members experience the enormous stress of seeing the patient critically ill and in an unpredictable condition. They also see other patients who may be dying, and they hear alarms sounding on a regular basis (Lower, Bonsack, & Guion, 2003).

Communication with family and visitors is often a low priority for ICU staff members, who are busy with critically ill patients (Greenwood, 1998). However, such communication is extremely important because the decisions made in ICU and NICU (neonatal intensive care unit) can involve end-of-life issues. These decisions are often fraught with ethical dilemmas. Who should make these decisions? Two prevalent, yet somewhat

expertise model: model in which the physician and the intensive care team are assumed to be best informed and most objective, and therefore best equipped to make end-of-life decisions.

negotiated model: decision-making model that allows decision making to be shared among the practitioners, patient, and family.

contradictory, models are called upon when answering this question (Leuthner, 2001). The **expertise model** implies that the physician and the intensive care team are best equipped to make end-of-life decisions. They are best informed and most objective. The **negotiated model** implies a sharing of the decision between the practitioners, patient, and family. Of course, in ICU, the patient is not always able to provide input, and so family and loved ones are left to represent the patient.

For ethical reasons, Leuthner and others argue in favour of the negotiated model because it reduces paternalism on the part of the practitioner and includes the family in one of the most important decisions they will ever face (Carter & Leuthner, 2002; Leuthner, 2001). A study of parents' wishes regarding end-of-life decisions in NICU has suggested that parents want the final call to be with the health care professionals because the burden of the decision is just too great for most parents to bear (Brinchmann, Forde, & Nortvedt, 2002). Having said this, the same authors advocate for keeping the family well informed and as involved as possible in this extremely difficult process.

We have looked at what it is like for adults to be in ICU with its collection of machines, tubes, and IV drips. But can you imagine a patient who weighs less than 1 kilogram (under 2 pounds) being hooked up to all this, caught in a battle for life? These are some of the patients in the neonatal intensive care unit. Some have been born prematurely, and then

Box 9-1

The Pediatric Intensive Care Unit

A prematurely born baby looks particularly vulnerable in a neonatal intensive care unit.
Getty Images

Joy Tompkins (2005) was a nurse working in pediatric intensive care when a 4-year-old girl was admitted with what was to be diagnosed as Guillain–Barré Syndrome, a nervous system disorder in which paralysis gradually moves up the body, leaving the patient dependent on life support. The condition tends to reverse itself in time, with movement and feeling gradually returning in reverse order of how paralysis had set in.

Thus, the nurse watched as her patient gradually became weaker and eventually motionless, requiring intubation and mechanical ventilation. Joy decided to plan out her patient's days as though they featured all the events of a normal 4-year-old and to communicate these to her as she lay still, able to respond only by blinking. Joy provided tape recordings of music and her family's voices (visiting was very limited when this patient was in pediatric intensive care [PCIU]).

Weeks passed this way. Finally, the paralysis began to recede. In Tompkins' words, "The disease left as silently as it arrived." Then came the day when that breathing tube could finally be removed:

Our eyes were locked on one another's, we counted to three and the physician pulled the breathing tube out. She coughed, her eyes widened, her pupils dilated, and her hands trembled as she reached up to her face to feel where the tube was once secured. Her hands moved toward me, she reached out and abruptly slapped my face! I was stunned and momentarily taken back. But I knew, she knew, we understood. It was finally over. Then she grabbed me, we hugged, and we cried. For the first time I could hear her voice—a wonderfully froggy sound. Two decades have passed, and still, it is her eyes that I remember.

taken quickly away from the delivery room to NICU. Other newborns (neonates) may be full-term births but may have suffered from a prenatal (before birth) or perinatal (during birth) condition that requires intensive care. It could be argued that the NICU is the most emotionally intense unit in the hospital, for both parents and staff.

Discharge

For some patients, leaving the hospital involves more than simply gathering up one's belongings and walking out the front door. It is often the case that further treatment is required or, at the very least, rest and general convalescence. As a result, there must be some form of support provided for patients after discharge. All of these considerations require **discharge planning**, a process in which post-hospital care is organized and risk is assessed (Tennier, 1997). By *risk*, we are referring to social problems, lack of support, and medical conditions that result in a high degree of dependency (Evans & Hendricks, 1993).

discharge planning: a process in which post-hospital care is organized and risks, such as social problems and lack of support, are assessed.

Imagine the possible sources of anxiety at discharge time for those parents whose babies spent the first weeks of their lives in NICU. Research in this area has discovered that parents' anxiety is related not only to the baby's condition (e.g., weight and central nervous system complications) but also the perceived personal and social resources of the parents (Auslander, Netzer, & Arad, 2003).

And what about the other end of the age spectrum? Elderly patients are likely to have a more difficult time at discharge because they have grown accustomed to hospital support and routine. Problems with discharge planning for elderly patients are compounded by the fact that the planning is time consuming, and so it must be started early. This means that discharge planning is taking place before the patient's medical condition has been clearly ascertained and effectively treated. One study that analyzed the discharge-planning process for 31 elderly patients discovered that, for 27 of the patients, their planning started before their medical status was clearly determined. As a result, discharge plans had to be altered in 26 of these 27 cases (Wells, 1997). As you can imagine, patients find these changes upsetting, especially when they lengthen the hospital stay. In fact, even the communication of early discharge decisions can be stressful because, at that point, the patient might have trouble imagining being capable of managing at home. One attempt to reduce the stress associated with discharge plans involves conducting an accurate assessment of the patient's cognitive functioning upon admission to hospital (Sands et al., 2003). This level of functioning helps predict a patient's ability to cope when discharged.

There are other challenges involved with discharge planning for elderly patients. Elderly patients may, for example, have other functional problems that are secondary to the medical condition being treated but still very important to consider regarding discharge. Can they walk unaided? Can they see and hear well? Also, what are the physical capabilities of the principal caregiver? This question is especially important if the caregiver is an elderly spouse. One way to take these functional limitations into account is to involve family members in the discharge-planning process. The study of the 31 patients mentioned above found that this involvement was sporadic (Wells, 1997), even though the staff regularly discussed discharge, or at least they thought they had (Rentsch, Luthy, Perneger, & Allaz, 2003). Thus, effective involvement of the family and good communication with them and among the multi-disciplinary health team can improve outcomes after discharge (Bauer, Fitzgerald, Haesler, & Manfrin, 2009).

The major dilemma in working with elderly patients is how to balance adequate care with the patient's desire for autonomy. Patients may have realistic worries about "never being the same again" after their hospital stay (Keefler, Duder, & Lechman, 2001). To cope with these worries, elderly patients may shun assistance or attempt to veto discharge plans that create an impression of dependence rather than independence. Social workers, psychologists, health care workers, and family members must help the patient make discharge plans that achieve this balance between safety and autonomy, and they must do so without being patronizing or dictatorial. The key is to involve the patient in the discharge-planning process as much as possible, which requires a sensitive understanding of the patient, the options available, and the patient's health. This understanding can be achieved only if all involved adopt a team approach.

Palliative Care

progressive illness: a condition that will continue to worsen in spite of treatment.

advanced illness: stage of illness at which death is imminent.

palliative care: care intended to maintain quality of life as best as possible for a patient who is in the advanced stage of an illness. The focus is the control of pain and other symptoms as opposed to the cure of the illness.

Most patients are discharged from the hospital because their condition is improving and their prognosis is good. Some patients, however, have illnesses that are **progressive**, meaning the patients will continue to worsen in spite of treatment; when a progressive illness is **advanced**, it is at a stage where death is imminent. For these patients, care shifts from an attempt to cure the illness to a regimen intended to control pain and other symptoms. A primary goal of care, then, is to provide a good quality of life (as much as possible) for the time remaining. Other goals include controlling symptoms, supporting family and making sure they are satisfied, and staying focused on patients' perceptions of purpose and meaning in their lives (Kaasa & Loge, 2003). These are the goals and focus of **palliative care**. This care involves compassionate communication; an understanding of patient and family values and goals of care; the relief of suffering; management of pain, depression, delirium, and other symptoms; an awareness of the processes of grief; and sensitivity for the soon-to-be bereaved survivors (Abrahm, 2003).

In Victoria, Deanna Hutchings has proposed a model for palliative care based on the Theory of Human Becoming that dovetails nicely with the fundamentals of palliative care. The model contains a number of important elements, including caring for the whole person and maintaining a necessary presence and dialogue with the dying person (Hutchings, 2002).

Once the decision has been made to move to palliative care goals, another important decision to be made is where the palliative care will be administered. There are three common choices—the hospital, the home, or a hospice. Hospice facilities represent a compromise between the comfort of home and the medical support of a hospital. At this point, we will focus more on the palliative care provided by hospitals. Having said this, it is important to note that hospital palliative care may also involve discharge planning and all the issues we discussed earlier in relation to that process, if the patient and family express a desire to move the site of care to the home or elsewhere. Because of this, palliative care is most successfully provided by multi disciplinary teams that include such people as physicians, nurses, social workers, chaplains, and psychologists. A review of studies assessing the effectiveness of such teams discovered that they yielded as good or better outcomes than individual planners concerning patient and family satisfaction, patients being cared for as they wished, a reduction of family anxiety, less patient pain, and better symptom control (Hearn & Higginson, 1998).

Staff members working in palliative care face death on a daily basis. To cope with this, they must shed the prevailing belief shared by most acute care workers that death is tantamount to failure (Payne, Dean, & Kalus, 1998). They must adjust their goals to make them consistent with those of palliative care. Moreover, they must come to grips with their own anxieties and fears about death. Perhaps this is why one study found that hospice nurses were less death avoidant and less concerned about their own death than were emergency room nurses (Payne et al., 1998).

While practitioners in acute care do everything they can to keep patients alive, practitioners working in palliative care must make difficult decisions that will actually result in a patient's death. Technology exists to keep patients alive virtually indefinitely—long after there is any hope that the patient will regain consciousness. Independent of debates about **euthanasia**, palliative care practitioners must decide when it has become futile to keep a patient artificially alive. It is a physician's responsibility to discuss a **do-not-resuscitate order**, stating that CPR or other interventions will not be used if the patient stops breathing.

DNR decisions are complex. Most practitioners believe that seriously ill patients deserve the right to be involved in resuscitation decisions. However, how does the physician decide which patients are sufficiently "seriously ill" to warrant that discussion? When this decision is made, the patient moves from the world of the living to that of the dying (Teno & Coppola, 1999). In some palliative care units, these discussions are initiated with patients who are expected to live less than 6 months. At this point, palliative care units provide what has been called a **mixed management model of care**. They prepare the patient for eventual death while at the same time providing life-sustaining treatments (Teno & Coppola, 1999).

euthanasia: the deliberate ending of a patient's life to relieve suffering.

do-not-resuscitate order: an order given by a physician indicating that CPR and other interventions are not to be used if the patient stops breathing.

mixed management model of care: the preparation of a patient for eventual death while at the same time providing life-sustaining treatments.

THE PSYCHOLOGICAL IMPACT OF MEDICAL PROCEDURES

Because so many people's experiences of hospitals come from having had an outpatient procedure, we will investigate the psychological impact of some of these procedures. In this analysis, we will make the point that there is always more to a medical procedure than meets the practitioner's eye. Patients attach considerable meaning to the process that may go well beyond the biomedical purpose of the procedure. To illustrate this, we will look at two common procedures—colonoscopy and mammography— to learn about the psychological impact of such procedures.

The Psychology of Colonoscopy

In Canada, colorectal cancer is the second leading cause of cancer-related death, with 9200 such deaths predicted in 2012 (Statistics Canada, 2012). The most common screening procedures for this type of cancer are colonoscopy and faecal occult blood test (FOBT). FOBT followed by colonoscopy (when FOBT yields positive results) has been estimated to reduce 10-year mortality due to colorectal cancer by 16.7 percent in Canada (Flanagan et al., 2003).

Colonoscopy decisions are affected by the kinds of cost–benefit analyses described in the health belief model (see chapter 1). Like all screening procedures designed to detect potentially serious illness, the psychological costs of colonoscopy include the possibility that the test will yield worrisome results. In addition, the procedure itself can be painful and anxiety-producing. Pain ratings for colonoscopy tend to be higher for women than for men, explained in part by the fact that women have longer colons (Ylinen, Vehviläinen-Julkunen, & Pietilä, 2009).

In Finland, where sedatives and pain medication are not routinely used for colonoscopies, about 58 percent of patients report at least some pain. Instead of sedatives, participants in a Finnish study were given what the authors called "peaceful talk", including calm and clear information regarding the procedure. Forty percent of patients receiving this during colonoscopy reported a significantly lower pain experience (Ylinen et al., 2009). In an American study of six patients undergoing colonoscopy, hypnosis was found to eliminate the need for sedation (Elkins et al., 2006).

The Psychology of Mammography

One valuable way to understand the potential negative psychological impact of a medical procedure is to consider its **invasiveness**. Invasiveness has both physical and psychological components. In a physical sense, health practitioners determine the invasiveness of a procedure by the extent to which it involves piercing the skin or entering the body with instruments—physically "invading" the body. In a psychological sense, a procedure is invasive if it has the potential to cause embarrassment, shame, or discomfort. This is often the result of procedures that intrude into intimate parts of the body (Weller & Hener, 1993). Not surprisingly, a patient's ability to adapt to a procedure is predicted, in large part, by the invasiveness of that procedure (Campbell-Heider & Knapp, 1993), although a procedure's potential results probably outweigh its invasiveness as a predictor of stressfulness (Kowalcek, Muhlhoff, Bachmann, & Gembruch, 2002).

Mammography is, at most, moderately invasive. Nonetheless, there is considerable anxiety surrounding the procedure, not so much because of what is done but because of what might be found, as indicated by the finding that post-mammography anxiety levels are best predicted by pre-exam anxiety levels. The *idea* of such screening is anxiety-producing (Brain et al., 2008).

Abnormal mammogram results can bring on fear, anxiety, and depression. This is also true for other screening tests, such as Pap tests for cervical cancer (Pasket & Rimer, 1995).

It could be argued that psychological distress is a necessary element of cancer screening, and a relatively small price to pay for the lives that are saved by early detection. However, estimates vary considerably regarding just how many lives are saved by cancer screening, especially mammography. Evidence is far greater for the benefits of screening for other forms of cancer, such as cancer of the cervix (Sasieni, Adams, & Cuzick, 2003).

When calculating the cost–benefit ratio of mammography or any other screening procedure, we must take **false-positive** results into consideration. These are results that indicate abnormality when none actually exists. A perfectly reliable test has no false positives, but mammograms are not perfectly reliable. The rate of false positives for mammograms is generally considered to be quite high. A study in Europe estimated the rate of false positives to vary between 1 and 14 percent, depending upon the callback procedures of the clinic (Lynge, Olsen, Fracheboud, & Patnick, 2003). This rate of false positives creates a dilemma regarding mammography screening, since it can put women through unnecessary anxiety, though evidence indicates that anxiety related to false-positive results is more short-term than long-term in duration (Brain, et al., 2008).

One form of false positive is a **benign breast biopsy**. In this case, women with abnormal mammograms are called back for a biopsy procedure, and the results show no evidence of malignancy. In Canada, negative results for biopsy after mammogram outnumber positive results 3 to 1, so the majority fit into the benign category (Public Health Agency

invasiveness: a measure of the extent to which hospital procedures, in a physical sense, involve piercing the skin or entering the body with instruments or, in a psychological sense, have the potential to cause embarrassment.

false-positive: result that indicates abnormality when none exists.

benign breast biopsy: a false-positive result that leads to women with abnormal mammograms being called back for a biopsy procedure, and the results show no evidence of malignancy.

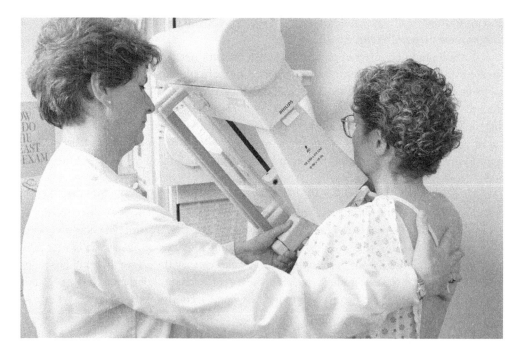

A woman undergoing mammography.
Alvis Upitis/The Image Bank/ Getty Images

of Canada, 2010b). A study of women who experienced a benign breast biopsy showed greater short-term psychological distress than for those in a healthy control group (Andrykowski et al., 2002). If a woman learns that her test has yielded abnormal results and that she is to return for follow-up testing, she will likely see herself as a cancer patient until proven otherwise. And even if follow-up tests prove negative, she may well think it is just a matter of time before the cancer appears for real (Wardle & Pope, 1992).

Regardless of how distressing a callback or negative biopsy might be, women who experience these false positives are not more likely to stop regular screening. In fact, they may be *more* likely to attend regular screening appointments, because they feel more susceptible to breast cancer.

PEOPLE

Very little of my work was glamorous in the TV drama sense, but much of it was intense.

A family physician (Coombs, 1998, p. 175).

It is important for health psychologists to understand the stresses health care providers experience on a daily basis. For example, it is of little use to tell family physicians they must spend more time listening to patients and explaining things to them if we have no appreciation for the number of patients those physicians must see in a given day. Similarly, a nurse may appear less compassionate than a patient would like simply because that nurse has a large patient load that includes some seriously ill people. In short, health psychology must be practised within the realities of the health care system.

In looking at what it is like to be a health care provider, our main objective is to provide some understanding of the realities of the work. The hope is that, through this understanding, health psychologists can be effective members of interprofessional teams that provide modern health care.

We will present a series of profiles of health practitioners and the work they do. Since we are not physicians, nurses, physiotherapists, or technologists (or other practitioners), we have relied on published research and first-hand interaction with practitioners and students to create these profiles. These profiles apply widely across the professions we will discuss. By the same token, we must never lose sight of the fact that there is considerable variation among practitioners. Some never experience stress or gender-related discrimination. Many find medical school to be quite straightforward and manageable. Others have been virtually paralyzed by these issues.

Also, the research that studies health professionals is more likely to focus on challenges than rewards, and so in this chapter you will read about these challenges. We need to know about the stresses and problems practitioners face. However, the majority of people working in these professions find this work extremely rewarding. Every working day, no matter how long and demanding it might be, people in these fields can say they were dedicated to helping others. In order to truly understand what these professionals experience, we urge you to talk to people who work in health care to get first-hand accounts of their work.

PHYSICIANS

After over a decade of declining numbers in the 1990s, Canada saw a 4 percent increase in physicians over 2011 (CIHI, 2014). According to the most recent figures, there are 189 doctors for every 100 000 Canadians. Also, for the first time, more physicians returned to Canada than left to practise in other countries between 2004 and 2008. In this section, we will explore reasons why people want to become physicians, and we will discuss some of the realities of day-to-day practice.

Physicians' Emotional Involvement in Their Work

At the beginning of this section on people working in health care, we quoted a family physician who said that his work wasn't as dramatic as television depictions but that it was still intense. It is important for health psychologists to learn to appreciate this intensity. One of the best ways to do this is to talk with physicians and get first-hand accounts. This, however, requires a close enough relationship for the physician to feel comfortable disclosing some personal feelings and accounts. We must remember, also, that physicians themselves report a reluctance to discuss emotional aspects of their work. Another way to gain insights into what physicians face on an emotional level is to read sections of medical journals in which physicians write candidly about dilemmas they have faced. For example, try reading the section entitled "The Left Atrium" in the *Canadian Medical Association Journal*, or "A Piece of My Mind" in the *Journal of the American Medical Association*.

In an issue of the *Canadian Medical Association Journal*, a physician describes one of his elderly patients. As you read this passage, notice the contrast between the clinical description provided in the first sentence and that which follows in the next two sentences:

> The history in her chart was all too familiar: 89-year-old woman from nursing home; Alzheimer's disease; inadequate oral intake; admitted with dehydration, hypernatremia and acute renal failure. She had a shock of frizzy white hair and a face crisscrossed with myriad fine wrinkles. Her eyes betrayed her confusion. (Hwang, 2006, p. 1138)

These sentences capture the very human nature of a physician's work.

In the *Journal of the American Medical Association*, a physician recounts a case involving an ultrasound exam confirming that a woman's fetus had no skull or brain. At first, he grappled with the question of who should inform the woman who has just undergone the exam. In this case, as the radiologist, he could have let her own doctor tell her, or perhaps the resident obstetrician. However, the woman could sense something was wrong. There was no avoiding the truth, and this was the time to present the upsetting news. The physician was empathetic but direct, and the woman sat in prolonged silence, trying to fathom this reality (Brown, 1988).

Few professions require such emotional conversations. Of course, not all conversations between patients and physicians involve negative emotions. Patients are elated by a normal childbirth and relieved when they are informed they are not seriously ill. The point is that such extreme emotional experiences are potentially exhausting and distracting. For this reason, most physicians find that they must learn to control their emotions, avoiding the peaks and valleys their patients may encounter. To do this requires the ability to distance oneself from one's patient. It is difficult, however, to do this and still make it clear that the physician truly cares for his or her patient's well-being.

Medical students learn to dehumanize their patients by referring to them as body parts rather than as people. This is one way to maintain emotional control. Another is to use humour, which can neutralize situations that would otherwise be very sad. For example, some physicians will use the initials *CTD* to describe a patient who is on a slow but inevitable decline to death; *CTD* stands for "circling the drain" (DiMatteo, 1991, p. 267).

Physicians and Stress

The responsibility inherent in being a physician has the potential to cause great stress. A study of more than 2000 Canadian physicians discovered that 38 percent described their practice as being very or extremely stressful (Burke & Richardsen, 1990). In addition to the basic responsibilities that come with caring for patients, there are other aspects of a physician's work that can add to the problem. For example, physicians often work under time pressure (Richardsen & Burke, 1991). If you have ever sat in your doctor's waiting room for any length of time, you will probably have noticed how often the phone rings as people try to make appointments. Many of these people want to see the doctor as soon as possible, and so they are "fit in." While we appreciate this consideration as patients, it makes for a hectic day for the physician, who must try to somehow strike a balance between giving people ample time and moving patients through in a timely fashion. And all of this is thrown into chaos if an emergency occurs. It is not surprising that work overload is cited by physicians as a significant source of stress (Aziz, 2004; Burke & Richardsen, 1990). A large 1998 study in Canada found that 62 percent of physicians considered their workload to be too heavy (Sullivan & Buske, 1998). This situation has persisted (Bergman, Ahmad, & Stewart, 2003).

Overload leads to **burnout**, a condition that was first identified among nurses but is now recognized in numerous health professionals, including physicians (Thomas, 2004). The symptoms of burnout have been well-documented. They include emotional exhaustion, perceived ineffectiveness, cynicism, and dissatisfaction with relations with co-workers (Spickard, Gabbe, & Christensen, 2002). Those experiencing burnout perceive a lack of correspondence between what they think they should be doing and what they actually are doing (Maslach & Leiter, 1997). The best way to prevent burnout is to focus on one's own

burnout: a condition that is similar to compassion fatigue and includes symptoms of physical exhaustion, depersonalization of patients, and feelings of discouragement and low accomplishment.

Are There Enough General and Family Practitioners in Canada?

In their final year of medical school, students declare their preferences regarding residency—the time during their training in which they move from having a general medical degree to being a practitioner. These choices provide indications of the distribution of the kinds of physicians we can expect in Canada. In recent years, fewer and fewer students have been choosing family and general practice. In 2003, 25 percent of the residency positions available in family medicine were unfilled (Wright, Scott, Woloschuk, & Brenneis, 2004). In 2009, the Canadian Collaborative Centre for Physician Resources estimated that the shortfall of family practitioners was greater than 1000 (Buske, 2009).

What are the consequences of this shortage? For one thing, 15 percent of Canadians have no family doctor (Statistics Canada, 2013), and more than 50 percent of these people have tried unsuccessfully to find one. Because the health of the population has been shown to improve with access to primary care physicians (Starfield, 1994), attempts are made to keep the ratio of general practitioners to specialists at 50:50 in Canada (Gutkin, 2003). There

are factors, however, that make this ratio difficult to maintain. In 2012, 34 percent of all medical school graduates picked family practice as their first choice for future practice (CaRMS, 2012). A number of factors explain the students' plans, including medical lifestyle (e.g., acceptable work hours), orientation to society (e.g., long-term relationships with patients), prestige, a focus on in-hospital care, and scope of patient problems. A person's values regarding these factors will influence choice regarding medical practice.

Others have argued that, while the values students bring to medical school are influential, so too are the experiences they have as medical students (McPherson, 2005). Thus, if family practice is presented as an attractive option, more people will opt for it.

One other solution stemming from this position is to allow practising specialists who have grown dissatisfied with their practice to re-certify as family practitioners. In addition, the reputation of family practice as featuring overwork and underpay must change (MacKean & Gutkin, 2003).

well-being throughout one's career. This can be done by spending more time with friends and family, focusing on spiritual and personal needs, finding meaning in work, setting limits at work, and maintaining a positive outlook (Weiner, Swain, Wolf, & Gottleib, 2001).

Of course, despite physicians' best efforts, some patients will die, and physicians must face the stress of communicating bad news to patients and their families (Ptacek & McIntosh, 2009). This stressor is more common in some specialties than others, such as oncology. In a study of this source of stress, 38 physicians were asked to recall a time when they had given a patient bad news. The physicians were then asked some questions based on their memory of the encounter. Most physicians followed published guidelines when giving bad news, though this did not eliminate the stress they felt when doing so. They felt that they had done an effective job of reducing their patients' distress but that their own discomfort and stress had started prior to the encounter and lasted beyond the end of the encounter. The conclusion of this research was that published guidelines on the giving of bad news are helpful in reducing patient distress, but more attention has to be paid to the distress felt by the physician (Ptacek, Fries, Eberhartd, & Ptacek, 1999).

Considerable research indicates that male and female physicians experience stress differently. For example, one study showed that workload, *per se*, was not a predictor of psychological distress for women (Gareis & Barnett, 2002). Instead, manageability of hours or schedule fit was such a predictor, which indicates that women physicians face a somewhat different set of stressors than men. Women face greater discrimination in the workplace and, in a larger context, experience strain between their work and family roles (Robinson, 2003). Still, female physicians tend to report higher degrees of job satisfaction than their male counterparts (Robinson, 2003), although an intergenerational comparison of female physicians whose mothers were also physicians found that daughters felt more stress and less satisfaction than their mothers had. This stress existed in spite of daughters' citing of more support mechanisms than their mothers had to help manage work–family conflicts (Shrier & Shrier, 2005). Perhaps this support is not keeping pace with increased expectations and workload.

There has been considerable research aimed at discovering the extent to which these stress levels put physicians at greater risk for suicide than the general public. One study in Britain reported that female physicians were more likely than females in the general public to commit suicide, whereas male physicians were *less* likely than males in the general population (Hawton, Clements, Sakarovitch, Simkin, & Deeks, 2001). Based on this, Hawton concluded that female physicians were at greater risk for suicide. However, another author pointed out that, because rates of suicide are lower for females generally, in fact, the rates for male and female physicians were not significantly different from one another (Verberne, 2002).

Uncertainty as a Source of Stress   Another significant source of stress that is not always obvious to the general public is **uncertainty**. We like to think that medicine is a precise science, but it is not. In an article by Lurie and Sox (1999), the authors make two important points regarding uncertainty. First, "Clinical examinations and other diagnostic tests are imperfect" (p. 493); and second, "The consequences of medical decisions are inherently uncertain at the decisive moment" (p. 493). This means that a given diagnosis is often accompanied by a degree of uncertainty, and **prognosis**, a prediction of how a medical condition will change in the future, is even more uncertain. Physicians work for the most part with probabilities rather than absolute certainties.

It is likely that the majority of patients do not have a good idea of how much uncertainty exists in medical decision making. In a study of this, patients were asked to estimate the accuracy with which diagnosis would be made for six different conditions (Hamm & Smith, 1998). Interestingly, the patients' estimates did not differ across conditions. This suggests that people have a general belief about the accuracy of medical science and that they apply that belief regardless of the condition in question. The medical truth is that some conditions are considerably easier to diagnose than others, and so certainty varies from one situation to the next. Furthermore, the patients' estimates of accuracy were quite unrealistic. In particular, they underestimated the likelihood of a false-positive diagnosis.

This level of faith in medical science only adds to the potential stressfulness of uncertainty for the physician. A patient thinks a physician should know and does know exactly what the diagnosis is and what the treatment should be, while, on the other side of the consultation, the physician is very aware of the level of uncertainty that exists. The physician's response to this situation ranges from communicating that uncertainty with a probability statistic through to denying the uncertainty altogether (Hamm & Smith, 1998).

A final point to make about uncertainty in medical decision making is that it is more common among those in general and family practice than among specialists. This is because physicians of all types tend to solve problems through pattern recognition. General practitioners see a wider range of symptoms; therefore, they have far too many patterns to remember and often too few of any particular symptom to even form a pattern in the physician's experience. Also, more problems are presented early in their history to

uncertainty: a significant source of stress for physicians resulting from the fact that the consequences of medical decisions are uncertain.

prognosis: a prediction of how a medical condition will change in the future.

general practitioners, before patterns have been well established. In contrast, specialists see a much narrower range of problems and symptoms, usually at a stage where the diagnosis has become clearer.

Physician Impairment   The conditions accompanying stress are doubly problematic for a physician. These conditions compromise not only the physician's own quality of life, but also the physician's ability to provide care to others. For these reasons, researchers looking at physician stress have coined the term **physician impairment**. It refers to a state in which stress-related symptoms interfere with the physician's ability to perform his or her job (Gold, 2004).

One of the most troubling causes of physician impairment is substance abuse. While alcoholism and drug addiction are no more prevalent among physicians, use of prescription drugs is, especially those drugs used to treat psychological distress, due in part to physicians' access to these drugs (O'Connor & Spickard, 1997; Ward, 2005). Issues of dependency have prompted a call to make these problems a health promotion issue for physicians (Brewster, 2001; Knight et al., 2002). Weir points out that it can be difficult for physicians to seek treatment because the admission of a drug or alcohol dependency can have implications for their licensing. As a result, physicians are more likely to deny their problems or suffer alone. By the time the problem surfaces in the workplace, it is probably well advanced. This reticence to seek treatment is unfortunate for many reasons, not the least of which is that recovery rates are around 80 percent when treatment is sought. This treatment is most effective when it is uninterrupted and residential, featuring family involvement and prudent return to practice with adequate follow-up and support (Weir, 2000).

physician impairment: a state in which stress-related symptoms interfere with physicians' abilities to perform their jobs.

Gender Issues in Medical Practice

No analysis of health care practitioners would be complete without a discussion of gender. Among physicians, men and women bring different attributes to their work, make somewhat different career choices, perceive their work differently, and communicate with their patients differently. Furthermore, patients' own gender influences their preferences for the gender of their physicians.

The "Feminization" of Medicine   In 1959, 6 percent of medical students in Canada were female. Thirty years later, that number had jumped to 44 percent. In 2011, 58 percent of medical students in Canada were female (Association of Faculties of Medicine of Canada, 2012; Burton & Wong, 2004). In terms of practice, in 1997, 25 percent of physicians practising in Canada were women (CIHI, 2001). By 2004, that percentage had grown to 30 percent (CIHI, 2006a), see Figure 9-2).

Regarding career choices, a study by researchers at l'Université de Laval, where 74 percent of the medical students were women (Burton & Wong, 2004), discovered that female physicians place more importance on their private lives when making professional life decisions than do their male counterparts (De Koninck, Bergeron, & Bourbonnais, 1997). Interviews with female physicians yielded some clear statements about the way values affected their career choices: "What is important for women is not the size of their practice, the income, or publications, but the type of practice, personal satisfaction, fulfilling needs . . ." (De Koninck et al., 1997, p. 1828). Another woman put it this way: "I didn't want to be just a doctor . . . I wanted a family, children . . . I wanted a life that I

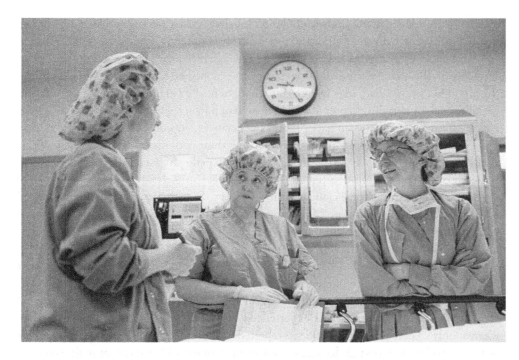

These practitioners are indicative of a growing proportion of females in the profession of medicine.
Helen King/Corbis

Figure 9-2 The Percentage of Female Students in Canadian Medical Schools Has Risen Sharply in Recent Generations

Source: Canadian Institute for Health Information. (2006a). Full-time equivalent physicians report: Canada, 2002–2003 and 2003–2004. Ottawa, Canada.

would call normal . . . I said to myself, if I go into neurosurgery, I'll never be able to" (De Koninck et al., 1997, p. 1829).

In a study of medical students at the University of Toronto, 27 percent of the men said they would choose surgery compared to only 10 percent of the women (Baxter, Cohen, & McLeod, 1996). This difference was based, in part, on perceptions regarding the lifestyle demands of the work and the amount of interaction (or lack thereof) surgeons have with patients. Other research with medical students has found that men say they

feminization of medicine: the trend toward increased proportions of female physicians in the profession.

want to work longer hours than women do and that women are more likely to want to spend leisure time with their family and friends (McFarland & Rhoades, 1998).

The trend toward increased proportions of female physicians has led some theorists to speculate on the changes this will bring to the profession. The **feminization of medicine**, as this trend has been called, may bring about changes to the balance between cure and care we talk about later in the chapter in our discussion of nursing. This trend may also affect the nature of interactions between patients and physicians (Levinson & Lurie, 2004).

Female physicians are more likely to involve their patients as partners in care decisions (Roter, Hall, & Aoki, 2002). More generally, female physicians are considered to be skilled providers of patient-centred care (Levinson & Lurie, 2004), which has a positive impact on treatment outcomes (Stewart, 1995). These outcomes may be further enhanced when physician and patient are of the same sex (Franks & Bertakis, 2003). This is good news for female patients, as the number of female physicians grows, but not so good for males, who might have more difficulty finding a male doctor (Levinson & Lurie, 2004).

Given that medicine has historically been male-dominated, it is not surprising that women physicians are more likely to perceive discrimination than men are (VanIneveld, Cook, Kane, & King, 1996). A study in Canada found that 70 percent of female internal medicine residents said they had experienced discrimination by attending physicians, whereas only 23 percent of male residents reported such discrimination. Similarly, 88 percent of female residents reported discrimination from patients (38 percent of male residents reported this), and 71 percent of female physicians reported discrimination from nurses, compared to 35 percent for male residents (VanIneveld et al., 1996). Female physicians were also much more likely than male residents to state that they had experienced sexual harassment from attending physicians, peers, and patients. In a study of more than 450 female physicians in Ontario, 76 percent said that they had experienced sexual harassment from patients (Phillips, 1996). In addition to the overt expressions of discrimination, there are what have been called "micro-inequities" (Robinson, 2003). These might include fewer opportunities for career advancement, social isolation, and a lack of recognition for good work.

In summary, physicians deal with numerous stressors and challenges throughout their careers, however rewarding they might find them. Demanding caseloads and hours, emotionally challenging communication, high expectations, and other realities of medical practice are some examples. Men and women bring different approaches to medical practice and different ways to deal with its challenges.

NURSES

Modern nursing in Canada is a profession facing many challenges. The constant changes in medical science demand that nurses stay absolutely current in their knowledge. The roles that nurses play in modern hospitals are expanding to include many advanced areas, such as transplant specialization and cardiac care. In fact, the area of advanced-practice nursing is a rapidly expanding one in Canada.

The Nature of Modern Nursing

caring: the role that most lay people think is the primary task of nurses.

curing: the role that most lay people think is the primary task of physicians.

When most lay people think of nurses, they think of people who are involved in **caring** for patients in hospital. This has been distinguished from the **curing** of people, which is more often associated with the physician's role (Barnes, 2005). In providing care, nurses make sure that medications are properly administered, that the patient's hygienic and dietary needs are taken care of, and that the emotional needs of the patient are considered as well. In general, nurses are patient advocates in the hospital setting. Of course, nurses work in settings other than hospitals, including community settings, as public health nurses, as home care nurses, and so on.

More recently, advanced training and re-definition of roles in modern nursing has given rise to **advanced-practice nursing**. The Canadian Nurses Association (CNA) defines advanced practice as "the role of a nurse working within a specialty area where superior clinical skills and judgement are acquired through a combination of experience and education" (CNA, 1997a, p. 2). In advanced practice, nurses' roles expand to include teaching, consultation, and research. Concerns have been expressed, however, that this might come at the expense of their caring role (Donnelly, 2003) and that the challenges brought on by multiple roles within the practice will increase nurses' stress levels (Cummings, Fraser, & Tarlier, 2003; Musclow, Sawhney, & Watt-Watson, 2002). However, if these concerns can be dealt with, they need not outweigh the benefits of providing nurses with the opportunity to contribute more fully to the care and cure of patients.

Nursing, then, is a profession in which ongoing education has become essential in order to keep up with advances in technology and nursing research. Many people entering the profession come in with a 4-year bachelor's degree in nursing rather than a registered nursing degree that may take 2 to 3 years to attain. It is clearly a field with exciting challenges. At the same time, nursing can be a very stressful profession, as we will see later in this section, and funding cutbacks in health care affect nursing significantly. Thus, nursing is a profession in which the demands are high and the resources often inadequate.

The CNA predicted a shortage of nurses in the order of 59 000–113 000 by the year 2001 (CNA, 1997b), with a 46 percent increase in demand for nurses. While there has been a small increase in the number of nurses practising in Canada since 2001, a significant shortage still exists as a result of an aging (and thus retiring) workforce in nursing (O'Brien-Pallas, Alksnis, & Wang, 2003) and a lack of young people entering the profession. In addition, the population in general is aging, putting increasing demands on the health care system.

advanced-practice nursing: nursing that includes teaching, consultation, and research within a specialty area where superior clinical skills and judgment are acquired through a combination of experience and education.

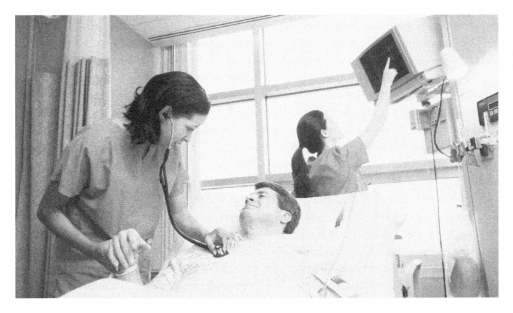

Modern nursing often requires advanced training and the ability to manage the stress of large patient loads.
Comstock/Stockbyte/Getty Images

There are a number of reasons why these aspects of modern nursing matter to health psychologists. First, increased demand combined with a shortage of resources is a recipe for stress. As we will see in this section, stress is a problem in nursing, for both nurses and patients. Burnout and stress are closely related. The second reason that health psychologists should be concerned with the changes in nursing is that people in health care are not immune to lifestyle-related illnesses—illnesses they spend so much time treating. Third, a considerable amount of hospital research in health psychology involves nurses. Nurses may be asked to administer research protocols in addition to their regular duties. When conducting this research, it is essential to have some understanding of the demands such involvement places on nurses' already hectic schedules and the implications that our conclusions and recommendations will have for nurses' work.

Stress in Nursing

People who work to alleviate suffering are susceptible to **compassion fatigue** (Schwam, 1998). Even for the most caring of people, there are limits to the amount of energy someone can dedicate to other people's welfare. When those limits are exceeded, nurses with compassion fatigue must either become less compassionate or reduce the number of patients they treat. For nurses who work in trauma-related settings, the symptoms of compassion fatigue mimic those of post-traumatic stress disorder, including anxiety, exhaustion, and sleep disruption. Closely related to compassion fatigue is burnout, which we have already discussed in this chapter.

The consequences of stress and its related conditions—compassion fatigue and burnout—are significant. One study found a demonstrated relationship between patient incidents, such as falling and medication errors, and nurses' scores on a stress index (Dugan et al., 1996). Not only do patients notice burnout when being cared for (Leiter et al., 1998), but also nurses with burnout miss more shifts, so patients may miss the nurses entirely (Parker & Kulik, 1995). Worse still, nurses who suffer prolonged burnout tend to leave the profession altogether (Parker & Kulik, 1995). Turnover can be problematic, given the important role nurses play and the resources dedicated to nursing education (Hayes et al., 2006). Moreover, nurse turnover is related to patient health outcomes. One study found that, with each loss of a full-time nurse in nursing homes, risk of infection increased by 30 percent and hospitalization by 80 percent (Zimmerman, Gruber-Baldini, Hebel, Sloane, & Magaziner, 2002).

The causes of stress are numerous and begin as soon as nurses enter nursing from training. In fact, the transition from student nurse to practitioner can be the first major source of stress. This has been called **reality shock** (Kramer, 1974) and is defined as the reaction to the discrepancy between a training environment and an actual work environment. Newly hired nurses report that they thought they had been adequately trained but quickly realize that they still have much to learn and that it must be learned quickly (Charnley, 1999). The sudden role shift from student to practising nurse can be frightening, since nurses now feel that they should know everything. They find it hard to cope with the volume of work and feel guilty when things don't get done in a timely way. New nurses sense a gap between the high standards of care they were taught and the lower standards that are the reality of nursing due to heavy demands and limited resources. One conflict many nurses must resolve is the one that exists between the nurturing, humanistic nature of nursing on one hand and the high-tech, high-traffic demands of modern medicine on the other. Finally, there is the stress of "learning the system," from finding out where supplies are kept to developing relationships with colleagues (Charnley, 1999).

For experienced nurses, stress appears to come from a number of sources, from the work environment to job responsibilities (Santos et al., 2003). The sheer volume of a nurse's work responsibilities and the need for multitasking in modern nursing are often-cited causes of stress. At any given moment, a nurse may be required to take numerous tests, manage supplies, complete paperwork, administer medications, and reassure worried family members (Flakus, 1998). Long hours can also be a problem as a number of hospitals have moved to 12-hour shifts. Stress has been shown to be higher for nurses in these shifts compared to their 8-hour counterparts (Hoffman & Scott, 2003). Also, nurses interviewed by University of Toronto researchers talked about an "effort–reward imbalance" in which the long hours, multitasking, and patient loads are not duly recognized (Hall & Kiesners, 2005).

It would stand to reason that some nursing specialties are more stressful than others. For example, oncology (pediatric oncology, in particular) can be very demanding. A study in Australia found that 70 percent of oncology nurses reported moderate to high degrees of emotional exhaustion (Barrett & Yates, 2002). Booth (1998) has studied the intense stress that accompanies unexpected patient death during surgery. This is particularly stressful because the surgical staff may feel that the death was caused by the intervention (and they may be correct). Even if the surgery was the only hope for the patient, staff are often left with the feeling that unexpected death during surgery was due to human error, whether it was or not. Few other professions feature doubts over one's own sense of competence combined with confrontations with mortality.

Stress is a significant problem in nursing but it is not insurmountable. There are ways in which nurses can cope effectively with the stressors of their job, and there are ways institutions can improve the work environment to reduce those stressors. For the nurses themselves, coping ability depends on social factors and personal factors (Boey, 1999). **Social factors**, as the term implies, refer to those elements of the nurse's social network, such as family, friends, and co-workers.

Personal factors include personality characteristics and coping strategies. For example, nurses with high self-esteem and a clear sense of control are less prone to stress. In terms of coping strategies, those who are more stress-resistant tend to avoid negative, emotion-focused coping. Instead, they use problem-focused coping, trying to find ways to make their job more manageable rather than dwelling on the frustration and anxiety they may feel. Another important personal factor is **psychological empowerment**, including finding the work meaningful, having a sense of autonomy (Kramer & Schmalenberg, 2003), feeling competent, and having a positive impact. Research at the University of Western Ontario has found that nurses with this sense of empowerment are more likely to stay in the profession and feel satisfied with their work (Laschinger, Finegan, Shamian, & Wilk, 2004).

The feeling of being in control that is so helpful in reducing stress can be greatly influenced by hospital management. Laschinger et al. (2004) calls supportive management and policies structural empowerment. According to the **job strain model**, a job with high strain is one that features both high demands and low control (Karasek, 1979). Policies intended to enhance nurses' sense of control have indeed been shown to reduce stress and burnout. Such policies include group meetings, better communication up and down the hierarchy, more say in job design, and so on (Felton, 1998). When these are in place, it is also likely that nurses will feel more committed to their institutions, which is another antidote to burnout (Hinds et al., 1998).

social factors in stress: the elements of a person's social network, such as family, friends, and co-workers, that affect ability to cope with job stressors.

personal factors in stress: personal characteristics, such as high self-esteem and a clear sense of control, that make some people better able to cope with the stressors of their job.

psychological empowerment in stress: a personal factor in stress that can include finding work meaningful, having a sense of autonomy, feeling competent, and having a positive impact.

job strain model: a model that suggests a job with high strain is one that includes high demands and low control.

OTHERS

Physicians and nurses are not the only health care professionals deserving of a health psychologist's attention. In this section, we will look at two other health care professions in which psychology can play a central role. Certainly, our list of professions discussed in this chapter is far from exhaustive. You are invited to think of ways in which psychology can make constructive contributions to the work of others providing health care.

Physiotherapists

In Case 9-1, you met May, a woman who had suffered a stroke that affected every aspect of her life. Many of the challenges that May and her physical therapist face as they work on May's rehabilitation are psychological in nature. In addition to knowing what May is capable of and what exercises to give her each day, Joyce must be sensitive to issues of motivation, adherence, mood, and social support.

Goal Setting   It is clear that physiotherapists (and also occupational therapists) must enter into a partnership with their patients if they hope to be successful. In other words, the relationship cannot be one in which the patient is passive and dependent upon the therapist. Nowhere is this more evident than in the area of goal setting (Barnes & Ward, 2000; Siegert & Taylor, 2004).

When setting goals for rehabilitation, it is important to acknowledge a difference between goals set in the hospital setting and those addressing integration back into the

CASE 9-1   THE LONG ROAD BACK

One of the most disturbing things for May was that she had no memory whatsoever for the event that had left her feeling so debilitated. One minute she felt fine, and the next she woke up in a hospital, having no idea how she got there. She did know, however, that something terrible had happened. This was because she could feel nothing in her right arm or right leg, and she couldn't talk.

May, who was 61 years old, had suffered a stroke, or cerebrovascular accident (CVA) as it is known medically. During the stroke, the blood supply to the left side of her brain had been cut off due to a blockage in an artery. May's family had been told that no one could say for sure just how profound her disability would be. It would depend on biology, medicine, some luck, and May's motivation for rehabilitation.

The first few days in the hospital, May did show some improvement. Some of her speaking ability returned, much to the relief of her family, but she still found verbal communication enormously frustrating. And she was experiencing great difficulty with movement; getting up to go to the bathroom was a major undertaking. She wondered how she and her husband would ever manage outside the hospital. These thoughts were so discouraging for May that there were times when she wished the stroke had just killed her and put an end to everything.

That cloud began to lift, however, when May met Joyce. Joyce was the physical therapist assigned to help May on her long road to rehabilitation. Joyce's skill and encouragement became vital to May, who found herself working harder than she had at any time in her life. Soon May started to feel like a professional athlete, training for the biggest game of her career.

The psychology of rehabilitation is as important for patients as sports psychology is for elite athletes.   Keith Brofsky/Photodisc/ Getty Images community (Playford et al., 2000). The former tend to be more short term and pragmatic in nature, relating to such things as mobility, hygiene, communication, and patient safety. The latter are more long term, addressing such things as social functioning.

Adherence

Closely related to goal setting is adherence (Sluijs, Kerssens, van der Zee, & Myers, 1998). The therapist cannot oversee all the work a patient must do. For improvement to occur, a patient like May must work diligently on rehabilitation on her own. She must adhere to the rehab regimen that she and the therapist have agreed on. All these factors are interrelated; for example, if May feels that she was part of the goal-setting process, she will feel more committed to achieving these goals and will be more likely to adhere to the regimen. Education, cognitive interventions, and behavioural interventions also affect adherence.

Behavioural Interventions

Most rehabilitation patients need some form of **external reinforcement**. That is to say, the physiotherapist, friends, family, and other practitioners must encourage and praise the patient's successes. For May, improvement will not be measured on a minute-to-minute basis. She will need to be reminded of what she can do today that she could not do during the early weeks of her rehabilitation. Also, May will need to find ways to **self-reinforce**. She must pat herself on the back and maybe even give herself tangible rewards for achieving certain goals. One of the best things about physical rehabilitation is that at least some of the success can be *measured objectively*. May can measure how much farther she has walked and how much more clearly she can speak as she progresses through the regimen. Objective criteria for success are the bread and butter of behavioural interventions. They allow for reinforcement to be directly contingent on desired behaviour and allow the patient and physiotherapist to *shape* the program by gradually increasing observable standards. Perhaps this is why therapists tend to set goals with their patients that are physical in nature, and thus objectively measurable. The downside is that psychological goals might get ignored by the practitioner adopting this focus (Wressle, Oberg, & Henriksson, 1999).

Cognitive Interventions

The power of effective behavioural interventions is clear in physical therapy. However, May's program cannot rely solely on behavioural strategies. It must also focus on her thinking, and that is the stuff of cognitive interventions. There are at least three areas in which this is crucial. First, May must be ready to make the necessary changes and to take on the challenges of rehabilitation (Wagner & McMahon, 2004).

Second, she must believe that she can reach an identified goal. You may remember from chapter 1 that we call these **efficacy beliefs**. These beliefs can be tricky to instil. It isn't usually enough to simply *tell* people that they are capable of doing something. Those messages must be based on some *evidence* that the patient will accept as being reasonable.

The third crucial target for cognitive interventions is the patient's **attributions**. These are the explanations people give for their successes and failures. In May's case, as with all patients, it will be essential that she attribute her success *internally* (Wiegmann & Berven, 1998). In other words, she must take credit for her improvement, citing things like her hard work and fighting spirit. If she tries to attribute her success to Joyce, her physiotherapist, Joyce must politely deflect that back to May.

Positive efficacy beliefs and internal attributions of success greatly increase the likelihood that May will adhere to her regimen when Joyce is not around. Most of all, these ways of thinking move May toward *independence*, which is an important goal of physical rehabilitation.

external reinforcement: the encouragement and praise from physiotherapists, friends, family, and other practitioners needed by rehabilitation patients for their successes.

self-reinforcement: praising oneself or rewarding oneself for accomplishments.

efficacy beliefs: the extent to which one thinks a course of action (e.g., a preventive behaviour or treatment) will actually work.

attributions: the explanations people give for events such as their successes and failures.

CHAPTER SUMMARY

- Describe key factors that influence our perception and interpretation of symptoms.

  Key factors include one's current mood or stress level. For example, being in a bad mood and experiencing stress both aggravate the experience of symptoms. Although the findings are not consistent, there do tend to be age and gender differences in the interpretation of symptoms.

- Apply a stage model to understand why people delay in seeking medical care.

  Patient delay can occur at the stage of appraisal delay (deciding that a symptom is a sign of illness), illness delay (the time between recognizing that one is ill and seeking care), behavioural delay (the time between deciding to seek care and actually making an appointment), scheduling delay (the time between scheduling an appointment and receiving medical attention), or treatment delay (the time between receiving medical attention and beginning treatment).

- Explain specific ways in which the procedures and rules within a hospital affect patients' sense of control and their ability to cope with being in hospital.

  Patients feel a loss of control in environments characterized as *total institutions*, in which many decisions are made for them.

  Patients sometimes respond to this loss of control using *reactance*, in which they disobey instructions in order to retain a sense of autonomy.

  Patients' sense of control is increased with the use of care plans that allow patients to be involved in decision making.

- Define "invasiveness" and place various medical procedures on a continuum of invasiveness, using this definition

  Invasiveness is defined in both physical and psychological terms. The procedures might invade the body physically or cause psychological distress in the form of embarrassment or anxiety.

  A colonoscopy would be considered more invasive than a mammogram for both, for example.

- Describe ways in which the nature of care and preparation for medical procedures can help patients cope.

  The provision of information that matches a patient's need for such information helps with coping. Also, providing patients with realistic expectations regarding recovery and treatment outcome is important, as is the introduction of relaxation techniques.

  Patients who are taught to self-monitor for emotion and symptom will cope better with hospital procedures.

- Describe psychological challenges associated with specific hospital departments (emergency, surgery, intensive care, discharge, and palliative care) and the coping and care needed to manage these challenges.

The emergency department is important as an entry point to the hospital and a place where patients may be in distress. Well-organized admission and triage procedures and adequate staffing are key factors in helping patients cope with this environment.

In addition to the list of considerations for good preparation, postoperative recovery focuses considerable attention on pain management. Patients can gain a sense of control over this via patient-controlled analgesics and other psychological techniques such as relaxation and distraction.

Time spent in intensive care is often disorienting and, of course, anxiety-producing for family members. A person's stay in ICU can be divided into stages, including the incommunication stage, the readaptation stage, and the reflection stage.

The discharge process requires considerable planning, especially for the frail elderly. This planning must take into account the capacity of family members and others to care for the patient when he or she returns home. The potential stressors on the family at this time must also be addressed.

In palliative care, the goals are to control symptoms, support the family, and focusing on the patients needs. This requires an awareness of the grief process.

■ Identify the major sources of stress and satisfaction for physicians.

Work overload is an often-cited source of stress for physicians

Decision-making uncertainty is another source

As is the emotional nature of interactions with patients, especially when giving bad news.

■ Describe the important role nurses play in patient care.

Nurses are "patient advocates." They interact extensively with hospitalized patients, looking after such things as medications, hygiene, and diet.

Some nurses become acute care nurse practitioners, combining knowledge, advanced skills, and greater professional autonomy to provide a level of care that is typically greater than that provided by most nurses.

■ Identify the major sources of stress in nursing.

In the early stages of their careers, nurses experience "reality shock," which results from the realization that actual nursing practice is different from what is encountered in training.

Work volume is another source of stress. This is made worse by a feeling that one has no control over one's work or work environment.

■ Understand the challenges associated with work in physical (and occupational) therapy.

Practitioners working in rehabilitation should work in partnership with patients to set mutually agreed-upon goals.

Adherence to rehabilitation plans is important and can be enhanced by effective use of behavioural and cognitive interventions.

Pain management is another important psychological issue in physical rehabilitation.

Chapter 10

From One to Many: Health on a Large Scale

denis_pc/Fotolia

Learning Objectives

After studying this chapter, you will be able to:

1. use the social ecological model to expand your understanding of the psychosocial approach to health.

2. list and explain common social determinants of health.

3. define vulnerability as it applies to health and provide examples of factors that increase vulnerability.

4. discuss ways in which culture relates to health and explain what is meant by culturally sensitive health care.

5. identify the major health challenges facing Canada's Aboriginal peoples and discuss ways in which these challenges can be overcome.

6. define harm reduction and provide examples of this public health approach.

7. cite historical and modern evidence to help explain public attitudes toward vaccination.

8. identify the elements of neighbourhood design that can affect our health, with specific reference to obesity.

"Why is Jason in the hospital?
Because he has a bad infection in his leg.

But why does he have an infection?
Because he has a cut on his leg and it got infected.

But why does he have a cut on his leg?
Because he was playing in the junk yard next to his apartment
building and there was some sharp, jagged steel there that he fell on.

But why was he playing in a junk yard?
Because his neighbourhood is kind of run down.
A lot of kids play there and there is no one to supervise them.

But why does he live in that neighbourhood?
Because his parents can't afford a nicer place to live.

But why can't his parents afford a nicer place to live?
Because his Dad is unemployed and his Mom is sick.

But why is his Dad unemployed?
Because he doesn't have much education and he can't find a job.

But why . . . ?"

From the Public Health Agency of Canada, What Makes Canadians Health or Unhealthy? http://www.phac-aspc.gc.ca/ph-sp/determinants/determinants-eng.php. Accessed October 4, 2012.

THE SOCIAL ECOLOGICAL MODEL: BUILDING ON THE BIOPSYCHOSOCIAL APPROACH TO UNDERSTAND BIG PICTURES

Our opening vignette, drawn from the website of the Public Health Agency of Canada, creates a link between a child's stay in hospital and his father's employment status. This takes the notion of distal causes to yet another level. With this in mind, in this chapter, we will expand our focus from the classic psychological analysis of the individual to the consideration of entire populations. This is a bit like going up in a helicopter and looking down from 3000 metres.

You may well ask why health psychologists need to take this helicopter ride in the first place. Isn't it enough to study individuals? No it isn't. Individuals do not exist in isolation from each other or from larger systems. In fact, attempts to understand and improve individual health often fail because these larger systems are not taken into account. It is naïve to think we can change an individual's health-related behaviour without understanding the extent to which that person's environment will support that change.

Think back to the first case you read about in this book (see chapter 1). Alan was admitted to hospital after having a heart attack. When you first encountered this case, you were asked to consider factors beyond the biological that could have accounted for Alan's heart attack and his possible recovery. We learned that Alan, as an individual, possessed certain characteristics and behaviours that put him at greater risk for his heart attack. Alan was quick to anger and he was hard-driving. He had a family to support. These realizations helped us understand the *biopsychosocial* approach to health.

In this chapter, we will expand further on the "social" piece of the biopsychosocial approach. Alan probably works for an organization that expects results, and lives within a community that sees status in financial success. Fortunately for Alan, he lives within a country with policies that make access to good health care more likely for him. The Healthy Heart program he would be directed toward would be accessible, in part, because of national and provincial policies that make it so.

As we describe these levels, you can imagine a collection of larger and larger circles emanating out from Alan the individual. These circles represent the **Social Ecological Model** (see Stokols, 1996). As Figure 10-1 illustrates, the Social Ecological Model places the individual in an ever-expanding set of contexts or systems. Stokols (1996) points out that these systems interact and combine to have a cumulative effect on our health. Health psychologists need to be cognizant of the individual's place within these systems.

Social Ecological Model: a model acknowledging that the individual is influenced by a collection of larger, inter-related, and cumulative contexts, such as organizations, communities, and governments.

Many major organizations and initiatives have adopted the Social Ecological Model, including the World Health Organization (Blas & Kurup, 2010, as cited in Golden & Earp, 2012), Active Canada 20/20, and the *Healthy People* Program in the United States (U.S. Department of Health and Human Services, 2000, as cited in Golden & Earp, 2012). In Canada, Langille and Rodgers (2010) analyzed physical activity in schools by considering

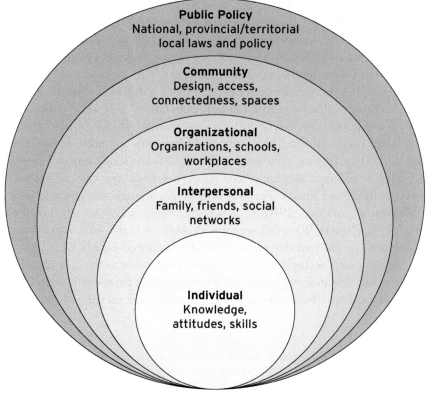

Figure 10-1 The Social Ecological Model

school board policies and societal pressures for academic achievement, as well as the individual behaviour of children. This represents a classic application of the Social Ecological Model.

Viewing things from 3000 metres isn't easy. Individuals are complex enough without considering the many inter-related systems in which they exist. This helps explain why most health promotion programs focus on the individual and interpersonal levels and do not take larger systems into account (Golden & Earp, 2012). In chapter 11, we will look more closely at health promotion and help you develop a greater understanding of the levels of the Social Ecological Model.

TRACKING HEALTH AND ILLNESS AT THE POPULATION LEVEL

To start our climb to elevations that allow us to see bigger pictures, we must first understand how the health of populations is studied. This is the work of **epidemiology**.

epidemiology: the study of changing patterns of health and disease across populations and geographic areas.

Epidemiology is concerned with the gathering and interpretation of information about disease occurrence and the general health of populations. Epidemiologists look at general patterns of health and, in particular, possible associations between exposure and disease. This could involve everything from contaminants in the air to poorly handled food. From these analyses, epidemiologists can often explain why a disease occurs and perhaps inform interventions that reduce its impact. They can also identify populations at risk and, more generally, describe the health status of populations.

Epidemiology literally means "the study of epidemics." Epidemiologists chart patterns of health and disease (primarily disease) across populations and geographic areas, studying the origin and distribution of health problems (Cockerham, 1998). Epidemiologists apply the Social Ecological Model. People working in the field include everyone from sociologists to physicians to meteorologists (for such things as air pollution data). Psychologists also work with epidemiological data. As we will see in this chapter, a basic understanding of illness patterns is very helpful to health psychologists.

Sometimes, the patterns being studied are quite stable over time. Change happens slowly, as in rates of dementia in an elderly population or of knee injuries in female athletes. Sometimes, however, a pattern can change rapidly. When this happens, epidemiologists need to determine if they are dealing with an outbreak. For example, on February 23, 2003, a 78-year-old woman took a flight from Hong Kong to Toronto. When she did, what would normally have been an everyday occurrence changed the lives of many people living in Canada. This was because the woman was suffering from Severe Acute Respiratory Syndrome (SARS). When she arrived in Toronto, she became the first case of SARS in Canada. What followed was an outbreak of this infectious disease that, in Canada, resulted in 250 probable cases and 40 deaths by mid-June of 2003.[1]

An outbreak such as this, featuring an illness that is new to the country and virtually new to the world, demands fast and decisive action. Before cures can be found, the nature of the disease itself must be determined. The detective work on this falls primarily to epidemiologists.

---

[1]Details regarding the SARS outbreak in Toronto have been taken from a Health Canada Report entitled "Epi-Update: Interim Report on the SARS Outbreak in the Greater Toronto Area, Ontario, Canada, April 24, 2003." Accessed on October 22, 2014, from http://www.virox.com/files_docs/content/pdf/en/download/RespiratoryInfections-Pu.pdf

To do their work, especially in outbreak analysis, epidemiologists often start with a single case, then trace back to its starting point. From there, they determine how widespread the problem has become. They then try to identify factors that all people with that problem share. The goal is to identify causes so that the problem can be eliminated or at least controlled. In doing this work, epidemiologists use terminology that health psychologists need to be familiar with.

For example, a case is one instance of the problem. The **index case** is the first identified case. In the SARS outbreak, the 78-year-old woman who arrived from Hong Kong was the index case. When she was admitted to hospital, she was visited by her family. As a result, six of them contracted SARS. Three of these family members visited their physician, who was then infected as well. One of the family members (Case B) went to a hospital emergency department on March 7, 2003. During his treatment in ER, he transmitted the disease to two paramedics, a firefighter, and four hospital staff. Three members of Case C's family also contracted SARS.

index case: the first identified instance of a medical problem.

Soon, other hospitals became involved, as did groups of people who were believed to have been exposed to probable cases outside hospital settings. As a result, the number of cases in Toronto increased dramatically over a short period of time.

There are many important psychological issues related to outbreaks. For example, it is often the case that the general public exaggerates the danger, creating a certain degree of hysteria. For the SARS outbreak, Canada decided to report both probable and suspect cases. The former refers to people who are showing all the defining symptoms and have been exposed to the disease. The latter refers to people who are displaying some of the symptoms but very possibly have not been exposed. Suspect cases rarely become probable cases. In British Columbia, there were 4 probable cases and 46 suspect cases. Because of this reporting strategy, the general public is presented with numbers that inaccurately reflect the risk of the disease. Also, the media might report lifetime prevalence numbers. These numbers would include people who had SARS and are recovered. This also results in an inflation of the magnitude of the problem.

This is not to say that SARS was not serious. It just hasn't been as serious as some members of the general public have come to believe. Some people began wearing surgical masks to protect themselves from a disease they had very little chance of being exposed to and despite the fact that the masks probably did nothing to protect the wearer.

As you will learn in chapter 11, "Health Promotion," fear does not always motivate people to engage in healthy behaviours. In the case of outbreak-induced panic, there is no guarantee that people will report symptoms promptly. Instead, they may try to carry on with their normal lives and risk the health of others by riding public transit and coming into contact with many other people.

SOCIAL DETERMINANTS OF HEALTH IN CANADA

Health Psychology focuses on psychological factors that help determine health. In this chapter, we have made the point that there are more macroscopic factors at work as well. People who work in health care call these larger forces **social determinants of health** (see Figure 10-2). This term refers, of course, to social conditions such as housing, employment, and the conditions in which one works, as well as the availability of things such as food and health care services (Raphael, 2004). Social determinants also refer to economic and political conditions, such as poverty and war. People focusing on social determinants

social determinants of health: factors such as housing, employment, socioeconomic status, and food availability that affect the health of populations.

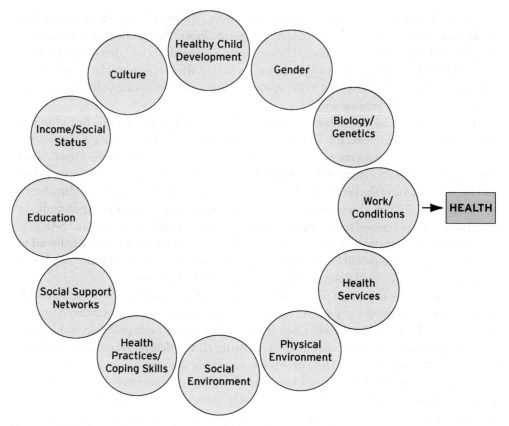

Figure 10-2 Social Determinants of Health in Canada

Source: Canadian Policy Research Networks (2006).

will refer to "upstream causes." The term reminds health practitioners and psychologists to pay attention to factors that may seem distant from the specific complaint affecting a patient or client, but nonetheless must be addressed if constructive interventions are to be implemented.

Purely biomedical approaches do not give adequate consideration to social determinants. Such determinants, which can also be placed within the Social Ecological Model, expand upon the "social" to the biopsychosocial model discussed in chapter 1.

THE VULNERABILITY OF POPULATIONS

When epidemiologists study health patterns and social determinants of health, they find that some populations are more likely than others to encounter a health problem and that determinants are not equitably distributed through the population. In fact, some populations are more likely to encounter a whole host of problems. These discoveries lead to the study of vulnerable populations. Vulnerability is the result of a number of factors. First, there is an increased likelihood of exposure to a threat. Second, a vulnerable population must deal with an increased likelihood that the threat will become a real problem. Third, these populations lack the resources to deal with that problem (Schröder-Butterfil & Marianti, 2006). Even in a developed country like

Canada, with a good health care system, there are many vulnerable populations. The elderly, street youth, and those living in poverty are just a few examples.

Indeed, the study of vulnerability in Canada takes us into highly contrasting worlds, from inner cities to remote wilderness. Those living in our inner-city environments face numerous vulnerabilities. These environments are defined, not only by their geographic location, but by the prevalence of poverty. They try to cope with a vast array of health issues and their psychological consequences, including poor nutrition and dental care, high rates of chronic disease, mental illness, and infection (Hay, Varga-Toth, & Hines, 2006).

The psychology of health-related vulnerability is complex and important, from the perspective of the vulnerable, as well as those who enjoy more privileged lives. For at-risk populations living in our inner cities, such as street youth, feelings of loneliness and entrapment may be experienced, along with thoughts of suicide (Kidd & Shahar, 2006).

According to a 2014 CBC report, 30 000 people are homeless in Canada every night (http://www.cbc.ca/news/canada/30-000-canadians-are-homeless-every-night-1.1413016; accessed on October 22, 2014). For the homeless, feelings of alienation and learned helplessness are common (Goodman, Saxe, & Harvey, 1991). You might be surprised to learn that, in places like Toronto, families represent the largest group of homeless people. They are not dealing with substance abuse or mental illness.

There are, all the same, clear reasons why homeless people experience psychological trauma. Becoming homeless would be traumatic enough for most people; however, this can be compounded by the day-to-day life associated with homelessness and the fact that many homeless people, especially women, experience trauma prior to becoming homeless (Goodman et al., 1991). Trauma of this kind can have significant consequences on physical health and health-related behaviours.

To appreciate the sharp contrast in living conditions and psychological issues experienced across Canada, compare these inner-city challenges with those described in Focus on Canadian Research 10-1.

Health across the Vast Expanse of Canada

Did you grow up in one of Canada's many rural or remote communities? If so, you will have some understanding of how, in a country as vast as Canada, many social determinants of health relate to geography. It comes as no surprise that one's health is closely tied to where one lives. One way to illustrate this quite clearly is to use epidemiological methods to compare urban and rural health status. There is the perhaps romantic belief that "life in the country" is healthier, with its fresh air, lack of concrete, and slower pace of life. Although all of this sounds bucolic enough, health statistics indicate that Canadians living in rural environments are not as healthy as most of their urban counterparts. Research reported by the Canadian Policy Research Networks (CPRN) (Hay et al., 2006) provides revealing evidence.

The first thing to understand is that Canada is so vast that the word "rural" does not adequately describe the range of living conditions outside cities. CPRN distinguishes between rural and remote contexts. Rural communities have fewer than 10 000 people living in them. Remote communities are usually but not always this small, but they are always distant from urban areas. To illustrate the difference, CPRN gives the example of Bethune, Saskatchewan. It is rural but not remote, being about 40 minutes from Regina. By contrast, Ulukhaktok, Northwest Territories, is remote and northern. It is accessible only by air and ship. How far do you have to travel to visit a physician? If you lived in a remote northern area, there would be a greater than 60 percent chance you would have to travel more than 100 kilometres for that visit.

On almost any dimension you can think of, the health status of rural Canadians is poorer than for those living in urban centres—illness related to lifestyle, injuries, poisoning, infant mortality, and life expectancy (Hay et al., 2006). Moreover, farming and mining have been called two of the most dangerous occupations in Canada, with mining being the most dangerous. Seventy percent of traumatic deaths in Canada occur in rural areas, despite the fact that only 30 percent of the population lives in these areas.

These health challenges are compounded by a relative lack of health care services in rural and remote areas. According to the CPRN report, about 17 percent of physicians live in rural areas to serve about 31 percent of Canada's population that lives in these areas. The numbers are worse for specialist practitioners.

There are also psychological factors that interact with these social determinants for this vulnerable population. Imagine being someone in a small rural community and being in need of psychiatric services or addiction counselling. If you are lucky, there might be one addiction counsellor in your community. Would you calmly walk in that person's building, passing many familiar faces in the town as you do so? The CPRN uses examples such as these to illustrate the potential stigma and violation of privacy associated with seeking some forms of health care in rural communities, even when that care is close at hand.

In summary, many people living in rural and remote communities would fit the definition of a vulnerable population. They have significant health challenges, and they lack the resources, personal, social, and systemic, to cope with them.

The remote northern community of Ulukhaktok, NWT. Studies indicate that the health status of people living in such communities is generally poorer than the health status of those living in urban centres.
GeoStock/Getty Images

CULTURE AND HEALTH

We know Canada to be a country of considerable cultural and ethnic diversity. Statistics Canada (2010) has projected that this diversity will increase further at least until 2030. By then, just over one-quarter of people living in Canada could have been born outside the country. Over 30 percent could belong to a visible minority, representing a doubling of the number from 2006. The most rapid increase in this category will likely be among those Canadian-born—the offspring of immigrants. It is predicted that 47 percent of second-generation Canadians will belong to a visible minority group by the year 2031. Minority groups will continue to concentrate in urban areas, with 71 percent living in Toronto, Montreal, or Vancouver. These calculations make a distinction between visible minorities and Aboriginal groups.

Much can be learned about the psychology of health and health care by studying health patterns of our immigrant populations. When these patterns are studied, it is common to find that immigrants report their health as being at least as good if not better than those born in Canada. Over time, however, these reports retreat to eventually be on a par with Canadian-born individuals. This pattern is common enough to be given a name. It is called the **"healthy immigrant effect,"** and it is not restricted to Canada (see Biddle, Kennedy, & McDonald, 2007, for Australia; Stephen et al., 1994, for the United States).

Researchers at Statistics Canada used longitudinal data from the National Population Health Survey to track self-reports of health status for immigrants, both European and non-European, and Canadian-born respondents (Ng, Wilkins, Gendron, & Berthelot, 2005). Their findings supported the existence of the "healthy immigrant effect." They started by pulling out all those respondents who reported their health to be good, very good, or excellent. They then followed their survey responses from 1994 to 2003. They found that non-European immigrants were more than twice as likely as those Canadian-born to show a deterioration in their self-reported health status, moving from the positive categories to either fair or poor. European immigrants, also including those from the United States, Australia and New Zealand, did not show this decline. Non-European immigrants were also about 1.5 times as likely as Canadian-born respondents to have become frequent visitors to doctors, though not more likely to be hospitalized.

Others have studied actual diagnosed conditions rather than self-reports of health status (McDonald & Kennedy, 2004). When actual chronic conditions are considered (either serious or non-life-threatening), we still see a decline in immigrant health. In both diagnosed and self-reported measures of health status, the decline continues only until it *converges* with the levels of native-born Canadians.

How can we explain this effect? Immigrants might start out with better reports and indications of health because they self-select before coming to Canada. Perhaps only those who feel fit enough for the challenge will consider emigrating. Also, Canada screens its potential immigrants' health prior to admission to the country, though this is not a particularly fine screen.

These factors might explain the positive early reports, but they don't explain the decline. The first place to look to find reasons for deterioration in health is the same places we would look for anyone. In this regard, immigrants were more likely to become inactive and gain weight than were those Canadian-born (McDonald & Kennedy, 2005). However, it has been suggested that reported declines happen too rapidly to be attributable to lifestyle changes (Newbold, 2005). Also, both European and non-European immigrants reported this decline in activity, but only non-Europeans reported a decline in

"healthy immigrant effect": the tendency for recent non-European immigrants to report their health as being above average upon arrival to Canada, but to report deterioration of their health over time.

health. This might be because non-Europeans are more likely to find themselves in vulnerable categories related to low socioeconomic status. Non-European immigrants are more likely to report difficulties securing long-term employment, for example. We can apply the Social Ecological Model here. Non-European immigrant health is, over time, affected by factors that sit at higher levels of the model—the organizational, community, or public policy—such as their social milieu and working conditions (Newbold, 2005).

Psychologically, it has been suggested that immigrants self-report poorer health status because they change their subjective standards of healthiness the longer they are in Canada. What seemed like good health in their home country comes to seem less than optimal in the affluent surroundings of Canada (McDonald & Kennedy, 2004).

Since non-European immigrants increase their number of visits to doctors, perhaps they become more likely to have conditions detected and feel that their health is deteriorating. While possible, this is not likely, since doctor visits increase quite rapidly upon immigration, reaching Canadian-born numbers, and then level out (McDonald & Kennedy, 2004). Measures of immigrant health decline don't co-vary with this pattern.

In medical cases reported by health care professionals or studied by students, it is common to include a brief description of the patient's race, ethnicity, or culture. One might read, "The patient was a 57-year-old Asian woman who came to the emergency department complaining of abdominal pain." Whether you are a student or a practitioner, it is important to ask just what each piece of this description adds to one's ability to respond appropriately to the case, and what still needs to be known before one can respond. For example, "abdominal pain" is a very general description. It could mean anything from minor gastrointestinal disruption to life-threatening illness. Certainly, if you asked practitioners what else they needed to know before they could provide a diagnosis, they would want to know more about that abdominal pain. Just where is it located? What brings it on? And so on.

The fact that this patient is Asian is at least as undifferentiating as is her abdominal pain. Yet, is it likely that practitioners would ask for more information in this regard? Just where in Asia is she from? Was she even born in Asia, or in Canada or elsewhere? How might this information help me provide appropriate care? These questions start to address the importance of culturally appropriate or culturally sensitive care.

What Is Culture?

culture: the values, behaviours, practices, and assumptions learned from our membership in groups that share them.

Entire disciplines, such as anthropology, are dedicated to the understanding of **culture**. Other disciplines borrow from this understanding to help them explore a myriad of phenomena that are influenced by culture. In this short section, we will just begin to venture into these very complex arenas so that you can start developing an appreciation for the fascinating, vital, and complicated issues related to culture and health.

There are many definitions of culture. Most make reference to shared meanings and practices. Members of a given culture will tend to agree on what actions are appropriate and what those actions mean. Canada's Centre for Intercultural Learning defines culture as "the values, behaviours, practices, assumptions we've learned from our membership in groups that share them." This definition posits that culture is learned. This learning helps define us and guide us regarding how to act and what things mean. The Centre for Intercultural Learning also observes: "Culture is vital because it enables its members to function with one another without the need to negotiate meaning at every moment" (Centre for Intercultural Learning, 2012; accessed on October 23, 2014, from http://www.intercultures.ca/cil-cai/overview-apercu-eng.asp?iso=ca).

How Culture Affects Health

Culture can be powerfully influential in our understanding of health, our health-related behaviours, and our interaction with health care systems. Culture will influence our interpretation of physical sensations, our perceived roles when we are in need of care, and our decisions about how to pursue care. It will also influence our day-to-day behaviours that affect the maintenance of our health. It will even influence what we think good health is.

Culture is also related to our earlier discussion of vulnerability. In Canada, health outcomes and access to health care are not equitably distributed across our many cultures. Some cultures would be considered privileged in this regard. Members of other cultures would report discrimination and racism. We have discussed differences in access to health care based on geographic location. Cultural differences also help predict differences in access to health care.

In cultural terms, privileged groups not only enjoy greater access to care, they make the rules regarding what warrants care and who deserves it. They make decisions regarding the allocation of resources. Thus, one's culture not only defines practices that can affect health, it can also play a major role in placing one on a continuum of privilege that affects access to resources and the very definition of what is healthy and what is not.

We have already introduced the "healthy immigrant effect," in which immigrants report better-than-average health upon arrival to their new country but gradually decline to levels comparable to local-born residents. The effects of culture, of course, intertwine with immigration, but they are also different. People bring their cultures when they immigrate. At the same time, people who have lived in Canada all their lives belong to cultures, and these affect health and health care completely independent of their country of origin.

Studies in the United States have revealed some clear ways in which the health care system responds differently to people depending upon their ethnicity or culture. Geiger (2001, citing Canto et al., 2000; Gornick, Eggers, & Reilly, 1996; Hannan et al., 1999) reports that African Americans, Hispanic Americans, and native Americans are less likely to receive such things as advanced cancer treatment, renal transplants, or coronary artery angioplasty or bypass surgery.

Even when treatment is provided, health care that is not sensitive to cultural differences runs the risk of prescribing regimens that will not be effectively followed (Nguyen & Achusim, 2002). One particularly poignant example is Lia Lee, the daughter of a Hmong family whose case was the subject of the book *The Spirit Catches You and You Fall Down* (Fadiman, 1997, as discussed by Malina, 2005). American physicians diagnosed Lia with epilepsy. Her parents, on the other hand, explained her seizures in terms of the presence of powerful and evil spirits that no medical regimen could overcome. Medical practitioners did not explore these beliefs. Instead, they reported the continual "non-compliance" of Lia's parents. Ultimately, Lia died from her condition.

Lia Lee's case is presented as an example of how not to provide culturally sensitive care. The tragic outcome supports this view. It must also be acknowledged that Fadiman spent many hours learning about Lia's parents' beliefs and how they explained their decision not to follow the prescribed regimens—hours that the attending physicians did not have. Instead, they were faced initially with a child experiencing a *grand mal* seizure in their emergency department.

It has been argued convincingly that, when our psychological resources are taxed or under considerable time and performance pressure, we rely on a system of thinking that reduces effort and allows for fast response. This system, called simply "System 1," (Kahneman, 2011) is contrasted with "System 2," in which information is carefully considered and the temptation to jump quickly from a seemingly recognizable pattern to familiar conclusions is resisted. It is likely that culturally sensitive care requires System 2 thinking, and this can seem like a luxury at times in the demanding world of health care.

What Is Required to Ensure the Best Possible Health for All, Regardless of Culture?

Luxury or not, it is imperative that health professionals develop the ability to provide culturally appropriate care. Without it, time and resources are wasted. Practitioners blame patients for not responding well, and patients write off practitioners as being uninterested in who the patients are and what they really need. The Lee family's belief in evil spirits is only one of many ways culture is manifest. One's role within a family, one's view of authority figures, and one's diet are other examples. It is of no value to simply tell a hypertensive patient to relax about her home life if that person feels personally responsible for her family's welfare, and feels that welfare is threatened in some way.

Gaps can be created when practitioners from one culture try to provide care for people from other cultures. In fact, it has been argued that health care providers bring two cultures to the encounter—the one they grew up in and the medical culture in which they were trained. Both can feel very foreign to the patient. **Culturally competent care** reduces these gaps. It is easier to describe what culturally competent care intends to produce than to define it as a discrete entity. For example, in a report presented to Ottawa's Capital District Health, Rhymes and Brown (2005) present Cross et al.'s (1989) definition, calling cultural competence that which enables individuals, agencies, and systems to work effectively in cross-cultural situations. It involves first developing an understanding of cultural factors and then designing systems that effectively acknowledge those factors (Betancourt, Green, Carrillo, & Ananeh-Firempong, 2003).

Perhaps cultural competence is difficult to define because it constitutes much more than a set of discernible skills. It is more a way of thinking than a checklist. Rhymes and Brown (2005) refer to McNaughton-Dunn's (2002) assertion that the provision of culturally competent care requires a change in world view of the person learning to be culturally competent. It requires a sharing of power between practitioners and patients as members of "equal but different cultures" (Rhymes & Brown, 2005, p. 2). Viewed this way, the development of cultural competence is as much about the psychology of change as it is about learning. It begins with an ability to critically reflect on one's own culturally based assumptions about one's self and others. This is no easy task, requiring that the learner "be humble to the process of cultural awareness" (p. 2).

The development of this competence might be better construed as a journey than an end in itself. This is a journey from incompetence to competence, from cultural destructiveness to eventual cultural proficiency (Lecca, Quervala, Nunes, & Gonzales, 1998)— from thinking that a child's parents are being continually non-compliant to an understanding of why they believe there is no medicine that can conquer an evil spirit.

culturally competent care: care that enables individuals, agencies, and systems to work effectively in cross-cultural situations. It involves first developing an understanding of cultural factors and then designing systems that effectively acknowledge those factors. It begins with an ability to critically reflect on one's own culturally based assumptions about one's self and others.

One of the real challenges to the provision of culturally competent care is acknowledging that people belong to groups that help define them without invoking stereotypes. Checklists that tell a practitioner what people from a given culture "are like" are rarely helpful. They do not encourage the practitioner to strike a balance between understanding a person's group membership and his or her autonomy as a unique individual. Treating people as individuals with a cultural heritage requires more careful and effortful "System 2" thinking." It cannot rely on quickly drawn conclusions based on stereotypes or personal theories based on one's looks.

Betancourt et al. (2003) provide an explanation of culturally competent care that includes these clinical considerations, but that also presents higher levels within the health care system as being part of the provision of culturally competent care. At the organizational level, attention must be paid to hiring practices for administrators and health care workers. Patients who interact with people from cultures similar to their own can more easily make sense of the health care system and thrive within it. Barriers are created by complex structures within health care. These structures can be inhibiting for anyone, much less someone coming from another culture. Cultural difficulties can be reduced by the introduction of people who can help with navigation of the health care system. This would also include adequate language interpreter services. Of course, all of these improvements require resources, and our health care system is already stretched in that regard. At the same time, it may be that the introduction of a more culturally diverse health care work force and navigators for the system might save money in the long run.

THE HEALTH OF CANADA'S ABORIGINAL PEOPLES

Of all of the relationship between culture and health in Canada, none is more prominent than the health of our aboriginal peoples. In chapter 7, "Chronic and Life-Threatening Illnesses," we made specific reference to Aboriginal health issues as they pertained to diabetes and HIV/AIDS. In this section, we will explore a wider range of issues related to Aboriginal health. There are many inequities and serious challenges that are revealed by this exploration—indeed, far more than we could adequately cover here.

Who Are Canada's Aboriginal Peoples?

Canada's Aboriginal population is not homogeneous. In fact, the term *Aboriginal* refers to a variety of groups in Canada. The language that is used, both officially and colloquially, to describe these groups carries its own collection of connotations. Our language is derived from documents produced by Health Canada. These documents make reference to four groups under the general heading "Aboriginal": First Nations people, who include North American Indians registered under the Indian Act; North American Indians not registered; Métis people; and Inuit people (*The Need for an Aboriginal Health Institute in Canada*, 2003a). Some of the issues discussed under the heading of "Aboriginal Health" apply to all these groups. Some, however, do not. The population of Aboriginal groups is growing faster than the general population in Canada. The Aboriginal population is generally younger as a result. Thirty-eight percent of that population is under the age of 15, compared to 21 percent of Canada's general population. Many of the health challenges faced by our Aboriginal peoples, therefore, relate to youth.

We refer to Aboriginal Peoples in the plural for a reason. There is considerable diversity within the term "Aboriginal."
Boomer Jerritt/All Canada Photos/Alamy

Health Challenges

Remember that the health of all Canadians is affected considerably by social determinants of health. These include factors such as living conditions, education, and economics. Figure 10-2 lists prominent social determinants. In chapter 11, "Health Promotion," we discuss health inequities existing in Canada today. Many of these inequities relate to social determinants of health. Thus, social determinants go a long way to explain why the health of our Aboriginal population is considerably poorer than that of other segments. Figures from 2004 reveal that life expectancy for First Nations males is 7 years shorter than for the non-Aboriginal males and First Nations females live an average of 5 years less than their non-Aboriginal counterparts (Health Canada, 2004). General violence, physical abuse, and sexual abuse are more common in Aboriginal communities, as are accidental deaths and injury among children. Add to this list infectious diseases, such as tuberculosis, which is 10 times more prevalent in First Nations and Inuit populations (Health Canada, 2004). Further challenges are presented in the form of substance abuse, which members of Aboriginal communities recognize as a serious problem (*Literature Review: Evaluation Strategies in Aboriginal Substance Abuse Programs: A Discussion*, 2002).

All of these challenges are significant, though two have received increased attention because of their severity: children's health and diabetes. We looked at diabetes in the Aboriginal population in chapter 7 (refer to Box 7-1). Add to those statistics a University of Manitoba study showing that Type II diabetes is four times as prevalent among First Nations people in that province (Martens et al., 2002). Children's health is a particular concern in Aboriginal communities, where 50 percent of children live in poverty (*The Need for an Aboriginal Health Institute in Canada*, 2003). The good news is that infant mortality rates are declining in these communities, though they are still well above the Canadian average (*The Need for an Aboriginal Health Institute in Canada*, 2003). Injury and accident-related death rates are four times greater than for non-Aboriginal children. And suicide rates are significantly higher.

As we have mentioned, substance abuse is another major problem, though this varies depending upon which Aboriginal population is being studied. In some cases, general consumption of alcohol might be lower for a given group compared to the non-Aboriginal population; however, a concentrated percentage of that Aboriginal group might be drinking to excess (*Literature Review: Evaluation Strategies in Aboriginal Substance Abuse Programs: A Discussion*, 2002). Solvent use is a problem particular to youth. Recent data on solvent use is hard to come by, though studies in the mid-1980s conducted in Manitoba and Quebec revealed that 2 to 3 percent of Aboriginal youth were using solvents beyond an experimental level and their median age was 12 to 13 years (Layne, 1987).

Addressing the Challenges

What is being done to help our Aboriginal population meet their health challenges? This is not a problem that governments can simply "throw money at," although funding is certainly necessary. Rather, solutions will be found by building partnerships among government, our Aboriginal peoples, and Canada's population at large. These partnerships must work at the community level because the Aboriginal tradition is such that the well-being of the individual is rooted in the health of the community (*Volume III: Gathering Strength*, 1996). Many programs focused at the community level have been called for and initiated by such national organizations as the First Nations and Inuit Health Branch (FNIHB) and the Assembly of First Nations Health and Social Secretariat.

Another priority of the Assembly of First Nations is called Health Renewal, involving the building of a framework to provide sustainable and effective health services. This priority could be supported by trained paraprofessionals within these communities, and it must be ensured that their roles are clear and valued by other health professionals (Minore & Boone, 2002). Bruce Minore and Margaret Boone, from the Centre for Rural and Northern Health Research at Lakehead University, have studied the work of Aboriginal paraprofessionals working in the communities of Northern Ontario.

A study of these communities reminds us that our Aboriginal population lives in every possible setting within the country. Unlike their urban counterparts, Inuit and First Nations people in Northern Ontario often live in remote and small communities. For them, the challenges we discussed earlier in this chapter related to remote communities can be added to other cultural factors. Some people might have one nurse, with physicians and others flying in once a month or so. Other communities share one nurse, who works with paraprofessionals within these communities. These are local people who have received training at institutions such as Nunavut Arctic College. Originally, indigenous paraprofessionals fulfilled a variety of roles, including community health representative, mental health worker, and addiction and alcohol program worker (Minore & Boone, 2002). Today, they are limited to health promotion and prevention activities (Minore, Jacklin, Boon, & Cromarty, 2009).

According to Minore and Boone, the success of the paraprofessional model depends upon the establishment of role clarity and consistency for these workers, clarity that is harder to achieve given the limitations to their roles and concerns regarding liability (Minore et al., 2009). It also depends upon the attitudes of the health professionals who work in these communities. While training programs seem quite good, the reality is that, when paraprofessionals enter their jobs, they are often unsure of their exact roles. A good example concerns patient confidentiality. In some cases, in an attempt to adhere strictly to confidentiality, paraprofessionals not only do not discuss a case informally with members of the community, but also might fail to share important information with a health care professional (Minore & Boone, 2002). One of the keys here is the education of rural health care workers. They must be helped to develop an awareness of the roles played by Aboriginal paraprofessionals in order to appreciate their contributions and to help them remain as contributing members of the team.

By 2012, the federal government transferred all of its responsibilities, resources, and infrastructure for Aboriginal health in British Columbia to the newly formed First Nations

Health Authority (FNHA). Up to now, health care in B.C. has been overseen by six health authorities. The FNHA is the first health authority to be defined by its people rather than by geography. The FNHA will be primarily responsible for on-reserve health programs such as primary care and public health programs, while the other six health authorities will still be responsible for acute care of first nations people (Vogel, 2011). The rest of the country will be watching with interest to gauge the impact of this new health authority.

The principle belief behind this move is that Canada's Aboriginal people are better served by health programs and services that they control. The work of Aboriginal physicians such as Dr. Lindsay Crowshoe supports this belief. His work at the Elbow River Healing Lodge in Calgary demonstrates the benefits of having Aboriginal people feeling connected to the care provided (Crowshoe, 2012). This connection comes from having a say in care and being cared for by Aboriginal practitioners. Crowshoe points out that, in addition to the immediate health concerns that bring Aboriginal people to the Health Lodge, there is the ever-present challenge of **historical trauma**, that must be acknowledge. Cultures that have been exposed to mass trauma through such forces as war and colonization feel the health effects for generations (Sotero, 2006).

This brief exploration of Aboriginal health cannot do justice to the scope of the problems and the efforts being taken to address them. However, we hope that you can develop some appreciation for each, and for the reasons why we must continue our commitment to helping Canada's Aboriginal peoples improve their health and general well-being.

historical trauma: negative health effects of mass trauma such as war and colonization that can be experienced for generations.

HARM REDUCTION AS A TREATING AND PREVENTING ILLNESS AT THE POPULATION LEVEL

Chapter 6 explores a range of behaviours that can compromise our health. Examples include cigarette smoking, overeating, and substance misuse. For individuals, psychologists hope to find ways to help them avoid or stop these behaviours. At a population level, the challenges change somewhat. While it is noble and worthwhile to help individuals control health-compromising behaviours, it becomes very difficult, if not impossible, to eliminate these behaviours across entire populations. Instead, the strategy expands to include harm reduction.

The assumption behind **harm reduction strategies** is that a given health-compromising behaviour cannot be entirely eliminated from a population, so it is logical to work to reduce its harmful effects. Harm reduction is evidence-based activity that can take place at a range of levels—from individual to macroscopic. Whatever the scope, the goal is to reduce harm. Initiated officially in 1990, harm reduction has become a more pressing topic as the potential harms of such things as drug use intensify, including HIV/AIDS and hepatitis (Erickson, Riley, Cheung, & O'Hare, 1997). We will see in this section that psychology figures prominently in the world of harm reduction, from helping people adopt harm-reducing behaviours through to understanding and affecting public attitudes toward harm reduction.

harm reduction strategy: attempts to reduce the harmful effects of a behaviour when faced with the reality that the health-compromising behaviour cannot be eliminated from a population.

Psychologically, harm reduction strategies are non-judgemental in nature. Rather than pass judgment on a behaviour, the strategies are designed to reduce its harmful effects. Trust and compassion are also important psychological factors. Harm reduction rejects a "just world belief" (Lerner, 1980) defined as the belief that people always get what they deserve. Instead, proponents of harm reduction believe that comprehensive health services are a right for all (see MacNeil & Pauly, 2010).

Regarding public attitudes, it might be difficult for the public to accept that harm reduction strategies do not indicate endorsement of health compromising behaviours, especially those that are illegal (Single, 1995). Nor do such strategies indicate that the health care system is "giving up" on people engaging in these behaviours. In fact, the exact opposite is true. A needle distribution program for heroin users living on city streets does not endorse heroin use. Rather, it acknowledges that heroin is highly addictive and that certain populations are particularly vulnerable. By distributing clean, unused needles, the risk of disease transmission and the harm associated with heroin use is reduced.

But people keep using, and this exacerbates a clash between *pragmatic* and *moral* foundations for one's beliefs about how to best deal with drug use. The pragmatic view holds that, if a method yields positive results, it should be employed. A moralistic view counters that some methods are just not right, even if they do have statistics to back them.

It might help resolve the dichotomous nature of the debate here to acknowledge that programs such as needle distribution and safe injection sites are presented in combination with rehabilitation and counselling programs. As you will see when we discuss research in this area, well-planned harm reduction strategies help improve the health of populations, not just for those engaging in health compromising behaviours, but for all of us.

British Columbia Harm Reduction Strategies and Services, in conjunction with the B.C. Centre for Disease Control, coordinates a number of harm reduction programs. These include peer support programs for people who use substances, needle distribution programs, outreach and education programs to encourage safer behaviour, substitute therapies that substitute illegal heroin with legal alternatives such as prescription heroin or non-injection methadone, and supervised consumption facilities (http://www.bccdc.ca/prevention/HarmReduction/default.htm. Accessed November 6, 2012).

Reducing the Harm of Injection Drug Use

It has been estimated that the number of illicit drug injections per year in the province of British Columbia was 24 951 144 between 2004 and 2006 (Harvard, Hill, & Buxton, 2008). During that same time period, there were 5 382 933 needle and syringe units distributed per year. This means that just over 20 percent of the required units were distributed. These and other products are distributed in keeping with the World Health Organization's goal to prevent HIV and hepatitis C in the population of injection drug users. The need to improve this distribution rate is pressing. In B.C., it is believed that over 80 percent of injection drug users have hepatitis C (Patrick et al., 2001).

Needle distribution or, as it is also called, needle exchange has been practised with government funding across Canada for over 30 years (MacNeil & Pauly, 2010). It can take place in a number of ways. For example, a fixed location can be established, familiar to injection drug users. Also, needles can be distributed via more portable methods, such as from vans. Although it may seem reasonable to favour the portable methods because they attempt to take the needles to the users, in fact, there is evidence to suggest that the fixed sites are more effective. This was discovered when the only fixed site in a large Canadian city was closed down and replaced by a portable needle exchange program (MacNeil & Pauly, 2010). The fixed site was closed in response to complaints from neighbours regarding open drug use, loitering, and garbage. Attempts to find another location proved unsuccessful.

To assess the impact of the closure, data was collected for a 5-month period following the location's closure. MacNeil and Pauly used police records, needle distribution, and client contact records before and after the closure. They also conducted interviews and focus groups with users and service providers. Finally, they observed mobile outreach programs for needle distribution, which consisted of a van and further distribution of needles from it on bicycle and on foot. This outreach was augmented by further distribution programs.

The fixed site provided more than clean needles. It also handled requests for housing and clothing, made hospital and transportation referrals, and provided counselling and education. The provision of these services, as well as nurse-led care, was reduced significantly when the fixed site was closed. Needle exchange activity also dropped of significantly—needle distribution by 40 percent and needle recovery by over 70 percent. It is estimated that thousands of needles are going unaccounted for, with many being shared or reused by an individual.

The psychological factors involved here are readily apparent but difficult to resolve. Some people have negative attitudes toward needle exchange programs, especially those that become a fixed element of their neighbourhood. The complaints voiced by neighbours of the fixed site were real. Schools and daycare centres were in the vicinity. At the same time, MacNeil and Pauly discovered that loitering actually increased when the site was closed. Police calls to an area two streets away from the former site tripled in the first month after closure. The authors concluded that the closure caused a spreading out of drug use across a larger area. The goal here is to reduce the "we/they" nature of these interventions and work toward strategies that reduce harm for both users and others in the community.

THE PSYCHOLOGY OF VACCINATION

A number of times in this chapter, we have contrasted public belief with research evidence. It can be a worrisome contrast, because the two are sometimes at odds, and it is the health of the population that is at stake. Another important example is vaccination.

To start our exploration of the psychology of vaccination, it would help to harken back to our discussion of the immune system in chapter 3. You might recall the concept of specific immunity. This refers to the immune system's ability to remember and recognize a pathogen and then produce immune cells to deal with it. We return to this concept now because vaccination relies on specific immunity. By introducing a safe dosage of a pathogen, vaccines cause the body's immune system to develop a memory for the pathogen and be ready to proliferate specific immune cells should the disease be encountered in fuller dosage at a later time.

As straightforward as this might sound, and with considerable epidemiological evidence indicating that vaccines can be effective in maintaining health at the population level, there are those who oppose their use. In the United Kingdom, just over half of people surveyed, regardless of whether or not they worked in health care settings, indicated that they would get immunized against swine flu (H1N1). The survey was conducted by telephone at the height of a second peek of swine flu outbreak in 2009. Reasons for refusing the vaccination were consistent with elements of the Theory of Reasoned Action, discussed in chapter 1. Some people were not concerned about the consequences of getting swine flu. Others questioned the efficacy and safety of the vaccine (Rubin, Potts, & Michie, 2011). Similar results and explanations have been found for health car workers in Canada (Marentette & El-Masri, 2011).

In 2014, the Fraser Valley B.C. communities of Abbotsford, Agassiz, Harrison Hot Springs, and Hope experienced an outbreak of measles, attributed to low vaccination rates in these communities. The area saw over 200 cases of the highly contagious and serious disease for which children under the age of 5 are at greatest risk. Health officials in this area believe that the outbreak would have been even worse if not for the increase in immunization rates during the outbreak.

One reason for the more general opposition among the public to vaccination is the rare co-occurrence of serious illnesses with vaccination. Because these illnesses have tended to involve children, the cases have become prominent and influential in spite of large amounts of evidence supporting vaccination. The most widely publicized concern is that flu vaccines can cause autism in children. For example, celebrities such as Jim Carey and Jenny McCarthy attended anti-vaccination rallies in the wake of McCarthy's son being diagnosed with autism.

The possible link between vaccination and autism has not been proven, and research claiming supposed links has been discredited (Godlee, Smith, & Marcovitch, 2011). However, another association that does have some research evidence is the possible relationship between the swine flu vaccination and a neurological disorder called Guillain–Barré Syndrome. Immunization for H1N1 (swine) flu in 1976 was first associated with the onset of Guillain–Barré Syndrome (GBS) in the United State (Evans, Cauchemez, & Hayden, 2009). GBS is a rare nervous system disorder that can result in motor paralysis and sensory changes. People rarely die from GBS, but intensive care interventions might be required and recovery can be a long process. The 1976 story is well worth exploring, because it tells us important things about the psychology of vaccination and perceived threat in the population.

The 1976 swine flu immunization program in the United States followed a swine flu outbreak among soldiers at Fort Dix, New Jersey. The vaccine was trialed on 7000 volunteers, then rolled out to 45 million people. Three elderly people who received the vaccine died of unrelated causes, but it was a time of heightened sensitivity to infection disease in the United States, on the heals of the appearance of legionnaires disease, so increased attention was drawn to the program. In fact, the program was halted, not because of the three deaths, but because it was believed that the incidence of GBS had become greater than would normally be expected.

Analysis showed that GBS was occurring in unvaccinated people at a rate of about one per million. Among the vaccinated, rates varied between 5 and 12 per million, depending upon age (Nachamkin, Allos, & Ho, 1998). (Younger people were less likely to develop GBS.) While this does represent an increase in the relative rate of GBS, the absolute number of people affected is low. Nevertheless, results of this kind warrant further investigation, and so future flu vaccine programs were monitored.

These studies have looked at a range of flu vaccines, not just for swine flu. Many of these studies found no link between GBS and flu vaccines. Some, including one conducted in Canada (Juurlink et al., 2006), have discovered small increases in GBS incidence related to vaccination. To complicate matters, some studies have found a link

Jim Carey, daughter Jane, and Jenny McCarthy at anti-vaccination rally. National Post, September 21, 2009.
Gene Young/Splash News/ Newscom

between GBS and having the flu (Sivadon-Tardy, 2009; Stowe, Andrews, Wise, & Miller, 2009). Thus, the current belief is that the link between flu vaccination and GBS remains somewhat uncertain, but very likely low.

Surveillance studies that monitor vaccination programs for adverse events like GBS are important, but they do not always provide definitive evidence of the existence or absence of an association. Better evidence is provided by clinical trials in which participants are assigned to either the vaccine or non-vaccine condition. In these trials, no association has been found between GBS and flu vaccination.

When determining a course of action in terms of the health of the population, risks associated with options must be compared. In other words, it is not enough to identify a very low risk of GBS in vaccination programs. This risk must be compared to what is likely to occur if there is no vaccination program. The collective burden of widespread influenza is probably greater than that of rare cases of GBS, but decisions based on such comparisons are still not easy.

Evidence regarding the efficacy and risks of vaccination is drawn more from epidemiology than from individual stories. The most convincing example of such epidemiology concerns smallpox. Once a serious worldwide disease, very widespread tracking of the disease combined with huge vaccination efforts led to the eradication of smallpox by 1977.

In Canada, smallpox vaccination was established on a widespread basis around 1940. In the 40 years prior to that, over 3400 cases had been documented. By 1946, smallpox had been virtually eliminated from the country. One suspected case appeared in Nova Scotia in 1949, thought to be brought in from the United States, and the last known case in the country was in 1962, brought to Canada from Brazil. The story of smallpox helped establish favourable public attitudes toward vaccination.

HEALTH AND THE BUILT ENVIRONMENT

By studying the health patterns of populations, we come to the clear and unsurprising conclusion that some populations are generally healthier than others. We have seen that this can be due to government policy, medical interventions, poverty, culture, and other demographic factors. For each of these, we move to the outer circles of the social ecological model. Another important predictor of differences in population health is where those populations live.

We have already looked at this in terms of general geography—urban versus rural versus remote settings. There is another important way to look at this, however—based not on geography, but on architecture, engineering, and planning. This is the stuff of what is called *the built environment*, and it plays a major role in our health and well-being.

Think for a moment about where you grew up, not in terms of whether it was urban, suburban, rural, or remote, but how it was built. Were there a lot of people in your neighbourhood? Was your school nearby? How about other places, like a park or a store? Did you walk or ride a bike to these places? Could you walk or ride your bike to most of your friends' houses? Or did you live in a suburban area where there were lots of cul-de-sacs, major roads without sidewalks, and large distances to cover to access the important things in your life?

Today, we know that the answers to these questions are related to our health. For some people, even though they may have grown up in a beautiful, affluent suburb, if they had to drive everywhere, their health was being compromised.

The things we will consider in this section relate closely to topics we discuss in other chapters. In chapter 5, "Health and Physical Activity," we talk about the health benefits of exercise, as well as psychological factors that affect whether people start and stay with

This neighbourhood has a high walkability factor.
Driendl Group/Getty images

exercise programs. In chapter 6, "Health-Compromising Behaviours," we talk about the prevalence and dangers of obesity, and about psychological and social factors that increase one's risk of being obese. In this section, we look at built environmental factors that, in some ways, over-ride psychological factors. Put simply, if some degree of exercise is required to fulfill basic needs such as shopping and seeing other people, then exercise is much more likely to happen, and obesity is less likely to occur.

The built environment, as the term suggests, consists of the roads, parks, and buildings in our lived worlds. These environments differ on a few clear dimensions, and these differences correlate with general health measures and, in particular, with obesity. In fact, some neighbourhoods might be **obesogenic**, which means their design increases the likelihood that residents will be obese. The most important health-related dimensions of a neighbourhood are **proximity, connectivity, density, and land use mix**. Each of these dimensions predicts the likelihood that people will choose non-motorized transport—most likely walking or cycling. Put simply, the more people walk or cycle, the less likely they are to be obese.

Proximity is defined as the straight-line distance between two points. Connectivity refers to just how close to that straight line you can travel on. It is determined by things like street design and sidewalk availability. Density is the ratio of dwellings to land area. Land use mix refers to the number of different types of use featured in an area, from residential to office to entertainment and so on (Saelens, Sallis, & Frank, 2003).

In chapter 5, we talk about exercise of a somewhat more intense nature—running or playing sports, for example. Here, we are talking about mild to moderate exercise. For this kind of exercise, the benefit isn't in its intensity so much as it is in its constancy. People who live in well-designed neighbourhoods walk or cycle virtually every day. It becomes their way of getting around. In this way, the built environment shapes their behaviour and their bodies.

With this in mind, we can see how the four dimensions come into play. Proximity refers to the distance to be travelled. If you are going to have coffee with a friend, you are more likely to walk or cycle to a coffee shop that is close by. As simple as this sounds, there are some neighbourhood designs that do not encourage walking even though that coffee shop is quite close. This is because the pathways for walking or cycling are not connected. Have you ever stayed in a hotel on the outskirts of a large city? Could you see the coffee shop or restaurant from your hotel but you needed to cross a freeway to get to it? This would be an example of close proximity but poor connectivity.

obesogenic neighbourhood: neighbourhood designed in such a way as to increase the likelihood its inhabitants will be obese.

proximity, density, connectivity, and land use mix: factors that are used to determine the healthiness of a built environment.

Calculating Your Neighbourhood's Walkability Score

As you read about the built environment, did you wonder about your current neighbourhood? Now, it is possible to conduct a quick assessment of your neighbourhood in terms of how obesogenic or healthy it is, thanks to the work of Dr. Larry Frank at the University of British Columbia and colleagues in the United States (Frank et al., 2010). To do this, researchers can calculate a neighbourhood's "walkability score." As the term suggests, this is a numerical measure of how easy it is to walk to things in your neighbourhood. The walkability of a neighbourhood is calculated by summing measures of residential density, mixed land use, connectivity, and retail floor area ratio. When the boundaries of a neighbourhood are defined, each of these factors can be calculated. For example, residential density is the ratio of residential dwellings to the land area dedicating to residences. High-rise apartments obviously feature more dwellings per piece of residential property. Land use is calculated by counting the number of units that are residential, retail, entertainment, office, or institutional in purpose. The more categories featured, the higher the mixed-use score. Connectivity is defined as the ratio of true intersections (at least three-way) and the land area of the neighbourhood. Finally, the ratio of retail floor area to retail land area indicates whether how much space is dedicated for things like parking lots and building setbacks from the street. The more land used, the better for walkability because pedestrian access tends to be better in this case. When adding up these factors, connectivity was given greater weight because it has been shown to exude greater influence on whether people choose to walk to destinations.

A neighbourhood's walk score uses these calculations and coverts the result to a score out of 100. You can find out your neighbourhood's walk score by visiting http://www.walkscore.com/ and entering your address.

Regarding density, there was a time when we might have thought that densely populated neighbourhoods were unhealthy, claustrophobic, and crime-ridden. Our thinking has changed dramatically in that regard. Neighbourhoods are now increasing density by putting apartments above shops or building "lane houses" in large backyards. This is because density increases the likelihood that people will walk or cycle. Think again about that friend you went to coffee with. If she lives a few blocks away, or on the same street, she will walk to your house and then to the coffee shop. In a sprawling suburb, on the other hand, there is probably at least one car ride involved in such an outing.

Finally, putting the coffee shop in the neighbourhood means that the land use is mixed. There is residential housing and commercial properties. The mix can be increased further by including theatres, fitness facilities, offices, and parks. The more mixed the land use, the less the proximity to needed amenities. Until recently, suburbs were considered attractive if they were designed for single use. Developments contained houses only. Everyone living in the houses then went to large malls to shop.

CHAPTER SUMMARY

- Use the Social Ecological Model to expand upon your understanding of the psychosocial approach to health.

    The social ecological model provides an expanded analysis of factors that affect health. It starts with the individual and then expands to encompass family and friends (the interpersonal), school and other institutions, the community, and public policy from government.

- List and explain common social determinants of health.

Social determinants of health include factors found in the outer circles of the social ecological model.

Factors include such things as culture, income, social status, friendship networks, and the physical environment.

■ Define vulnerability as it applies to health, and provide examples of factors that increase vulnerability.

Vulnerable populations are those form whom social determinants of health are not favourable, making them more susceptible to health problems.

Examples of vulnerable populations include the homeless, those living in remote locations, and those of lower socioeconomic status.

■ Discuss ways in which culture relates to health, and explain what is meant by culturally sensitive health care.

Culture will influence our interpretation of physical sensations, our perceived roles when we are in need of care, and our decisions about how to pursue care. It will also influence our day-to-day behaviours that affect the maintenance of our health. It will even influence what we think good health is.

Culturally competent care is required. This involves first developing an understanding of cultural factors and then designing systems that effectively acknowledge those factors.

■ Identify the major health challenges facing Canada's Aboriginal peoples, and discuss ways in which these challenges can be overcome.

Aboriginal people experience significantly more health problems than do non-Aboriginal Canadians, from diabetes to HIV/AIDS to shorter life expectancy.

One approach to reducing these health disparities is to give more control to Aboriginal peoples for their own health care. One recent example of an attempt to do this is British Columbia's First Nations Health Authority.

■ Define harm reduction, and provide examples of this public health approach.

The assumption behind harm reduction strategies is that a given health-compromising behaviour cannot be entirely eliminated from a population, so it is logical to work to reduce its harmful effects.

Examples include needle distribution programs, peer support programs, and substitute therapies for heroin addiction.

■ Cite historical and modern evidence to help explain public attitudes toward vaccination.

Positive attitudes toward vaccination were shaped by the success of vaccination programs to combat smallpox. These were successful to the point that smallpox as deemed eradicated as of 1977.

Negative attitudes have been created by unproven concerns that vaccination can cause autism, and evidence that, in rare cases, Guillain–Barré Syndrome has been associated with swine flu vaccine.

■ Identify the elements of neighbourhood design that can affect our health, with specific reference to obesity.

The key elements of the built environment that can affect the activity levels of the people living in them are proximity, connectivity, density, and mixed land use.

Chapter 11
Health Promotion

kentoh/Shutterstock

Learning Objectives

After studying this chapter, you will be able to:

1. define health promotion.
2. explain how health promotion has developed in Canada.
3. apply the concepts of self-care and mutual aid to the goals of health promotion.
4. apply the health belief model and the theory of reasoned action to the goals of health promotion.
5. apply theories of social psychology with the goal of improving the effectiveness of health promotion programs.
6. explain the precede-proceed model.
7. list the standards by which health promotion programs are evaluated.

In September of her grade 12 year, Rachel's school held a TADD Day (Teens Against Drinking and Driving). She had never heard of TADD, so she went to see what it was all about. Besides, most of her friends said they were going. Rachel took an "Alcohol Knowledge Inventory Test" and discovered that she knew less about the effects of alcohol than she thought. She learned the TADD slogan: "Keep Dreams Alive—Don't Drink and Drive." And she learned that other students were hoping to start a TADD Chapter in her school.

When the TADD group did get started, Rachel decided to join after learning that the risk of being involved in a fatal crash went up astronomically when driving impaired, and that teens were particularly vulnerable in this regard. The TADD group focused on four elements: attitudes about alcohol and drug use, the act of driving while impaired, the consequences of that act, and alternatives to impaired driving.

Rachel and her friends may well be concerned about impaired driving. According to Mothers Against Drunk Driving, motor vehicle crashes are the leading cause of death for people between the ages of 15 and 25, and alcohol is considered to be a factor in 45 percent of those crashes. Also, though 16- to 25-year-olds made up 13 percent of the Canadian population in 2006, they accounted for 33 percent of all alcohol-related crash deaths.

We could try to reduce these numbers through strict legislation and law enforcement, and we would likely see some positive effect. However, there would be a greater impact felt if school programs such as TADD could become widespread. In this program, the population involved, in this case adolescents, takes some responsibility for addressing a health-related problem. They do the work to change attitudes and behaviour, with the ultimate goal of affecting health. This is the essence of health promotion, and it is a very important way for populations to get healthy and stay healthy.

While many definitions of health promotion have been put forward, most refer to strategies intended to maintain or improve the health of large populations. The World Health Organization (WHO) defines **health promotion** simply as "the process of enabling people to increase control over, and to improve, their health" (1986). Yet even with this seemingly straightforward definition, health promotion takes many forms—from smoking-cessation programs to patient education, public awareness campaigns, and political activism—and this makes it difficult to state in concrete terms just what health promotion is (Ontario Health Promotion e-Bulletin, 2006).

health promotion: strategies intended to maintain or improve the health of large populations.

Health promotion strategies, such as TADD, are often undertaken at a federal level of government. They are, therefore, usually very large, making their effectiveness difficult to measure directly. Furthermore, the challenges inherent in attempting to change attitudes and behaviour on such a large scale are daunting. Yet, governments must persevere despite these difficulties, because effective health promotion is essential to our well-being.

Health promotion is also practised at an international level. The WHO Health Promotion Department uses political and sociological approaches to try to improve the health of the world's citizens. A good example of one of their initiatives is the *Mega Country Network*. This network attempts to affect health worldwide by involving the world's most populous countries. The program includes 11 countries with populations of 100 million or more, accounting for more than 60 percent of the world's population (e.g., see www.who.int/school_youth_health/mega/en/). It includes such goals as the promotion of healthy diets and physical activity and the elimination of tobacco use.

Canada has played an active role in the WHO health promotion initiatives and has developed its own health promotion strategy. Here we begin by looking at the development of this work in Canada. This should provide you with a general sense of what health promotion entails.

CANADA AS A WORLDWIDE LEADER IN HEALTH PROMOTION

Canadian governments have actually been in the business of health promotion since the 1700s. Back then, the main task was regulatory in nature, coming up with regulations regarding sanitation and rules of operation for hospitals. In the early 1900s, once these regulations were firmly in place, the focus was shifted to educating the general public about the value of proper sanitation (Badgley, 1994).

In the first half of the 1900s, provincial health promotion programs were started in Ontario (1921), Manitoba (1929), Quebec (1943), and Newfoundland (1949). National programs followed—for example, *ParticipAction,* aimed at increasing Canadians' activity levels (started in 1971); the *Hole in the Fence* program, to curtail drug use (started in 1973); and *Dialogue on Drinking* (started in 1976).

Other examples of health promotion programs in Canada include the Aboriginal Head Start Program On Reserve (AHSOR), Aboriginal Head Start in Urban and Northern Communities (AHSUNC), Community Action Program for Children (CAPC), and the many other programs offered to all Canadians by the Public Health Agency of Canada—such as Stairway to Health, which encourages people to take the stairs rather than the elevator when at work.

In Canada, successful health promotion has been a clearly stated goal of federal governments since at least the mid-1970s. The kick-start came in 1974 from, then Minister of Health and Welfare, Marc Lalonde's paper, *A New Perspective on* the Health of Canadians. In it, he identified lifestyle as an important factor in health and well-being and, as such, an important target for health promotion and education.

In 1986, then Minister of Health and Welfare, Jake Epp published *Achieving Health for All: A Framework for Health Promotion* (Epp, 1986). In it, Epp referred to the World Health Organization's definition of health promotion and applied it to Canada. Most importantly, in that paper Epp presented a very useful framework for health promotion.

This framework is given in Table 11-1. Its categories sum up what health promotion is all about. Note the scope of the goals; everyone in the country should find some

Table 11-1 Canada's Framework for Health Promotion: Achieving Health for All

Health Challenge	Reducing inequities	Increasing prevention	Enhancing coping
Health Promotion Mechanism	Self-care	Mutual aid	Healthy environments
Implementation Strategy	Fostering participation	Strengthening community services	Coordinating healthy public policy

Source: Epp J. (1986). Achieving health for all: A framework for health promotion. *Canadian Journal of Public* Health, 77, 393–430. Reproduced with the permission of the Minister of Public Works and Government Services Canada, 2010.

relevance in the framework. Note also the implications regarding locus of responsibility. All health promotion programs place the primary responsibility for good health on the individual rather than on medical staff or medical facilities.

Consistent with this emphasis on personal responsibility is the World Health Organization's reference to control in its definition of health promotion. Also note that self-care and mutual aid are cited as health promotion mechanisms in the Canadian framework. In other words, one goal of health promotion is to encourage people to look after themselves. Another is to encourage them to look after each other. A cynical view of these goals might suggest that they represent ways in which the government is shirking its responsibility to look after us. The reply to that cynicism is that there are limits to how much a government can do to look after its citizens, and having personal agency over one's health is, in itself, healthy.

In fact, some authors have argued that, if health promotion is to be truly effective, it must be based on a social movement rather than a government edict (Labonte, 1990; O'Neill, Rootman, & Pederson, 1994). In other words, the real promoters of healthy choices must be the general public. For example, we know we are getting somewhere in terms of health promotion when parents won't start the car until every child's seatbelt is fastened. Another example of success can be found in the number of community-initiated programs that have been started independent of federal or provincial mandates.

Labonte (1987) provides a three-level framework for successful community-oriented health promotion. His analysis provides a useful taxonomy of health promotion and is very reminiscent of the biopsychosocial approach we introduced in chapter 1.

The first level identified by Labonte is **medical**. This level of health promotion is disease-based and the goal is disease treatment. For example, a community might develop a program to help people recover from heart attacks or devote funding to finding a cure for cancer. The second level deals with **public health**. This level is behaviour-based and the goal is disease prevention. A good example of a behaviour-based intervention would be the promotion of safe sex, or anti-drinking-and-driving programs. The third level is **socioenvironmental**. At this level, the orientation is toward social change and public health policy. Examples include such things as legislation to reduce poverty or school board policies to provide lunches for school children.

The second and third levels of Labonte's model are concerned with **social determinants of health**. These include such factors as income and social status, social support networks, education, employment/working conditions, personal health practices and coping skills, healthy child development services, gender, and culture (Public Health Agency of Canada, 2011. Retrieved on November 2, 2014, from http://www.phac-aspc.gc.ca/ph-sp/determinants/index-eng.php#What). There is considerable evidence to indicate that these determinants have a greater impact on our population's health than does medical science (International Centre for Health and Society, 2003).

Of course, one of the goals of health promotion at the governmental level is to save the governments money on health expenditures. In Canada, where health care is socialized, total health expenditures reached $207 billion in 2012 (Canadian Institute for Health Information, 2012a). This works out to $5948 per capita. When we consider that a great deal of that money is spent on treating conditions that are preventable, we can see why health promotion is important from a fiscal as well as a medical perspective.

People who study health at the sociological level of the biopsychosocial approach will argue that saving money and saving lives are often accomplished by the same strategies. These strategies focus on prevention more than cure, and they feature messages that are intended to affect self-care behaviour, usually through attitude change. We now take a closer

medical level of health promotion: the orientation is disease-based and the goal is disease treatment.

public health level of health promotion: the orientation is behaviour-based and the goal is disease prevention.

socioenvironmental level of health promotion: the orientation is toward social change and public health policy.

social determinants of health: factors such as housing, employment, socioeconomic status, and food availability that affect the health of populations.

look at Canada's health promotion framework to develop an understanding of what forms these strategies can take.

The Goals of Health Promotion in Canada

In chapter 1, we traced the major topics of health psychology as they have developed over the years. As we work through Canada's framework for health promotion, you will see that a number of these same topics receive attention. Look for potential applications of research on coping, social support, and stress reduction as examples. You will also see that the level of emphasis is far broader than the purely biological. In keeping with the biopsychosocial approach, you will find elements in the framework related to individual psychology (e.g., self-care), sociology (e.g., strengthening community health services), and geography (e.g., healthy environments).

Health Challenges   When Canadians think of their health care system, they are more likely to think of its equity than its inequity. It is, after all, a system designed to promote and provide equal access for all. However, the truth is that inequities exist and they pose a challenge for the Canadian health care system. These inequities may be based on many factors, including differences in geography, culture, age, education, income, or labour-force status. For example, fewer than 6 percent of people in the highest-income bracket in Canada rate their health as only fair or poor compared to 27 percent in the lowest income group (Tremblay, Ross, & Berthelot, 2002). These income-related disparities also apply to infant mortality rates and life expectancy (Wilkins, Berthelot, & Ng, 2002). Significant inequities also exist between Aboriginal and non-Aboriginal communities. A study of Aboriginal people living off reserves showed their self-reported health to be poorer than that of a non-Aboriginal population matched for socioeconomic level and health behaviours (Tjepkema, 2002).

The debate over the introduction of privatized health care options often involves issues of equity. Most Canadians would like to see surgical wait lists shortened, and one way to do that is allowing those willing to pay to enter a separate system, taking them out of the general wait list, and providing them with more timely care. However, will this produce a two-tiered system in which those who can afford the private option receive the care they need while others do not? This debate is playing itself out in the courts, with cases such as the one brought to the Quebec Supreme Court by Dr. Jacques Chaoulli, a family physician in Montreal, and his patient George Zeliotis (*Chaoulli vs. the Attorney General of Quebec*). They argued that Mr. Zeliotis should not have to endure the painful wait for hip surgery because the province of Quebec (like other provinces) does not allow people to use private health insurance to pay for health services. After having their case turned down at the provincial level, Chaoulli and Zeliotis appealed to the Supreme Court of Canada. The Court ruled in favour by a vote of four to three. The outcomes of cases like these will shape the future of Canada's health care system and, subsequently, the health promotion strategies that accompany it.

Changing demographics provide another challenge for Canadian health care. As a population, an increasing percentage of us are in older age categories. We need to know about the ways in which our health needs change as we age (Chen & Wilkins, 1998). Age-related health concerns are not restricted to seniors, however. We know that our adolescent population has its own set of health promotion issues as well. Central among these are risk-related behaviours, such as cigarette smoking (Chen & Millar, 1998). It is the job of health promotion to influence these behaviours. Another pressing age-related problem in Canada is childhood obesity. For children aged 5 to 11, 19 percent of boys and 6 percent of girls are obese (Statistics Canada, 2012b).

Does Income Matter When It Comes to Health?

When it comes to health promotion research, Canada is a world leader. The primary sources of data for this research are the National Population Health Surveys. Other large national databases are also used, such as the Canadian Human Mortality Data Base and the Canadian Community Health Survey.

Researchers using the Canadian Human Mortality Data Base and census data from 1971 to 1996 have been able to assess income-based differences in mortality across the country. Causes of death were analyzed using international coding standards, though residents of long-term care facilities were excluded because census data that would indicate household income level do not apply well to institutions.

Income was divided into five equal categories, called *quintiles,* from richest to poorest. In these categories, total number of deaths and deaths by various causes were calculated. Using this methodology, it is possible to track changes in mortality rates for various groups over time. For example, researchers discovered that income-related disparities in life expectancy diminished by well over 1 year for both men and women between 1971 and 1996. Also, infant mortality rates for Canada's highest income bracket have dropped from 10.2 infants per 1000 births in 1971 to 4.0 in 1996. In the poorest quintile, infant morality has dropped over the same period from 20 to 6.4 per 1000 births. You can see some important trends here. First, there has been a significant drop in infant mortality rates overall. Second, that drop has been greater among those in the lowest quintile while those in the top quintile still have better numbers (Wilkins et al., 2002).

The nature of people's occupations can be another source of health-related inequity. This is due, in part, to the differences in stress levels associated with various jobs (Wilkins & Beaudet, 1998). We also know that certain risk-related behaviours are more common among people in particular occupations. For example, in 1994 and 1995, 43 percent of people working in construction, transportation, and mining smoked cigarettes daily. By comparison, only 18 percent of people in the so-called white-collar occupations smoked every day (Gaudette, Richardson, & Huang, 1998). In 2011, it was estimated that over 2.9 million non-smoking Canadians were exposed regularly to second-hand smoke (see Physicians for a Smoke-Free Canada, 2012).

Health Promotion Mechanisms

How can we best use health promotion strategies to meet Canada's health challenges laid out in the framework in Table 11-1? The framework provides three answers: (1) We must be encouraged to look after ourselves, (2) we must be encouraged to look after each other, and (3) we must make our environments healthier by reducing pollution, improving safety, and reducing inequities.

As we review these health promotion mechanisms, notice again where the *locus of responsibility* is placed—squarely on the shoulders of the citizen. Remember that this is a key assumption of the health promotion process. Spending money to encourage people to look after themselves rather than having the government look after them costs considerably less and results in better quality of life. It has been estimated that obesity alone costs the Canadian health care system more than $4.3 billion a year. Inactivity costs a whopping $5.3 billion (Katzmarzyk & Janssen, 2004). Imagine the savings in money and the reduction of health problems if at least some of those people could be convinced to manage their diets in a healthier way.

Hence the rationale for an emphasis on **self-care**. Self-care refers to such things as exercise, diet, risk behaviours, voluntary screening, and regular medical checkups. Effective health promotion programs have measurable effects on these behaviours and, consequently, the general health of Canadians.

self-care: behaviours such as exercise, diet, voluntary screening, and regular medical checkups that people engage in to promote their health.

Utilization of effective screening programs is a form of self-care. In the late 1940s, the province of British Columbia became one of the first places in the world to introduce regular screening for cervical cancer (Wardle & Pope, 1992). The test used in this screening is called a **Pap test (or Pap smear)**. When compared to screening tests for other kinds of cancer, the Pap test is considered to be among the most effective. By *effective*, we mean that it is an accurate early detection strategy that has significantly helped reduce cervical cancer mortality rates. The death rate from cervical cancer has declined by almost 50 percent since the Pap test was introduced. The current survival rate is estimated to be 74 percent over 5 years (Public Health Agency of Canada, 2009. Retrieved on November 2, 2014, from http://www.phac-aspc.gc.ca/cd-mc/cancer/cervical_cancer_figures-cancer_du_col_uterus-eng.php). However, women between the ages of 40 and 60, who are more at risk for cervical cancer than are their younger counterparts, have Pap test participation rates of about 75 percent (Canadian Partnership Against Cancer, 2011). So there are still many women who are not benefitting from testing.

The Canadian Pap test data illustrates a truism in health promotion—the work never ends. To be sure, there is tangible success; the majority of women in Canada do have Pap tests. Between 2006 and 2008, 74 percent of women between the ages of 20 and 69 had received a Pap test in the previous 3 years (Forte, Lockwood, McLachlin, Fekete, & Bryant, 2012).

The issue of smoking cessation also fits in the self-care category. In spite of what we know about the dangers of cigarette smoking, health promotion in this particular area of self-care runs into problems brought on by the social pressure and addiction that accompany smoking. Attempts to simply frighten people away from cigarettes have been discouragingly unsuccessful (Becker & Janz, 1987; Sutton & Eiser, 1984). The relative ineffectiveness of this approach obviously makes health promotion more difficult. Parading grim statistics or blackened lung tissue in front of people isn't enough to make them avoid smoking.

The good news is that smoking is on the decline in Canada, even among youth aged 15 to 19. In 1999, 28 percent of this age group smoked. By 2008, that number had dropped to 15 percent (Health Canada, 2010b). Even with this trend, though, we have a long way to go with health promotion in this area, especially considering the fact that most smokers start when they are young. Programs must involve much more than simple appeals to fear. Later in this chapter, we will look more closely at the use of fear appeals and what must be added to make them effective.

Improving self-care among citizens is a fundamental objective of any health promotion program. But because people do not live in isolation from one another, in addition to looking after ourselves we must also look after each other. We have a responsibility to family, friends, loved ones, and for that matter, society as a whole when it comes to health and safety. This responsibility is highlighted in the Canadian framework by the promotion mechanism called **mutual aid**.

A large body of literature in health psychology supports the framework's inclusion of mutual aid as an important promotion mechanism. The general conclusion of this literature is that it is healthy to have other people around (for a review, see Suls & Wallston, 2003). Mortality rates are lower in communities featuring a high level of social integration; close-knit communities are healthier.

Health psychologists are very interested in **social support**—that collection of interpersonal resources we have at our disposal to help us avoid or cope with difficult times in our lives. Social support is remarkably beneficial. Research indicates that strong support systems affect a number of health indicators, including how long a person can expect to live (Ross & Mirowsky, 2002).

In this book, we refer often to social support. It is an important resource when coping with stress, which we discussed in detail in chapter 2. Also, as we have mentioned, social support is a critical factor in people's ability to cope with serious illness, a topic we looked at in chapter 7.

It is important to know that social support doesn't always "just happen." Also, some people benefit from it more than others do. And social support comes in a number of different forms, some of which are easier to promote than others. We turn now to factors that affect the amount of support a person might receive, in an attempt to determine specific goals of health promotion strategies in the area of mutual aid.

Perhaps the most important point to make at the outset of this exploration is that social support is related to other elements of Canada's health promotion framework—most notably *reducing inequities*. For example, seniors who live on low incomes have less support than their more affluent counterparts. We also know that, as people get older, their number of unmet needs increases in terms of health-related social assistance (Chen & Wilkins, 1998).

To understand how health promotion can be used to help reduce these inequities, we must divide social support into two general types, based on the source of the support. First, there is **naturally occurring support**. This is the support we get from friends, relatives, co-workers, and others in our own social networks. If you have just had triplets, you might have friends or family over to help out with meals or household chores, or to look after the babies so you can get some sleep. This would be an example of naturally occurring support.

The other kind of support is called **agency-provided support**. This is support that is provided by agencies and organizations formed to fill the void when naturally occurring support is either lacking or unavailable. Imagine that you had those triplets just after moving to a new city where you didn't know a soul. You might be relieved to find that there was a support group for parents of multiple births in that city. This would be a group made up of people like you who help each other and find community resources to provide further help.

When we study social support in the context of serious illness, we find that many people who are seriously ill don't have many people "like them" who share their illness. For example, wives of prostate cancer patients can be loving and extremely supportive, but they can't have had prostate cancer. For this reason, prostate cancer support groups are popular among men who want information and empathy that can come only from other patients. This is another important reason for agency-provided support.

What is the main job of health promotion here? In terms of mutual aid, health promotion campaigns must encourage the creation of support groups and attendance at them. This is especially true for segments of our population in which support is less available, as well as for people whose ability to cope can be improved by spending time with others who have similar illnesses or other health problems.

We have just seen that social support can be categorized in terms of its source. Social support can also be categorized by its type (for an application, see Cardenas, 2006). For example, we can receive **practical support**, sometimes called *tangible support,* which includes help with the demands of daily living—getting meals, going to medical appointments, mowing the lawn, and so on. Also, there is **informational support**, which could include such things as being told about treatment options, typical recovery times from treatment or injury, or what to do to speed recovery. Finally, there is **emotional support**. This is provided by people who take the time to understand our fears and frustrations, who help calm us during anxious times, who help bring our moods up, or who distract us from our worries.

When we know the types of support that people need, we can do a better job of providing that support. Imagine how you would respond if you found out that a close friend

naturally occurring support: the support we obtain from friends, relatives, co-workers, and others in our own social networks.

agency-provided support: social support provided by agencies and organizations that have been formed to fill the void when naturally occurring support is either lacking or unavailable.

practical support: help with the demands of daily living, such as getting meals and rides to the doctor.
informational support: the provision of information such as treatment options or typical recovery times from a treatment or injury.
emotional support: support provided by people who take the time to understand our fears and frustrations, who help calm us during anxious times, who help bring our moods up, or distract us from our worries.

had just been diagnosed with cancer. You might know exactly what to do. On the other hand, you might have no experience with receiving this kind of news and so feel awkward. Do you call your friend right away or do you wait? If you call, what do you say? What should you do? What can you do to help? These are difficult questions that can paralyze us.

If you knew that people diagnosed with cancer need practical, informational, and emotional support, you might be better able to answer those difficult questions and provide support. Perhaps your friend needs a ride to an appointment. Maybe her kids need rides to school. Or perhaps there is something your friend needs to know, and you might be in a position to find out. In terms of emotional support, maybe you just need to be there to listen. The point is that we can use health promotion to educate people about these ways of providing support. Furthermore, we can promote the clear benefits of providing this support. In chapter 7, you found data from studies proving that mutual aid in the form of social support is of tremendous benefit to people with serious illnesses. For now, it is important to know that good health promotion programs can increase the likelihood that such support is forthcoming and that it will be effective by ensuring that it matches people's needs (Reynolds, 2001).

In examining Canada's health promotion framework, you will see that mutual aid isn't the only element for which social support is relevant. Consider also the two implementation strategies of *fostering public participation* and *strengthening community health services*. While these strategies clearly require the involvement of professionals from a variety of segments of the health care system, they also require the participation of the general public. Support groups obviously grow out of public participation, and they are commonly offered through community health service facilities.

In this section, we have used Canada's health promotion framework to provide some examples of the challenges faced by people working in health promotion. The number of health promotion programs that could be mounted in a country as vast and varied as Canada is virtually infinite. However, by using the framework, we can consolidate this number to a very manageable set of goals. We must find ways to promote self-care and mutual aid, and we must reduce health-related inequities. These goals are not unique to Canada. Indeed, they are common to health promotion programs worldwide.

USING PSYCHOLOGICAL PRINCIPLES TO PROMOTE HEALTHY LIVING

Now that we know what the main goals and challenges are for health promotion in Canada, we will turn to the ways psychology can be used to help achieve these goals. In this section, we will draw on the major theories of health psychology that we introduced in chapter 1. We will also look closely at theories taken from social psychology.

Prominent Theories in Health Psychology Applied to Health Promotion

Much of health promotion is targeted at people's thinking. The assumption here is that one way to change behaviour is to change the beliefs relating to that behaviour. From chapter 1, you will recall that this line of reasoning is consistent with the **health belief model**, the **theory of reasoned action**, and the **theory of planned behaviour**.

These theories share two important elements: (1) the importance of people's beliefs regarding their vulnerability to a threat and (2) the effectiveness of a given course of

health belief model: analyzes health behaviour in terms of the belief that a health threat exists and the belief that a given course of action will affect the threat.

theory of reasoned action: a theory that behaviour is preceded by intention, and that our intention is influenced by beliefs about the behaviour and subjective norms.

theory of planned behaviour: behaviour is preceded by intention and that our intention is influenced not only by subjective norms and beliefs about the efficacy of the behaviour, but also by the belief that one is actually capable of performing the behaviour.

action to reduce that threat. In addition, it is important that people place a high value on their health. Because these beliefs and values are important to health-related behaviour, many health promotion programs are designed specifically to affect them.

Health promotion programs, then, must provide information regarding the likelihood that someone will suffer a health problem (vulnerability information) and advice on how one can reduce that likelihood (information regarding efficacy of preventive behaviours).

The theory of reasoned action and the theory of planned behaviour both acknowledge that people weigh the potential *costs* and *gains* of a given behaviour before adopting it. With this knowledge in mind, health promotion programs geared toward physical activity, such as Stairway to Health, focus on the gains rather than the costs of taking the stairs instead of the elevator. They emphasize the fun of exercise, not the fatigue that may result. These programs make the point that physical activity can be convenient, uplifting, and healthy. In so doing, they target people's beliefs regarding cost and gain. For some examples of these programs and messages, visit the Health Canada website and click on Healthy Living (www.hc-sc.gc.ca). The theories of health psychology are called on to form the foundation of health promotion programs. These programs also rely on research findings from the field of *social psychology*. This is because health promotion involves *persuasion,* which is a social phenomenon.

The Social Psychology of Health Promotion

Persuasion is the attempt to change people's attitudes and beliefs. An **attitude** is a cognition in which a person *evaluates* some target. Attitudes involve words such as *good* or *bad* and verbs such as *like* or *dislike*. Health promotion programs attempt to change attitudes when they try to persuade people that low-fat diets are *good,* and that people should *like* them. We might call this *health advertising*.

In chapter 1, we defined a *health belief* as something we think to be true concerning our health. More generally, beliefs are our personal encyclopedias of the world. They are the things we consider to be true. Beliefs are related to attitudes but different from them in that beliefs are not evaluative in nature. For example, we might hold the *belief* that yogurt contains less fat than ice cream, and this belief might support the attitude that yogurt is *good* for us.

Health promotion programs try to affect what people believe to be true and what they *like* and consider *good*. Over the years, social psychologists have conducted extensive research on persuasion (for a detailed review, see Olson & Maio, 2003). Well-proven principles have emerged from this research that can be applied to health promotion. Several examples follow.

The Elaboration Likelihood Model of Persuasion Research investigating people's attitudes toward political candidates has discovered that there are basically two routes through which these attitudes are influenced (Petty & Cacioppo, 1981). The first, called the **central route**, refers to the use of logic, facts, and reason. Political campaigns using the central route present statistics and logical arguments in favour of a given candidate or perhaps in opposition to a candidate. Health promotion programs using this route will present statistics and medical facts.

The second way that people's attitudes toward political candidates are influenced is called the **peripheral route**. This involves an appeal to emotion and general impression. Political campaigns using this route will focus on the looks and charisma of the candidate. Health promotion campaigns using the peripheral route feature healthy-looking people or show graphic depictions of the potential horrors resulting from risk behaviour.

persuasion: the attempt to change people's attitudes and beliefs.

attitude: a cognition in which a person evaluates some object or idea.

central route to persuasion: the use of logic, facts, and reason to affect someone's attitude.

peripheral route to persuasion: attempts to affect attitude by appealing to emotion and general impression.

Research in social psychology shows that some people are influenced more by central routes and others more by peripheral routes. This means that health promotion campaigns must cover both bases. Statistical presentations, which make use of a central route, must be packaged well to appeal to people who are more influenced by peripheral routes.

A number of studies have applied the elaboration likelihood model to health promotion. In the area of AIDS prevention, for example, it has been suggested that there might be problems with programs focused exclusively on providing facts. People may become overloaded with information if it is not packaged in ways that arouse constructive emotional responses (Mulvihill, 1996). An example of this packaging is short films, which have been shown to be effective in engendering positive attitudes toward prevention behaviour (Igartua, Cheng, & Lopes, 2003).

Fear Appeals: An Example of Health Promotion by the Peripheral Route

One fairly obvious application of the peripheral route is the use of what are called **fear appeals**. The term is self-explanatory. The assumption, of course, is that we can change people's behaviour by presenting frightening accounts of what will happen to them if they continue a given behaviour (e.g., smoking) or if they don't adopt a behaviour (e.g., dental hygiene).

There is considerable theoretical support for this assumption. For example, main components of the theory of planned behaviour include *perceived threat* and *personal vulnerability*. Fear appeals are designed to intensify people's beliefs regarding this threat and the extent to which they are vulnerable. In other words, **threat perception**, the belief that a threat is real and that we are vulnerable to it, is more important than simple fear arousal.

Long before the introduction of the theory of planned behaviour, Hovland and colleagues' **drive-reduction theory** was used to explain fear appeals. Drive-reduction theory argues that we are driven to reduce the tension brought about by deprivation or other states to which we have an aversion (Hovland, Janis, & Kelley, 1953). According to this theory, fear appeals should work because we are driven to reduce fear, and when we are successful, the behaviour that we use to reduce the fear is reinforced.

The Extended Parallel Process Model (Witte, 1992) forwards three possible outcomes of fear appeals. People are motivated to control the danger, control the fear, or to not respond at all. The goal of fear appeals is to motivate people to control the danger, such as avoiding cigarette smoking. If, the fear arousal is *too high,* the person will be more likely to engage in either fear control (such as avoiding the message) or non-responding (Maloney, Lapinski, & Witte, 2011). There are a number of reasons for this, but the main one is that frightening messages present situations and outcomes that appear to be so awful that we don't think we can deal with them effectively no matter what we do. As a result, the recommended behaviour looks ineffective in comparison to the potentially catastrophic nature of the threat. For example, can I really prevent the devastating effects of cancer by eating broccoli? In answering this question, many people would see a mismatch in strength between the threat and the threat-reducing behaviour and so remain uninfluenced. They carry on with their old behaviour because the high-fear message makes the situation look too hopeless to do anything about. In this case, we don't believe in the *efficacy* of the behaviour to deal with the threat. Modern analysis of the mechanisms behind fear appeals indicates that, to be effective, efficacy messages should be presented in a one-to-one ratio with appeals to fear (Carcioppolo et al., 2013).

These efficacy messages address two forms—**response efficacy** (the belief that the behaviour will reduce the threat) and **self-efficacy** (the belief that one can carry out the behaviour). Another problem with high-fear messages is that our self-efficacy suffers

fear appeals: the attempt to change people's behaviour by presenting frightening accounts of what could happen to them if they continue a given behaviour or if they don't adopt a behaviour.

threat perception: the belief that a threat is real and that we are vulnerable to it.

drive-reduction theory: suggests we are driven to reduce the tension brought about by deprivation or other negative states.

response efficacy: the perception that a threat-reducing strategy will work.

self-efficacy: an individual's perception of his or her ability to succeed at a particular task at a specific time.

Posters like this one take advantage of fear appeals.
Province of British Columbia

when we are afraid. To illustrate this, ask yourself how reassured you would be by instructions on how to employ a backup parachute in the event that the main chute doesn't open. Imagine yourself listening to these instructions. In the event that you were plummeting to earth under the full force of gravity, are you confident that you would be able to carry out those backup instructions? Or would you be too afraid to remember the instructions and carry them out correctly? Confidence levels vary from person to person under such circumstances.

Concerning health promotion, we might undermine people's confidence in their ability to perform self-examinations for cancer if we portray cancer in particularly frightening ways. This may be why 54 percent of women who were sent a reassuring letter listing "encouraging facts" about breast cancer made an appointment for a mammogram, whereas only 42 percent made an appointment after receiving an anxiety-arousing letter listing "worrisome facts." Interestingly, only 38 percent made an appointment when they received a standard letter listing no facts at all (Kendall & Hailley, 1993).

The point is that the effectiveness of fear appeals depends very much on people's *responses* while frightened. Efficacy beliefs represent one kind of response. **Self-accountability** represents another. As the term implies, self-accountability refers to the extent to which a person feels responsible for a given emotion or situation. This applies not only to fear appeals, but also to appeals to guilt and regret (Inman & Zeelenberg, 2002). Passyn and Sujan (2006) illustrate the distinction between fear and guilt appeals with a slogan used by the Partnership for a Drug-Free America: "Smoking pot may not kill you, but it will kill your mother" —a slogan aimed at guilt rather than fear.

Appeals that feature guilt or fear demonstrate that we can frame a message in either positive or negative ways. **Message framing**, then, refers to the extent to which positive or negative aspects of an outcome are emphasized. Loss-framed messages emphasize the negative results of not engaging in a behaviour, and gain-framed messages emphasize the positive effects of engaging in a behaviour. A theory from cognitive psychology called *prospect theory* suggests that loss-framing will work best in some situations and gain-framing will work best in others (Tversky & Kahneman, 1981). Specifically, loss-framed messages should be more effective when addressing risky behaviour, like getting a Pap test, which carries the risk of having cancer detected. Using sunscreen, on the other hand, is a behaviour that does not feature the risk of detection. A recent meta-analysis of studies investigating the effects of framing has shown that, as prospect theory would predict, gain-framing is more effective for prevention-related messages. The review did not find, however, that loss-framed messages were better for detection-related messages (Gallagher & Updegraff, 2012). See Table 11-2 for examples of loss- and gain-framed messages.

What can we conclude from our analysis of fear appeals as a health promotion strategy? Clearly, messages that do nothing more than frighten people without addressing response efficacy, self-efficacy, or self-accountability are likely to be ineffective. On the other hand, if we arouse fear or guilt, send the message that the person is responsible for the existence of these emotions, and accompany that with a convincing argument that there are ways to address the problem within the capabilities of the people receiving the message, then we increase our chances of success. "Success" in terms of health promotion means that people will pay attention to our message, remember it, and behave in ways that are consistent with it by reducing health risks and increasing well-being. (For a detailed theoretical analysis of fear appeals, see Maloney et al., 2011).

The Application of Other Social-Psychological Principles to Health Promotion
We know that the more often people hear a message, the more likely they are to be influenced by it (Zajonc, 1968). Advertisers have known this for decades, as evidenced by the number of times we will see the same commercial in a 30-minute television program. Slogans take advantage of the repetition effect by being repeated in every different ad that appears in a given campaign. Health promotion campaigns could take greater advantage of slogans, just as advertisers do. Imagine the effect if a health promotion campaign had come up with the phrase "Just Do It."

self-accountability: the extent to which a person feels personally responsible for a given emotion or situation.

message framing: the extent to which positive or negative aspects of an outcome are emphasized in a health promotion message.

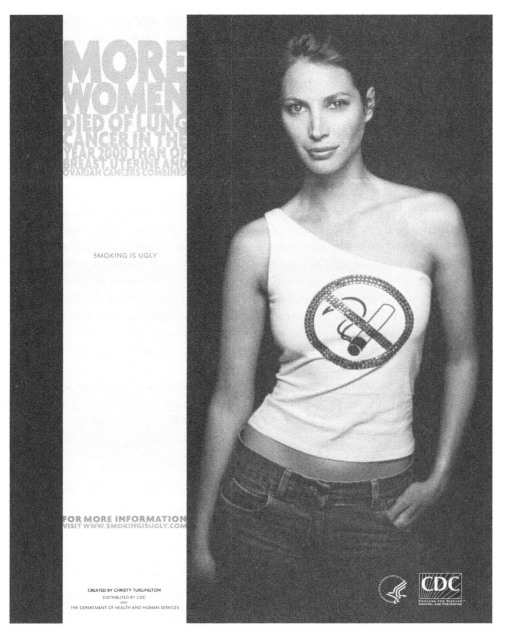

Supermodel Christy Turlington represents a peripheral approach to health promotion.
Centres for Disease Control and Prevention

Table 11-2 Examples of Loss-Framed and Gain-Framed Health Promotion Messages

	Loss-Framed Message	Gain-Framed Message
High-Risk Behaviour (Detection)	Failing to detect cervical cancer early via a Pap test can cost you your life.	Detecting cervical cancer early via a Pap test can save your life.
Low-Risk Behaviour (Prevention)	By not using sunscreen, you could contract skin cancer and die.	By using sunscreen, you greatly reduce your risk of getting skin cancer.

Loss-framed messages emphasize the downside of not engaging in a health behaviour. Gain-framed messages emphasize the upside of that behaviour.

Of course, advertising campaigns are far more than just repeated words and phrases. We must also consider who is saying those words. When we adopt a central route to persuasion, we want to use people who are credible and people who are seen as knowledgeable and believable. Not surprisingly, research has shown that sources perceived to be credible tend to be more persuasive than non-credible ones (Teasdale & Yardley, 2011). If we are mounting an anti-smoking campaign, for example, we might want to put a physician on camera. If it is an anti-drinking-and-driving program, we could use a police officer who is often first on the scene of motor vehicle accidents.

If, on the other hand, we are using a peripheral approach, we will focus on the *attractiveness* of our speaker or we might want to pick someone who is famous. This is why anti-drug-abuse campaigns use professional athletes as speakers.

Good health promotion campaigns use both credible and popular speakers. As an example, imagine that you are asked to design a program to reduce the incidence of drinking and driving at high school graduations. In Ontario, 32 percent of the students in grades 7 to 13 reported being a passenger in a car driven by a drunk driver. Fifteen percent of those with driver's licences reported driving within an hour after consuming two or more drinks, and 20 percent reported driving within an hour after using cannabis (Adlaf, Mann, & Paglia, 2003). Your counterattack programs for high schools, aimed at affecting the drinking and driving behaviour, would be most effective if they combined messages from first-response police officers (because they are highly *credible*) and school presidents (because they are *popular*).

A health promotion program must consider the audience's *knowledge level*. When talking to small audiences, people in health promotion can make educated guesses about an audience's knowledge level. However, this is much more challenging when planning national campaigns. How much do people know about heart anatomy, for example? One study showed that people could provide adequate definitions for 72 percent of a list of 50 commonly used medical terms (Thompson & Pledger, 1993).

Obviously, Canadians vary tremendously in their knowledge of medical language and procedures. For this reason, good health promotion campaigns must be basic enough to include as many people as possible without insulting anyone's intelligence. This can be a tricky balance to achieve.

Complicating the issue of knowledge is *literacy*. In Canada, those who report being in poor health are more likely to have low literacy scores, especially among the nation's senior citizens (Statistics Canada, 2005c).

In addition, there are people in Canada who are not fluent in English or French. According to Statistics Canada census figures, more than 450 000 people in Canada cannot understand spoken English or French. That figure represents 1.6 percent of our population. In British Columbia, 2.6 percent of the population cannot understand spoken English or French. Effective health promotion campaigns for these segments of our population must be either highly visual or multilingual.

Poole and Ting (1995) discovered that Indo-Canadian maternity patients scored lower on tests of knowledge of hospital procedures, baby care, and self-care than did Euro-Canadian patients. Language barriers are cited as a significant reason for these differences. It is clear, from studies such as this, that patient education and health promotion will be more effective when presented in a person's native language and, preferably, by people of the same cultural background.

In summary, we have seen that theories of psychology can and must be applied to the design and implementation of health promotion campaigns. When we consider these theories, we develop a greater appreciation for the complexities of health promotion. Changing the minds and behaviour of large groups of people is no easy task. The good news is that people who can be convinced to change their behaviour often come to endorse that behaviour and go on to carry out health promotion for others.

LOOK BEFORE YOU LEAP: THE PRECEDE-PROCEED MODEL

People working in health promotion benefit greatly from a model that guides them in the planning of their programs. This provides not only structure and direction for the planning process, but also a set of criteria by which an existing program can be assessed. This is exactly what the precede-proceed model does (Green & Kreuter, 1991). The model was designed as a way to facilitate and analyze health promotion programs from the planning stages through to their implementation and impact.

There are two key attributes to the model. One is the identification of components involved in the planning, implementation, and evaluation of health promotion programs. The other is the identification of causal pathways among these components. Table 11-3 presents the model. The "precede" phases of the model relate to the *planning* of health promotion programs. The "proceed" phases relate to the *implementation* and *evaluation* of that program. By examining Table 11-3, you can see that the model has an element of symmetry that helps clarify it conceptually. We begin by moving from right to left across the top of the model and then proceed by moving from left to right across the bottom.

Table 11-3 The Precede-Proceed Model of Health Promotion Planning, Implementation, and Evaluation

←PRECEDE

Phase 5	Phase 4	Phase 3	Phase 2	Phase 1
Administrative and policy diagnosis	Educational and organizational diagnosis	Behavioural and environmental diagnosis	Epidemiological diagnosis	Social diagnosis
Health promotion	Predisposing factors			
Health education	Reinforcing factors	Behaviour and lifestyle	Health	Quality of life
Policy regulation organization	Enabling factors	Environment		

Phase 6	Phase 7	Phase 8	Phase 9
Implementation	Process evaluation	Impact evaluation	Outcome evaluation

PROCEED→

Source: Green & Kreuter (1991). *Health promotion planning: An educational and environmental approach.* Mountainview, CA: Mayfield Publishing. Adapted by permission.

In so doing, we end up where we started, with a focus on health and quality of life. We can walk through the phases of the model to develop an appreciation for its logic.

We begin in phase 1 by diagnosing quality of life. If there were no problems here, there would be no need to continue with our health promotion plan. However, there are always problems because no population is completely free of disease, disability, and accidents. In phase 2, we would conduct an epidemiological diagnosis to identify patterns of health and illness in our population. In terms of causation, the model assumes that these health patterns affect quality of life. Phase 3 requires a diagnosis of behavioural and environmental factors that explain our epidemiological data. We are now beginning to create a causal pathway from behaviour and environment to health to quality of life. In phase 4, we assess factors affecting behaviour and environment. What biological, psychological, or social factors influence behaviour? (This should remind you of the biopsychosocial model.) What factors affect environment? In phase 5, the final phase of planning, we would devise programs and policies meant to create optimal environments that are physically healthy and that reinforce healthy behaviours.

Now we are ready to "proceed," which is to say implement our plan and evaluate its effects. In phase 6, we would implement our education programs, new health policies, environmental regulations, and so on. These may take advantage of some of the psychological theories we discussed earlier in the chapter. To begin assessing the effectiveness of these programs, we would enter the process evaluation phase (phase 7). At this point, we evaluate the extent to which our programs affect the factors that predispose people to healthy behaviour and reinforce that behaviour. In addition, we may also be trying to bring about conditions that foster improvements in people's physical environments. In phase 8, we assess impact by measuring changes in behaviour, lifestyle, and environment since the program began. These changes should, in turn, bring about better health and, ultimately, better quality of life. This brings us back to where we started.

A good example of the implementation of the precede-proceed model is a program that was designed to decrease work-related disability for people with arthritis. This program employed self-management strategies and occupational therapist consultants. The next step (phase 4 of the precede-proceed model) in this case might be to identify factors that would predispose a person to self-manage and use professional consultations well. Now we are ready to design a health promotion program that takes advantage of psychological theory to improve work productivity and self-confidence for people with arthritis (Lacaille et al., 2008).

When we move in the "proceed" direction, we would implement our program and evaluate the extent to which it brings about predisposing and reinforcing factors that favoured successful work lives (phase 7). Next, we would evaluate the extent to which these events actually had an impact on the workers' behaviour and, more generally, their satisfaction (phase 8). Finally, we would need to determine whether the workers' health had improved and, along with it, their quality of life.

The precede-proceed model has been tested in more than 600 published studies, addressing everything from timely follow-up after an abnormal mammogram (Arnsberger et al., 2006) to the prevention of unintentional injury (Trifiletti, Gielen, Sleet, & Hopkins, 2005), making it the most widely tested model of its kind. One of the advantages of the model is that it works in conjunction with any other model or theory of health promotion design. For example, in phase 5, planners could use the health belief model as their guide, trying to educate people about their vulnerability and efficacy beliefs. The model

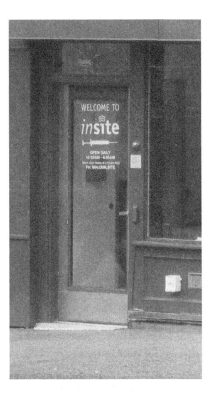

Community programs such as Insite, operated by Vancouver Coastal Health, provide examples of the ways in which the precede-proceed model of health promotion planning can be applied.
Vancouver Coastal Health

has been criticized for being too individually oriented, with its emphasis on behaviour and lifestyle (Luschen, Cockerham, & Kunz, 1996). An expanded model might take the social and cultural context of that behaviour into consideration.

ASSESSING THE EFFECTIVENESS OF HEALTH PROMOTION PROGRAMS

Health promotion programs are labour-intensive initiatives that can be expensive. It is important, therefore, to find ways to assess their effectiveness. In health promotion, the magnitude of the interventions and the desired effects can make evaluation of impact difficult. Fawcett et al. (2001) identify no fewer than 12 challenges inherent in evaluating health promotion programs that are pitched at the community level. These authors point out that it can be difficult to identify just what is determining the health of the community, much less evaluating programs designed to affect those determinants. Furthermore, some of the endpoints of health promotion, such as "community capacity" or "quality of life," while important, are abstract in nature.

For example, getting definitive measures of changes in rates of child abuse and domestic violence on a population level can be difficult. For one thing, under-reporting is often a problem. And then there is the lag time between the implementation of a promotion program and the benefit that is realized. Some health promotion benefits, such as reduced cardiovascular disease, can take years to realize. These are just some of the challenges identified by Fawcett and his colleagues.

In spite of these challenges, health promotion programs must be evaluated, not just to satisfy the curiosity of policy makers, program planners, and researchers, but also for the good of the communities the programs are designed to support (Judd, Frankish, & Moulton, 2001). The key to effective evaluation of health promotion programs is to engage all relevant parties in the process. Judd and colleagues point out that an evaluation system that follows the values and goals of health promotion, as we have discussed in this chapter, must be collaborative, democratic, participatory, and open.

Based on these goals, the standards applied to the evaluation of health promotion programs come in a number of forms, which have been nicely articulated by Judd and colleagues (2001). For example, **arbitrary standards** are based on decisions made by some outside body regarding what a community needs. Contrast these with community-based **experiential standards**, which are based on what experience has told the community it needs. There are **historical standards**, which are based on comparisons to other programs or to the program in question at an earlier time in its existence. **Normative standards** determine a program's impact by assessing national averages in areas such as literacy, mortality and morbidity, and self-reports of health. **Scientific standards** draw similar statistical comparisons but with data published in scientific literature. Finally, there are **propriety standards**, which take ethics and legalities into account, and **feasibility standards**, which are used to evaluate a program based on this practicality or sustainability (St. Leger, 2005).

Once standards have been identified to use for our evaluation, there are well-defined steps that can be followed (Rootman, Godstadt, Polvin, & Springett, 2001; see Table 11-4).

In summary, while it is not easy, it is imperative to evaluate health promotion programs. The key is to apply appropriate standards that are consistent with the goals of health promotion and the needs of the community in question. These standards must be applied via careful steps, starting with a thorough knowledge of the program and leading to effective action informed by the evaluation.

arbitrary standards: standards used to evaluate health promotion programs forwarded by a body that exists outside the community involved in the promotional campaign.

experiential standards: standards used to evaluate health promotion programs based on direct experiences of the community involved in the promotional campaign.

historical standards: standards used to evaluate health promotion programs based on comparisons to other programs or to the same program at an earlier time.

normative standards: standards used to evaluate health promotion programs using statistics, such as national averages, that describe the health issue being addressed.

Table 11-4 Steps Involved in the Evaluation of Health Promotion Initiatives

Steps	Considerations
Step 1: Describing the program	Develop a familiarity with the program you are evaluating in terms of its context, goals, and constituents.
Step 2: Identifying the issues and questions	What needs to be known about the program? What do the program's constituents mean when they ask "Is the program working?"
Step 3: Designing the data collection process	Will qualitative and/or quantitative methods be used? What will your sources be?
Step 4: Collecting the data	Careful and systematic data collection is required.
Step 5: Analysing and interpreting the data	Will you be looking for themes? Is your analysis theory-driven?
Step 6: Making recommendations	What can you confidently conclude from your analysis and what will you tell the constituents?
Step 7: Dissemination	Who should be made aware of your evaluation?
Step 8: Taking action	What should be done as a result of your evaluation?

Source: Based on Rootman recommendations, referenced from: Rootman, I., Godstadt, M., Polvin L., and Springett, J. (2001). A framework for health promotion evaluation. In Rootman, I. et al. (eds.). *Evaluation in health promotion: Principles and perspectives*. Copenhagen, WHO Regional Office for Europe, 2001 (WHO Regional Publications, European Sewries, No. 92, pp. 7–38).

A FINAL WORD ABOUT HEALTH PROMOTION

In this chapter on health promotion, we have made repeated reference to self-care and mutual aid, making the point that, with these goals in mind, the locus of responsibility for health is placed on individuals and groups. As you read through these sections, you might have wondered about the fairness of this locus of responsibility. If we lived in a world that featured perfect social justice, it would be reasonable to place major responsibility for health on the individual. However, we do not live in such a world.

Obviously, some people are in a much better position to engage in healthy behaviour than are others. Healthy diets tend to be more expensive than unhealthy ones. Opportunities for physical activity are not evenly distributed among Canadians. Health disparities can be mapped by postal codes, and an analysis of this shows that social determinants of health manifest themselves differently across these environments.

In this chapter, by referring to social determinants of health, health disparities, and personal responsibility for health, we are espousing what has been called a **co-production process** related to the promotion of health (Schmidt, 2009). By this, we mean that the responsibility for health must be shared among centralized health bureaucracies, individuals, and communities.

scientific standards: standards used to evaluate health promotion programs using data published in scientific literature describing similar programs or health issues.

propriety standards: standards used to evaluate health promotion programs that take legal and ethical issues into account.

feasibility standards: standards used to evaluate health promotion programs based on the practicality or sustainability of the program.

co-production process: a process whereby the responsibility for health is shared among centralized health bureaucracies, individuals, and communities.

CHAPTER SUMMARY

- Define health promotion.

  The World Health Organization defines health promotion as the process of enabling people to increase control over and to improve their health.

- Explain how health promotion has developed in Canada.

  Health promotion has a long history in Canada, dating back to the 1700s. Programs began developing at the provincial level in the 1920s with a focus on proper sanitation. From there, national programs began to flourish in the 1970s.

  One example is "Achieving Health for All: A Framework for Health Promotion," published in 1986. A key goal for health promotion in Canada is the reduction of health disparities.

- Apply the concepts of self-care and mutual aid to the goals of health promotion.

  An important goal of health promotion programs is to have individuals and communities look after themselves and each other. A key mechanism for this is social support. This support, which can be naturally occurring or agency-provided, takes at least three forms: practical, informational, and emotional.

- Apply the health belief model and the theory of reasoned action to the goals of health promotion.

  Major elements of most health promotion programs are drawn from the health belief model and the theory of reasoned action. They include perceived vulnerability, perceived seriousness, and cost/gain analysis. Health promotion programs communicate messages about how a given condition could affect anyone (vulnerability), could be serious and still easy to treat (low cost/high gain), and that treatment could be effective (efficacious).

■ Apply theories of social psychology with the goal of improving the effectiveness of health promotion programs.

Social psychological theories relevant to health promotion come from the study of persuasion. For example, the elaboration-likelihood model identifies central and peripheral routes to persuasion. Central routes present facts and figures, appealing to the cognitive dimension of attitudes. Peripheral routes appeal to emotion. Good health promotion programs follow both routes. The peripheral route sometimes features fear appeals. Such appeals are effective only if they are accompanied by ways in which the emotion can be reduced through dealing with the fear-arousing problem.

■ Explain the precede-proceed model

The precede-proceed model is a nine-phase model in which the first five phases (precede) describe the diagnosis of the problem and the design of a plan to address the problem. The remaining four phases (proceed) describe the implementation of the plan and the evaluation of the process and outcomes.

■ List the standards by which health promotion programs are evaluated.

Health promotion programs are difficult to evaluate because they are often large in scale, and the outcomes can be abstract. The standards applied to the evaluation process may be arbitrary (some outside body decides what a community needs), experiential (based on the real experiences of the community), historical (based on the status of the community at an earlier time), normative (based on national averages), scientific (based on other research), or based on propriety (ethics and legalities) and feasibility.

Glossary

A

A-delta fibres the afferent peripheral fibres that are associated with transmitting sharp, distinct pain

acceleration–deceleration anjury a type of concussion that occurs when an immobile head is hit by a moving object or a moving head hits an immobile object

acceptance the final stage of Kübler-Ross's theory of death and dying, in which people achieve a peaceful acceptance of their own death

acquired immune deficiency syndrome (AIDS) a disease caused by the human immunodeficiency virus (HIV); after infection, the body's compromised immune system makes it susceptible to a host of other infections

active leisure a positive experience that is associated with activities such as hobbies, playing a musical instrument, and exercise

active-passive model situation in which patients are unable to participate in their care or to make decisions because of their medical condition

acupuncture an ancient Chinese pain control technique that involves the insertion of fine needles to create stimulation to the peripheral nerves

acute illness an illness with a defined beginning and end

acute pain pain that lasts less than 6 months and serves to warn of impending tissue damage or the need for convalescent rest

acute stressor a stressor that is immediate in its duration and proximity

addiction the state of being physically or psychologically dependent on a substance

addictive smokers smokers who develop a psychological dependence on smoking and are keenly aware when they are not smoking

adherence the degree to which patients carry out the behaviours and treatments that physicians and other health professionals recommend

adjuvant therapy therapy used in conjunction with other therapy

adrenal cortex the outer portion of the adrenal gland; at times of stress supplies hormones to the body that provide energy and increase blood pressure, but that can adversely affect the body's ability to resist and recover from disease

adrenal medulla the central portion of the adrenal gland; secretes catecholamines (containing both adrenaline and noradrenaline) when the hypothalamus initiates the stress response

advanced illness stage of illness at which death is imminent

advanced-practice nursing nursing that includes teaching, consultation, and research within a specialty area where superior clinical skills and judgment are acquired through a combination of experience and education

aerobic exercise exercise, such as jogging, that involves the increased consumption of oxygen over an extended period of time

afferent (sensory) neurons nerve cells that conduct impulses from a sense organ to the central nervous system, or from lower to higher levels in the spinal cord and brain

agency-provided support social support provided by agencies and organizations that have been formed to fill the void when naturally occurring support is either lacking or unavailable

alarm the initial phase of Selye's General Adaptation Syndrome in which the body mobilizes its defences against a stressor

alcohol dependency syndrome model a theory suggesting that for a variety of reasons people do not exercise control over their drinking, and this leads to problem drinking

alcohol myopia a drinker's decreased ability to engage in insightful cognitive processing

allostatic load the long-term physiological impact of chronic exposure to stress

anaerobic exercise exercise, such as sprinting, in which intense effort is expended over a short period of time, resulting in an oxygen debt

anger a reaction that often follows denial when people are confronted with novel and severe trauma, as identified by Kübler-Ross

angioplasty a procedure in which a bubble-like device is inserted into the artery at the point of the blockage, thus expanding the artery and allowing for better blood flow

anorexia nervosa an eating disorder that is characterized by a dramatic reduction in food intake and extreme weight loss due to an extreme fear of gaining weight

anticipatory nausea nausea that is felt before a chemotherapy treatment begins, explained in terms of classical conditioning

antidepressants medications that reduce the depression that frequently accompanies pain; it is also believed that they affect pain-related neurotransmitters

antiemetic medication medication intended to reduce nausea and vomiting

arbitrary standards standards used to evaluate health promotion programs forwarded by a body that exists outside the community involved in the promotional campaign

asymptomatic conditions there are not accompanied by palpable symptoms or sensations

attitude a cognition in which a person evaluates some object or idea

attributions the explanations people give for events such as their successes and failures

autonomic activity physiological processes that cannot be consciously controlled, such as heart rate, respiration rate, blood pressure, hand surface temperature, and skin conductance

aversion therapy therapy that includes pairing a behaviour that one is attempting to eliminate with some unpleasant stimulus so that the undesired behaviour will elicit negative sensations

B

bargaining a response, identified by Kübler-Ross, that may occur when a person is confronted with novel and severe trauma; includes trying to do things that will buy more time

behavioural medicine a branch of medicine concerned with the relationship between health and behaviour; the focus is usually on remediation

beliefs as person variables pre-existing notions, both personal and cultural, that influence appraisal, and thus stress, by determining the meaning given to the environment

benefit finding attitude or technique often referred to as finding the "silver lining in the cloud," which appears to aid in post-traumatic growth

benign breast biopsy a false-positive result that leads to women with abnormal mammograms being called back for a biopsy procedure, and the results show no evidence of malignancy

benign-positive appraisal a cognitive process by which an event is appraised to involve outcomes that are positive and may enhance well-being

bereavement emotions attendant upon the loss of a close friend or loved one

binge eating disorder (BED) compulsive overeating or bingeing; unlike bulimia nervosa, BED uses no compensatory measure or purge to counteract the binge

biofeedback the recording of physiological measures through electronic instruments that provide immediate feedback concerning physiological state in an attempt to modify physiological processes

biological imbedding the process by which experience has permanent effects on the expression of our genetic coding and, subsequently, on a range of biological processes this coding affects

biomedical model an approach suggesting that health is best understood in terms of biology

biopsychosocial approach a model that suggests that biological, psychological, and social factors are all involved in any given state of health or illness

biopsychosocial communication suggests that biological, psychological, and social factors are all involved in any given state of health or illness

blunters patients who avoid information

body dysmorphic disorder condition in which individuals who suffer from eating disorders do not perceive their bodies accurately

body mass index (BMI) measure of obesity calculated by dividing one's weight in kilograms by height in metres squared

Bulimia nervosa an eating disorder that involves recurrent episodes of binge eating followed by purging

box scale a scale on which people rate and report their pain by choosing the number that best indicates the degree of pain that they are experiencing from a series of numbers in boxes ranging from "no pain" to "worst pain imaginable"

burnout a condition that is similar to compassion fatigue and includes symptoms of physical exhaustion, depersonalization of patients, and feelings of discouragement and low accomplishment

C

C-fibres the afferent peripheral fibres that are associated with transmitting diffuse, dull, or aching pain

cardiac invalidism anxiety regarding a subsequent heart attack causes patients to curtail their activity levels far more than required by their actual disease status

caring the role that most lay people think is the primary task of nurses

central control trigger in the gate control theory of pain, a specialized system of large-diameter, rapidly conducting fibres that activate selective cognitive processes that then influence, by way of descending fibres, the opening and closing of the gate

central nervous system the division of the nervous system that is composed of the brain and the spinal cord

central route to persuasion the use of logic, facts, and reason to affect someone's attitude

centrally acting analgesics pain-killing medications that operate on the central nervous system by imitating the effects of the body's endogenous pain relief system

challenge appraisal appraisal in which, though an event is perceived to be stressful, the focus is one of positive excitement and potential for growth

chemotherapy treatment used in addition to surgery and/or radiation therapy when it is suspected that cancer has metastasized, or to help prevent it from doing so

chronic condition a condition that doesn't go away or get better

chronic intractable benign pain continuous pain that varies in intensity

chronic pain pain lasting for longer than 6 months

chronic progressive pain continuous pain that gradually intensifies as a person's condition worsens

chronic recurrent pain intermittent intense episodes of acute pain followed by relief

cognitive appraisal assessment of whether or not an event is stressful

cognitive reappraisal and restructuring therapy sometimes used with cardiac patients, in which they learn to think differently about the things that make them angry and to make behavioural changes, such as learning to control their breathing

cognitive restructuring a technique whereby maladaptive, stress-producing cognitions are identified and replaced with ones that are more appropriate cognitive transactional models models that emphasize the relationship between a person and his or her environment and the appraisal that the individual makes of the situation

collectivist one who considers him- or herself to be part of a greater whole and who considers individualism to be less important than allegiance to the group

commitments as person variables values that influence appraisal by determining the importance of a particular encounter and that affect the choices made to achieve a desired outcome

compassion fatigue a lack of energy among health care professionals, particularly nurses, who are constantly working in an environment in which suffering is common

compliance the degree to which patients carry out the behaviours and treatments that physicians and other health professionals recommend

concussion (closed head injury) a bruising of the brain that can result in severe neurocognitive deficits, permanent disability, and even death

consumerist communication the use of the physician as a consultant who answers questions rather than asking them

coping strategies that an individual employs to deal with stresses caused by the ever-changing demands of the environment

coping goal the objective of a coping response (which is usually to reduce the impact of stress)

coping outcomes the specific outcomes of a coping response

coping response an intentional physical or mental act that is initiated in response to a stressor

co-production process a process whereby the responsibility for health is shared among centralized health bureaucracies, individuals, and communities

coronary artery bypass graft (CABG, or bypass surgery) a procedure in which healthy arteries from other parts of the body, often the legs, are grafted into the coronary artery system to bypass blocked arteries

cost-gain belief an individual's assessment of the costs associated with a course of action (e.g., effort, discomfort, embarrassment, or inconvenience) compared to the benefit of the behaviour to the individual's health

creative non-adherence a patient's intentional modifying or supplementing of a recommended treatment regimen

culture the values, behaviours, practices, and assumptions learned from our membership in groups that share them

culturally competent care care that enables individuals, agencies, and systems to work effectively in cross-cultural situations. It involves first developing an understanding of cultural factors and then designing systems that effectively acknowledge those factors. It begins with an ability to critically reflect on one's own culturally based assumptions about one's self and others.

curing the role that most lay people think is the primary task of physicians

cytokines increase the body's capacity to produce inflammation, and help heal wounds and fight infection

D

day care patient a person who goes to the hospital for a procedure or test that is more involved than, for example, routine radiography, but does not stay overnight

deep brain stimulation a surgical procedure that involves implanting an electrode that delivers electrical signals to the brain

dehumanization the tendency to see people as objects or body parts rather than human beings

delayed gratification term used by behaviourists to describe a situation in which there is a time lag between a behaviour and its reinforcement

delta alcoholism the inability to abstain

denial a coping strategy in which people deny that distressing events exist or that negative emotions are being felt

depersonalization taking away a person's sense of individuality

depression a common mental disorder of varying severity and impact that features depressed mood, loss of interest or pleasure, feelings of guilt or low self-worth, disturbed sleep or appetite, low energy, and poor concentration

discharge planning a process in which post-hospital care is organized and risks, such as social problems and lack of support, are assessed

disease model (of problem drinking) a theory that suggests that alcoholism is a disease resulting from the physical properties of alcohol

diseases of adaptation health problems that are the result of long-term neurological and hormonal changes caused by ongoing stress

disempowering care patient care that yields dependence and results in learned helplessness

disfigurement a potential physical result of cancer surgery that can have serious psychological consequences

distraction a pain management technique in which the patient focuses attention on something other than the sensation of pain

do-not-resuscitate order an order given by a physician indicating that CPR and other interventions are not to be used if the patient stops breathing

drive-reduction theory a theory that suggests we are driven to reduce the tension brought about by deprivation or other negative states

duration temporal situational factor involved in stress appraisal

E

efficacy beliefs the extent to which one thinks a course of action (e.g., a preventive behaviour or treatment) will actually work

ego orientation a goal perspective that focuses on success and failure, with success often coming at other people's expense

electroencephalograph (EEG) an instrument that assesses pain by measuring electrical activity in the brain electromyograph (EMG) an instrument that assesses pain by measuring electrical activity in muscles

emotion-focused coping coping by focusing on ways to reduce the emotional impact of a disease without trying to cure it

emotional-approach coping coping by facing emotional responses to a disease and dealing effectively with those responses

emotional arousal a source of efficacy expectation in which individuals assess their emotional level and evaluate their capabilities accordingly; for example, high levels of emotion may be thought to be debilitating and predictive of failure

emotional support support provided by people who take the time to understand our fears and frustrations, who help calm us during anxious times, who help lift our moods up, or who distract us from our worries

empowering care patient care that yields independence and results in learned mastery

endocrine system a system of the body that controls glandular responses to stress; responds more slowly than the nervous system but the effects can persist for weeks

endogenous opioids opiate-like substances produced within the body that regulate pain

enumerative assay a lab test done to count cells (typically white blood cells) as they exist in the bloodstream

environmental tobacco smoke (ETS or second-hand smoke) smoke that is in the air we breathe because of others' smoking

epidemiology the study of changing patterns of health and disease across populations and geographic areas

ethanol (ethyl alcohol) the alcohol used in beverages

eustress a positive, yet stressful, experience

euthanasia the deliberate ending of a patient's life to relieve suffering

event uncertainty the inability to predict the probability of an event which, as a result, increases the stress response

evoked potentials electrical responses produced by stimuli

exercise psychology the study of the influence that sport and exercise have on one's psychology and behaviour

exhaustion the third phase in Selye's General Adaptation Syndrome; the body experiences fatigue and immunocompromise because of the severity or duration of a stressor

expanded biomedical communication includes numerous closed-ended medical questions and moderate levels of biomedical and psychosocial exchange between physician and patient

experiential standards standards used to evaluate health promotion programs based on direct experiences of the community involved in the promotional campaign

expertise model model in which the physician and the intensive care team are assumed to be best informed and most objective, and therefore best equipped to make end-of-life decisions

external imagery a technique in which an individual becomes a passive and external third-person observer of his or her own actions

external reinforcement the encouragement and praise from physiotherapists, friends, family, and other practitioners needed by rehabilitation patients for their successes

F

false-positive result that indicates abnormality when none exists

family-oriented care in comprehensive cancer care, the family becomes the patient because for virtually every cancer patient there is a family and a collection of close friends who are also affected by the disease

fear appeals the attempt to change people's behaviour by presenting frightening accounts of what could happen to them if they continue a given behaviour or if they don't adopt a behaviour

feasibility standards standards used to evaluate health promotion programs based on the practicality or sustainability of the program

feminization of medicine the trend toward increased proportions of female physicians in the profession

fetal alcohol spectrum disorder (FASD) the name used to describe the range of disabilities caused by prenatal exposure to alcohol; these effects are permanent

fight-or-flight response the body's complex autonomic reaction when faced with a perceived threat

functional tests of immunity tests done to assess the immune system at work

G

gamma alcoholism loss of control once drinking begins

gastric banding a minimally invasive surgical procedure that involves placing a band around the stomach so that a person feels full after consuming only a small amount of food

gastric bypass radical surgical intervention to control extreme obesity, in which a small pouch is created at the bottom of the esophagus to limit food intake

gate control theory suggests that a neural mechanism in the dorsal horns of the spinal cord acts like a gate that can increase or decrease the flow of nerve impulses from peripheral fibres to the central nervous system, thereby influencing the sensation of pain

General Adaptation Syndrome (GAS) the three-stage response of the body to stressors as identified by Selye: alarm, resistance, and exhaustion

germ theory the discovery that many illnesses are caused by the activity of microorganisms, such as bacteria

gestational diabetes a temporary condition affecting 2 to 4 percent of all pregnant women

global measures of quality of life a general or overall assessment of quality of life without focusing on specific aspects

glucocorticoids substances released by the adrenal glands upon stimulation from the sympathetic division when one is under stress

gradient of reinforcement the gradual weakening of a behaviour the further it gets in time from the reinforcement of that behaviour

grief deep sorrow, usually in response to bereavement

guidance-cooperation model communication in which the patient seeks advice from the physician and answers the questions that are asked, but the physician is responsible for determining the diagnosis and treatment

guided imagery a form of relaxation that relies on distraction, in which the participant is told to imagine a calm, peaceful, and pleasant image

H

habitual smokers smokers who smoke without the awareness that they are doing so

hallucinogens drugs that dramatically affect perception, emotions, and mental processes; can cause hallucinations

harm/loss appraisal a type of stressful appraisal, at the time of the primary appraisal, that involves significant physical or psychological loss

harm reduction strategy attempts to reduce the harmful effects of a behaviour when faced with the reality that the health-compromising behaviour cannot be eliminated from a population

Health Action Process Approach (HAPA) approach that divides health behaviours into a motivations phase and a volitional phase

health belief model a model that analyzes health behaviour in terms of the belief that a health threat exists and the belief that a given course of action will affect the threat

health promotion strategies intended to maintain or improve the health of large populations

health psychology the application of psychological principles to the diagnosis and treatment of illness as well as to people's attempts to maintain health and well-being

"healthy adherer" effect greater adherence to health-promoting behaviours, such as medication adherence, is indicative of overall healthy behaviour

"healthy immigrant effect" the tendency for recent non-European immigrants to report their health as being above average upon arrival to Canada, but to report deterioration of their health over time

help-intended communication communication that includes support, especially emotional support

highly active antiretroviral treatment (HAART) a treatment for AIDS that has been shown to significantly increase life expectancy

historical standards standards used to evaluate health promotion programs based on comparisons to other programs or to the same program at an earlier time

historical trauma negative health effects of mass trauma such as war and colonization that can be experienced for generations

homeostasis the dynamic physiological response on the part of the body to maintain a stable internal state in spite of the demands of the environment

human immunodeficiency virus (HIV) a virus that gradually breaks down the body's immune system, making it

susceptible to a host of other infections, eventually resulting in AIDS

hypermetabolic a physiological state in which the metabolic rate is higher than normal, as occurs in the fight-or-flight response

hypnosis an altered state of consciousness

hypoglycemia low blood sugar

hypometabolic state a state of the body in which the heart slows, blood pressure drops, breathing is slow and easy, and muscle tension decreases

hypothalamus a portion of the brain that initiates the stress response in both the nervous system and the endocrine system

I

imminence interval during which an event is being anticipated; the more imminent an event, the more intense the appraisal

immunocompetence the extent to which an immune system is functioning properly to ward off microorganisms

impression management approach when people believe they are being observed they will eat less than when they believe no one is watching

incommunication stage a period in ICU during which a patient is either unconscious or barely conscious

index case the first identified instance of a medical problem

individualist one who focuses on independence and self-reliance rather than placing group needs above his or her own

information-motivation-behavioural skills model a theory maintaining that there are a number of steps one must go through to successfully achieve safe sex practices

informational support the provision of information such as treatment options or typical recovery times from a treatment or injury

insulin-dependent diabetes (Type 1) a condition in which a person produces very little or no insulin and as a result is required to take insulin on a daily basis, usually by way of self-administered injection

internal imagery technique in which an individual imagines being inside his or her body, experiencing a given situation

internality–externality hypothesis assertion that in people of normal weight, feelings of hunger and satiety come from within, in the form of internal stimuli (e.g., hunger pangs or feelings of fullness), whereas obese people are more likely to determine their level of hunger in response to external stimuli (e.g., time of day, smell, or sight of food)

intrusive cognitions unwanted thoughts, often visual in nature, related to the patient's ideas about cancer and death

invasiveness a measure of the extent to which hospital procedures, in a physical sense, involve piercing the skin or entering the body with instruments or, in a psychological sense, have the potential to cause embarrassment

irrelevant appraisal a cognitive process by which an event is appraised as having no implications for the individual's well-being

isokinetic exercise exercise that involves placing tension on a muscle group through a complete range of motion

isometric exercise exercise that involves the contraction of a muscle group against an immovable object without movement in the body

isotonic exercise exercise that involves using weights or calisthenics to place tension on the muscle through the shortening or lengthening of the muscle group

J

job strain model a model that suggests a job with high strain is one that includes high demands and low control

L

leptin hormone that responds to weight loss by increasing hunger levels until the person's weight returns to its ideal or target level

limbic system a system of the brain that is responsible, in part, for emotion in the stress response

local anaesthetics pain-relieving chemicals that can be applied topically but are much more effective when injected at the site where the pain originates

lock-out interval the time period between allowable dosages, when patient-controlled analgesia is used; a device is set by a practitioner to control this period

M

malignant neoplasms cancerous growths that may be treated by radiation and chemical therapy

medical jargon technical language used by a physician that is sometimes unintelligible to the patient

medical level of health promotion the orientation is disease-based and the goal is disease treatment

meditation a form of relaxation in which one attempts to focus attention fully on a single thought or image

message framing the extent to which positive or negative aspects of an outcome are emphasized in a health promotion message

metastasized spread (frequently used to denote the spread of cancer)

mitogen a relatively harmless substance that stimulates immune cell activity as though the immune cell were acting against an invading cell or antigen

mixed management model of care the preparation of a patient for eventual death while at the same time providing life-sustaining treatments

modelling a technique used to reduce stress associated with fear-provoking situations, in which observing a model coping well with a situation facilitates a similar response by the observer in a similar situation

modelling or matching effect people tend to eat the same amount as those in their presence

monitors patients who welcome information and seek it out

multidimensional measures of quality of life assessment that includes specific aspects of quality of life, such as physical, emotional, and social functioning

multilevel explanations explanations that use medical jargon followed by further explanation using everyday language

muscle dysmorphia condition characterized by belief that one's body is not sufficiently lean and muscular; clinically significant distress or impairment in social, occupational, or other areas of functioning; and a primary focus on being too small or inadequately muscular

mutual aid responsibility to family, friends, loved ones, and even society as a whole when it comes to health and safety

mutual-participation model health care model in which the physician and patient make joint decisions about every aspect of care

myocardial infarction (MI) heart attack caused by lack of blood flow to the heart

myocardial ischemia a lack of blood flow to the heart muscle

N

narcotics pain-killing drugs that work by binding to opiate receptors in the central nervous system

narrowly biomedical communication characterized mainly by biomedical talk, closed-ended medical questions, and very little discussion of psychosocial issues

naturally occurring support the support we obtain from friends, relatives, co-workers, and others in our own social networks

navigator often a nurse, community health worker, or social worker, who helps patients diagnosed with serious illnesses find their way through the sometimes complicated world of hospitals and treatment

negative-affect smoker a smoker who smokes to reduce negative affect, such as anxiety, distress, fear, or guilt

negotiated model decision-making model that allows decision making to be shared between the practitioners, patient, and family

nervous system one of the two major components of the physical response to stress; made up of the central nervous system and the peripheral nervous system

neuromatrix theory an extension to the gate control theory, with greater emphasis placed on the brain's role in pain perception

nicotine-replacement therapy stop-smoking technique that provides some form of nicotine to replace that previously obtained through smoking

NK cell cytotoxic activity assay test in which the proliferation and effectiveness of NK cells is measured after they have been exposed to diseased cells

NK cell lysis destroying tumour cells by exposing them to NK cells

nociceptors the afferent nerve endings that respond to pain stimuli

non-adherence failure to follow the advice of the health professional; the inability to stay with an exercise program non-discrepant responses physician responds to the patient's questions using the same sophistication of vocabulary that the patient uses

non-insulin-dependent diabetes (Type 2) a condition in which a person does not produce enough insulin or is not able to use insulin effectively

normative standards standards used to evaluate health promotion programs using statistics, such as national averages, that describe the health issue being addressed

novelty the extent to which an individual's previous experience with a situation influences the appraisal process

O

obesity condition characterized by having an excess of body fat; Health Canada and the World Health Organization define obesity as a BMI of 30.0 or greater

obesogenic neighbourhood neighbourhood designed in such a way as to increase the likelihood its inhabitants will be obese

oncology the study and treatment of cancer

operant pain pain that is reinforced by a person's environment

outpatient a person who goes to the hospital for a procedure or test but does not stay overnight

outcome goals goals that are concerned with the results or outcomes of events and usually involve comparisons to others

P

pain behaviours alterations in behaviour by a person experiencing pain to either reduce the pain or to prevent it from getting worse

pain threshold the point at which the intensity of a stimulus is perceived as painful

pain tolerance the duration of time or intensity at which a person is willing to endure a stimulus beyond the point where it began to hurt

palliative care care intended to maintain the best possible quality of life for a patient who is in the advanced stage of an illness. The focus is the control of pain and other symptoms as opposed to the cure of the illness

pancreas a gland that secretes insulin and glucagon as a function of blood sugar levels

Pap test (or Pap smear) a test done to screen for cervical cancer

parasympathetic nervous system the component of the autonomic system that re-establishes homeostasis in the system and promotes the reconstructive process following a stressful experience

participant modelling a technique used to reduce stress in which, subsequent to an individual observing a model coping with an anxiety evoking situation, the person is encouraged to engage in the behaviour while receiving reassurance from the model

passive leisure a positive experience that is associated with lack of activity (e.g., listening to music, daydreaming)

passive smoking the breathing of environmental tobacco smoke

patient-centred care approach in which patients and families become active members of the treatment team

patient-controlled analgesia (PCA) analgesic administration that is independently controlled by the patient

perceived behavioural control the belief that a specific behaviour is within one's control

performance accomplishments actual experiences of mastery, considered to be the most influential source of self-efficacy

performance goals goals that describe an outcome that can be achieved independently of others' performances

periaqueductal gray area an area of the midbrain that is involved in pain reception

peripheral nervous system division of the nervous system that is made up of the somatic nervous system and the autonomic nervous system (which is further divided into the sympathetic and the parasympathetic nervous systems)

peripheral route to persuasion attempts to affect attitude by appealing to emotion and general impression

peripherally acting analgesics non-narcotic medications that decrease pain by reducing inflammation at the site of tissue damage; they also inhibit the synthesis of neurochemicals in the peripheral nervous system that facilitate the transmission of pain impulses

person variables variables, paticularly commitments and beliefs, that interact with situation variables to affect the appraisal of a situation's stressfulness

personal control a factor that influences a person's ability to cope with stress; personal controlcan be achieved either behaviourally or cognitively

personal factors in stress personal characteristics, such as high self-esteem and a clear sense of control, that make some people better able to cope with the stressors of their job

personal resources resources that are available to people in their own lives to help them reduce the potential for stressful events and cope with stressful situations as they occur

persuasion the attempt to change people's attitudes and beliefs

phantom limb pain the experience of pain in an absent body part

phenomenologically according to a person's own report on the phenomenon

physical activity the expenditure of energy, either purposely or without intention, as a result of bodily movements produced by skeletal muscles as part of leisure or work activities

physical therapy therapy involved in the rehabilitation of muscle, bone, joint, or the results of nerve disease

physical fitness physiological functioning (including cardiorespiratory endurance, muscular endurance, muscular strength, body composition, and flexibility) that influences the ability to perform physical activity

physician impairment a state in which stress-related symptoms interfere with physicians' abilities to perform their jobs

pituitary gland a gland located in the brain; described as the "master" gland because it controls other glands through the hormones it secretes; most of these hormones have an indirect impact on stress

positive-affect smoker a smoker who smokes to attain positive affect (e.g., increased stimulation, relaxation, or gratification of sensorimotor needs)

positive psychology approach that encourages psychologists to use fewer negative or problem-focused frameworks and to focus more on effective human functioning

post-concussion syndrome symptoms experienced subsequent to a concussion, such as memory problems, difficulties in concentration, headaches, dizziness, and irritability

post-traumatic growh positive psychological or lifestyle outcome from an experience with a life-threatening illness

practical support help with the demands of daily living, such as getting meals and rides to the doctor

predictability a characteristic of the environment that allows an individual to prepare for an event and therefore reduce the stress involved

primary appraisal the initial evaluation of a situation

problem-focused coping coping by actively addressing the stressors associated with a disease, such as cancer, and its treatment

process goals goals that focus on specific processes that a performer will be concerned with during a performance

prognosis a prediction of how a medical condition will change in the future

progressive illness a condition that will continue to worsen in spite of treatment

progressive muscular relaxation (PMR) a technique in which a person achieves relaxation by flexing and gradually relaxing muscle groups

propriety standards standards used to evaluate health promotion programs that take legal and ethical issues into account

protease inhibitor medication that can significantly prolong the lives of people living with AIDS

proximity, density, connectivity, and land use mix factors that are used to determine the healthiness of a built environment

psychological empowerment in stress a personal factor in stress that can include finding work meaningful, having a sense of autonomy, feeling competent, and having a positive impact

psychological methods in sport techniques such as relaxation, goal-setting, and imagery, which are used to develop psychological skills

psychological skills in sport arousal or attentional control implemented to enhance performance

psychoneuroimmunology (PNI) the study of the relationship between psychological states and the functioning of the immune system

psychosocial communication includes substantial psychosocial exchange between physician and patient

public health level of health promotion the orientation is behaviour-based and the goal is disease prevention

Q

quality of life the extent to which symptoms and treatment affect a person's physical, social, cognitive, and emotional functioning

R

radiation therapy a form of cancer treatment in which radiation is used to shrink or destroy tumours

radical surgery cancer surgery that requires the removal of a considerable amount of normal tissue

reactance behaving counter to recommendations in response to feeling that one has lost personal control over health behaviours; the non-compliant behaviours and attitudes of patients who perceive hospital rules and regimens to be unacceptable challenges to their freedom

readaptation stage a period in ICU when a patient can sense a struggle to recover and recognizes his or her dependence on machines

reality shock the reaction to the discrepancy between a training environment and an actual work environment

reappraisal a continuous experience in which existing appraisals of situations are changed or modified on the basis of new information

reflection stage a period during which a patient who was in ICU tries to piece together his or her recent experience

relaxation techniques techniques to reduce anxiety to manageable levels so that energy can be used to positively influence performance; based on the principle that we cannot be relaxed and tense at the same time

relaxation skills techniques to reduce anxiety to manageable levels so that the energy can be used to positively influence performance; based on the principle that we cannot be relaxed and tensed at the same time

relocation stress (translocation stress) the stress caused by being separated from those things that were keeping patients alive—the one-on-one care and the technology

resilience concept in positive psychology that describes "good outcomes in spite of serious threats to adaptation or development"

resistance a set of physiological responses that allow a person to deal with a stressor; the second phase of Selye's General Adaptation Syndrome in which the body mobilizes its resources if the source of stress moves from acute to chronic

respondent pain pain that occurs in response to noxious stimulation or tissue damage

response efficacy belief the perception that a threat-reducing strategy will work

restraint theory an explanation for eating behaviour that claims that external sensitivity is linked to *restrained eating* (or strict dieting), rather than to body weight, and that overeating is more likely in people who restrain their eating

reticular formation complex system running through the middle of the brain stem that serves as a communication network to filter messages between the brain and the body

rotational injury a type of concussion resulting from a blow to the side of the head

S

scientific standards standards used to evaluate health promotion programs, using data published in scientific literature based on similar programs or health issues

second-impact syndrome the result when an athlete who has suffered a concussion returns to activity too soon and receives another blow to the head that can result in much greater trauma to the brain than that initially experienced

secondary appraisal an individual's evaluation of their ability to cope with a situation following the primary appraisal

sedatives medications, such as barbiturates, that affect pain indirectly by reducing anxiety and helping the patient to sleep

self-accountability the extent to which a person feels personally responsible for a given emotion or situation

self-awareness model the theory that drinking makes people less self-aware because it inhibits the use of normal complex information-processing strategies, such as memory and information acquisition

self-care behaviours such as exercise, diet, voluntary screening, and regular medical checkups that people engage in to promote their health

self-efficacy an individual's perception of his or her ability to succeed at a particular task at a specific time

self-management strategies strategies used to help people overcome the environmental conditions that perpetuate smoking

self-reinforcement praising oneself or rewarding oneself for accomplishments

self-talk sport psychology concept to describe one of the methods athletes use to correct bad habits, focus attention, modify activation, increase self-confidence and efficacy, and maintain exercise behaviour

set-point theory the idea that the body contains a set-point that works like a thermostat; when a person gains weight, biological control mechanisms diminish caloric intake; when a person loses weight, similar mechanisms increase hunger levels until the weight returns to its ideal or target level

Shiatsu massage sustained massage pressure on specific points of the body; according to the beliefs of practitioners Shiatsu massage releases blockages in the flow of energy through the body

sites of cancer types of cancer as defined by the location of the tumour

situation variables variables that interact with person variables to influence the appraisal of a situation

social comparison monitoring of the opinions and experiences of others to determine what is right and wrong, normal and abnormal; also subsequent use of this information to help with decision making

social determinants of health factors such as housing, employment, socioeconomic status, and food availability that affect the health of populations

social dominance a risk factor for coronary disease that is independent of hostility; social dominance is described as "a set of controlling behaviours, including the tendency to cut off and talk over the interviewer"

Social Ecological Model a model acknowledging that the individual is influenced by a collection of larger, inter-related, and cumulative contexts, such as organizations, communities, and governments

social facilitation approach this approach states that people tend to eat more when in the presence of others

social factors in stress the elements of a person's social network, such as family, friends, and co-workers, that affect ability to cope with job stressors

social learning model this theory, when applied to drinking behaviour, proposes that people drink because they experience positive reinforcement for doing so or because they observe others drinking and model the behaviour

social support a collection of interpersonal resources that people have at their disposal to help them avoid or cope with difficult times in their lives

socioenvironmental level of health promotion the orientation is toward social change and public health policy

sport an activity that involves rules or limits, a sense of history, an aspect of winning and losing, and an emphasis on physical exertion in the context of competition

sport psychology the study of the influence of psychological factors on sport behaviour

stages of change model model containing six linear stages: precontemplation, contemplation, action, maintenance, termination, and relapse

states and traits psychological concepts that distinguish between short-term conditions (states) and enduring characteristics (traits)

stimulant a drug that increases alertness, decreases appetite and the need for sleep, and may produce intense feelings of euphoria and a strong sense of well-being

stimulation-produced analgesia (SPA) freedom from pain as a result of electrical stimulation

stress the non-specific mental or somatic result of any demand upon the body

stress-buffering hypothesis the theory that social support has an indirect effect and acts as a buffer to protect individuals from the negative effects of stress

stress-diathesis model model that examines the interaction between the environment and heredity, often referred to as *nature versus nurture*; this model proposes that predisposing factors in an individual may determine whether or not a physical effect is experienced in the presence of stressful events

stress inoculation training a technique designed to help people cope effectively with stressful events; includes reconceptualizing events in less stressful ways, improving coping strategies, and applying the reconceptualized cognitive and behavioural approach to relevant stressors

stress-intrusion scores a measure of the impact a stressful event has on a person's life

stress literacy the degree to which an individual (or community) understands the effects of stress

stress management techniques techniques that have been developed specifically to help people cope with stress either directly or indirectly

stress response a response that reflects a spontaneous emotional or behavioural reaction to stress, rather than a deliberate attempt to cope

Stress response dampening effect the hypothesis suggesting that people do not respond as strongly psychologically or physiologically to stressors if they have been drinking.

stressful appraisal a cognitive process by which an event is appraised to involve harm/loss, threat, or challenge at the time of the primary appraisal

subjective norms beliefs regarding what others think we should do and the extent to which we are motivated to go along with these people

Swedish massage slow, gentle stroking movements to warm and relax tissue and stimulate blood circulation

sympathetic nervous system the system responsible for the "fight or flight" response when triggered by the hypothalamus (e.g., faster heart beat, increased blood pressure)

systematic desensitization a technique to help people cope with fear and anxiety by combining relaxation with gradual exposure to the fear-inducing stimulus

T

tangible support help with the demands of daily living, such as getting meals and rides to the doctor

task orientation a goal perspective in which individuals derive satisfaction from the sense of competence experienced as they improve; the focus is on effort and their own performance rather than that of others

temporal uncertainty lack of knowledge as to when an event will occur, which can result in stress

tension reduction hypothesis the hypothesis that people drink alcohol because of its tension-reducing properties

theory of planned behaviour behaviour is preceded by intention and that intention is influenced not only by subjective norms and beliefs about the efficacy of the behaviour, but also by the belief that one is actually capable of performing the behaviour

theory of reasoned action a theory that behaviour is preceded by intention, and that our intention is influenced by beliefs about the behaviour and subjective norms

threat appraisal an appraisal at the time of the primary appraisal that involves the anticipation of harm or loss

threat perception the belief that a threat is real and that we are vulnerable to it

thyroid gland an important gland in the stress response because it produces thyroxine, which increases blood pressure and respiration rate, and affects mental processes

total institution an institution that takes responsibility for the total care and control of its inhabitants

tranquillizers medications such as diazepam (Valium) that affect pain indirectly by reducing patient anxiety

transcendental meditation (TM) a technique of meditation to reduce stress introduced by Maharishi Mahesh Yogi in the late 1950s

transcutaneous electrical nerve stimulation (TENS) a pain control technique that involves placing an electrode on the surface of the skin and applying electrical stimulation

triage the sorting and classifying of patients to determine priority of need and proper location and means of treatment

type A behaviour pattern behaviours include impatience, time urgency, aggressiveness, hostility, and competitiveness; originally believed to be predictive of coronary heart disease

U

uncertainty a significant source of stress for physicians resulting from the fact that the consequences of medical decisions are uncertain

uniformity myth belief that all patients should receive the same amount of information in their preparation for a hospital stay regardless of their personal styles of coping with stress

upper respiratory tract infection (URTI) one of a collection of illnesses, such as colds, coughs, and bronchitis

V

verbal descriptor scale a rating scale on which people are asked to describe their pain by choosing the phrase that most closely resembles the pain that they are experiencing

verbal persuasion to verbally persuade others that they have the skills to perform a particular task—to talk them into it

vicarious experience experience that is gained through observing or visualizing others perform a skill, which can alert one to one's own capabilities and raise one's sense of self-efficacy

visual analog scale (VAS) a scale on which people rate and report their pain by marking a point on a line anchored by the phrase "no pain" and by a phrase such as "worst pain imaginable"

vulnerability physically, the adequacy of an individual's resources; psychologically, a threat to something that an individual values

W

withdrawal the unpleasant symptoms people experience when they stop using a substance to which they are addicted

References

A

Abascal, J.R., Brucato, D., & Brucato, L. (2001). *Stress mastery: The art of coping gracefully*. Englewood Cliffs, NJ: Prentice-Hall.

Abbott, R.D., Rodriguez, B.L., Burchfiel, C.M., & Curb, J.D. (1994). Physical activity in older middle-aged men and reduced risk of stroke: The Honolulu Heart Program. *American Journal of Epidemiology, 139*, 881–893.

Abdeshi, S.K., Hashemipur, M.A., Mesgarzadeh, V., Shahidi Payam, A., & Halaj Monfared, A. (2013). Effect of hypnosis on induction of local anaesthesia, pain perception, control of haemorrhage and anxiety during extraction of third molars: A case-control study. *Journal of Craniomaxillofacial Surgery, 41*(4), 310–315.

Abrahm, J.L. (2003). Update in palliative medicine and end-of-life care. *Annual Review of Medicine, 54*, 53–72.

Abroms, L., Jorgensen, C.M., Southwell, B.G., Geller, A.C., & Emmons, K.M. (2003). Gender differences in young adults' beliefs about sunscreen use. *Health Education Behavior, 30*(1), 29–43.

Active Canada 20/20. (2012). Accessed at www.activecanada 2020.ca/active-canada-20-20

Ader, R., Felton, D.L., & Cohen, N. (1981). *Psychoneuroimmunology*. New York: Academic Press.

Adlaf, E.M., Mann, R.E., & Paglia, A. (2003). Drinking, cannabis use and driving among Ontario students. *Canadian Medical Association Journal, 168*(5), 565–566.

Aiello-Laws, L., Reynolds, J., Deizer, N., Peterson, M., & Bakitas, M. (2009). Putting evidence into practice: What are the pharmacological interventions for nociceptive and neuropathic cancer pain in adults? *Clinical Journal of Oncology Nursing, 13*(6), 649–655.

Ajzen, I. (1985). From intentions to actions: A theory of planned behaviour. In J. Kuhland & J. Beckman (Eds.), *Action-control: From cognitions to behavior* (pp. 11–39). Heidelberg, Germany: Springer.

Ajzen, I. (1991). The theory of planned behavior. *Organizational Behavior and Human Decision Processes, 50*, 179–211.

Ajzen, I., & Fishbein, M. (1980). *Understanding attitudes and predicting social behaviour*. Englewood Cliffs, NJ: Prentice-Hall.

Akil, H., Owens, C., Gutstein, H., Taylor, L., Curran, E., & Watson, S. (1998). Endogenous opioids: Overview and current issues. *Drug and Alcohol Dependence, 51*, 127–140.

Albertsen, P. (1998, November). *A competing risk analysis of outcomes associated with men treated conservatively for clinically localized prostate cancer*. Paper presented at the Cancer Care: Quality of Life and Outcomes Symposium, Chicago, IL.

Alderman, B.A., Rogers, T.J., Landers, D.M., Arent, S.M., & Johnson, T.A. (2006). *The influence of physical activity and fitness on stress: A meta-analysis*. Unpublished manuscript.

Aldwin, C.M. (1994). *Stress, coping and development: An integrative perspective*. New York: Guilford Press.

Alexander, C.N., Robinson, P., Orme-Johnson, D.W., Schneider, R.H., & Walton, K.G. (1994). The effects of transcendental meditation compared to other methods of relaxation and meditation in reducing risk factors, morbidity, & mortality. *Homeostasis, 35*, 243–263.

Alford, C., Hamilton-Morris, J., & Verster, J.C. (2012). The effects of energy drink in combination with alcohol on performance and subjective awareness. *Psychopharmacology, 222*, 519–532.

Alon, E., Jaquenod, M., & Schaeppi, B. (2003). Post-operative epidural versus intravenous patient-controlled analgesia. *Minerva Anestesiologica, 69*(5), 443–437.

Alonso, J., Black, C., Norregaard, J.C., Dunn, E., Anderson, T.F., Espallargues, M., Bernth-Petersen, P., & Anderson, G.F. (1998). Cross-cultural differences in the reporting of global functional capacity: An example in cataract patients. *Medical Care, 36*(6), 868–878.

Alves, C.R., Gualano, B., Takao, P.P., Avakian, P., Fernandes, R.M., Morine, D., et al. (2012, August). Effects of acute physical exercise on executive functions: A comparison between aerobic and strength exercise. *Sport Exercise Psychology, 34*(4), 539–549.

Alvord, M.K., & Grados, J.J. (2005). Enhancing resilience in children: A proactive process. *Professional Psychology: Research and Practice, 36*, 238–245.

Ambady, N., Laplante, D., Nguyen, T., Rosenthal, R., Chaumeton, N., & Levinson, W. (2002). Surgeons' tone of voice: A clue to malpractice history. *Surgery, 132*(1), 5–9.

American Medical Association. (2013). Guidelines for physician-patient electronic communication. Retrieved March 14, 2013, from http://www.ama-assn.org/ama/pub/about-ama/our-people/member-groups-sections/young-physicians-section/advocacy-resources.page?

American Pain Society. (2005). *Guidelines for the management of cancer pain in adults and children.* Glenview, IL: Author.

American Pain Society. (2013). *Pain: Current understanding of assessment, management and treatments.* Retrieved July 25, 2013, from www.americanpainsociety.org/education/content/enduringmaterials.html

American Psychiatric Association. (2013). *Diagnostic and statistical manual of mental disorders* (5th ed.). Washington, DC: Author.

Anand, B.K., & Chhina, G.S. (1961). Investigations on yogis claiming to stop their heart beats. *Indian Journal of Medical Research, 49,* 90–94.

Anand, B.K., Chhina, G.S., & Singh, B. (1961a). Studies on Shri Ramand Yogi during his stay in an air-tight box. *Indian Journal of Medical Research, 49,* 82–89.

Anand, B.K., Chhina, G.S., & Singh, B. (1961b). Some aspects of electroencephalographic studies in yogis. *EEG and Clinical Neurophysiology, 13,* 452–456.

Anda, R.F., Dong, M., Brown, D.W., Felitti, V.J., Giles, W.H., Perry, G.S., et al. (2009). The relationship of adverse childhood experiences to a history of premature death of family members. *BMC Public Health, 9,* 106.

Andersen, B.L., Cacioppo, J.T., & Roberts, D.C. (1995). Delay in seeking a cancer diagnosis: Delay stages and psychophysiological comparison processes. *British Journal of Social Psychology, 34,* 33–52.

Anderson, B.L., Farrar, W.B., Golden-Kreutz, D., Kutz, L.A., MacCallum, R., Courtney, M.E., et al. (1998). Stress and immune responses after surgical treatment for regional breast cancer. *Journal of the National Cancer Institute, 90,* 30–36.

Anderson, R., Freedland, K., Clouse, R., & Lustman, P. (2001). Prevalence of comorbid depression in adults with diabetes. A meta-analysis. *Diabetes Care, 24,* 1069–1078.

Andrykowski, M.A., Carpenter, J.S., Studts, J.L., Cordova, M.J. Cunningham, L.L.C., Beacham, A., et al. (2002). Psychological impact of benign breast biopsy: A longitudinal, comparative study. *Health Psychology, 21*(5), 485–494.

Andreoli, A.V., Keller, S.E., Rabaeus, M., Marin, P., Bartlett, J.A., & Taban, C. (1993). Depression and immunity: Age, severity, and clinical course. *Brain, Behavior, and Immunity, 7,* 279–292.

Anshel, M. (2005). *Applied exercise psychology: A practitioner's guide to improving client health and fitness.* New York: Springer.

Antall, G.F., & Kresevic, D. (2004). The use of guided imagery to manage pain in an elderly orthopaedic population. *Orthopaedic Nursing, 23,* 335–340.

Antoni, M.H. (2003). *Stress management intervention for women with breast cancer.* Washington, DC: American Psychological Association.

Antshel, K.M. (2002). Integrating culture as a means of improving treatment adherence in the Latino population. *Psychology, Health & Medicine, 7,* 435–449.

Ariely, D., & Loewenstein, G. (2006). The heat of the moment: The effect of sexual arousal on sexual decision making. *Journal of Behavioral Decision Making, 19,* 87–98.

Armitage, C.J., & Conner, M. (2000). Social cognition models and health behaviour: A structured review. *Psychology and Health, 15,* 173–189.

Armitage, C.J., Norman, P., & Conner, M. (2002). Can the Theory of Planned Behaviour mediate the effects of age, gender and multidimensional health locus of control? *British Journal of Health Psychology, 7,* 299–316.

Arnett, J.L., Martin, R.M., Streiner, D.L., & Goodman, J.T. (1987). Hospital psychology in Canada. *Canadian Psychology, 28,* 161–171.

Arnsberger, P., Fox, P., Ryder, P., Nussey, B., Zhang, X., & Otero-Sabogal, R. (2006). Timely follow-up among multicultural women with abnormal mammograms. *American Journal of Health Behavior, 30*(1), 51–61.

Aronoff, G.M. (2000). Opioids in chronic pain management: Is there a significant risk of addiction? *Current Review of Pain, 4,* 112–121.

Aspinwall, L.G., & Taylor, S.E. (1997). A stitch in time: Self-regulation and proactive coping. *Psychological Bulletin, 121,* 417–436.

Association of Faculties of Medicine of Canada. (2012). *Canadian medical education statistics.* http://www.afmc.ca/publications-statistics-e.php. Accessed December 6, 2012.

Astle, S.J. (1996). The experience of loss in athletes. *Journal of Sports Medicine and Physical Fitness, 26,* 279–284.

Atkins, D., & Cullen, T. (2013). The future of health information technology: Implications for research. *Medical Care, 51,* S1–S3.

Audrain-McGovern, J., Rodriguez, D., & Kassel, J.D. (2009). Adolescent smoking and depression: Evidence for self-medication and peer-smoking mediation. *Addiction, 104,* 1743–1756.

Auslander, G.K., Netzer, D., & Arad, I. (2003). Parental anxiety following discharge from hospital of their very low birth weight infants. *Family Relations: Interdisciplinary Journal of Applied Family Studies, 52*(1), 12–21.

Austenfeld, J.L., & Stanton, A.L. (2004). Coping through emotional approach: A new look at emotion, coping, and health-related outcomes. *Journal of Personality, 72*(6), 1335–1363.

Austin, B.S. (2013). Closing the "know-do" gap: Training public health professionals in eating disorders prevention via case-method teaching. *International Journal of Eating Disorders, 46*(5), 533–537.

Ayanian, J.Z., & Cleary, P.D. (1999). Perceived risks of heart disease and cancer among cigarette smokers. *Journal of the American Medical Association, 281*, 1019–1021.

Aziz, A. (2004). Sources of perceived stress among American medical doctors: A cross-cultural perspective. *Cross-Cultural Management, 11*(4), 28–39.

B

Barber, J. (1986). Hypnotic analgesia. In A.D. Holzman & D.C. Turk (Eds.), *Pain management: A handbook of psychological treatment approaches* (pp. 151–167). New York: Pergamon Press.

Badgley, R.F. (1994). Health promotion and social change in the health of Canadians. In A. Pederson, M. O'Neill, & I. Rootman (Eds.), *Health promotion in Canada: Provincial, national and international perspectives* (pp. 200–239). Toronto: Saunders.

Bagozzi, R.P. (1992). The self-regulation of attitudes, intentions, and behavior. *Social Psychology Quarterly, 29*, 178–204.

Bahrke, M.S., & Morgan, W.P. (1978). Anxiety reduction following exercise and meditation. *Cognitive Therapy and Research, 2*, 323–334.

Bailey, R.K., Geyen, D.J., Scott-Gurnell, K., Hipolito, M.M.S., Bailey, T.A., & Beal, J.M. (2005). Understanding and treating depression among cancer patients. *International Journal of Gynecological Cancer, 15*(2), 203–208.

Bair, M.J., Robinson, R.L., Eckert, G.J., Stang, P.E., Croghan, T.W., & Kroenke, K. (2004). Impact of pain on depression treatment response in primary care. *Psychosomatic Medicine, 66*, 17–22.

Baker, C., & Melby, V. (1996). An investigation into the attitudes and practices of intensive care nurses toward verbal communication with unconscious patients. *Journal of Clinical Nursing, 5*, 185–192.

Balfour, L., Silverman, A., Tasca, G., Kowal, J., Seatter, R., & Cameron, W. (2003). Stress and depression related to lower immune system functioning among people with HIV (PHAS). Presentation to the 64th Annual Conference of the Canadian Psychological Association, June 12, Hamilton, Ontario.

Ball, G.D.C., & McCargar, L.J. (2003). Childhood obesity in Canada: A review of prevalence estimates and risk factors for cardiovascular diseases and type 2 diabetes. *Canadian Journal of Applied Physiology, 28*, 117–140.

Bandura, A. (1977). Self-efficacy: Toward a unifying theory of behavior change. *Psychological Review, 84*, 191–215.

Bandura, A. (1986). *Social foundations of thought and action: A social cognitive theory.* Englewood Cliffs, NJ: Prentice-Hall.

Bandura, A. (1990). Perceived self-efficacy in the exercise of personal agency. *Journal of Applied Sport Psychology, 2*, 128–163.

Bandura, A. (1991). Self-efficacy mechanism in physiological activation and health-promotion behavior. In J. Madden IV (Ed.), *Neurobiology of learning, emotion, and affect* (pp. 229–269). New York: Raven Press.

Bandura, A. (1997). *Self-efficacy: The exercise of control.* New York: Freeman.

Bannister, R. (1955). *The four-minute mile.* New York: Dodd, Mead.

Barling, N.R., & Moore, S.M. (1996). Prediction of cervical cancer screening using the theory of reasoned action. *Psychological Reports, 79*, 77–78.

Barnes, E. (2005). Caring and curing: Paediatric cancer services since 1960. *European Journal of Cancer Care, 14*(4), 373–380.

Barnes, M.P., & Ward, A.B. (2000). *Textbook of rehabilitation medicine.* Oxford: Oxford University Press.

Barnett, R.C., Steptoe, A., & Gareis, K.C. (2005). Marital-role quality and stress-related psychobiological indicators. *Annals of Behavioral Medicine, 30*(1), 36–43.

Barrett, L., & Yates, P. (2002). Oncology/haematology nurses: A study of job satisfaction, burnout, and intention to leave the specialty. *Australian Health Review: A Publication of the Australian Hospital Association, 25*(3), 109–121.

Barson, J.R., Morganstern, I., & Leibowitz, S.F. (2010). Galanin and consummatory behavior: Special relationship with dietary fat, alcohol and circulating lipids. In T. Hokfelt (Ed.), *Galanin* (pp. 87–111). Basel, Switzerland: Springer Basel.

Bartley, E.J., & Fillingim, R.B. (2013). Sex differences in pain: A brief review of clinical and experimental findings. *British Journal of Anaesthesia, 11*, 52–58.

Battino, R. (2000). *Guided imagery and other approaches to healing.* Carmarthen, UK: Crown House.

Battista, S.R., Stewart, S.H., & Ham, L.S. (2010). A critical review of laboratory-based studies examining the relationships of social anxiety and alcohol intake. *Current Drug Abuse Reviews, 3*(1), 3–22.

Bauer, M., Fitzgerald, L., Haesler, E., & Manfrin, M. (2009). Hospital discharge planning for frail older people and their family. Are we delivering best practice? A review of the evidence. *Journal of Clinical Nursing, 18*, 2539–2546.

Baum, A., & Posluszny, D.M. (1999). Health psychology: Mapping biobehavioral contributions to health and illness. *Annual Review of Psychology, 50*, 137–163.

Baxter, N., Cohen, R., & McLeod, R. (1996). The impact of gender on the choice of surgery as a career. *American Journal of Surgery, 172*, 373–376.

BC Centre for Disease Control. (2013). *Overview of HIV/AIDS*. Retrieved December 3, 2014, from http://www.bccdc.ca/dis-cond/a-z/_h/HIVAIDS/overview/default.htm

Beard, H. (2005). Does intermediate care minimize relocation stress for patients leaving the ICU? *Nursing in Critical Care, 10*(6), 272–278.

Beck, A. (1963). Thinking and depression: 1. Idiosyncratic content and cognitive distortions. *Archives of General Psychiatry, 9*, 324–333.

Beck, A. (1976). *Cognitive therapy and the emotional disorders.* New York: International Universities Press.

Becker, C.B., Smith, L.M., & Ciao, A.C. (2006). Peer-facilitated eating disorder prevention: A randomized effectiveness trial of cognitive dissonance and media advocacy. *Journal of Counseling Psychology, 53*(4), 550–555.

Becker, M.H. (1974). The health belief model and sick role behavior. *Health Education Monographs, 2*, 409–419.

Becker, M.H., & Janz, N.K. (1987). On the effectiveness and utility of health hazard/health risk appraisal in clinical and nonclinical settings. *Health Services Research, 22*, 537–551.

Beckman, H.B., & Frankel, R.M. (1984). The effect of physician behavior on the collection of data. *Annals of Internal Medicine, 101*, 692–696.

Beecher, H.K. (1959). *Measurement of subjective responses.* New York: Oxford University Press.

Behar, R. (2006). Gender-related aspects of eating disorders: A psychosocial view. In P.I. Swain (Ed.), *New developments in eating disorders research* (pp. 37–63). Hauppauge, NY: Nova.

Beisecker, A., & Beisecker, T. (1990). Patient information-seeking behaviors when communicating with doctors. *Medical Care, 28*, 19–28.

Belle Brown, J. (2003). Time and the consultation. In R. Jones, N. Britten, & L. Culpepper (Eds.), *Oxford textbook of primary medical care* (pp. 190–194). Oxford, England: Oxford University Press.

Ben-Eliyahu, S., Page, G.G., & Schleifer, S.J. (2007). Stress, NK cells, and cancer: Still a promissory note. *Brain, Behavior, and Immunity, 21*, 881–887.

Bennenbroek, F.T.C., Buunk, B.P., van der Zee, K.I., & Grol, B. (2002). Social comparison and patient information: What do cancer patients want? *Patient Education & Counseling, 47*, 5–12.

Bennett, K.K., Compas, B.E., Beckjord, E., & Glinder, J.G. (2005). Self-blame and distress among women with newly diagnosed breast cancer. *Journal of Behavioral Medicine, 28*(4), 313–323.

Bensing, J.M., Roter, D.L., & Hulsman, R.L. (2003). Communication patterns of primary care physicians in the United States and the Netherlands. *Journal of General Internal Medicine, 18*, 335–342.

Bensing, J., Rimondini, M., & Visser, A. (2013). What patients want. *Patient Education and Counseling, 90*, 287–290.

Benso, A., Casanueva, F.F., Ghigo, E., & Granata, R. (Eds.). (2013). *The grehlin system.* Basel, Switzerland: Karger.

Benson, H. (1975). *The relaxation response.* New York: William Morrow.

Benson, H., Beary, J.F., & Carol, M.P. (1974). The relaxation response. *Psychiatry, 37*, 37–46.

Ben-Zur, H. (2002). Monitoring/blunting and social support: Associations with coping and affect. *International Journal of Stress Management, 9*(4), 357–373.

Berger, B.G., & Tobar, D.A. (2007). Physical activity and quality of life: Key considerations. In G. Tenenbaum & R.C. Eklund (Eds.), *Handbook of sport psychology* (3rd ed., pp. 598–620). New Jersey: John Wiley & Sons.

Bergman, B., Ahmad, F., & Stewart, D.E. (2003). Physician health, stress and gender at a university hospital. *Journal of Psychosomatic Research, 54*(2), 171–178.

Bernstein, D.A., & Borkovec, T.D. (1973). *Progressive relaxation training: A manual for the helping professions.* Champaign, IL: Research Press.

Betancourt, J.R., Green, A.R., Carrillo, J.E., & Ananeh-Firempong, O. (2003). Defining cultural competence: A practical framework for addressing racial/ethnic disparities in health and health care. *Public Health Reports, 118*, 293–302.

Bierut, L.J. (2011). Genetic vulnerability and susceptibility to substance dependence. *Neuron, 69*(4), 618–627.

Bigby, J., & Perez-Stable, E.J. (2004). The challenges of understanding and eliminating racial and ethnic disparities in health. *Journal of General Internal Medicine, 19*, 201–203.

Biddle, N., Kennedy, S., & McDonald, J.T. (2007). Health assimilation patterns among Australian immigrants. *Economic Record, 83*(260), 16–30.

Biddle, S.J.H., & Mutrie, N. (2001). *Psychology of physical activity: Determinants, well-being and interventions.* New York: Routledge.

Bingefors, K., & Isacson, D. (2004). Epidemiology, co-morbidity, and impact on health-related quality of life of self-reported headache and musculoskeletal pain—A gender perspective. *European Journal of Pain, 8,* 435–450.

Birmingham, C.L., Su, J., Hlynsky, J.A., Goldner, E.M., & Gao, M. (2005). The mortality rate from anorexia nervosa. *International Journal of Eating Disorders, 38*(2), 143–146.

Bish, A., Ramirez, A., Burgess, C., & Hunter, M. (2005). Understanding why women delay in seeking help for breast cancer symptoms. *Journal of Psychosomatic Research, 58*(4), 321–326.

Bishop, S.R., & Warr, D. (2003). Coping, catastrophizing and chronic pain in breast cancer. *Journal of Behavioral Medicine, 26*(3), 265–281.

Bjordal, J.M., Johnson, M.I., & Ljunggreen, A.E. (2003). Transcutaneous electrical nerve stimulation (TENS) can reduce postoperative analgesic consumption. A meta-analysis with assessment of optimal treatment parameters for postoperative pain. *European Journal of Pain, 7*(2), 181–188.

Blair, M.J., Robinson, R.L., Eckert, G.J., Stang, P.E., Croghan, T.W., & Kroenke, K. (2004). Impact of pain on depression treatment response in primary care. *Psychosomatic Medicine, 66,* 17–22.

Blair, S.N., Kohl, H.W., Paffenberger, R.S., Clark, D.G., Cooper, K.H., & Gibbons, L.W. (1989). Physical fitness and all-cause mortality: A prospective study of healthy men and women. *Journal of the American Medical Association, 262,* 2395–2401.

Blanchard, E.B. (1987). Long-term effects of behavioral treatment of chronic headache. *Behavior Therapy, 18,* 375–385.

Blanchard, E.B. (2000). Headaches. In A.E. Kazdin (Ed.), *Encyclopedia of psychology: Vol. 4* (pp. 67–70). Washington, DC: American Psychological Association.

Blanchard, E.B., Andrasik, F., Guarnieri, P., Neff, D.F., & Rodichok, L.D. (1987). Two-, three-, and four-year follow-up on the self-regulatory treatment of chronic headache. *Journal of Consulting and Clinical Psychology, 55,* 257–259.

Blanchard, E.B., Appelbaum, K.A., Guarnieri, P., Morrill, B., & Dentinger, M.P. (1987). Five year prospective follow-up on the treatment of chronic headache with biofeedback and/or relaxation. *Headache, 27,* 580–583.

Blanchard, E.B., & Haynes, M.R. (1975). Biofeedback treatment of a case of Raynaud's disease. *Journal of Behavior Therapy and Experimental Psychiatry, 6,* 230–234.

Blanchard, J., & Lurie, N. (2004). R-E-S-P-E-C-T: Patient reports of disrespect in the health care setting and its impact on care. *Journal of Family Practice, 53,* 721–730.

Blane, C., Hughes, C.M., & McElnay, J.C. (2006). The impact of depressive symptoms and psychosocial factors on medication adherence in cardiovascular disease. *Patient Education and Counseling, 60*(2), 187–193.

Blas, E., & Kurup, A.S. (Eds.). (2010). *Equity, determinants and public health programs.* Geneva: World Health Organization.

Bloom, J.R., & Kessler, L. (1994). Emotional support following cancer: A test of the stigma and social activity hypothesis. *Journal of Health and Social Behavior, 35,* 118–133.

Boehm, J.K., Peterson, C., Kivimaki, M., & Kubzansky, L.D. (2011). Heart health when life is satisfying: Evidence from the Whitehall II cohort study. *European Heart Journal, 32*(21), 2672–2677.

Boey, K.W. (1999). Distressed and stress resistant nurses. *Issues in Mental Health Nursing, 20,* 33–54.

Bogart, L.M., & Delahanty, D.L. (2004). Psychosocial models. In T. Boll, R.G. Frank, A. Baum, & J.L. Wallander (Eds.), *Handbook of clinical health psychology: Volume 3. Models and perspectives in health psychology* (pp. 201–248). Washington, DC: American Psychological Association.

Bogart, L.M., & Helgeson, V.S. (2000). Social comparisons among women with breast cancer: A longitudinal investigation. *Journal of Applied Social Psychology, 30*(3), 547–575.

Bogg, T., & Roberts, B.W. (2004). Conscientiousness and health-related behaviours: A meta-analysis of the leading behavioural contributors to mortality. *Psychological Bulletin, 130,* 887–919.

Boisvert, J.A., & Harrell, W.A. (2009). Homosexuality as a risk factor for eating disorder symptomatology in men. *Journal of Men's Studies, 17,* 210–225.

Boldt, J., Thaler, E., Lehmann, A., Papsdorf, M., & Isgro, F. (1998). Pain management in cardiac surgery patients: Comparison between standard therapy and patient-controlled analgesia regimen. *Journal of Cardiothoracic and Vascular Anesthiology, 12,* 654–658.

Bonham, V.L. (2001). Race, ethnicity, and pain treatment: Striving to understand the causes and solutions to the disparities in pain treatment. *Journal of Law, Medicine and Ethics, 29,* 52–68.

Booth, M.J. (1998). Nurse anesthetist reaction to the unexpected or untimely death of patients in the operating room. *Holistic Nursing Practice, 13,* 51–58.

Borland, R., Wilson, N., Fong, G.T., Hammond, D., Cummings, K.M., Yong, H.H., et al. (2009). Impact of graphic and text warnings on cigarette packs: Findings from four countries over five years. *Tobacco Control: An International Journal, 18*(5), 358–364.

Boroditsky, R., Fisher, W., & Sand, M. (1996). The 1995 Canadian contraception study. *Journal SOGC, 18*(Suppl.), 1–31.

Boscarino, J.A. (1997). Diseases among men 20 years after exposure to severe stress: Implications for clinical research and medical care. *Psychosomatic Medicine, 59,* 605–614.

Bosy-Westphal, A., Hinrichs, S., Jauch-Chara, K., Hitze, B., Later, W., Wilms, B., et al. (2008). Influence of partial sleep deprivation on energy balance and insulin sensitivity in healthy women. *Obesity Facts, 1,* 266–273.

Boucard, G.K., Albinet, C.T., Bugaiska, A., Bouquet, C.A., Clarys, D., & Audiffren, M. (2012). Impact of physical activity on executive functions in aging: A selective effect on inhibition among old adults. *Journal of Sport and Exercise Psychology, 34*(6), 808.

Bozoian, S., Rejeski, W.J., & McAuley, E. (1994). Self-efficacy influences feeling states associated with acute exercise. *Journal of Sport and Exercise Psychology, 16,* 326–333.

Bracegirdle, H. (1995). Children's stereotypes of visibly physically impaired targets: An empirical study. *British Journal of Occupational Therapy, 58,* 25–27.

Brady, J.V., Porter, R.W., Conrad, D.G., & Mason, J.W. (1958). Avoidance behavior and the development of duodenal ulcers. *Journal of the Experimental Analysis of Behavior, 1,* 69–72.

Brain, K., Henderson, B.J., Tyndel, S., Bankhead, C., Watson, E., Clements, A., et al. (2008). Predictors of breast cancer-related distress following mammography screening in younger women on a family history breast screening programme. *Psycho-Oncology, 17,* 1180–1188.

Brannon, L., & Feist, J. (2000). *Health psychology: An introduction to behavior and health* (4th ed.). Belmount, CA: Wadsworth/Thompson Learning.

Brannon, L., & Feist, J. (2007). *Health psychology: An introduction to behavior and health* (6th ed.). Toronto: Thomson Wadsworth.

Bray, G.A., & Tartaglia, L.A. (2000). Medicinal strategies in the treatment of obesity. *Nature, 404,* 672–677.

Brehm, J.W. (1966). *A theory of psychological reactance.* New York: Academic Press.

Breivik, H., Collette, B., Ventafridda, V., Cohen, R., & Gallacher, D. (2006). Survey of chronic pain in Europe: Prevalence, impact on daily life, and treatment. *European Journal of Pain, 10*(4), 287–333.

Brennan, M.J., & Liebermann, J.A., III. (2009). Sleep disturbances in patients with chronic pain: Effectively managing opioid analgesia to improve outcomes. *Current Medical Research and Opinion, 25*(5), 1045–1055.

Brewer, B.W. (1994). Review and critique of models of psychological adjustment to athletic injury. *Journal of Applied Sport Psychology, 6,* 87–100.

Brewer, B.W. (2001). Psychology of sport injury rehabilitation. In R.N. Singer, H.A. Hausenblas, & C.M. Janelle (Eds.), *Handbook of Sport Psychology* (2nd ed., pp. 767–809). New York: Wiley.

Brewer, B.W. (2010). The role of psychological factors in sport injury rehabilitation outcomes. *International Review of Sport and Exercise Psychology, 3,* 40–61.

Brewster, J.M. (2001). Helping physicians with alcohol problems. *CMAJ, 164*(2), 179.

Brewin, C.R., Watson, M., McCarthy, S., Hyman, P., & Dayson, D. (1998). Intrusive memories and depression in cancer patients. *Behaviour Research and Therapy, 36,* 1131–1142.

Brinchmann, B.S., Forde, R., & Nortvedt, P. (2002). What matters to the parents? A qualitative study of parents' experiences with life-and-death decisions concerning their premature infants. *Nursing Ethics, 9*(4), 388–404.

Brink, E., Karlson, B.W., & Hallberg, L.R.-M. (2002). To be stricken with acute myocardial infarction: A grounded theory study of symptom perception and care-seeking behaviour. *Journal of Health Psychology, 7*(5), 533–543.

Brockmeyer, T., Holtforth, M.G., Bents, H., Kammerer, A., Herzog, W., & Friederich, H.C. (2012), The thinner the better: Self-esteem and low body weight in anorexia nervosa. *Clinical Psychology and Psychotherapy, 20*(4), 1771.

Broderick, J.E., Junghaenel, D.U., & Turk, D.C. (2004). Stability of patient adaptation classifications on the multidimensional pain inventory. *Pain, 109,* 94–102.

Brondel, L., Rober, M.A., Nougues, P.M., Touyarou, P., & Davenne, D. (2010). Acute partial sleep deprivation increases food intake in healthy men. *American Journal of Clinical Nutrition, 91*(6), 1550–1559.

Brondolo, E., & Mas, F. (2001). Cognitive-behavioral strategies for improving medication adherence in patients with bipolar disorder. *Cognitive and Behavioral Practice, 8*(2), 137–147.

Brown, C. (2005). Injuries: The psychology of recovery and rehab. In S. Murphy (Ed.), *The sport psych handbook* (pp. 215–236). Champaign, IL: Human Kinetics.

Brown, I. (2014). Faster, stronger—Deadlier: Why do elite athletes sneer at risk and tempt the gods, and why do we encourage them? *The Globe and Mail,* February 14, 2014.

Brown, C.A., & Mehler, P.S. (2011). Medical complications of self-induced vomiting. *Eating Disorders, 21*(4), 287–294.

Brown, D.L. (1988). No pretending not to know. *Journal of the American Medical Association, 260*, 2720.

Brown, M.A., & Stetz, K. (1999). The labor of caregiving: A theoretical model of caregiving during potentially fatal illness. *Qualitative Health Research, 9*, 182–197.

Bruch, H. (1973). Eating disorders. *Obesity, anorexia nervosa and the person within*. New York: Basic Books.

Bruch, H. (1978). *The golden cage: The enigma of anorexia nervosa*. Cambridge, MA: Harvard University Press.

Bruch, H. (1982). Anorexia nervosa: Therapy and theory. *American Journal of Psychiatry, 139*, 1531–1538.

Bruch, H. (2001). *The golden cage: The enigma of anorexia nervosa*. Cambridge, MA: Harvard University Press.

Brucker, P.S., Yost, K., Cashy, J., Webster, K., & Cella, D. (2005). General population and cancer patients norms for the Functional Assessment of Cancer Therapy—General (FACT-G). *Evaluation & the Health Professions, 28*(2), 192–211.

Brunton, P. (1972). *A search in secret India*. New York: Samuel Weiser.

Buckalew, L.W. (1991). Patients' compliance: The problem and directions for psychological research. *Psychological Reports, 68*, 348–350.

Buckworth, J., & Dishman, R.K. (2007). Exercise adherence. In G. Tenenbaum & R.C. Eklund (Eds.), *Handbook of sport psychology* (3rd ed., pp. 509–536). New Jersey: John Wiley & Sons.

Bulik, C.M., Sullivan, P.F., & Kendler, K.S. (2003). Genetic and environmental contributions to obesity and binge eating. *International Journal of Eating Disorders, 33*, 293–298.

Bulik, C.M., Sullivan, P.F., Tozzi, F., Furberg, H., Lichtenstein, P., & Pedersen, N.L. (2006). Prevalence, heritability, and prospective risk factors for anorexia nervosa. *Archives of General Psychiatry, 63*, 305–312.

Burack, J.H., Barrett, D.C., Stall, R.D., Chesney, M.A., Ekstrand, M.L., & Coates, T.J. (1993). Depressive symptoms and CD4 lymphocyte decline among HIV-infected men. *Journal of the American Medical Association, 270*, 2568–2573.

Burack, R.C., & Carpenter, R.R. (1983). The predictive value of the presenting complaint. *Journal of Family Practice, 16*, 749–754.

Burgess, C., & Ramirez, A. (2006). Response to the letter to the editor from Professor Friedrich Stiefel on "Understanding why women delay in seeking help for breast cancer symptoms." *Journal of Psychosomatic Research, 60*(3), 309–310.

Burgoon, M., Callister, M., & Hunsaker, F.G. (1994). Patients who deceive: An empirical investigation of patient-physician communication. *Journal of Language and Social Psychology, 13*, 443–468.

Burke, R.J., & Richardsen, A.M. (1990). Sources of satisfaction and stress among Canadian physicians. *Psychological Reports, 67*, 1335–1344.

Burt, R.D., Dinh, K.T., Peterson, A.V., Jr., & Sarason, I.G. (2000). Predicting adolescent smoking: A prospective study of personality variables. *Preventive Medicine, 30*(2), 115–125.

Burton, D., Naylor, S., & Holliday, B. (2001). Goal setting in sports: Investigating the goal effectiveness paradox. In R.N. Singer, H.A. Hausenblas, & C.M. Janelle (Eds.), *Handbook of Sport Psychology* (2nd ed., pp. 497–528). New York: Wiley.

Burton, D., & Weiss, C.L. (2008). The fundamental goal concept: The path to process and performance success. In T. Horn (Ed.), *Advances in sport psychology* (3rd ed., pp. 339–375). Champaign, IL: Human Kinetics.

Burton, K.R., & Wong, I.K. (2004). A force to contend with: The gender gap closes in Canadian medical schools. *Canadian Medical Association Journal, 170*(9), 1385–1386.

Bush, D.E., Ziegelstein, R.C., Tayback, M., Richter, D., Stevens, S., Zahalsky, H., et al. (2002). Even minimal symptoms of depression increase mortality risk after acute myocardial infarction. *American Journal of Cardiology, 89*, 112–113.

Buske, L. (2009). Family physician shortfall estimates. Canadian Collaborative Centre for Physician Resources.

Byrne, D. (1977). Social psychology and the study of sexual behavior. *Personality and Social Psychology Bulletin, 3*, 3–30.

C

Cafri, G. Olivardia, R., & Thompson, J.K. (2008). Symptom characteristics and psychiatric comorbidity among males with muscle dysmorphia. *Comprehensive Psychiatry, 49*, 374–379.

Calle, E.E., Thun, M.J., Petrelli, J.M., Rodriguez, C., & Heath, C.W. (1999). Body-mass index and mortality in a prospective cohort of U.S. adults. *The New England Journal of Medicine, 341*, 1097–1105.

Calzavara, L.M., Bullock, S.L., Myers, T., Marshall, V.W., & Cockerill, R. (1999). Sexual partnering and risk of HIV/STD among Aboriginals. *Canadian Journal of Public Health, 90*, 186–191.

Calzavara, L.M., Burchell, A.N., Levovic, G., Myers, T., Remis, R.S., Rabould, J., et al. (2012). The impact of stressful life events on unprotected anal sex among gay and bisexual men. *AIDS and Behavior, 16*, 633–643.

Cameron, L. (1997). Screening for cancer: Illness perceptions and illness worry. In K.J. Petrie & J.A. Weinman (Eds.), *Perceptions of health and illness: Current research and applications* (pp. 291–322). Amsterdam: Harwood.

Campbell, C.M., Edwards, R.R., & Fillingim, R.B. (2005). Ethnic differences in responses to multiple experimental pain stimuli. *Pain, 113*, 20–26.

Campbell, S.H., & Birdsell, J.M. (1994). Knowledge, beliefs, and sun protection behaviors of Alberta adults. *Preventive Medicine, 23*, 160–166.

Campbell-Heider, N., & Knapp, T.R. (1993). Toward a hierarchy of adaptation to biomedical technology. *Critical Care Nursing Quarterly, 16*(3), 42–50.

Cameron, L., Leventhal, E.A., & Leventhal, H. (1995). Seeking medical care in response to symptoms and life stress. *Psychosomatic medicine, 57*, 1–11.

Canadian Cancer Society. (2013). *Canadian cancer statistics 2012.* Canadian Cancer Society, Statistics Canada, Provincial/Territorial Cancer Registries, Public Health Agency of Canada.

Canadian Cancer Society. (2014). *Lung cancer.* Retrieved December 1, 2014, from http://www.cancer.ca/en/cancer-information/cancer-type/lung/statistics/?region=on

Canadian Fitness and Lifestyle Research Institute. (2009). Barriers to physical activity in children. *2009 Physical Activity Monitor: Facts and Figures, Bulletin 3.*

Canadian Institute for Health Information. (2001). *Full-time equivalent physicians report: Canada, 1996/97 to 1998/99.* Ottawa, ON: Author.

Canadian Institute for Health Information. (2005). *Public health programs and prevention account for, on average, only 3% of health spending, says OECD.* Retrieved April 24, 2006, from secure.cihi.ca/cihiweb/dispPage.jsp?cw_page=media_08nov2005_e

Canadian Institute for Health Information. (2006a). *Full-time equivalent physicians report: Canada, 2002–2003 and 2003–2004.* Ottawa, ON: Author.

Canadian Institute for Health Information. (2012a). *National health expenditure trends, 1975–2012.* Ottawa, ON: Author.

Canadian Institute for Health Information. (2012b). *All-cause readmission to acute care and return to the emergency department.* Ottawa, ON: Author.

Canadian Medical Association. (2005). *Physician guidelines for on-line communication with patients.* Retrieved March 14, 2013, from https://www.cma.ca/Assets/assets-library/document/en/advocacy/CMA_Social_Media-e.pdf

Canadian Mental Health Association. (2014). *Eating disorders.* Retrieved http://www.cmha.ca/mental_health/facts-about-eating-disorders/

Canadian Nurses Association. (1997a). Out in front—Advanced nursing practice. *Nursing Now: Issues and Trends in Canadian Nursing,* January.

Canadian Nurses Association. (1997b). *The future supply of registered nurses: A discussion paper.* Ottawa, ON: Author.

Canadian Pain Society. (2014, June). *Pain: Current understanding of assessment, management and treatments.* Retrieved from www.canadianpainsociety.ca/pdf/pain_fact_sheet_en.pdf

Canadian Partnership Against Cancer. (2011). *Cervical Cancer Screening in Canada: Monitoring Program Performance 2006–2008. Canadian Partnership Against Cancer.* Toronto, Canada.

Canadian Resident Matching Service. (2012). *R-1 match reports—2012.* Retrieved on October 19, 2014, from http://www.carms.ca/assets/upload/pdfs/2012R1_MatchResults/7_Discipline%20Choices%20of%20Canadian%20Applicants_en.pdf

Cannon, W.B. (1932). *The wisdom of the body.* New York: Norton.

Cannon, W.B. (1939). *The wisdom of the body* (2nd ed.). New York: Norton.

Cano, A., & de C. Williams, A.C. (2010). Social interaction in pain: Reinforcing pain behaviors or building intimacy? *Pain, 149*, 9–11.

Canto, J.G., Allison, J.J., Kiefe, C.I., Fincher, C., Farmer, R., Sekar, P., Person, S., & Weissman, N.W. (2000). Relation of race and sex to the use of reperfusion therapy in Medicare beneficiaries with acute myocardial infarction. *New England Journal of Medicine, 342*(15), 1094–1100.

Cappelli, M., Surh, L., Walker, M., Korneluk, Y., Humphreys, L., Verma, S., et al. (2001). Psychological and social predictors of decisions about genetic testing for breast cancer in high-risk women. *Psychology, Health & Medicine, 6*(3), 321–333.

Carcioppolo, N., Jensen, J.D., Wilson, S.R., Collins, W.B., Carrion, M., & Linnemeier, G. (2013). Examining HPV threat-to-efficacy ratios in the Extended Parallel Process Model. *Health Communication, 28*(1), 2028.

Cardaciotto, L., Herbert, J.D., Forman, E.M., Moitra, E., & Farrow, V. (2008, June). The assessment of present-moment awareness and acceptance: The Philadelphia Mindfulness Scale. *Assessment, 15*(2), 204–223.

Cardenas, V. (2006). The relationship between social support and depression among Latina and Caucasian dementia caregivers. *Dissertation Abstracts International: Section B; The Sciences and Engineering, 66* (7–B), 39–42.

Cardi, V., & Treasure, J. (2010). Treatments in eating disorders: Towards future directions. *Minerva Psichiatrica, 51*(3), 191–206.

Carlson, C.R., & Hoyle, R.H. (1993). Efficacy of abbreviated progressive muscle relaxation training: A quantitative review of behavioral medicine research. *Journal of Consulting and Clinical Psychology, 61*, 1059–1067.

Carlsson, C.P.O., & Sjolund, B.H. (2001). Acupuncture for chronic low back pain: A randomized placebo-controlled study with long-term follow-up. *Clinical Journal of Pain, 17*, 296–305.

Carney, R.M., Freedland, K.E., & Veith, R.C. (2005). Depression, the autonomic nervous system, and coronary heart disease. *Psychosomatic Medicine, 67*(Suppl. 1), S29–S33.

Carney, R.M., & Jaffe, A.S. (2002). Treatment of depression following acute myocardial infarction. *Journal of the American Medical Association, 288*(6), 750–751.

Carter, B.S., & Leuthner, S.R. (2002). Decision making in the NICU—Strategies, statistics, and "satisficing." *Bioethics Forum, 18*(3–4), 7–15.

Casperson, C.J., Powell, K.E., & Christenson, G.M. (1985). Physical activity, exercise, and physical fitness: Definitions and distinctions for health-related research. *Public Health Reports, 100*, 126–131.

Cassidy, J.D., Carroll, L.J., Cote, P., Lemstra, M., Berglund, A., & Nygren, A. (2000). Effect of eliminating compensation for pain and suffering on the outcome of insurance claims for whiplash injury. *New England Journal of Medicine, 342*, 1179–1186.

Cassidy, K., Reid, G.J., McGrath, P.J., Finely, G.A., Smith, D.J., Morley, C., et al. (2002). Watch needle, watch TV: Audiovisual distraction in preschool immunization. *Pain Medicine, 3*, 108–118.

Castro, C.M., Wilson, C., Wang, F., & Scillinger, D. (2007). Babel babble: Physicians' use of unclarified medical jargon with patients. *American Journal of Health Behavior, 31*(Suppl. 1), S85–S95.

Catania, J.A., Kegeles, S.M., & Coates, T.J. (1990). Towards an understanding of risk behavior: An AIDS risk reduction model (ARRM). *Health Education Quarterly, 17*, 53–72.

Catz, S.L., Kelly, J.A., Bogart, L.M., Genosch, E.G., & McAuliffe, T.L. (2000). Patterns, correlates, and barriers to medication adherence among persons prescribed new treatments for HIV disease. *Health Psychology, 19*, 124–133.

Cawley, J. (2011). *The Oxford handbook of the social science of obesity.* Oxford University Press: Toronto.

CCSA. (2008). CCSA *roadside survey shows more drivers using drugs than alcohol.* Retrieved November 20, 2014, from www.ccsa.ca/Resource%20Library/ccsa0115382009_e.pdf

CCSA. (2010). *Clearing the smoke on cannabis series highlights.* Retrieved July 1, 2010, from www.ccsa.ca/Resource%20Library/ccsa-11797-2009.pdf

CCSA. (2013, March). *First do no harm: Responding to Canada's prescription drug crisis. Prescription drug misuse.* Retrieved November 20, 2014, from http://www.ccsa.ca/Resource%20Library/Canada-Strategy-Prescription-Drug-Misuse-Report-en.pdf

CCSA. (2014). *Canada's low-risk alcohol drinking guidelines.* Retrieved November 20, 2014, from http://www.ccsa.ca/Eng/topics/alcohol/drinking-guidelines/Pages/default.aspx

Cella, D.F., Tulsky, D.S., Gray, G., Saraflan, B., Linn, E., Bonomi, A., et al. (1993). The Functional Assessment of Cancer Therapy Scale: Development and validation of the general measure. *Journal of Clinical Oncology, 11*, 570–579.

Chambers, C.T., Cassidy, K.L., McGrath, P.J., Gilbert, C.A., & Craig, K.D. (1996). *Child facial coding system: A manual.* Nova Scotia and Vancouver: Dalhousie University and University of British Columbia.

Chang, Y., & Etnier, J.L. (2009). Exploring the dose-response relationship between resistance exercise intensity and cognitive function. *Journal of Sport and Exercise Psychology, 31*, 640–656.

Chang, Y.K., Tsai, C.L., Hung, T.M., Cheung So, E., Chen, F.T., & Etnier, J.L. (2011). Effects of acute exercise on executive function: A study with a tower of London Task. *Journal of Sport & Exercise Psychology, 33*(6), 847–865.

Chapman, C.R. (1984). New directions in the understanding and management of pain. *Social Science and Medicine, 19*, 1261–1277.

Chapple, A., Ziebland, S., & McPherson, A. (2004). Stigma, shame, and blame experienced by patients with lung cancer: Qualitative study. *British Medical Journal, 328*(7454), n.p.

Chaput, J.P., Despres, J.P., Bouchard, C., & Tremblay, A. (2011). Short sleep duration preferentially increases abdominal adiposity in adults: Preliminary evidence. *Clinical Obesity, 1*, 141–146.

Chaput, J.P., & Tremblay, A. (2007). Does short sleep duration favor abdominal adiposity in children? *International Journal of Pediatric Obesity, 2*, 188–191.

Charnley, F. (1999). Occupational stress in the newly qualified staff nurse. *Nursing Standard, 13*(29), 33–36.

Chassin, L., Presson, C.C., Pitts, S.C., & Sherman, S.J. (2000). The natural history of cigarette smoking from adolescence to adulthood in a Midwestern community sample. Multiple trajectories and their psychosocial correlates. *Health Psychology, 19*, 223–231.

Chaves, J.F., & Barber, T.X. (1976). Hypnotic procedures and surgery: A critical analysis with applications to "acupuncture analgesia." *American Journal of Clinical Hypnosis, 18*(4), 217–236.

Chen, E.H., Shofer, F.S., Dean, A.J., Hollander, J.E., Baxt, W.G., Robey, J.L., et al. (2008). Gender disparity in analgesic treatment of emergency department patients with acute abdominal pain. *Academic Emergency Medicine, 15,* 414–418.

Chen, J., & Millar, W.J. (1998). Age of smoking initiation: Implications for quitting. *Health Reports, 9*(4), 39–46.

Chen, J., Ng, E., & Wilkins, R. (1996). The health of Canada's immigrants in 1994–1995. *Health Reports, 7,* 42.

Chen, J., & Wilkins, R. (1998). Seniors' needs for health-related personal assistance. *Health Reports, 10*(1), 39–50.

Chen, X., & Siu, L.L. (2001). Impact of the media and the Internet on oncology: Survey of cancer patients and oncologists in Canada. *Journal of Clinical Oncology, 19*(23), 4291–4297.

CHSRF–Canadian Health Services Research Foundation. (2006). *Myth: Medical malpractice lawsuits plague Canada. Mythbusters.* Retrieved November 20, 2014, from http://www.cfhi-fcass.ca/SearchResultsNews/06-03-01/70e601b8-487a-44d0-b390-4e4a0a453493.aspx

Chyun, D.A., Melkus, G.D., Katten, D.M., Price, W.J., Davey, J.A., Grey, N., et al. (2006). The association of psychological factors, physical activity, neuropathy, and quality of life in type 2 diabetes. *Biological Research for Nursing, 7*(4), 279–288.

Cinciripini, P.M., & Floreen, A. (1982). An evaluation of a behavioral program for chronic pain. *Journal of Behavioral Medicine, 5,* 375–389.

Clague, J., Cinciripini, P., Blalock, J., Wu, X., & Hudmon, K.S. (2010). The D2 dopamine receptor gene and nicotine dependence among bladder cancer patients and controls. *Behavior Genetics, 40*(1), 49–58.

Clark, J. (1998, November). *Prostate cancer quality of life: Patient centered measures of health outcomes.* Paper presented at the Cancer Care: Quality of Life and Outcomes Symposium, Chicago, IL.

Classen, C., Butler, L.D., Koopman, C., Miller, E., DiMiceli, S., Giese-Davis, J., et al. (2001). Supportive-expressive group therapy and distress in patients with metastatic breast cancer. *Archives of General Psychiatry, 58*(5), 494–501.

Claydon, L.S., Chesterton, L.S., Barlas, P., & Sim, J. (2011). Dose–specific effects of transcutaneous electrical nerve stimulation (TENS) on experimental pain: A systematic review. *Clinical Journal of Pain, 27*(7), 635–647.

Clements, P.T., DeRanieri, J.T., Vigil, G.J., & Benasutti, K.M. (2004). Life after death: Grief therapy after the sudden traumatic death of a family member. *Perspectives in Psychiatric Care, 40*(4), 149–154.

Clowers, M. (2002). Young women describe the ideal physician. *Adolescence, 37,* 695–704.

Coambs, R.B., Jensen, P., Her, M.H., Ferguson, B.S., Jarry, J.L., Wong, J.S.W., et al. (1995). *Review of the scientific literature on the prevalence, consequences, and health costs of noncompliance and inappropriate use of prescription medication in Canada.* Ottawa, ON: Pharmaceutical Manufacturers Association of Canada, University of Toronto Press.

Cockerham, W.M. (1998). *Medical sociology* (7th ed.). Upper Saddle River, NJ: Prentice Hall.

Cohen, L., Fouladi, R.T., & Katz, J. (2005). Preoperative coping strategies and distress predict postoperative pain and morphine consumption in women undergoing abdominal gynecologic surgery. *Journal of Psychosomatic Research, 58*(2), 201–209.

Cohen, M.R., & Smetzer, J. (2005). Patient-controlled analgesia safety issues. *Journal of Pain & Palliative Care Pharmacotherapy, 19*(1), 45–50.

Cohen, S., Doyle, W.J., Skoner, D.P., Fireman, P., Gwaltner, J.M., Jr., & Newsom, J.T. (1995). State and trait negative affect as predictors of objective and subjective symptoms of respiratory viral infections. *Journal of Personality and Social Psychology, 68,* 139–169.

Cohen, S., & Herbert, T.B. (1996). Health psychology: Psychological factors and physical disease from the perspective of human psychoneuroimmunology. *Annual Review of Psychology, 47,* 113–142.

Cohen, S., Rodriguez, M.S., Feldman, P.J., Rabin, B.S., & Manuck, S.B. (2002). Reactivity and vulnerability to stress-associated risk for upper respiratory illness. *Psychosomatic Medicine, 64,* 302–310.

Cohen, S., & Wills, T.A. (1985). Stress, social support, and the buffering hypothesis. *Psychological Bulletin, 98,* 310–357.

Coiagluri, B., Roscoe, J.A., Morrow, G.R., Atkins, J.N., Giguere, J.K., & Colman, L.K. (2008). How do patient expectancies, quality of life, and postchemotherapy nausea interrelate? *Cancer, 113*(3), 654–661.

Collins, J.L., La Pean, A., O'Tool, F., Eskra, K.L., Roedl, S.J., Tluczek, A., & Farrell, M.H. (2013). Factors that influence parents' experiences with results disclosure after newborn screening identifies genetic carrier status for cystic fibrosis or sickle cell hemoglobinopathy. *Patient Education and Counseling, 90,* 378–385

Compo, N.S., Evans, J.R., Carol, R.N., Kemp, D., Villalba, D., Ham, L.S., & Rose, S. (2011). Alcohol intoxication and memory for events: A snapshot of alcohol myopia in a real-world drinking scenario. *Memory, 19*(2), 202–210.

Concheiro, A., Diaz, E., Luaces, C., Pou, J., & Garcia, J. (2001). Triage criteria in a emergency department. *Anales Espanoles de Pediatria, 54*(3), 233–237.

Cook, J.A., Grey, D., Burke, J., Cohen, M.H., Gurtman, A.C., Richardson, J.L., et al. (2004). Depressive symptoms and AIDS-related mortality among a multisite cohort of HIV-positive women. *American Journal of Public Health, 94*(7), 1133–1140.

Cooke, M.W., Arora, P., & Mason, S. (2003). Discharge from triage: Modelling the potential in different types of emergency department. *Emergency Medicine Journal, 20*(2), 131–133.

Coombs, R.H. (1998). *Surviving medical school.* Thousand Oaks, CA: Sage.

Cooper, L.A., Roter, D.L., Johnson, R.L., Ford, D.E., Steinwachs, D.M., & Powe, N.R. (2003). Patient-centered communication, ratings of care, and concordance of patient and physician race. *Annals of Internal medicine, 139*, 907–915.

Corbière, M., Sullivan, M.J.L., Stanish, W.D., & Adams, H. (2007). Pain and depression in injured workers and their return to work: A longitudinal study. *Canadian Journal of Behavioral Science, 39*(1), 23–31.

Cordova, M.J., Cunningham, L.L.C., Carlson, C.R., & Andrykowski, M.A. (2001). Posttraumatic growth following breast cancer: A controlled comparison study. *Health Psychology, 20*(3), 176–185.

Coulter, A. (2002). Patients' views of the good doctor. *British Medical Journal, 325*, 668–669.

Courneya, K.S., Friedenreich, C.M., Sela, R.A., Quinney, H.A., Rhodes, R.E., & Handman, M. (2003). The group psychotherapy and home-based physical exercise (grouphope) trial in cancer survivors: Physical fitness and quality of life outcomes. *Psycho-Oncology, 12*(4), 357–374.

Cousson-Gélie, F., Irachabal, S., Bruchon-Schweitzer, M., Dihuydy, J.M., & Lakdja, F. (2005). Dimensions of Cancer Locus of Control Scale as predictors of psychological adjustment and survival in breast cancer patients. *Psychological Reports, 97*(3), 699–711.

Coyne, J., Aldwin, C., & Lazarus, R.S. (1981). Depression and coping in stressful episodes. *Journal of Abnormal Psychology, 90*, 439–447.

Coyne, J.C., & Racioppo, M.W. (2000). Never the twain shall meet? Closing the gap between coping research and clinical intervention research. *American Psychologist, 55*, 655–664.

Coyne, J.C., Thombs, B.D., Stefanek, M., & Palmer, C. (2009). Time to let go of the illusion that psychotherapy extends the survival of cancer patients: Reply to Kraemer, Kuchler, and Spiegel (2009). *Psychological Bulletin, 135*(2), 179–182.

Cox, H. (1973). *The seduction of the spirit.* New York: Simon and Schuster.

Cox, R.H. (2002). *Sport psychology: Concepts and applications* (5th ed.). Boston: McGraw-Hill.

Cox, R.H. (2007). *Sport psychology: Concepts and applications* (6th ed.). New York: McGraw-Hill.

Cox, R.H. (2012). *Sport psychology: Concepts and applications* (7th ed.). New York: McGraw-Hill.

Cramer, J.A. (2004). A systematic review of adherence with medications for diabetes. *Diabetes Care, 27*, 1218–1224.

Crepaz, N., & Marks, G. (2002). Towards an understanding of sexual risk behavior in people living with HIV: A review of social, psychological, and medical findings. *AIDS, 16*, 135–149.

Critchley, J.A., & Capewell, S. (2003). Mortality risk reduction associated with smoking cessation in patients with coronary heart disease. *Journal of the American Medical Association, 290*, 86–97.

Cross, T., Bazron, B., Dennis, K., & Isaacs, M. (1989). *Towards a culturally competent system of care, Volume I.* Washington, DC: Georgetown University Child Development Center, CASSP Technical Assistance Center.

Crowshoe, L. (2012). Guiding concepts of an urban Aboriginal health centre. Presentation to the Canadian Conference on Medical Education, April 17, Banff, Alberta.

Csikszentmihalyi, M. (1997). *Finding flow.* New York: Basic Books.

Cullinane, C.A., Chu, D.Z.J., & Mamelak, A.N. (2002). Current surgical options in the control of cancer pain. *Cancer Practice, 10*, s21–s26.

Cumming, J., & Ramsey, R. (2009). Imagery interventions in sport. In S.D. Mellalieu & S. Hanton (Eds.), *Advances in applied sport psychology: A review* (pp. 5–36). London: Routledge.

Cummings, G.G., Fraser, K., & Tarlier, D.S. (2003). Implementing advanced nurse practitioner roles in acute care: An evaluation of organizational change. *Journal of Nursing Administration, 33*(3), 139–145.

Cunningham, J.A. (1999). Resolving alcohol-related problems with and without treatment: The effects of different problem criteria. *Journal of Studies on Alcohol, 60*(4), 463–466.

Curt, G.A., Breitbart, W., Cella, D., Groopman, J.E., Horning, S.J., Itri, L.M., et al. (2000). Impact of cancer-related fatigue on the lives of patients: New findings from the Fatigue Coalition. *The Oncologist*, 353–360.

Cuthbertson, B.H., Hull, A., Strachan, M., & Scott, J. (2004). Post-traumatic stress disorder after critical illness requiring general intensive care. *Intensive Care Medicine, 30*, 450–455.

D

Dalal, S., & Melzack, R. (1998). Potentiation of opioid analgesia by psychostimulant drugs: A review. *Journal of Pain and Symptom Management, 16*, 245–253.

Dando, T.M., & Perry, C.M. (2004). Aprepitant: A review of its use in the prevention of chemotherapy-induced nausea and vomiting. *Drugs, 64*(7), 777–794.

Danish, S.J., Nellen, V.C., & Owens, S.S. (1996). Teaching life skills through sport: Community-based programs for adolescents. In J.L. Van Raalte & B. Brewer (Eds.), *Exploring sport and exercise psychology* (pp. 205–225). New York: American Psychological Association.

Danish, S.J., Pettipas, A.J., & Hale, B.D. (1993). Life development intervention for athletes: Life skills through sports. *The Counseling Psychologist, 21*, 352–385.

David, D., Ruttenberg, D.H., & Bovberg, D.H. (2006). Relations between coping responses and optimism-pessimism in predicting anticipatory psychological distress in surgical breast cancer patients. *Personality and Individual Differences, 40*, 203–213.

Davidson, K.W., Gidron, Y., Mostofsky, E., & Trudeau, K.J. (2007). Hospitalization cost offset of a hostility intervention for coronary heart disease patients. *Journal of Consulting and Clinical Psychology, 75*(4), 657–662.

Davidson, R.J., Kabat-Zinn, J., Schumacher, J., Rosenkranz, M., Muller, D., Santorelli, S.F., et al. (2003). Alterations in brain and immune function produced by mindfulness meditation. *Psychosomatic Medicine, 65*, 564–570.

Davis, M., Eschelman, E.R., & McKay, M. (2008). *The relaxation and stress reduction workbook* (6th ed.). Oakland: New Harbinger.

Dawber, T.R. (1980). *The Framingham Study: The epidemiology of atherosclerotic disease.* Cambridge: Harvard University Press.

DeBraganza, N., & Hausenblas, H.A. (2010). Media exposure of the ideal physique on women's body dissatisfaction and mood: The moderating effects of ethnicity. *Journal of Black Studies, 40*(4), 700–716.

de Boer, D., Delnoij, D., & Rademakers, J. (2013). The importance of patient-centered care for various patient groups. *Patient Education and Counseling, 90*, 405–410.

Degenhardt, L., & Hall, W. (2006). Is cannabis use a contributory cause of psychosis? *Canadian Journal of Psychiatry, 51*(9), 556–565.

De Koninck, M., Bergeron, P., & Bourbonnais, R. (1997). Women physicians in Québec. *Social Science and Medicine, 44*, 1825–1832.

de Kooker, M. (2008). Mind, immunity and health: The science and clinical applications of psychoneuroimmunology. *Continuing Medical Education, 26*(1), 18–20.

Deledda, G., Moretti, F., Rimondini, M., & Zimmerman, C. (2013). How patients want their doctor to communicate: A literature review on primary care patients' perspective. *Patient Education and Counseling, 90*, 297–306.

del Rio, E.F., Becona, E., & Duran A.L. (2011). Subtypes of smokers who attend psychological treatment in order to stop smoking. *Substance Use and Misuse, 46*(9), 1113–1123.

Demyttenaere, K., Bruffaerts, R., Lee, S., Posada–Villa, J., Kovess, V., Angermeyer, M.C., et al. (2007). Mental disorders among persons with chronic back or neck pain: Results from the World Mental Health Surveys. *Pain, 129*(3), 332–342.

Deveugele, M., Derese, A., De Bacquer, D., van den Brink-Muinen, A., Bensing, J., & De Maesener, J. (2004). Is the communicative behavior of GPs during the consultation related to diagnosis? A cross-sectional study in six European countries. *Patient Education and Counseling, 54*(3), 283–289.

Devine, E.C. (2003). Meta-analysis of the effect of psychoeducational interventions on pain in adults with cancer. *Oncology Nursing Forum, 30*(1), 75–89.

De Wit, R., Herrstedt, J., Rapoport, B., Carides, A.D., Guoguang-Ma, J., Elmer, M., et al. (2004). The oral NK1 antagonist, aprepitant, given with standard antiemetics provides protection against nausea and vomiting over multiple cycles of cisplatin-based chemotherapy: A combined analysis of two randomised, placebo-controlled phase III clinical trials. *European Journal of Cancer, 40*(3), 403–510.

DiGirolamo, A., Thompson, N., Martorell, R., Fein, S., & Grummer-Strawn, L. (2005). Intention or experience? Predictors of continued breastfeeding. *Health Education & Behavior, 32*(2), 208–226.

Dillard, J., & Hirchman, L.A. (2002). *The chronic pain solution.* New York: Bantam.

Dillbeck, M.C., & Orme-Johnson, D.W. (1987). Physiological differences between transcendental meditation and rest. *American Psychologist, 42*, 879–880.

DiMatteo, M.R. (1991). *The psychology of health, illness, and medical care: An individual perspective.* Pacific Grove, CA: Brooks/Cole.

DiMatteo, M.R. (1994). Enhancing patient adherence to medical recommendations. *Journal of the American Medical Association, 271*, 79–83.

DiMatteo, M.R. (1995). Health psychology research: The interpersonal challenges. In G.G. Brannigan & M.R. Merrens (Eds.), *The social psychologists: Research adventures* (pp. 207–221). New York: McGraw-Hill.

DiMatteo, M.R. (2004a). Social support and patient adherence to medical treatment: A meta-analysis. *Health Psychology, 23*, 207–218.

DiMatteo, M.R. (2004b). Variations in patients' adherence to medical recommendations: A quantitative review of 50 years of research. *Medical Care, 42*(3), 200–209.

DiMatteo, M.R., & DiNicola, D.D. (1982). *Achieving patient compliance: The psychology of the medical practitioner's role.* New York: Pergamon.

DiMatteo, M.R., Giordani, P.J., Lepper, H.S., & Croghan, T.W. (2002). Patient adherence and medical treatment outcomes: A meta-analysis. *Medical Care, 40*(9), 794–811.

DiMatteo, M.R., Lepper, H.S., & Croghan, T.W. (2001). Depression is a risk factor for noncompliance with medical treatment: Meta-analysis of the effects of anxiety and depression on patient adherence. *Archives of Internal Medicine, 160,* 2101–2107.

DiMatteo, M.R., & Martin, L.R. (2002). *Health psychology.* Boston: Allyn & Bacon.

Dimeo, F. (2002). Radiotherapy-related fatigue and exercise for cancer patients: A review of the literature and suggestions for future research. *Frontiers of Radiation Therapy and Oncology, 37,* 49–56.

Dimeo, F.C. (2001). Effects of exercise on cancer-related fatigue. *Cancer, 92*(6, Suppl.), 1689–1693.

Dimeo, F.C., Stieglitz, R.D., Novelli-Fischer, U., Fetscher, S., & Keul, J. (1999). Effects of physical activity on the fatigue and psychologic status of cancer patients during chemotherapy. *Cancer, 85,* 2273–2277.

Dinh, K.T., Sarason, I.G., Peterson, A.V., & Onstad, L.E. (1995). Children's perception of smokers and nonsmokers: A longitudinal study. *Health Psychology, 14,* 32–40.

DiNicola, D.D., & DiMatteo, M.R. (1984). Practitioners, patients, and compliance with medical regimens: A social psychological perspective. In A. Baum, S.E., Taylor, & J.E. Singer (Eds.), *Handbook of psychology and health: Vol. 4. Social psychological aspects of health* (pp. 55–84). Hillsdale, NJ: Erlbaum.

Dirkzwager, A.J., van der Velden, P.G., Grievink, L., & Yzermans, C.J. (2007). Disaster-related posttraumatic stress disorder and physical health. *Psychosomatic Medicine, 69,* 435–440.

Dishman, R.K. (Ed.). (1988). *Exercise adherence: Its impact on public health.* Champaign, IL: Human Kinetics.

Dishman, R.K. (2001). The problem of exercise adherence: The problem of sloth in nations with market economies. *Quest, 53,* 279–294.

Distefan, J.M., Pierce, J.P., & Gilpin, E.A. (2004). Do favorite movie stars influence adolescent smoking initiation? *American Journal of Public Health, 94*(7), 1239–1244.

Doll, R., Stephen, J., Barroetavena, M.C., Linden, W., Poole, G., Ng, E., et al. (2003). Patient navigation in cancer care: Program delivery and research in British Columbia. *Canadian Oncology Nursing Journal, 13*(3), 193.

Doll, R., Stephen, J., Barroetavena, M.C., Linden, W., Poole, G., & Fyles, G. (2005). *Patient navigation in cancer care.* Final Report. Vancouver: BC Cancer Agency.

Donnelly, G. (2003). Clinical expertise in advanced practice nursing: A Canadian perspective. *Nurse Education Today, 23*(3), 168–173.

Donohue, K.F., Curtin, J.J., Patrick, C.J., & Lang, A.R. (2007). Intoxication level and emotional response. *Emotion, 7,* 103–112.

Dorner, T.E., Stronegger, W.J., Rebhandl, E., Rieder A., & Freidl, W. (2010). The relationship between various psychosocial factors and physical symptoms reported during primary-care health examinations. *Wiener Klinische Wochenschrift, 122,* 103–9.

Douglas Mental Health Institute. (2012). *Ask the expert.* Retrieved December 1, 2014, from http://www.douglas.qc.ca/expert_advices?id=91

Dovidio, J.F., Pagotto, L., & Hebl, M.R. (2011). Implicit attitudes and discrimination against people with physical disabilities. In R.L. Wiener & S.L. Willborn (Eds.), *Disability and aging discrimination: Perspectives in law and psychology* (pp. 157–183). New York: Springer.

Dowling, E., Yabroff, K.R., Mariotto, A., McNeel, T., Zeruto, C., & Buckman D. (2010). Burden of illness in adult survivors of childhood cancers. *Cancer, 116*(15), 3712–3721.

Dracup, K. (2009). The challenge of reducing prehospital delay in patients with acute coronary syndrome. *Circulation. Cardiovascular Quality and Outcomes, 2,* 144–145.

Drapeau, M. (2012, November). Introduction to the special issue on sports and exercise psychology. *Canadian Psychology, 53*(4), 259–260.

Driskell, J.E., Copper, C., & Moran, A. (1994). Does mental practice enhance performance? *Journal of Applied Psychology, 79,* 481–492.

Drozda, D.J., Allen, S.R., Standiford, D.A., Turner, A.M., & McCain, G.C. (1997). Personal illness models of diabetes: Parents of preadolescents and adolescents. *Diabetes Education, 23,* 550–557.

Dubbert, S. (2002). Physical activity and exercise: Recent advances and current challenges. *Journal of Consulting and Clinical Psychology, 70,* 526–536.

Dube, S.R., Fairweather, D., Pearson, W.S., Felitti, V.J., Anda, R.F., & Croft, J.B. (2009). Cumulative childhood stress and autoimmune diseases in adults. *Psychosomatic Medicine, 71,* 243–250.

Duda, J.L. (1992). Motivation in sport settings: A goal perspective approach. In G. Roberts (Ed.), *Motivation in sport and exercise* (pp. 57–91). Champaign, IL: Human Kinetics.

Duda, J.L., & Hall, H. (2001). Achievement goal theory in sport: Recent extensions and future directions. In R.N. Singer, H.A. Hausenblas, & C.M. Janelle (Eds.), *Handbook of sport psychology* (2nd ed., pp. 417–443). New York: Wiley.

Dugan, J., Lauer, E., Bouquot, Z., Dutro, B.K., Smith, M., & Widmeyer, G. (1996). Stressful nurses: The effect on patient outcomes. *Journal of Nursing Care Quality, 10*(3), 46–58.

Dumont, C., St. Onge, M., Fougeyrollas, P., & Renaud, L.A. (1998). Perceived burden in family caregivers with physical disabilities. *Canadian Journal of Occupational Therapy, 65,* 258–270.

Dunkel-Schetter, C. (1984). Social support and cancer: Findings based on patient interviews and their implications. *Journal of Social Issues, 40*(4),77–98.

Dunn, J., Steginga, S.K., Occhipinti, S., & Wilson, K. (1999). Evaluation of a peer support program for women with breast cancer—Lessons for practitioners. *Journal of Community and Applied Social Psychology, 9,* 13–22.

Dutra, L., Stathopoulou, G., Basden, S.L., Leyro, T.M., Powers, M.B., & Otto, M.W. (2008). A meta-analytic review of psychosocial interventions for substance use disorders. *American Journal of Psychiatry, 165,* 179–187.

E

Eaton, D.K., Kann, L., Kinchen, S., Shanklin, S., Ross, J., Hawkins, J., et al. (2010). Youth risk behavior surveillance–United States, 2009. *MMWR. Surveillance Summaries: Morbidity And Mortality Weekly Report. Surveillance Summaries/CDC, 59*(5), 1–142.

Echemendia, R.J., Iverson, G.L., McCrea, M., Broshek, D.K., Gioia, G.A., Sautter, S.W., et al. (2012). Role of Neuropsychologists in the Evaluation and Management of Sport-Related Concussion: An Inter-Organization Position Statement. *Archives of Clinical Neuropsychology, 27*(1), 119–122.

Edelman, S. (2005). Relationship between psychological factors and cancer: An update of the evidence. *Clinical Psychologist, 9*(2), 45–53.

Edwards, G., & Gross, M.M. (1976). Alcohol dependence: Provisional description of a clinical syndrome. *British Medical Journal,* 1058–1061.

Edwards, R.R., Haythornthwaite, J.A., Sullivan, M.J., & Filingim, R.B. (2004). Catastrophizing as a mediator of sex differences in pain: Differential effects for daily pain versus laboratory-induced pain. *Pain, 111,* 335–341.

Ekkekakis, P., Backhouse, S.H., Gray, C., & Lind, E. (2008). Walking is popular among adults but is it pleasant? A framework for clarifying the link between walking and affect as illustrated in two studies. *Psychology of Sport and Exercise, 9,* 246–264.

Elkins, G., White, J., Patel, P., Marcus, J., & Perfect, M.M. (2006). Hypnosis to manage anxiety and pain associated with colonoscopy for colorectal cancer screening: Case studies and possible benefits. *International Journal of Clinical and Experimental Hypnosis, 54*(4), 416–431.

Ellis, A. (1962). *Reason and emotion in psychotherapy.* New York: Lyle Stuart.

Ellis, A. (1975). *How to live with a "neurotic"* (rev. ed.). New York: Crown.

Ellis, A. (1994). The sport of avoiding sports and exercise: A rational emotive behavior therapy perspective. *The Sport Psychologist, 8,* 248–261.

Ellis, A., & Grieger, R. (1977). *Handbook of rational-emotive therapy.* New York: Springer.

Ellis, D.A., Naar-King, S., Frey, M., Templin, T., Rowland, M., & Cakan, N. (2005). Multisystemic treatment of poorly controlled Type 1 diabetes: Effects on medical resource utilization. *Journal of Pediatric Psychology, 30*(8), 656–666.

Ellison, L.F., Morrison, H.I., de Groh, M., & Villeneuve, P.J. (1999). Health consequences of smoking among Canadian smokers: An update. *Chronic Diseases in Canada, 20,* 36–39.

Elton-Marshall, T., Leatherdale, S.T., & Burkhalter, R. (2011). Tobacco, alcohol and illicit drug use among Aboriginal youth living off-reserve: Results from the Youth Smoking Survey. *Canadian Medical Association Journal, 183*(8), E4880–E486.

Emanuel, E.J., & Emanuel, L.L. (1992). Four models of the physician-patient relationship. *Journal of the American Medical Association, 267,* 2221–2226.

Engebretson, T.O., Clark, M.M., Niaura, R.S., Phillips, T., Albrecht, A., & Tilkemeier, P. (1999). Quality of life and anxiety in a phase II cardiac rehabilitation program. *Medical Science in Sports Exercise, 31,* 216–223.

Engel, G.L. (1977). The need for a new medical model: A challenge for biomedicine. *Science, 196,* 129–136.

Ephraim, P.L., Wegener, S.T., MacKenzie, E.J., Dillingham, T.R., & Pezzin, L.E. (2005). Phantom pain, residual limb pain, and back pain in amputees: Results of a national survey. *Physical Medicine and Rehabilitation, 86,* 1910–1919.

Epp, J. (1986). Achieving health for all: A framework for health promotion. *Canadian Journal of Public Health, 77,* 393–430.

Epstein, L.H., & Cluss, P.A. (1982). A behavioral medicine perspective on adherence to long-term medical regimens. *Journal of Consulting and Clinical Psychology, 50,* 950–971.

Erickson, M.H. (1967). An introduction to the study and application of hypnosis for pain control. In J. Lassner (Ed.), *Hypnosis and psychosomatic medicine* (p. 83). New York: Springer.

Erickson, P.G., Riley, D.M., Cheung, Y.W., & O'Hare, P.A. (Eds.) (1997). *Harm reduction; A new direction for drug policies and programs.* University of Toronto Press.

Eriksen, M., Mackay, J., & Ross, H. (2012). *The tobacco atlas* (4th ed.). Atlanta, GA: American Cancer Society. www.TobaccoAtlas.org

Ernst, E., Lee, M.S., & Choi, T.Y. (2011). Acupuncture: Does it alleviate pain and are there serious risks? A review of reviews. *Pain, 152*(4), 755–764.

Estabrooks, P.A. (2000). Sustaining exercise participation through group cohesion. *Sport Science Reviews, 28,* 63–67.

Etnier, J.L., Salazar, W., Landers, D.M., Petruzzello, S.J., Han, M., & Nowell, P. (1997). The influence of physical fitness and exercise upon cognitive functioning: A meta-analysis. *Journal of Sport and Exercise Psychology, 19,* 249–277.

Evans, D., Cauchemez, S., & Hayden, F.G. (2009). "Prepandemic" immunization for novel influenza viruses, "Swine Flu" vaccine, Guillain-Barre Syndrome, and the detection of rare severe adverse events. *Journal of Infectious Disease, 200,* 321–328.

Evans, D.L., Folds, J.D., Petitto, J.M., Golden, R.N., Pedersen, C.A., Corrigan, M., et al. (1992). Circulating natural killer cell phenotypes in men and women with major depression. *Archives of General Psychiatry, 49,* 388–395.

Evans, P.D., Doyle, A., Hucklebridge, F., & Clow, A. (1997). Positive but not negative life-events predict vulnerability to upper respiratory illness. *British Journal of Health Psychology, 2,* 339–348.

Evans, P., Hucklebridge, K., & Clow, A. (2003). *Mind, immunity and health: The science of psychoneuroimmunology.* London: Free Association Books.

Evans, R.L., & Hendricks, R.D. (1993). Evaluating hospital discharge planning: A randomized clinical trial. *Medical Care, 31,* 358–370.

Evans, R.W., & Penzien, D.B. (2003). Your headache is a cow. *Headache, 43,* 168–169.

F

Facione, N.C., & Giancarlo, C.A. (1998). Narratives of breast symptom discovery and cancer diagnosis: Psychologic risk for advanced cancer at diagnosis. *Cancer Nursing, 21,* 430–440.

Facione, N.C., Miaskowski, C., Dodd, M.J., & Paul, S.M. (2002). The self-reported likelihood of patient delay in breast cancer: New thoughts for early detection. *Preventive Medicine, 34,* 397–407.

Fadiman, A. (1997). *The spirit catches you and then you fall down: A Hmong child, her American doctors, and the collision of two cultures.* New York: Farrar, Straus, and Giroux.

Fagundes, C.P., Glaser, R., & Kiecolt-Glaser, J.K. (2013). Stressful early life experiences and immune dysregulation across the lifespan. *Brain, Behaviour, and Immunity, 27,* 8–12.

Fagundes, C.P., Glaser, R., Malarkey, W.B., & Kiecolt-Glaser, J.K. (2013). Childhood adversity and herpesvirus latency in breast cancer survivors. *Health Psychology, 32*(3), 337–344.

Farooqui, I.S., Matarese, G., Lord, G.M., Keogh, J.M., Lawrence, E., Agwu, C., et al. (2002). Beneficial effects of leptin on obesity, T cell hyporesponsiveness, and neuroendocrine/metabolic dysfunction of human congenital leptin deficiency. *The Journal of Clinical Investigation, 110,* 1093–1103.

Faulkner, M. (2001). The onset and alleviation of learned helplessness in older hospitalized people. *Aging & Mental Health, 5*(4), 379–386.

Fawcett, S.B., Paine-Andrews, A., Francisco, V.T., Schultz, J., Richter, K.P., Berkley-Patton, J., et al. (2001). Evaluating community initiatives for health and development. In I. Rootman, M. Goodstadt, B. Hyndman, D.V. McQueen, L. Potvin, J. Springett, & E. Ziglio (Eds.), *Evaluation in health promotion: Principles and perspectives.* World Health Organization Regional Publications, European Series, No. 92.

Fawzy, N.W., Secher, L., Evans, S., & Giuliano, A.E. (1995). The positive appearance centre: An innovative concept in comprehensive psychosocial cancer care. *Cancer Practice, 3*(4), 233–238.

Fedoroff, I.C., Blackwell, E., & Speed, B. (2014). Evaluation of group and individual change in a multidisciplinary pain management program. *The Clinical Journal of Pain, 30*(5), 399–408.

Felton, G.M., Parsons, M., & Bartoces, M.G. (1997). Demographic factors: Interaction effects on health promoting behavior and health related factors. *Public Health Nursing, 14,* 361–367.

Felton, J.S. (1998). Burnout as a clinical entity—Its importance in health care workers. *Occupational Medicine, 48*, 237–250.

Feltz, D.L. (1988). Self-confidence and sports performance. In K.B. Pandolf (Ed.), *Exercise and sport sciences reviews* (pp. 423–457). New York: MacMillan.

Feltz, D.L., & Lirgg, C.D. (2001). Self-efficacy beliefs in athletes, teams, and coaches. In R.N. Singer, H.A. Hausenblas, & C.M. Janelle (Eds.), *Handbook of sport psychology* (2nd ed., pp. 340–361). New York: Wiley.

Feltz, D.L., Short, S.E., & Sullivan, P.J. (2008). *Self-efficacy in sport*. Champaign, IL: Human Kinetics Press.

Ferguson, E., & Cassaday, H.J. (1999). The Gulf War and illness by association. *British Journal of Psychology, 90*, 459–475.

Ferguson, E., & Cassaday, H.J. (2002). Theoretical accounts of Gulf War Syndrome: From environmental toxins to psychoneuroimmunology and neurodegeneration. *Behavioral Neurology, 13*, 133–147.

Fernandez-Espejo, E., Viveros, M.-P., Nunez, L. Elllenbroek, B.A., & de Fonseca, F.R. (2009). Roles of cannabis and endocannabinoids in the genesis of schizophrenia. *Psychopharmacology, 206*, 531–549.

Ferrell, B., Smith, S., Cullinane, C., & Melancon, C. (2003). Symptom concerns of women with ovarian cancer. *Journal of Pain and Symptom Management, 25*(6), 528–538.

Ferrell, B.R., Novy, D., Sullivan, M.D., Banja, J., Dubois, M.Y., Gitlin, M.C., et al. (2001). Ethical dilemmas in pain management. *Journal of Pain, 2*, 171–180.

Festinger, L. (1954). A theory of social comparison processes. *Human Relations, 7*, 117–140.

Fillingim, R.B., & Edwards, R.R. (2001). The association of hormone replacement therapy with experimental pain responses in postmenopausal women. *Pain, 92*, 229–234.

Fillmore, K.M., Kerr, W.C., & Stockwell, T. (2006). Moderate alcohol use and reduced mortality risk: Systematic error in prospective studies. *Addiction Research and Theory, 14*(2), 101–

Finley, A., Chambers, C.T., McGrath, P.J., & Walsh, T. (1999, October). Further validation of the Parents' Postoperative Pain Measure. Poster session presented at the annual meeting of the American Pain Society, Fort Lauderdale, FL.

Fischer, M.A., Stedman, M.R., Lii, J., Vogeli, C., Shrank, W.H., Brookhart, M.A., et al. (2010). Primary medication non-adherence: Analysis of 195,930 electronic prescriptions. *Journal of General Internal Medicine, 25*(4), 284–290.

Fischer, S., Smith, G.T., & Anderson, K.G. (2003). Clarifying the role of impulsivity in bulimia nervosa. *International Journal of Eating Disorders, 33*(4), 406–411.

Fishbein, M., & Ajzen, I. (1975). *Belief, attitude, intention, and behavior: An introduction to theory and research.* Reading, MA: Addison-Wesley.

Fisher, C.A., Hetrick, S.E., & Rushford, N. (2010). Family therapy for anorexia nervosa. *Cochrane Database of Systematic Reviews 4*: CD004780.

Fisher, J.D., & Fisher, W.A. (1998). Theoretical approaches to individual level change in HIV risk behavior. In J. Peterson & R. Diclemente (Eds.), *HIV prevention handbook* (pp. 3–53). New York: Plenum.

Fisher, J.D., Fisher, W.A., & Shuper, P.A. (2009). The information-motivation-behavioural skills model of HIV preventive behavior. In R.J. DiClemente, R.A. Crosby, & M.C. Kegler (Eds.), *Emerging theories in health promotion practice and research* (2nd ed., pp. 21–63). San Francisco: Jossey-Bass.

Fisher, W.A., & Fisher, J.D. (1998). Understanding and promoting sexual and reproductive health behavior: Theory and method. *Annual Review of Sex Research, 9*, 39–76.

Flakus, B.J. (1998). Stress relief for critical care nurses. *Nursing Management, 29*, 48D, 48H–48J.

Flament, M.F., Bissada, H., & Spettigue, W. (2012). Evidence-based pharmacotherapy. *International Journal of Neuropsychopharmacology, 15*(2), 189–207.

Flanagan, W.M., Le Petit, C., Berthelot, J.M., White, K.J., Coombs, B.A., & Jones-McLean, E. (2003). Potential impact of population-based colorectal cancer screening in Canada. *Chronic Diseases in Canada, 24*(4), 81–88.

Flegal, K.M., Kit, B.K., Orpana, H., & Graubard, B.I. (2013). Association of all-cause mortality with overweight and obesity using standard body mass index categories: A systematic review and meta-analysis. *Journal of the American Medical Association, 309*, 71–82.

Fleshner, M., & Laudenslager, M.L. (2004). Psychoneuroimmunology: Then and now. *Behavioral and Cognitive Neuroscience Review, 3*(2), 114–130.

Flocke, S.A., Miller, W.L., & Crabtree, B.F. (2002). Relationships between physician practice style, patient satisfaction, and attributes of primary care. *Journal of Family Practice, 5*(10), 835–840.

Flor, H., Nikolajsen, L., & Staehelin Jensen, T. (2006). Phantom limb pain: A case of maladaptive CNS plasticity? *Nature Reviews Neuroscience, 7*, 873–881.

Folkins, C.H., & Syme, W.E. (1981). Physical fitness training and mental health. *American Psychologist*, 373–389.

Fong, G.T., Hammond, D., Laux, F.L., Zanna, M.P., Cummings, K.M., Borland, R., et al. (2004). The near-universal experience of regret among smokers in four countries: Findings from the International Tobacco

Control Policy Evaluation Survey. *Nicotine Tobacco Research, 6*(3), S341–S451.

Fontaine, K.R., Redden, D., Wang, C., Westfall, A.O., & Allison, D.B. (2003). Years of life lost due to obesity. *Journal of the American Medical Association, 289*(2), 187–193.

Fordyce, W.E. (1976). *Behavioral methods for chronic pain and illness.* St. Louis: C.V. Mosby.

Forester, B., Kornfeld, D.S., Fleiss, J.L., & Thompson, S. (1993). Group psychotherapy during radiotherapy: Effects on emotional and physical distress. *American Journal of Psychiatry, 150,* 1700–1706.

Forte, T., Lockwood, G.A., McLachlin, C.M., Fekete, S., & Bryant, H.E. (2012). A first look at participation rates in cervical cancer Screening programs in Canada. *Current Oncology, 19*(5), 269–271.

Fox, K.R. (2000). The effects of exercise on physical self-perceptions and self-esteem. In S.J.H. Biddle, K.R. Fox, & S.H. Boutcher (Eds.), *Physical activity and psychological well-being* (pp. 88–117). London: Routledge & Kegan Paul.

Fox, R., & Gourlay, Y.J. (2000). The impact of highly active antiretroviral combination therapy in HIV infected patients in Glasgow. *Health Bulletin (Edinb), 58*(4), 309–315.

Fraguela, J.A.G., Martin, A.L., & Trinanes, E.R. (2003). Drug abuse prevention in the school: Four-year follow-up of a programme. *Psychology in Spain, 7,* 29.

Francis, L., & Barling, J. (2005). Organizational injustice and psychological strain. *Canadian Journal of Behavioural Science, 37,* 250–261.

Franco-Bronson, K. (1996). The management of treatment-resistant depression in the medically ill. *Psychiatric Clinics of North America, 19,* 329–350.

Frank, L.D., Sallis, J.F., Saelens, B.E., Leary, L., Cain, K., Conway, T.L., et al. (2010). The development of a walkability index: Application to the Neighbourhood Quality of Life Study. *British Journal of Sports Medicine, 44*(13), 924–933.

Frank, M.G., Hendricks, S.E., Johnson, D.R., Wieseler, J.L., & Burke, J.W. (1999). Antidepressants augment natural killer cell activity: In vivo and in vitro. *Neuropsychobiology, 39,* 18–24.

Frankel, R., & Beckman, H. (1989). Evaluating the patient's primary problem(s). In M. Stewart & D. Roter (Eds.), *Communicating with medical patients* (pp. 86–98). Newbury Park, CA: Sage Publications.

Franks, P., & Bertakis, K.D. (2003). Physician gender, patient gender, and primary care. *Journal of Women's Health, 12,* 73–80.

Frappier, J.Y., Kaufman, M., Baltzer, F., Elliott, A., Lane, M., Pinzon, J., et al. (2008). Sex and sexual health: A survey of Canadian youth and mothers. *Paediatrics & Child Healthy, 13*(1), 25–30.

Frasure-Smith, N., & Lesperance, F. (2003). Depression and other psychological risks following myocardial infarction. *Archives of General Psychiatry, 60*(6), 627–636.

Frasure-Smith, N., & Lespérance, F. (2008). Depression and anxiety as predictors of 2-year cardiac events in patients with stable coronary artery disease. *Archives of General Psychiatry, 65*(1), 62–71.

Frasure-Smith, N., Lesperance, F., & Talajic, M. (1993). Depression following myocardial infarction: Impact on 6-month survival. *Journal of the American Medical Association, 270,* 1860–1861.

Frasure-Smith, N., & Prince, R. (1985). The Ischemic Heart Disease Life Stress Monitoring Program: Impact on mortality. *Psychosomatic Medicine, 47,* 431–445.

Fraze, J.L., Uhrig, J.D., Davis, K.C., Taylor, M.K., Lee, N.R., Spoeth, S., et al. (2009). Applying core principles to the design and evaluation of the "Take Charge. Take the Test" campaign: What worked and lessons learned. *Public Health, 123*(Suppl. 1), e23–e30.

Fredericks, L.E., & Evans, F.J. (2001). *The use of hypnosis in surgery and anesthesiology: Psychological preparation of the surgical patient.* Springfield, IL: Charles C. Thomas.

Fredrickson, B.L. (2001). The role of positive emotions in positive psychology: The broaden-and-build theory of positive emotions. *American Psychologist, 56,* 218–226.

Freeman, N., Friedman, R.S., Bartholow, B.D., & Wulfert, E. (2010). Effects of alcohol priming on social disinhibition. *Experimental and Clinical Psychopharmacology, 18*(2), 135–144.

Frey Law, L.A., Evans, S., Knudtson, J., Nus, S., Scholl, K., & Sluka, K.A. (2008). Massage reduces pain perception and hyperalgesia in experimental muscle pain: A randomized, controlled trial. *The Journal of Pain, 9*(8), 714–721.

Friedman, H.S., Tucker, J., Tomlinson-Keasey, C., Schwartz, J., Wingard, D., & Criqui, M.H. (1993). Does childhood personality predict longevity? *Journal of Personality and Social Psychology, 65,* 176–185.

Friedman, J.M. (2000). Obesity in the new millennium. *Nature, 404,* 632–634.

Friedman, J.M. (2003). A war on obesity, not the obese. *Science, 299,* 856–858.

Friedman, M., & Rosenman, R.H. (1959). Association of specific overt behavior pattern with blood and cardiovascular findings—Blood cholesterol level, blood clotting time, incidence of arcus senilis, and clinical coronary artery disease. *Journal of the American Medical Association, 162,* 1286–1296.

Friedman, M., & Rosenman, R.H. (1974). *Type A behavior and your heart*. New York: Knopf.

Frigon, J.-Y. (2004). Biobehavioural and cognitive determinants of adolescent girls' involvement in sexual risk behaviours: A test of three theoretical models. *Canadian Journal of Human Sexuality, 13*(1), 29–44.

Frisoni, G.B., Fedi, V., Geroldi, C., & Trabucchi, M. (1999). Cognition and perception of physical symptoms in the community-dwelling elderly. *Behavioral Medicine, 25*, 5–12.

Fuchs-Lacelle, S., & Hadjistavropoulos, T. (2004). Development and preliminary validation of the pain assessment checklist for seniors with limited ability to communicate. *Pain Management Nursing, 5*, 37–49.

Fuchs-Lacelle, S., Hadjistavropoulos, T., & Lix, L. (2008). Pain assessment as intervention: A study of older adults with severe dementia. *Clinical Journal of Pain, 24*, 697–707.

Fumaz, C.R., Gonzalez-Garcia, M., Borras, X., Muñoz-Moreno, Perez-Alvarez, N., Mothe, B., et al. (2012). Psychological stress is associated with high levels of IL-6 in HIV-1 infected individuals on effective combined antiretroviral treatment. *Brain, Behavior, and Immunity, 26*, 568–572.

G

Gagliese, L., & Katz, J. (2003). Age differences in postoperative pain are scale dependent: A comparison of measures of pain intensity and quality in younger and older surgical patients. *Pain, 103*, 11–20.

Gagliese, L., & Melzack, R. (1997). Age differences in the quality of chronic pain: A preliminary study. *Pain Research and Management, 2*, 157–162.

Gagliese, L., Weizblit, N., Ellis, W., & Chan, V.W.S. (2005). The measurement of postoperative pain: A comparison of intensity scales in younger and older surgical patients. *Pain, 117*(3), 412–420.

Galdas, P.M., Cheater, F., & Marshall, P. (2005). Men and health help-seeking behavior: Literature review. *Journal of Advanced Nursing, 49*, 616–623.

Gall, T.L., Charbonneau, C., Clarke, N.H., Grant, K., Joseph, A., & Shouldice, L. (2005). Understanding the nature and role of spirituality in relation to coping and health: A conceptual framework. *Canadian Psychology, 46*, 88–104.

Gall, T.L., & Cornblat, M.W. (2002). Breast cancer survivors give voice: A qualitative analysis of spiritual factors in long-term adjustment. *Psycho-Oncology, 11*(6), 524–535.

Gallagher, K.M., & Updegraff, J.A. (2012). Health message framing effects on attitudes, intentions, and behaviour: A meta-analytic review. *Annals of Behavioral Medicine, 43*, 101–116.

Garber, M.C. (2004). The concordance of self-report with other measures of medication adherence: A summary of the literature. *Medical Care, 42*, 649–652.

Gardner, F.L., & Moore, Z.E. (2006). *Clinical sport psychology*. Champagne, IL: Human Kinetics.

Gardner, F.L., & Moore, Z.E. (2007). *The psychology of enhancing human performance: The Mindfulness-Acceptance-Commitment (MAC) approach*. New York: Springer Publishing.

Gardner, F.L., & Moore, Z.E. (2010). Acceptance-based behavioral therapies and sport. In S. Hanrahan, & M. Andersen (Eds.), *Handbook of applied sport psychology* (pp. 186–193). New York: Routledge.

Gardner, F.L., & Moore, Z.E. (2012). Mindfulness and acceptance models in sport psychology: A decade of basic and applied scientific advancements. *Canadian Psychology, 53*(4), 309–318.

Gardner, J., & Wilkinson, P. (2011). Is family therapy the most effective treatment for anorexia nervosa? *Psychiatria Danubina* (Suppl. 1), S175–S177.

Gareis, K.C., & Barnett, R.C. (2002). Under what conditions do long work hours affect psychological distress: A study of full-time and reduced-hours female doctors. *Work & Occupations, 29*(4), 483–497.

Gatchel, R.J. (2005). *Clinical essentials of pain management*. Washington, DC: American Psychological Association.

Gathchel, R.J., & Oordt, M.S. (2003). Coping with chronic or terminal illness. In R.J.O. Gatchel & M.S. Oordt (Eds.), *Clinical health psychology and primary care: Practical advice and clinical guidance for successful collaboration* (pp. 213–233). Washington, DC: American Psychological Association.

Gaudette, L.A., Richardson, A., & Huang, S. (1998). Which workers smoke? *Health Reports, 10*(3), 35–45.

Gauthier, N., Thibault, P., & Sullivan, M.J. (2011). Catastrophizers with chronic pain display more pain behaviour when in a relationship with a low catastrophizing spouse. *Pain Research Management, 16*(5), 293–299.

Gauvin, L. (1990). An experiential perspective on the motivational features of exercise and lifestyle. *Canadian Journal of Sport Sciences, 15*, 51–58.

Gauvin, L., Levesque, L., & Richard, L. (2001). Helping people initiate and maintain a more active lifestyle: A public health framework for physical activity promotion research. In R.N. Singer, H.A. Hausenblas, & C.M. Janelle (Eds.), *Handbook of sport psychology* (2nd ed., pp. 718–739). New York: Wiley.

Gauvin, L., & Spence, J.C. (1995). Psychological research on exercise and fitness: Current research trends and future challenges. *The Sport Psychologist, 9*, 434–448.

Gauvin, L., Steiger, H., & Brodeur, J.-M. (2008). Eating-disorder symptoms and syndromes in a sample of urban-dwelling Canadian women: Contributions toward a population health perspective. *International Journal of Eating Disorders, 42*, 158–165.

Gavel-Cruz, M., & Weinshenker, D. (2009). Mechanisms of disulfiram-induced cocaine abstinence: Antabuse and cocaine relapse. *Molecular Interventions, 9*(4), 175–187.

Gavin, L., Steiger, H., & Brodeur, J.M. (2008). Eating-disorder symptoms and syndromes in a sample of urban-dwelling Canadian women: Contributions toward a population health perspective. *International Journal of Eating Disorders, 42*(2), 158–165.

Gay, M., Philippot, P., & Luminet, O. (2002). Differential effectiveness of psychological interventions for reducing osteoarthritis pain: A comparison of Erickson hypnosis and Jacobson relaxation. *European Journal of Pain, 6*, 1–16.

Geiger, J. (2001). Racial stereotyping and medicine: The need for cultural competence. *Canadian Medical Association Journal, 164*(12), 1699–1700.

Geist, R., Heinmaa, M., Katzman, D., & Stephens, D. (1999). A comparison of male and female adolescents referred to an eating disorder program. *Canadian Journal of Psychiatry, 44*, 374–378.

Gellaitry, G., Cooper, V., Davis, C., Fisher, M., Date, H.L., & Horne, R. (2005). Patients' perception of information about HAART: Impact on treatment decisions. *AIDS Care, 17*, 367–376.

Gendolla, G.H., Abele, A.E, Andrei, A., Spurk, D., & Richter, M. (2005). Negative mood, self-focused attention, and the experience of physical symptoms: The joint impact hypothesis. *Emotion, 5*(2), 131–144.

George, T.R. (1994). Self-confidence and baseball performance: A causal examination. *Journal of Sport and Exercise Psychology, 16*, 381–399.

Georgiades, K., Boyle, M.H., Duku, E., & Racine, Y. (2006). Tobacco use among immigrant and nonimmigrant adolescents: Individual and family level influences. *Journal of Adolescent Health, 38*(4), e1–e7.

Gibson, S.J., & Chambers, C.T. (2004). Pain over the lifespan: A developmental perspective. In T. Hadjistavropoulos & K.D. Craig (Eds.), *Pain: Psychological perspectives* (pp. 113–153). Mahwah, NJ: Erlbaum.

Gilbar, O. (1989). Who refuses chemotherapy: A profile. *Psychological Reports, 64*, 1291–1297.

Giles, B.E., & Walker, J.S. (2000). Sex differences in pain and analgesia. *Pain Reviews, 7*, 181–193.

Gill, D. (2006). Sport psychology and fitness activities. In J. Doasil (Ed.), *The sport psychologist's handbook* (pp. 589–615). Chichester, England. John Wiley & Sons.

Gilpin, E.A., Pierce, J.P., & Parkas, A.J. (1997). Duration of smoking abstinence and success in quitting. *Journal of the National Cancer Institute, 89*, 572–576.

Gilpin, E.A., White, V.M., & Pierce, J.P. (2005). What fraction of young adults are at risk for future smoking, and who are they? *Nicotine & Tobacco Research, 7*(5), 747–759.

Girdano, D.A., Dusek, D.E., & Everly, G.S. (2005). *Controlling stress and tension*. San Francisco: Pearson Education.

Glantz, S.A. (2004). Smoking in movies: A major problem and a real solution. Erratum. *Lancet, 363*(9404), 250.

Glantz, S. (June, 2009). *Smoking in the movies*. Paper presented at the UK National Smoking Cessation Conference, London, UK. Retrieved July 1, 2010, from www.uknscc.org/2009_UKNSCC/mp3/stanton_glantz.html

Glaser, R., Pearson, G.R., Bonneau, R.H., Esterling, B.A., Atkinson, C., & Kiecolt-Glaser, J.K. (1993). Stress and memory T-cell response to the Epstein-Barr virus in healthy medical students. *Health Psychology, 12*, 435–442.

Glaser, R., & Kiecolt-Glaser, J.K. (2005). Science and society: Stress-induced immune dysfunction: Implications for health. *Nature Reviews: Immunology, 5*(3), 243–251.

Glaser, R., Padgett, D.A., Litsky, M.L., Baiocchi, R.A., Yang, E.V., Chen, M., et al. (2005). Stress-associated changes in the steady-state expression of latent Epstein-Barr virus: Implications for chronic fatigue syndrome and cancer. *Brain, Behavior, and Immunity, 19*, 91–103.

Glassman, A.H., & Shapiro, P.A. (1998). Depression and the course of coronary artery disease. *American Journal of Psychiatry, 155*, 4–11.

Gmel, G., Gutjahr, E., & Rehm, J. (2003). How stable is the risk curve between alcohol and all-cause mortality and what factors influence the shape? A precision-weighted hierarchical meta-analysis. *European Journal of Epidemiology, 18*, 631–642.

Godin, G., Maticka-Tyndale, E., Adrien, A., Manson-Singer, S., Willms, D., & Cappon, P. (1996). Cross-cultural testing of three social cognitive theories: An application to condom use. *Journal of Applied Social Psychology, 26*, 1556–1586.

Godlee, F., Smith, J., & Marcovitch, H. (2011). Wakefield's article linking MMR vaccine and autism was fraudulent. *British Medical Journal, 342*, c7452.

Goedhuys, J., & Rethans, J.J. (2001). On the relationship between the efficiency and the quality of the consultation: A validity study. *Family Practice, 18*(6), 592–596.

Goffman, E. (1961). *Asylums*. New York: Anchor.

Gold, M.S. (2004). Physician health and impairment. *Psychiatric Annals, 34*(10), 736–741.

Goldberg, R.J., Gurwitz, J.H., & Gore, J.M. (1999). Duration of, and temporal trends (1994–1997) in, prehospital delay in patients with acute myocardial infarction. *Archives of Internal Medicine, 159,* 2141–2146.

Golden, S.D., & Earp, J.L. (2012). Social ecological approaches to individuals and their contexts: Twenty years of health promotion interventions. *Health Education and Behavior, 39*(3), 364–372.

Goldsmith, D.J. (2004). *Communicating social support.* New York: Cambridge University Press.

Gollwitzer, P.M. (1993). Goal achievement: The role of intentions. In W. Stroebe & M. Hewstone (Eds.), *European review of social psychology, 4* (pp. 141–185). Chichester, UK: Wiley.

Goodheart, C.D., & Lansing, M.H. (1997). *Treating people with chronic disease: A psychological guide.* Washington, DC: American Psychological Association.

Goodman, G., & Dooley, D. (1976). A framework for help-intended communication. *Psychotherapy: Theory, Research and Practice, 13,* 106–117.

Goodman, L., Saxe, L., & Harvey, M. (1991). Homelessness as psychological trauma. Broadening perspectives. *American Psychologist, 46*(11), 1219–1225.

Goodwin, P.J., Leszcz, M., Ennis, M., Koopmans, J., Vincent, L., Guther, H., et al. (2001). The effect of group psychosocial support on survival in metastatic breast cancer. *New England Journal of Medicine, 345*(24), 1719–1726.

Gott, C.M., Rogstad, K.E., Riley, V., & Ahmed-Jushuf, I. (1999). Delay in symptom presentation among a sample of older GUM clinic attenders. *International Journal of STD & AIDS, 10,* 43–46.

Gott, M. (2006). Sexual health and the new ageing. *Age and Ageing, 35,* 106–107.

Gornick, M.E., Eggers, P.W., & Reilly, T.W. (1996). Effects of race and income on mortality and use of services among Medicare beneficiaries. *New England Journal of Medicine, 335,* 791–799.

Gortmaker, S.L., Must, A., Perrin, J.M., Sobol, A.M., & Dietz, W.H. (1993). Social and economic consequences of overweight in adolescence and young adulthood. *The New England Journal of Medicine, 329,* 1008–1012.

Gotay, C., Katzmarzyk, P., Janssen, I., Dawson, M., Aminoltejari, K., & Bartley, N. (2013). Updating the Canadian obesity maps: An epidemic in progress. *Canadian Journal of Public Health, 104* (1). Retrieved from cancerprevent.ca/sites/cancerprevent.ca/files/documents/Obesity-in-Canadian-adults_2000-2012-new.pdf

Gough, I.R., Furnival, C.M., Schilder, L., & Grove, W. (1983). Assessment of the quality of life of patients with advanced cancer. *European Journal of Cancer and Clinical Oncology, 19*(8), 1161–1165.

Gould, D., & Damarjian, N. (1996). Imagery training for peak performance. In J.L. Van Raaalte & B.W. Brewer (Eds.), *Exploring sport and exercise psychology* (pp. 25–50). Washington, DC: American Psychological Association.

Government of Canada. (2013). National anti-drug strategy. Retrieved July 17, 2013, from http://www.national-antidrugstrategy.gc.ca/prevention/index.html

Graham, K., Bernards, S., Wilsnack, S.C., & Gmel, G. (2011). Alcohol may not cause partner violence but it seems to make it worse: A cross national comparison of the relationship between alcohol and severity of partner violence. *Journal of Interpersonal Violence, 26*(8), 1503–1523.

Grams, G.D., Herbert, C., Heffernan, C., Calam, B., Wilson, M.A., Grzybowski, S., et al. (1996). Haida perspectives on living with non-insulin-dependent diabetes. *Canadian Medical Association Journal, 155,* 1563–1568.

Gravely-Witte, S., Leung, Y.W., Nariani, R., Tamim, H., Oh, P., Chan, V.M., et al. (2010). Effects of cardiac rehabilitation referral strategies on referral and enrollment rates. Nature Reviews. *Cardiology, 7*(2), 87–96.

Gray, F., Chretien, F., Vallat-Decouvelaere, A.V., & Scaravilli, F. (2003). The changing pattern of HIV neuropathology in the HAART era. *Journal of Neuropathology and Experimental Neurology, 62*(5), 429–440.

Green, E.E., Green, A.M., & Walters, E.D. (1972). Biofeedback for mind-body self-regulation: Healing and creativity. *Fields . . . Within Fields, 5,* 105–114.

Green, L., & Kreuter, M. (1991). *Health promotion planning: An educational and environmental approach.* Mountain View, CA: Mayfield Publishing.

Greenberg, J.S., & Pargman, D. (1989). *Physical fitness: A wellness approach* (2nd ed.). Englewood Cliffs, NJ: Prentice-Hall.

Greene, M.G., Hoffman, S., Charon, R., & Adelman, R. (1987). Psychosocial concerns in the medical encounter: A comparison of the interactions of doctors with their old and young patients. *The Gerontologist, 27*(2), 164–168.

Greenwood, J. (1998). Meeting the needs of patients' relatives. *Professional Nurse, 14,* 156–158.

Gregoire, I., Kalogeropoulos, D., & Corcos, J. (1997). The effectiveness of a professionally led support group for men with prostate cancer. *Urological Nursing, 17,* 58–66.

Greist, J.H. (1984). *Exercise in the treatment of depression. Coping with mental stress: The potential and limits of exercise intervention.* Washington, DC: National Institute of Mental Health.

Griffin, J.A., Umstattd, M.R., & Usdan, S.L. (2010). Alcohol use and high-risk sexual behavior among collegiate women: A review of research on alcohol myopia theory. *Journal of American College Health, 58*(6), 523–532.

Groesz, L.M., Levine, M.P., & Murnen, S.K. (2002). The effect of experimental presentation of thin media images on body satisfaction: A meta-analytic review. *International Journal of Eating Disorders, 31*(1), 1–16.

Gross, R., Bilker, W.B., Friedman, H.M., Coyne, J.C., & Strom, B.L. (2002). Provider inaccuracy in assessing adherence and outcomes with newly initiated antiretroviral therapy. *AIDS, 16*, 1835–1837.

Grossarth-Maticek, R., & Eysenck, H.J. (1990). Personality, stress and disease: Description and validation of a new inventory. *Psychological Reports, 66*, 355–373.

Grossman, P., Niemann, L., Schmidt, S., & Walach, H. (2004). Mindfulness-based stress reduction and health benefits: A meta-analysis. *Journal of Psychosomatic Research, 57*, 35–43.

Grunau, R.V.E., & Craig, K.D. (1987). Pain expression in neonates: Facial action and cry. *Pain, 28*, 395–410.

Grunberg, S.M., Deuson, R.R., Mavros, P., Geling, O., Hansen, M., Cruciani, G., et al. (2004). Incidence of chemotherapy-induced nausea and emesis after modern antiemetics. *Cancer, 100*, 2261–2268.

Grusser, S.M., Winter, C., Muhlnickel, W., Denke, C., Karl, A., Villringer, K., et al. (2001). The relationship of perceptual phenomena and cortical reorganization in upper extremity amputees. *Neuroscience, 102*, 263–272.

Gruzelier, J. (2003). Self-hypnosis and immune function, health, wellbeing, and personality. *Australian Journal of Clinical & Experimental Hypnosis, 31*(2), 153–161.

Gunzerath, L., Faden, V., Zakhari, S., & Warren, K. (2004). National Institute on Alcohol Abuse and Alcoholism report on moderate drinking. *Alcoholism: Clinical and Experimental Research, 28*, 829–847.

Gura, T. (2003). Cellular warriors at the battle of the bulge. *Science, 299*, 846–849.

Gushue, G.V., & Brazaitis, S.J. (2003). Lazarus and group psychotherapy: AIDS in the era of protease inhibitors. *Counseling Psychologist, 31*(3), 314–342.

Gutkin, C. (2003). Medical schools' accountability for physician resources. *Canadian Family Physician, 49*, 263.

Guttman, N. (1993). Information exchange in medical encounters: Problems and problems. In B.D. Ruben and N. Guttman (Eds.), *Caregiver patient communications* (pp. 151–168). Dubuque, IA: Kendall Hunt.

H

Haan, N. (1993). The assessment of coping, defense, and stress. In L. Goldberger & S. Breznitz (Eds.), *Handbook of stress: Theoretical and clinical aspects* (2nd ed., pp. 258–273). New York: Free Press.

Haake, M., Müller, H.H., Schade-Brittinger, C., Schade-Bittinger, C., Basler, H.D., Schäefer, H., et al. (2007). German Acupuncture Trials (GERAC) for chronic low back pain: Randomized, multicenter, blinded, parallel-group trial with 3 groups. *Archives of Internal Medicine, 167*, 1892–1898.

Hackfort, D., & Spielberger, C.D. (1988). *Anxiety in sports: An international perspective.* New York: Hemisphere.

Hadjistavropoulos, H.D., Craig, K.D., Grunau, R.E., & Johnston, C.C. (1994). Judging pain in newborns: Facial and cry determinants. *Journal of Pediatric Psychology, 19*, 485–491.

Hadjistavropoulos, H.D., Craig, K.D., Grunau, R.E., & Whitfield, M.F. (1997). Judging pain in infants: Behavioural, contextual, and developmental determinants. *Pain, 73*, 319–324.

Hadjistavropoulos, H.D., & de C. Williams, A.C. (2004). Psychological interventions in chronic pain. In T. Hadjistavropoulos & K.D. Craig (Eds.), *Pain: Psychological perspectives* (pp. 271–301). Mahwah, NJ: Erlbaum.

Hadjistavropoulos, T. (2004). Ethics for psychologists who treat, assess, and/or study pain. In T. Hadjistavropoulos & K.D. Craig (Eds.), *Pain: Psychological perspectives* (pp. 327–344). Mahwah, NJ: Lawrence Erlbaum Associates.

Hadjistavropoulos, T., Gibson, S., & Fine, P. (2011). Pain in older persons: A brief clinical guide. In M. Lynch, K.D. Craig, & P. Peng (Eds.), *Clinical pain management: A practical guide* (pp. 311–318). London: Wiley.

Hadjistavropoulos, T., LaChapelle, D., MacLeod, F., Snider, B., & Craig, K.D. (2000). Measuring movement–exacerbated pain in cognitively impaired frail elders. *Clinical Journal of Pain, 16*, 54–63.

Hadjistavropoulos, T., von Baeyer, C., & Craig, K.D. (2001). Pain assessment in persons with limited ability to communicate. In D.C. Turk & R. Melzack (Eds.), *Handbook of pain assessment* (2nd ed., pp. 134–152). New York: Guilford.

Hadlow, J., & Pitts, M. (1991). The understanding of common terms by doctors, nurses and patients. *Social Science and Medicine, 32*, 193–196.

Hahn, D.B., Payne, W.A., Gallant, M., & Crawford, S. (2003). *Focus on health*. Toronto: McGraw-Hill Ryerson.

Halberstadt, A.L., & Geyer, M.A. (2011). Multiple receptors contribute to the behavioral effects of indoleamine hallucinogens. *Neuropharmacology, 61*(3), 364–381.

Halfens, R.G. (1995). Effect of hospital stay on health locus-of-control beliefs. *Western Journal of Nursing Research, 17*, 156–167.

Hall, C.R. (2001). Imagery in sport and exercise. In R.N. Singer, H.A. Hausenblaus, & C.M. Janelle (Eds.), *Handbook of sport psychology* (2nd ed., pp. 529–549). New York: Wiley.

Hall, H. (2011). Acupuncture's claims punctured: Not proven effective for pain, not harmless. *Pain, 152*(4), 711–712.

Hall, J.A., & Roter, D.L. (2007). Physician-patient communication. In H.S. Friedman & R. Cohen Silver (Eds.), *Foundations of health psychology* (pp. 325–357). New York: Oxford University Press.

Hall, L.M., & Kiesners, D. (2005). A narrative approach to understanding the nursing work environment in Canada. *Social Science & Medicine, 61*(12), 2482–2491.

Hall, S., & Smith, A. (1996). Investigation of the effects and aftereffects of naturally occurring upper respiratory tract illness on mood and performance. *Physiology and Behavior, 59*, 569–577.

Halmi, K.A., Agras, W.S., Crow, S., Mitchell, J., Wilson, G.T., Bryson, S.W., et al. (2005). Predictors of treatment acceptance and completion in anorexia nervosa: Implications for future study designs. *Archives of General Psychiatry, 62*, 776–781.

Hamill, S., & Dickey, M. (2005). Cultural competence: What is needed in working with Native Americans with HIV/AIDS? *Journal of the Association of Nurses in AIDS Care, 16*, 64–69.

Ham, O.K. (2005). The intention of future mammography screening among Korean women. *Journal of Community Health Nursing, 22*(1), 1–13.

Hamm, R.M., & Smith, S.L. (1998). The accuracy of patients' judgments of disease probability and test sensitivity and specificity. *Journal of Family Practice, 47*, 44–52.

Hammond, D., Fong, G.T., McDonald, P.W., Brown, K.S., & Cameron, R. (2004). Graphic Canadian cigarette warning labels and adverse outcomes: Evidence from Canadian smokers. *American Journal of Public Health, 94*(8), 1442–1445.

Hammond, D., Fong, G.T., McDonald, P.W., Cameron, R., & Brown, K.S. (2003). Impact of the graphic Canadian warning labels on adult smoking behaviour. *Tobacco Control, 12*, 391–395.

Hammond, D., McDonald, P.W., Fong, G.T., Brown, K.S., & Cameron, R. (2004). The impact of cigarette warning labels and smoke-free bylaws on smoking cessation: Evidence from former smokers. *Canadian Journal of Public Health, 95*(3), 201–204.

Hanewinkel, R., & Sargent, J.D. (2007). Exposure to smoking in popular contemporary movies and youth smoking in Germany. *American Journal of Preventive Medicine, 32*, 466–473.

Hannan, E.L., van Ryn, M., Burke, J., Stone, D., Kumar, D., Arani, D., et al. (1999). Access to coronary bypass surgery by race/ethnicity and gender among patients who are appropriate for surgery. *Medical Care, 37*(1), 68–77.

Hanson, R.G. (1986). *The joy of stress*. Fairway, KS: Andrews, McMeel and Parker.

Harandi, A.A., Esfandani, A., & Shakibaei, F. (2004). The effect of hypnotherapy of procedural pain and state anxiety related to physiotherapy in women hospitalized in a burn unit. *Contemporary Hypnosis, 21*, 28–34.

Hardy, J., Roberts, R., & Hardy, L. (2009). Awareness and motivation to change negative self-talk. *The Sport Psychologist, 23*, 435–450.

Hardy, J., Oliver, E., & Tod, D. (2009). A framework for the study and application of self-talk in sport. In S.D. Mellalieu & S. Hanton (Eds.), *Advances in applied sport psychology: A review* (pp. 37–74). London: Routledge.

Hardy, L., Jones, G., & Gould, D. (1996). *Understanding psychological preparation for sport: Theory and practice of elite performers*. Chichester, England: John Wiley and Sons.

Harper, D.C. (1999). Presidential address: Social psychology of difference: Stigma, spread, and stereotypes in childhood. *Rehabilitation Psychology, 44*, 131–144.

Harrington, J., Noble, L.M., & Newman, S.P. (2004). Improving patients' communication with doctors: A systematic review of intervention studies. *Patient Education and Counseling, 52*(1), 7–16.

Hart, I., & Poole, G.D. (1995). Individualism and collectivism and considerations in cross-cultural health research. *Journal of Social Psychology, 135*, 97–99.

Hart, T.A., & Heimberg, R.G. (2005). Social anxiety as a risk factor for unprotected intercourse among gay and bisexual male youth. *AIDS and Behavior, 9*(4), 505–512.

Harvard, S.S., Hill, W.W., & Buxton, J.A. (2008). Harm reduction product distribution in British Columbia. *Canadian Journal of Public Health, 99*(6), 446–450.

Hashmi, J.A., & Davis, K.D. (2010). Women experience greater heat pain adaptation and habituation than men. *Pain, 145*, 350–357.

Haskard Zolnierek, K.B., & DiMatteo, M.R. (2009). Physician communication and patient adherence to treatment: A meta-analysis. *Medical Care, 47*(8), 826–834.

Haskard Zolnierek, K.B., DiMatteo, M.R., Mondala, M.M., Zhang, Z., Martin, L.R., & Messiha, A.H. (2009). Development and validation of the Physician-Patient Humor Rating Scale. *Journal of Health Psychology, 14*(8), 1163–1173.

Haskell, W.L., Alderman, E.L., Fair, J.M., Maron, D.J., Mackey, S.F., Superko, H.R., et al. (1994). Effects of intensive multiple risk factor reduction on coronary atherosclerosis and clinical cardiac events in men and women with coronary artery disease: The Stanford Coronary Risk Intervention Project (SCRIPT). *Circulation, 89*, 975–990.

Haug, M.R., Musil, C.M., Warner, C.D., & Morris, D.L. (1997). Elderly persons' interpretation of a bodily change as an illness symptom. *Journal of Aging Research, 9*, 529–552.

Haupt, E., Herrmann, R., Benecke-Timp, A., Vogel, H., Haupt, A., & Walter, C. (1996). The KID Study II: Socioeconomic baseline characteristics, psycho-social strain, standard of current medical care education of the Federal Insurance for Salaried Employees' Institution (BfA) diabetic patients in inpatient rehabilitation. Kissingen Diabetes Intervention Study. *Experimental Clinics in Endocrinology and Diabetes, 104*, 378–386.

Hawton, K., Clements, A., Sakarovitch, C., Simkin, S., & Deeks, J.J. (2001). Suicide in doctors: A study of risk according to gender, seniority and specialty in medical practitioners in England and Wales, 1979–1995. *Journal of Epidemiology & Community Health, 55*(5), 296–300.

Hay, D., Varga-Toth, J., & Hines, E. (2006). Frontline health care in Canada: Innovations in delivering services to vulnerable populations. Ottawa, ON: Canadian Policy Research Networks.

Hay, P. (2013). A systematic review of evidence for psychological treatments in eating disorders: 2005–2012. *International Journal of Eating Disorders, 46*(5), 462–269.

Hayden, J.A., van Tulder, M.W., & Tomlinson, G. (2005). Systematic review: Strategies for using exercise therapy to improve outcomes in chronic low back pain. *Annals of internal Medicine, 142*, 776–785.

Hayes, L.J., O'Brien-Pallas, L., Duffield, C., Shamain, J., Buchan, J., Hughes, F., et al. (2006). Nursing turnover: A literature review. *International Journal of Nursing Studies, 43*(2), 237–263.

Hayes, S.C., Strosahl, K., & Wilson, K.G. (1999). *Acceptance and Commitment Therapy: An experiential approach to behavior change.* New York: Guilford Press.

Haynes, R.B., Ackloo, E., Sahota, N., McDonald, H.P., & Yao, X. (2008). Interventions for enhancing medication adherence. *Cochrane Database of Systematic Reviews, 2.* Retrieved June 30, 2010, from www.mrw.interscience.wiley.com/cochrane/clsysrev/articles/CD000011/frame.html

Haynes, R.B., McKibbon, K.A., & Kanani, R. (1996). Systematic review of randomized trials of interventions to assist patients to follow prescriptions for medications. *Lancet, 348*, 383–386.

Haynes, S.G., Feinleib, M., & Kannel, W.B. (1980). The relationship of psychosocial factors to coronary heart disease in the Framingham Study: I. Methods and risk factors. *American Journal of Epidemiology, 107*, 362–383.

Haynes, S.G., McDonald, H.P., & Garg, A.X. (2002). Helping patients follow prescribed treatment. *Journal of the American Medical Association, 288*, 2880–2883.

Hays, K. (1999). *Working it out: Using exercise in psychotherapy.* Washington, DC: American Psychological Association.

Hays, K.F. (2002). The enhancement of performing excellence among performing artists. *Journal of Applied Sport Psychology, 14*, 299–312.

Health Canada. (2000). *Preventing substance use problems among young people: A compendium of best practices.* Ottawa, ON: Health Canada Publications.

Health Canada. (2002). *AIDS: The AIDS/HIV files.* Retrieved July 25, 2003, from www.hc-sc.gc.ca/english/feature/aids/symptoms_main.html

Health Canada. (2003a). *The need for an Aboriginal health institute in Canada.* Ottawa, ON: Health Canada.

Health Canada. (2003b). *Canadian tobacco use monitoring survey 2002: Environmental tobacco smoke: At home, at work and in public places.* Retrieved July 17, 2003, from www.hc-sc.gc.ca/hecs-sesc/tobacco/research/ctums/2001/2001ets.html

Health Canada. (2004). *Quitting smoking.* Retrieved November 18, 2014, from http://hc-sc.gc.ca/hc-ps/tobac-tabac/quit-cesser/index-eng.php

Health Canada. (2009a). *Salvia divinorum.* Retrieved November 18, 2014, from http://hc-sc.gc.ca/ahc-asc/media/nr-cp/_2011/2011_29fs-eng.php

Health Canada. (2009b). *Straight facts about drugs and drug abuse.* Retrieved November 3, 2010, from publications.gc.ca/collections/Collection/H39-65-2000E.pdf

Health Canada. (2009c). *A statistical profile on the health of First Nations in Canada: Determinants of Health, 1999 to 2003.* Retrieved July 15, 2013, from http://www.hc-sc.gc.ca/fniah-spnia/pubs/aborig-autoch/2009-stats-profil/index-eng.php#fig10

Health Canada. (2010a). *Safe use of energy drinks*. Retrieved November 18, 2014, from www.has.uwo.ca/hospitality/nutrition/pdf/safeuse_energydrinks.pdf

Health Canada. (2010b). *Drug and alcohol use statistics: Major findings from the Canadian Alcohol and Drug Use Monitoring Survey (CADUMS) 2009*. Retrieved July 1, 2010, from www.hc-sc.gc.ca/hc-ps/drugs-drogues/stat/index-eng.php

Health Canada. (2011). *Health labels for cigarettes and little cigars*. Retrieved July 15, 2013, from http://www.hc-sc.gc.ca/hc-ps/tobac-tabac/legislation/label-etiquette/cigarette-eng.php

Health Canada. (2013a). *Canadian Tobacco Use Monitoring Survey 2011*. Retrieved July 15, 2013, from http://www.hc-sc.gc.ca/hc-ps/tobac-tabac/research-recherche/stat/index-eng.php

Health Canada. (2013b). *Healthy living: Nicotine addiction*. Retrieved November 18, 2014, from www.healthycanadians.gc.ca/healthy-living-vie-saine/tobacco-tabac/addiction-dependance-eng.php

Health Canada. (2014). *Canadian guidelines for body weight classification in adults*. Retrieved November 18, 2014, from www.hc-sc.gc.ca/hpfb-dgpsa/onpp-bppn/bmi_chart_java_e.html

Health on the Net Foundation. (2014). Retrieved November 18, 2014, from http://www.hon.ch

Hearn, J., & Higginson, T.J. (1998). Do specialist palliative care teams improve outcomes for cancer patients? A systematic literature review. *Palliative Medicine, 12,* 317–332.

Heatherton, T.F., Herman, C.P., & Polivy, J. (1992). Effects of distress on eating: The importance of ego-involvement. *Journal of Personality and Social Psychology, 62,* 801–803.

Hebebrand, J., & Hinney, A. (2009). Environmental and genetic risk factors in obesity. *Child and Adolescent Psychiatric Clinics of North America, 18,* 83–94.

Hemingway, H., & Marmot, M. (1999). Psychosocial factors in the aetiology and prognosis of coronary heart disease: Systematic review of prospective cohort studies. *British Medical Journal, 318,* 1460–1467.

Helft, P.R., Hlubocky, F., & Daugherty, C.K. (2003). American oncologists' views of Internet use by cancer patients: A mail survey of American Society of Clinical Oncology members. *Journal of Clinical Oncology, 21*(5), 942–947.

Hendriks, H.F.J. (2007). Moderate alcohol consumption and insulin sensitivity: Observations and possible mechanisms. *Annals of Epidemiology, 17*(5, Suppl.), S40–S42.

Hendricks, L.E., & Hendricks, R.T. (1998). Greatest fears of type 1 and type 2 patients about having diabetes: Implications for diabetes educators. *Diabetes Education, 24,* 168–173.

Herbert, T.B., & Cohen, S. (1993). Stress and immunity in humans: A meta-analytic review. *Psychosomatic Medicine, 55,* 364–379.

Herbert, T.B., Cohen, S., Marsland, A.L., Bachen, E.A., Rabin, B.S., Muldoon, M.F., et al. (1994). Cardiovascular reactivity and the course of immune response to an acute psychological stressor. *Psychosomatic Medicine, 56,* 337–344.

Herman, C.P., Fitzgerald, N.E., & Polivy, J. (2003). The influence of social norms on hunger ratings and eating. *Appetite, 41,* 15–20.

Herman, C.P., Koenig-Nobert, S., Peterson, J.B., & Polivy, J. (2005). Matching effects on eating: Do individual differences make a difference? *Appetite, 45,* 108–109.

Herman, C.P., & Mack, D. (1975). Restrained and unrestrained eating. *Journal of Personality, 43*(4), 647–660.

Herman, C.P., & Polivy, J. (1980). *Restrained eating*. In A.J. Stunkard (Ed.), *Obesity* (pp. 593–606). Philadelphia: Saunders.

Herman, C.P., & Polivy, J. (2005). Normative influences on food intake. *Physiology & Behavior, 86,* 762–772.

Herman, C.P., & Polivy, J. (2008). External cues in the control of food intake in humans: The sensory-normative distinction. *Physiology & Behavior, 5,* 722–728.

Herman, C.P., Roth, D.A., & Polivy, J. (2003). Effects of the presence of others on food intake: A normative interpretation. *Psychological Bulletin, 129,* 873–886.

Herr, K. (2011). Pain assessment strategies in older patients. *The Journal of Pain, 12*(3), S3–S13.

Herrmann, C.K., Brand-Driehorst, S., Kaminsky, B., Leibing, E., Staats, H., & Rüger, U. (1998). Diagnostic groups and depressed mood as predictors of 22-month mortality in medical inpatients. *Psychosomatic Medicine, 60,* 570–577.

Hertzman, C., & Boyce, T. (2010). How experience gets under the skin to create gradients in developmental health. *Annual Review of Public Health, 31,* 329–347.

Hewitt, M., & Rowland, J.H. (2002). Mental health service use among adult cancer survivors: Analysis of the National Health Interview Survey. *Journal of Clinical Oncology, 20,* 4581–4590.

Hickman, S.E., Tilden, V.P., & Tolle, S.W. (2004). Family perceptions of worry, symptoms, and suffering in the dying. *Journal of Palliative Care, 20*(1), 20–27.

Hickok, J.T., Roscoe, J.A., Morrow, G.R., King, D.K., Atkins, J.N., & Fitch, T.R. (2003). Nausea and emesis remain significant problems of chemotherapy despite prophylaxis with 5-hydroxytryptamine-3 antiemetics: A University of Rochester James P. Wilmot Cancer Center Community Clinical Oncology Program Study of 360 cancer patients treated in the community. *Cancer, 97*(11), 2880–2886.

Hicks, C.L., von Baeyer, C.L., Spafford, P.A., van Korlaar, I., & Goodenough, B. (2001). The Faces Pain Scale—Revised: Toward a common metric in pediatric pain measurement. *Pain, 93*(2), 173–183.

Hilgard, E.R., & Hilgard, J.R. (1975). *Hypnosis in the relief of pain.* Los Altos, CA: Kaufman.

Hill, J.O., Wyatt, H.R., Reed, G.W., & Peters, J.C. (2003). Obesity and the environment: Where do we go from here? *Science, 299,* 853–855.

Hilton, S., Hunt, K., Emslie, C., Salinas, M., & Ziebland, S. (2008). Have men been overlooked? A comparison of young men and women's experiences of chemotherapy-induced alopecia. *Psycho-Oncology, 17,* 577–583.

Hinds, P.S., Sanders, C.B., Srivastava, D.K., Hickey, S., Jayawardene, D., Milligan, M., et al. (1998). Testing the stress-response sequence model in paediatric oncology nursing. *Journal of Advanced Nursing, 28,* 1146–1157.

HIV/AIDS among Aboriginal persons in Canada: A continuing concern. (2003). Ottawa, ON: Health Canada, Centre for Infectious Disease Prevention and Control.

Hjermstad, M.J., Fayers, P.M., Haugen, D.F., Caraceni, A., Hanks, G.W., Loge, J.H., et al. (2010). Studies comparing numerical rating scales, verbal rating scales, and visual analogue scales for assessment of pain intensity in adults: A systematic literature review. *Journal of Pain and Symptom Management, 41*(6), 1073–1093.

Hoek, H.W. (2006). Incidence, prevalence and mortality of anorexia nervosa and other eating disorders. *Current Opinion in Psychiatry, 19*(4), 389–394.

Hoffman, A.J., & Scott, L.D. (2003). Role stress and career satisfaction among registered nurses by work shift patterns. *Journal of Nursing Administration, 33*(6), 337–342.

Hoffmann, D.E., & Tarzian, A.J. (2001). The girl who cried pain: A bias against women in the treatment of pain. *The Journal of Law, Medicine and Ethics, 29,* 13–27.

Hoffman, H.G. (2004). Virtual-reality therapy. *Scientific American, 291*(2), 58–65.

Hoffman, H.G., Richards, T.L., Bills, A.R., Van Oostrom, T. Magula, J., Seibel, E.J., et al. (2006). Using MRI to study the neural correlates of virtual reality analgesia. *CNS Spectrums, 11*(1), 45–51.

Hoffman, H.G., Patterson, D.R., Magula, J., Carrougher, G.J., Zeltzer, K., Dagadakis, S., et al. (2004). Water-friendly virtual reality pain control during wound care. *Journal of Clinical Psychology, 60*(2), 189–195.

Hoffman, H.G., Sharar, S.R., Coda, B., Everett, J.J. Ciol, M., Richards, T., & Patterson, D.R. (2004). Manipulating

presence influences the magnitude of virtual reality analgesia. *Pain, 111,* 162–168.

Hogg, R., Lima, V., Sterne, J.A., Grabar, S., Battegay, M., Bonarek, M., et al. (2008). Life expectancy of individuals on combination antiretroviral therapy in high-income countries: A collaborative analysis of 14 cohort studies. *Lancet, 372,* 293–299.

Holland, K.D., & Holahan, C.K. (2003). The relation of social support and coping to positive adaptation to breast cancer. *Psychology & Health, 18,* 15–29.

Holly, P., Kennedy, P., Taylor, A., & Beedie, A. (2003). Immediate breast reconstruction and psychological adjustment in women who have undergone surgery for breast cancer: A preliminary study. *Psychology, Health & Medicine, 8*(4), 441–452.

Holmes, P.S., & Collins, D.J. (2001). The PETTLEP approach to motor imagery: A functional equivalence model for sport psychologists. *Journal of Applied Sport Psychology, 13*(1), 60–83.

Holroyd, A. (2006). *Attitudes toward aging implications for a caring profession.* Unpublished manuscript, Department of Nursing, Vancouver Island University, Nanaimo, Canada.

Homo-Delarche, F., Fitzpatrick, F., Christeff, N., Nunez, E.A., Bach, J.F., & Dardenne, M. (1991). Sex steroids, glucocorticoids, stress and autoimmunity. *Journal of Steroid Biochemistry and Molecular Biology, 40,* 619–637.

HON Code of Conduct for Medical and Health Web Sites. (2003, April 23). Health on the Net Foundation. Retrieved July 1, 2003, from www.hon.ch/

Hong, T.B., Oddone, E.Z., Dudley, T.K., & Bosworth, H.B. (2006). Medication barriers and anti-hypertensive medication adherence: The moderating role of locus of control. *Psychology, Health & Medicine, 11*(1), 20–28.

Hood, K.K., Rausch, J.R., & Dolan, L.M. (2011). Depressive symptoms predict change in glycemic control in adolescents with type 1 diabetes: Rates, magnitude, and moderators of change. *Pediatric Diabetes,* 718–723.

Hoskins, C.N., Baker, S., Sherman, D., & Bohlander, J. (1996). Social support and patterns of adjustment to breast cancer. *Scholarly Inquiry For Nursing Practice, 10,* 99–123.

Hovland, C.I., Janis, I.L., & Kelley, H.H. (1953). *Communication and persuasion: Psychological studies of opinion change.* New Haven, CT: Yale University Press.

Howard, G., Wagenknecht, L.E., Burk, G.L., Diez-Roux, A., Evans, G.W., McGovern, P., et al. (1998). Cigarette smoking and progression of atherosclerosis: The Atherosclerosis Risk in Communities (ARIC) Study. *Journal of the American Medical Society, 279,* 119–124.

Howard, V.A., & Thurber. (1998). The interpretation of infant pain: Physiological and behavioral indicators. *Pediatric Nursing, 13*(3), 164–174.

Hsieh, A.Y., Tripp, D.A., Ji, L.J., & Sullivan, M.J.L. (2010). Comparisons of catastrophizing, pain attitudes, and cold-pressor pain experience between Chinese and European Canadian young adults. *Journal of Pain, 11*, 1187–1194.

Hsieh, A.Y., Tripp, D.A., & Ji, L.J. (2011). The influence of ethnic concordance and discordance on verbal reports and nonverbal behaviours of pain. *Pain, 152*(9), 2016–2022.

Humbke, K.L., Brown, D.L., Welder, A.N., Fillion, D.T., Dobson, K.S., & Arnett, J.L. (2004). A survey of hospital psychology in Canada. *Canadian Psychology, 45*(1), 31–41.

Hunter, J.P., Katz, J., & Davis, K.D. (2005). Dissociation of phantom limb phenomena from stump tactile spatial acuity and sensory thresholds. *Brain, 128*, 308–320.

Hurley, A.D., Tomasulo, D.J., & Pfadt, A.G. (1998). Individual and group psychotherapy approaches for persons with mental retardation and developmental disabilities. *Journal of Developmental and Physical Disabilities, 10*, 365–386.

Hutchings, D. (2002). Parallels in practice: Palliative nursing practice and Parse's theory of human becoming. *American Journal of Hospital Palliative Care, 19*(6), 408–414.

Huth, M.M., Broome, M.E., & Good, M. (2004). Imagery reduces children's post-operative pain. *Pain, 110*, 439–448.

Hwang, S.W. (2006). Discharge day. *Canadian Medical Association Journal, 174*(8), 1138–1139.

I

Igartua, J.J., Cheng, L., & Lopes, O. (2003). To think or not to think: Two pathways towards persuasion by short films on AIDS prevention. *Journal of Health Communication, 8*(6), 513–528.

Ilacqua, G.E. (1994). Migraine headaches: Coping efficacy of guided imagery training. *Headache, 34*, 99–102.

Inman, J.J., & Zeelenberg, M. (2002). Implementation regret in repeat purchase versus switching decisions: The attenuating role of decision justifiability. *Journal of Consumer Research, 29*, 116–128.

International Centre for Health and Society. (2003). *Social determinants of health: The solid facts* (2nd ed.). World Health Organization, Europe.

Irwin, M., Daniels, M., Smith, T.L., Bloom, E., & Weiner, H. (1987). Impaired natural killer cell activity during bereavement. *Brain, Behavior, and Immunity, 1*, 98–104.

Irwin, M., Lacher, U., & Caldwell, C. (1992). Depression and reduced natural killer cytotoxicity: A longitudinal study of depressed patients and control subjects. *Psychological Medicine, 22*, 1045–1050.

Irwin, M.R., & Miller, A.H. (2007). Depressive disorders and Immunity: 20 years of progress and discovery. *Brain, Behavior, and Immunity, 21*(4), 374–383.

Irwin, M., Patterson, T., Smith, T.L., Caldwell, C., Brown, S.A., Gillin, J.C., et al. (1990). Reduction of immune function in life stress and depression. *Biological Psychiatry, 27*, 23–30.

Irwin, M.R., Pike, J.L., Cole, J.C., & Oxman, M.N. (2003). Effects of a behavioral intervention, tai chi chih, on varcella-zoster virus specific immunity and health functioning in older adults. *Psychosomatic Medicine, 65*, 823–830.

ITC Project. (2012a). Health warnings on tobacco packaging: ITC cross country comparison report. University of Waterloo, Waterloo, Ontario, Canada.

ITC Project. (2012b). Smoke free policies: ITC cross country comparison report. University of Waterloo, Waterloo, Ontario, Canada.

Iverson, S.A., Howard, K.B., & Penney, B.K. (2008). Impact of Internet use on health-related behaviors and the patient-physician relationship; A survey-based study and review. *The Journal of the American Osteopathic Association, 108*(12), 699–711.

Iwai, K. (1996). 1: The self-image of muscular dystrophy inpatients and the psychological effects of their disease. *Japanese Journal of Special Education, 33*(5), 1–6.

J

Jackson, S.A., & Csikszentmihalyi, M. (1999). *Flow in sports.* Champaign, IL: Human Kinetics.

Jacobs, G.D. (2001). Clinical applications of the relaxation response and mind-body interventions. *Journal of Alternative and Complementary Medicine, 7*(Suppl. 1), 92–101.

Jacobsen, P.B., & Hann, D.M. (1998). Cognitive-behavioral interventions. In J.C. Holland (Ed.), *Psycho-oncology* (pp. 717–729). New York: Oxford University Press.

Jacobson, A.M., & Weinger, K. (1998). Treating depression in diabetic patients; Is there an alternative to medications? *Annals of Internal Medicine, 129*, 656–657.

Jacobson, E. (1938). *Progressive relaxation: A physiological and clinical investigation of muscle states and their significance in psychology and medical practice* (2nd ed.). Chicago: University of Chicago Press.

Jacobson, P.D., Bovbjerg, D.H., Schwartz, M.D., Hudis, C.A., Gilewski, T.A., & Norton, L. (1995). Conditioned emotional distress in women receiving chemotherapy for breast cancer. *Journal of Consulting and Clinical Psychology, 63*, 108–114.

Jacox, A., Carr, D.B., & Payne, R. (1994). New guidelines for management of pain in patients with cancer. *New England Journal of Medicine, 330*(9), 651–655.

Janssen, I. (2013). The public health burden of obesity in Canada. *Canadian Journal of Diabetes, 37*(2), 90–96.

Janssen, S.M., & Lagro-Janssen, A.L.M. (2012). Physician's gender, communication style, patient preferences and patient satisfaction in gynecology and obstetrics: A systematic review. *Patient Education and Counseling, 89*, 221–226.

Jasnowski, M.L., Holmes, D.S., & Banks, D.L. (1988). Changes in personality associated with changes in aerobic and anaerobic fitness in women and men. *Journal of Psychosomatic Research, 32*, 273–276.

Jellinek, E.M. (1960). *The disease concept of alcoholism.* New Haven, CT: College and University Press.

Jemmott, J.B., III, Borysenko, M., Chapman, R., McClelland, D.C., Chapman, R., Meyer, D., & Benson, H. (1983). Academic stress, power motivation, and decrease in secretion rate of salivary secretory Immunoglobulin A. *Lancet,* 1400–1402.

Jenkins, C.D. (1996). Where there's hope, there's life. *Psychosomatic Medicine, 58*, 122–124.

Jenkins, N., Lawton, J., Douglas, M., Walker, S., Finnie, R., Porteous, M., & Hallowell, N. (2013). How do index patients participating in genetic screening programmes for familial hypercholesterolemia (FH) interpret their DNA results? A UK-based qualitative study. *Patient Education and Counseling, 90*, 372–377.

Jensen, M.P., & Karoly, P. (2001). Self-report scales and procedures for assessing pain in adults. In D.C. Turk & R. Melzack (Eds.), *Handbook of pain assessment* (2nd ed., pp. 15–34). New York: Guilford.

Jensen, M.P., Turner, J.A., Romano, J.M., & Strom, S.E. (1995). The Chronic Pain Coping Inventory: Development and preliminary validation. *Pain, 60*, 203–216.

Joachim, G., & Acorn, S. (2000). Stigma of visible and invisible chronic conditions. *Journal of Advanced Nursing, 32*(1), 243–248.

Job, E. (2003). *Learning to show "it hurts": The role of developmental factors in predicting young children's use of self-report scales for pain.* Unpublished master's thesis, University of British Columbia, Vancouver, British Columbia.

Johnson, R.L., Roter, D., & Powe, D.R. (2004). Patient race/ethnicity and quality of patient-physician communication during medical visits. *American Journal of Public Health, 94*, 2084–2090.

Johnson, R.L., Saha, S., Arbelaez, J.J., Beach, M.C., & Cooper, L. (2004). Racial and ethnic differences in patient perceptions of bias and cultural competence in health care. *Journal of General Internal Medicine, 19*, 101–110.

Johnson Thornton, R.L., Powe, N.R., Roter, D., & Cooper, L.A. (2011). Patient-physician social concordance, medical visit communication and patients' perceptions of health care quality. *Patient Education and Counseling, 85,* e201–e208.

Johnston, K.L., & White, K.M. (2003). Binge-drinking: A test of the role of group norms in the theory of planned behaviour. *Psychology and Health, 18*, 63–77.

Jonasson, G., Carlsen, K.H., Sodal, A., Jonasson, C., & Mowinckel, P. (1999). Patient compliance in a clinical trial with inhaled budesonide in children with mild asthma. *European Respiratory Journal, 14*, 150–154.

Jones, G. (2002). Performance excellence: A personal perspective on the link between sport and business. *Journal of Applied Sport Psychology, 14*, 268–281.

Jones, L.W., Courneya, K.S., Fairey, A.S., & Mackey, J.R. (2005). Does the theory of planned behavior mediate the effects of an oncologist's recommendation to exercise in newly diagnosed breast cancer survivors? Results from a randomized controlled trial. *Health Psychology, 24*(2), 189–197.

Jorenby, D.E., Leischow, S.J., Nides, M.A., Rennard, S.I., Johnston, J.A., Hughes, A.R., et al. (1999). A controlled trial of sustained-release bupropion, a nicotine patch, or both for smoking cessation. *New England Journal of Medicine, 340*, 685–691.

Judd, J., Frankish, J., & Moulton, G. (2001). Setting standards in the evaluation of community-based health promotion programs—A unifying approach. *Health Promotion International, 16*(4), 367–380.

Julien, R.M., Advokat, C.D., & Comaty, J. (2011). *A primer of drug action* (12th ed.). New York: Worth.

Juurlink, D.N., Stukel, T.A., Kwong J., Kopp, A., McGeer, A., Upshur, R.E., et al. (2006). Guillain-Barre syndrome after influenza vaccination in adults: A population-based study. *Archives of Internal Medicine, 166*, 2217–2221.

Jurgens, C.Y. (2006). Somatic awareness, uncertainty, and delay in care-seeking in acute heart failure. *Research in Nursing and Health, 29*(2), 74–86.

K

Kaasa, S., & Loge, J.H. (2003). Quality of life in palliative care: principles and practice. *Palliative Medicine, 17*(1), 11–20.

Kabat-Zinn, J. (1993). Mindfulness meditation: Health benefits of an ancient Buddhist practice. In D. Goleman & J. Gurin (Eds.), *Mind/body medicine: How to use your mind for better health* (pp. 259–275). Yonkers, NY: Consumer Reports Books.

Kabat-Zinn, J. (2003). Mindfulness-based interventions in context: Past, present, and future. *Clinical Psychology: Science and Practice, 10*(2), 144–156.

Kahn, B.E., & Wansink, B. (2004). The influence of assortment structure on perceived variety and consumption quantities. *Journal of Consumer Research, 30*, 519–533.

Kahn, H.A. (1963, July). The relationship of reported coronary heart disease mortality to physical activity of work. *American Journal of Public Health Nation's Health, 53*(7), 1058–1067.

Kahneman, D. (2011). *Thinking fast and slow.* New York: Farrar, Straus and Giroux.

Kahneman, D., & Miller, D.T. (1986). Norm theory: Comparing reality to its alternatives. *Psychological Review, 80,* 136–153.

Kambouropoulos, N. (2003). The validity of the tension-reduction hypothesis in alcohol cue-reactivity research. *Australian Journal of Psychology, 55*(S1), 6.

Kanayama, G., & Pope, H.G., Jr. (2011). Gods, men, and muscle dysmorphia. *Harvard Review of Psychiatry, 19,* 95–98.

Kangas, M., Henry, J.L., & Bryant, R.A. (2002). Posttraumatic stress disorder following cancer: A conceptual and empirical review. *Clinical Psychology Review, 22,* 499–524.

Ka'opua, L.S.I., & Mueller, C.W. (2004). Treatment adherence among Native Hawaiians living with HIV. *Social Work, 49,* 55–62.

Kappesser, J., Williams, A.C., & Prkachin, K.M. (2006). Testing two accounts of pain underestimation. *Pain, 124,* 109–116.

Kaplan, R.A., Rossell S.L., Enticott, P.G., & Castle, D.J. (2013). Own-body perception in body dysmorphic disorder. *Cognitive Neuropsychiatry, 18*(6), 594–614.

Kaplan, R.M., Sallis, J.F., & Patterson, T.L. (1993). *Health and human behavior.* New York: McGraw-Hill.

Kaplan, S.H., Gandek, B., Greenfield, S., Rogers, W., & Ware, J.E. (1995). Patient and visit characteristics related to physicians' participatory decision-making style: Results from the Medical Outcomes Study. *Medical Care, 33,* 1176–1187.

Kaps, E.C. (1994). The role of the support group, "Us Too." *Cancer, 74,* 2188–2189.

Karaca, I., Ilkay, E., Akbulut, M., & Yavuzkir, M. (2003). Treatment of in-stent restenosis with excimer laser coronary angioplasty. *Japanese Heart Journal, 44*(2), 179–186.

Karasek, R. (1979). Job demands, job decision latitude, and mental strain: Implications for job design. *Administrative Science Quarterly, 24,* 285–310.

Karl, A., Muhlnickel, W., Kurth, R., & Flor, H. (2004). Neuroelectric source imaging of steady-state movement-related cortical potentials in human upper extremity amputees with and without phantom limb pain. *Pain, 110,* 90–102.

Karageorghis, C.I., & Priest, D.L. (2012, March). Music in the exercise domain: a review and synthesis (Part II). *International Review of Sport and Exercise Psychology, 5*(1), 67–84.

Katz, J., Wowk, A., Culp, D., & Wakeling, H. (1999). A randomized, controlled study of the pain- and tension-reducing effects of 15 minute workplace massage treatments versus seated rest for nurses in a large teaching hospital. *Pain Research and Management, 4*(2), 81–88.

Katz, R.C., Flasher, L., Cacciapaglia, H., & Nelson, S. (2001). The psychosocial impact of cancer and lupus: A cross validation study that extends the generality of "benefit finding" in patients with chronic disease. *Journal of Behavioral Medicine, 24*(6), 561–571.

Katzmarzyk, P.T., & Janssen, I. (2004). The economic costs associated with physical inactivity and obesity in Canada: An update. *Canadian Journal of Applied Physiology, 29*(2), 90–115.

Katzmarzyk, P.T., Craig, C.L., & Bouchard, C. (2001). Underweight, overweight and obesity: Relationship with mortality in the 13-year follow-up of the Canada Fitness Survey. *Journal of Clinical Epidemiology, 54,* 916–920.

Kavussanu, M., & McAuley, E. (1996). Exercise and optimism: Are highly active individuals more optimistic? *Journal of Sport and Exercise Psychology, 18,* 264–280.

Keefe, F.J., Williams, D.A., & Smith, S.J. (2001). Assessment of pain behaviors. In D.C. Turk & R. Melzack (Eds.), *Handbook of pain assessment* (2nd ed., pp. 170–189). New York: Guilford.

Keefler, J., Duder, S., & Lechman, C. (2001). Predicting length of stay in an acute care hospital: The role of psychosocial problems. *Social Work in Health Care, 33*(2), 1–16.

Kehr, B.A. (2004). Computer-enhanced treatment compliance. *Behavioral Health Management, 24*(2), 44–48.

Keller, A., Litzelman, K., Wisk, L.E., Maddox, T., Cheng, E.R., Creswell, P.D., et al. (2012). Does the perception that stress affects health matter? *Health Psychology, 31*(5), 677–684.

Kelly, B., Raphael, B., Judd, F., Perdices, M., Kernutt, G., Burnett, P., et al. (1998). Posttraumatic stress disorder in response to HIV infection. *General Hospital Psychiatry, 20,* 345–352.

Kelly, G.A., Blake, C., Power, C., O'Keeffe, D., & Fullen, B.M. (2011). The association between chronic low back pain and sleep: A systematic review. *Clinical Journal of Pain, 27*(2), 169–181.

Kelly, J.A. (1998). Group psychotherapy for persons with HIV and AIDS-related illnesses. *International Journal of Group Psychotherapy, 48,* 143–162.

Kelly, J.F., Stout, R.L., Magill, M., & Tonigan, J.S. (2011). The role of Alcoholics Anonymous in mobilizing adaptive social network changes: A prospective lagged mediational analysis. *Drug and Alcohol Dependence, 114,* 119–126.

Kelly, K.M., Ajmera, M., Bhattacharjee, S., Vohra, R., Hobbs, G., Chaudhary, L., et al. (2013). Perception of cancer recurrence risk: More information is better. *Patient Education and Counseling, 90,* 361–366.

Kelner, K., & Helmuth, L. (2003). Obesity—What is to be done? *Science, 299,* 845.

Kemeny, M.E. (2005). The psychobiology of stress. In G. Miller & E. Chen (Eds.), *Current directions in health psychology* (pp. 55–63). Washington, DC: Pearson Education.

Kendall, C., & Hailley, B.J. (1993). The relative effectiveness of three reminder letters on making and keeping mammogram appointments. *Behavioral Medicine, 19,* 29–34.

Kendall-Tackett, K. (2009). Psychological trauma and physical health: A psychoneuroimmunology approach to etiology of negative health effects and possible interventions. *Psychological Trauma: Theory, Practice, and Policy, 1,* 35–48.

Kennedy, D.P., Tucker, J.S., Pollard, M.S., Go, M.H., & Green, H.D. (2011). Adolescent romantic relationships and change in smoking status. *Addictive Behaviors, 36*(4), 320–326.

Kennedy, J., & Morgan, S. (2009). Cost-related prescription nonadherence in the United States and Canada: A system-level comparison using the 2007 International Health Policy Survey in Seven Countries. *Clinical Therapy, 31*(1), 213–219.

Kenkel, M.B., Deleon, P.H., Mantell, E.O., & Steep, A.E. (2005). Divided no more: Psychology's role in integrated health care. *Canadian Psychology, 46*(4), 189–202.

Keogh, E. (2006). Sex and gender differences in pain: A selective review of biological and psychosocial factors. *Journal of Men's Health and Gender, 3,* 236–243.

Keogh, E. (2009). Sex differences in pain. In R.J. Moore (Ed.), *Biobehavioral approaches to pain* (pp. 125–148). New York: Springer Science and Business Media.

Keogh, E., Bond, F.W., Hanmer, R., & Tilson, J. (2005). Comparing acceptance- and control-based coping instructions on the cold-pressor pain experiences of healthy men and women. *European Journal of Pain, 9*(5), 59–81.

Kern, M.L., & Friedman, H.S. (2008). Do conscientious individuals live longer? A quantitative review. *Health Psychology, 27,* 505–512.

Kerns, R.D., Turk, D.C., & Rudy, T.E. (1985). The West Haven-Yale Multidimensional Pain Inventory. *Pain, 23,* 345–356.

Keski-Rahkonen, A., Bulik, C.M., Neale, B.M., Rose, R.J., Rissanen, A., & Kaprio, J. (2005). Body dissatisfaction and drive for thinness in young adult twins. *International Journal of Eating Disorders, 37*(3), 188–199.

Kidd, S., & Shahar, G. (2008). Resilience in homeless youth: The key role of self-esteem. *American Journal of Orthopsychiatry 78*(2), 163–172.

Kiecolt-Glaser, J. (2003). Chronic stress and age-related increases in the proinflammatory cytokine IL-6. *Proceedings of the National Academy of Science, 100,* 9090–9095.

Kiecolt-Glaser, J.K., Fisher, J.D., Ogrocki, P., Stout, J.C., Speicher, C.E., & Glaser, R. (1987). Marital quality, marital disruption, and immune function. *Psychosomatic Medicine, 49,* 13–34.

Kiecolt-Glaser, J.K., Glaser, R., Shuttleworth, E.C., Dyers, C.S., Ogroki, P., & Speicher, C.E. (1987). Chronic stress and immunity in family caregivers of Alzheimer's disease victims. *Psychosomatic Medicine, 49,* 523–535.

Kiecolt-Glaser, J.K., Gouin, J.-P., & Hantsoo, L. (2010). Close relationships, inflammation, and health. *Neuroscience and Biobehavioral Reviews, 35*(1), 33–38.

Kiecolt-Glaser, J.K., Kennedy, S., Malkoff, S., Fisher, L., Speicher, C.E., & Glaser, R. (1988). Marital discord and immunity in males. *Psychosomatic Medicine, 50,* 213–229.

Kiecolt-Glaser, J.K., Marucha, P.T., Atkinson, C., & Glaser, R. (2001). Hypnosis as a modulator of cellular immune dysregulation during acute stress. *Journal of Consulting & Clinical Psychology, 69,* 674–682.

Kiecolt-Glaser, J.K., McGuire, L., Robles, T.F., & Glaser, R. (2002a). Psychoneuroimmunology: Psychological influences on immune function and health. *Journal of Consulting and Clinical Psychology, 70,* 537–547.

Kiecolt-Glaser, J.K., McGuire, L., Robles, T.F., & Glaser, R. (2002b). Emotions, morbidity, and mortality: New perspectives from psychoneuroimmunology. *Annual Review of Psychology, 53,* 83–107.

Kiesler, D.J. (1966). Some myths of psychotherapy research and the search for a paradigm. *Psychological Bulletin, 65,* 110–136.

Kinder, L.S., Bradley, K.A., Katon, W.J., Ludman, E., McDonell, M.B., & Bryson, C.L. (2008). Depression, posttraumatic stress disorder, and mortality. *Psychosomatic Medicine, 70,* 20–26.

King, K.M., & Teo, K.K. (1998). Cardiac rehabilitation referral and attendance: Not one and the same. *Rehabilitation Nursing, 23*, 246–251.

King, S., Chambers, C.T., Huguet, A., MacNevin, R.C., McGrath, P.J., Parker, L., et al. (2011). The epidemiology of chronic pain in children and adolescents revisited: A systematic review. *Pain, 152*(12), 2729–2738.

Kingston, G. (1999). Concussion leaves a gap in Long's memory. *Vancouver Sun*, October 18.

Kingston K., & Wilson K. (2009). The application of goal setting in sport. In S. Mellalieu & S. Hanton (Eds.), *Advances in applied sport psychology: A review* (pp. 75–123). New York: Routledge.

Kircaldy, B.D., & Shephard, R.J. (1990). Therapeutic implications of exercise. *International Journal of Sport Psychology, 21*, 165–184.

Kirschenbaum, D. (1998). Using sport psychology interventions to improve health psychology outcomes. *The Health Psychologist, 20*, 16–23.

Kirschenbaum, K.S. (1997). Prevention of sedentary lifestyles: Rationale and methods. In W.P. Morgan (Ed.), *Physical activity and mental health* (pp. 33–48). Washington, DC: Taylor and Francis.

Kishchuk, N., Tremblay, M., Lapierre, J., Heneman, B., & O'Loughlin, J. (2004). Qualitative investigation of young smokers' and ex-smokers' view on smoking cessation methods. *Nicotine and Tobacco Research, 6*, 491–500.

Kissane, D. (2009). Beyond the psychotherapy and survival debate: The challenge of social disparity, depression and treatment adherence in psychosocial cancer care. *Psycho-Oncology, 18*(1), 1–5.

Kiyohara, C., & Ohno, Y. (2010). Sex differences in lung cancer susceptibility: A review. *Gender Medicine, 7*(5), 381–401.

Klump, K., McGue, M., & Iacono, W.G. (2000). Age differences in genetic and environmental influences on eating attitudes and behaviors in preadolescent and adolescent female twins. *Journal of Abnormal Psychology, 109*, 239–251.

Knight, J.R., Sanchez, L.T., Sherritt, L., Bresnahan, L.R., Silveria, J.M., & Fromson, J.A. (2002). Monitoring physician drug problems: Attitudes of participants. *Journal of Addictive Diseases, 21*(4), 27–36.

Knutson, K.L., & van Cauter, E. (2008). Associations between sleep loss and increased risk of obesity and diabetes. *Annals of the New York Academy of Sciences, 1120*(Suppl. 1), 287–304.

Komaroff, A.L. (2003, March 7). *An update on the obesity problem.* Journal Watch (General). Retrieved July 9, 2003, from general-medicine.jwatch.org/cgi/content/full/2003/307/8

Komproe, I.H., Rijken, M., Ros, W.J.G., Winnubst, J.A.M., & Harm't, H. (1997). Available support and received support: Different effects under stressful circumstances. *Journal of Social and Personal Relationships, 14*, 59–77.

Kop, W.J., & Gottdiener, J.S. (2005). The role of immune system parameters in the relationship between depression and coronary artery disease. *Psychosomatic Medicine, 67*(Suppl. 1), S37–S41.

Korol, C.T., & Craig, K.D. (2001). Pain from the perspectives of health psychology and culture. In S.S. Kazarian & E.R. Evans (Eds.), *Handbook of cultural health psychology* (pp. 241–265). San Diego: Academic Press.

Kotalik, J. (2012). Controlling pain and reducing misuse of opioids: Ethical considerations. *Canadian Family Physician, 58*, 381–385.

Kowalcek, I., Muhlhoff, A., Bachmann, S., & Gembruch, U. (2002). Depressive reactions and stress related to prenatal medicine procedures. *Ultrasound in Obstetrics and Gynecology, 19*(1), 18–23.

Kozlowski, L.T. (1979). Psychological influences on cigarette smoking. In Krasnegor, N.A. (Ed.), *The behavioural aspects of smoking* (pp. 99–125). NIDA Research Monograph 26. U.S. Department of Health, Education, and Welfare, Public Health Service, Alcohol, Drug Abuse, and Mental Health Administration, National Institute on Drug Abuse. DHEW Publication No. 79-882.

Kozlowski, L.T., & Herman, C.P. (1984). The interaction of psychosocial and biological determinants of tobacco use: More on the boundary model. *Journal of Applied Social Psychology, 14*, 244–256.

Kraemer, H.C., Kuchler, T., & Spiegel, D. (2009). Use and misuse of the CONSORT guidelines to assess research findings: Comment on Coyne, Stefanek, and Palmer (2007). *Psychological Bulletin, 135*, 173–178.

Kraetschmer, N., Sharpe, N., Urowitz, S., & Deber, R.B. (2004). How does trust affect patient preferences for participation in decision-making? *Health Expectations: An International Journal of Public Participation in Health Care & Health Policy, 7*(4), 317–326.

Kramer, A.F., Hahn, S., Cohen, N.J., Banich, M.T., McAuley, E., Harrison, C.R., et al. (1999). Ageing, fitness and neurocognitive function. *Nature, 400*, 418–419.

Kramer, M. (1974). *Reality shock—Why nurses leave nursing.* St. Louis, MO: CV Mosby.

Kramer, M., & Schmalenberg, C.E. (2003). Magnet hospital staff nurses describe clinical autonomy. *Nursing Outlook, 51*, 13–19.

Krantz, D.S., Grunberg, N.E., & Baum, A. (1985). Health psychology. *Annual Review of Psychology, 36,* 349–383.

Kruger, J., Galuska, D.A., Serdula, M.K., & Jones, D.A. (2004). Attempting to lose weight: Specific practices among U.S. adults. *American Journal of Preventive Medicine, 26,* 402–406.

Krupat, E., Fancey, M., & Cleary, P.D. (2000). Information and its impact on satisfaction among surgical patients. *Social Science & Medicine, 51*(12), 1817–1825.

Kübler-Ross, E. (1969). *On death and dying.* New York: Macmillan.

Kubzansky, L.D., Martin, L.T., & Buka, S.L. (2009). Early manifestations of personality and adult health: A life course perspective. *Health Psychology, 28,* 364–372.

Kuehn, B.M. (2006). Report reviews secondhand smoke risks: Some scientists question level. *Journal of the American Medical Association, 296*(8), 922–953.

Kuhl, D. (2003). *What dying people really want: Practical wisdom for the end of life.* New York: Public Affairs Publishing.

Kummervold, P.E., & Johnsen, J.A. (2011). Physician response time when communicating with patients over the Internet. *Journal of Medical Internet Research, 13*(4), e79.

Kurtz, S.M. (2002). Doctor-patient communication: Principles and practices. *Canadian Journal of Neurological Sciences, 29*(2), S23–S29.

Kurtz, M.E., Kurtz, J.C., Given, C.W., & Given B. (1995). Relationship of caregiver reactions and depression to cancer patients' symptoms, functional states and depression: A longitudinal view. *Social Science and Medicine, 40,* 837–846.

Kurtz, S.M., Silverman, J., Benson, J., & Draper, J. (2003). Marrying content and process in clinical method teaching: Enhancing the Calgary Cambridge guides. *Academic Medicine, 78*(8), 802–809.

Kuuppelomäki, M., & Lauri, S. (1998). Cancer patients' reported experiences of suffering. *Cancer Nursing, 21,* 364–369.

L

La Via, M.F., Munno, I., Lydiard, R.B., Workman, E.W., Hubbard, J.R., Michel, Y., et al. (1996). The influence of stress intrusion on immunodepression in generalized anxiety disorder patients and controls. *Psychosomatic Medicine, 58,* 138–142.

Labonte, R. (1987). Community health promotion strategies. *Health Promotion, 16,* 5–10, 32.

Labonte, R. (1990). Health promotion: From concepts to strategies. In G. Eikenberg (Ed.), *The seeds of health: Promoting wellness in the '90s* (pp. 129–146). Ottawa, ON: Canadian College of Health Service Executives.

Lacaille, D., White, M.A., Rogers, P.A., Backman, C.L., Gignac, M.A., & Esdaile, J.M. (2008). A proof-of-concept study of the "Employment and Arthritis: Making It Work" program. *Arthritis and Rheumatism, 59*(11), 1647–1655.

Ladwig, K.H., & Dammann, G. (1997). Psychological adaptation after successful out-of-hospital resuscitation. *Journal of Psychosomatic Research, 43*(6), 559–564.

Ladwig, K.H., Schoefinius, A., Dammaun, G., Danner, R., Gurtler, R., & Herrmann, R. (1999). Long-acting psychotraumatic properties of a cardiac arrest experience. *American Journal of Psychiatry, 156,* 912–919.

Laforge, R.G., Greene, G.W., & Prochaska, J.O. (1994). Psychosocial factors influencing low fruit and vegetable consumption. *Journal of Behavioral Medicine, 17,* 361–374.

Lalonde, M. (1974). *New perspectives on the health of Canadians.* Ottawa, ON: Information Canada.

Landers, D.M., & Arent, S.M. (2001). Physical activity and mental health. In R.N. Singer, H.A. Hausenblas, & C.M. Janelle (Eds.), *Handbook of sport psychology* (2nd ed., pp. 740–765). New York: Wiley.

Landers, D.M., & Arent, S.M. (2007). Physical activity and mental health. In G. Tenenbaum & R.C. Eklund (Eds.), *Handbook of sport and exercise psychology* (3rd ed., pp. 469–491). Hoboken, NJ: John Wiley & Sons.

Landers, D.M., & Petruzzello, S.J. (1994). Physical activity, fitness, and anxiety. In C. Bouchard, R.J. Shephard, & T. Stephens (Eds.), *Physical activity, fitness, and health: International proceedings and consensus statement* (pp. 868–882). Champaign, IL: Human Kinetics.

Langille, J.-L.D., & Rodgers, W.M. (2010). Exploring the influence of a social ecological model on school-based physical activity. *Health Education and Behavior, 37*(6), 879–894.

Laschinger, H.K.S., Finegan, J.E., Shamian, J., & Wilk, P. (2004). A longitudinal analysis of the impact of workplace empowerment on work satisfaction. *Journal of Organizational Behavior, 25*(4), 527–545.

Lau, R.R., Hartman, K.A., & Ware, J.E., Jr. (1986). Health as a value: Methodological and theoretical considerations. *Health Psychology, 5,* 25–43.

Lavie, C.J., Milani, R.V., Cassidy, M.M., & Gilliland, Y.E. (1999). Effects of cardiac rehabilitation and exercise training programs in women with depression. *American Journal of Cardiology, 83,* 1480–1483.

Lavin, D., & Groarke, A. (2005). Dental floss behaviour: A test of the predictive utility of the Theory of Planned Behaviour and the effects of making implementation intentions. *Psychology, Health & Medicine, 10*(3), 243–252.

Layne, N. (1987). *Solvent use/abuse among the Canadian Registered Indian and Inuit population. An overview paper.* Unpublished report. Ottawa, ON: National Native Alcohol and Drug Abuse Program.

Lazarus, R.S. (1999). *Fifty years of the research and theory of R.S. Lazarus: An analysis of historical and perennial issues.* Mahwah, NJ: Erlbaum.

Lazarus, R.S. (2006). *Stress and emotion.* New York: Springer.

Lazarus, R.S., & Folkman, S. (1984). *Stress, appraisal, and coping.* New York: Springer.

LCC. (2013). Lung Cancer Canada newsletter. Retrieved July 15, 2013, from www.lungcancercanada.ca

Leathart, A. (1994). Communication and socialisation (1): An exploratory study and explanation for nurse-patient communication in ITU. *Intensive and Critical Care Nursing, 10*, 93–104.

Leatherdale, S.T., Cameron, R., Brown, K., Jolin, M.A., & Kroeker, C. (2006). The influence of friends, family, and older peers on smoking among elementary school students: Low-risk students in high-risk schools. *Preventive Medicine: An International Journal Devoted to Practice and Theory, 42*(3), 218–222.

Leatherdale, S.T., Maske, S., & Kroder, C. (2006). Sex differences in how older students influence younger student smoking behaviour. *Addictive Behaviors, 31*(8), 1308–1318.

Lecca, P., Quervala, I., Nunes, J., & Gonzales, H. (1998). *Cultural Competency in Health, Social and Human Services: Directions for the Twenty-First Century.* New York: Garland Publishing.

Lee, A., & Poole, G. (2005). An application of the transactional model to the analysis of chronic illness narratives. *Qualitative Health Research, 15*(3), 346–364.

Lee, F.J., Stewart, M., & Brown, J.B. (2008). Stress, burnout, and strategies for reducing them: What's the situation among Canadian family physicians? *Canadian Family Physician, 54*, 234.

Lee, R.S., Kochman, A., & Sikkema, K.J. (2002). Internalized stigma among people living with HIV-AIDS. *AIDS & Behavior, 6*(4), 309–319.

Leit, R.A., Gray, J.J., & Pope, H.G., Jr. (2002). The media's representation of the ideal male body: A cause for muscle dysmorphia? *International Journal of Eating Disorders, 13*(3), 334–338.

Leit, R.A., Pope, H.G., Jr., & Gray, J.J. (2000). Cultural expectations of muscularity in men: The evolution of playgirl centerfolds. *International Journal of Eating Disorders, 29*(1), 90–93.

Leiter, M., Harvie, P., & Frizzel, C. (1998). The correspondence of patient satisfaction and nurse burnout. *Social Science and Medicine, 47*, 1611–1617.

Lenz, E.R., & Perkins, S. (2000). Coronary artery bypass graft surgery patients and their family member caregivers: Outcomes of a family-focused staged psychoeducational intervention. *Applied Nursing Research, 13*(3), 142–150.

Lerner, M.J. (1980). *The belief in a just world: A fundamental delusion.* New York: Plenum.

Le Scanff, C., & Taugis, T. (2002). Stress management for police special forces. *Journal of Applied Sport Psychology, 14*, 330–343.

Leserman, J., Jackson, E.D., Petitto, J.M., Golden, R.N., Silva, S.G., Perkins, D.O., et al. (1999). Progression to AIDS: The effects of stress, depressive symptoms, and social support. *Psychosomatic Medicine, 61*(3), 397–406.

Lester, S.R., Brown, J.R., Aycock, J.E., Grubbs, S.L., & Johnson, R.B. (2010). Use of saliva for assessment of stress and its effect on the immune system prior to gross anatomy practical examinations. *Anatomical Sciences Education, 3*(4), 160–167.

Leszcz, M., & Goodwin, P.J. (1998). The rationale and foundations of group psychotherapy for women with metastatic breast cancer. *International Journal of Group Psychotherapy, 48*, 245–273.

Letizia, M., Creech, S., Norton, E., Shanahan, M., & Hedges, L. (2004). Barriers to caregiver administration of pain medication in hospice care. *Journal of Pain and Symptom Management, 27*(2), 114–124.

Lett, H.S., Davidson, J., & Blumenthal, J.A. (2005). Non-pharmacologic treatments for depression in patients with coronary heart disease. *Psychosomatic Medicine, 67*(Suppl. 1), S58–S62.

LeUnes, A., & Nation, J.R. (2002). *Sport psychology* (3rd ed.). Pacific Grove, CA: Wadsworth.

Leuthner, S.R. (2001). Decisions regarding resuscitation of the extremely premature infant and models of best interest. *Journal of Perinatology, 21*(3), 193–198.

Levant, R.F. (2005). Graduate education in clinical psychology for the twenty-first century: Educating psychological health care providers. *Journal of Clinical Psychology, 61*(9), 1087–1090.

Leventhal, E.A., Hansell, S., Diefenbach, M., Leventhal, H., & Glass, D.C. (1996). Negative affect and self-report of physical symptoms: Two longitudinal studies of older adults. *Health Psychology, 15*, 193–199.

Leventhal, H., Weinman, J., Leventhal, E.A., & Phillips, L.A. (2008). Health psychology: The search for pathways between behavior and health. *Annual Review of Psychology, 59*, 477–505.

Levin, J.S., & Puchalski, C.M. (1997). Religion and spirituality in medicine: Research and education. *Journal of the American Medical Association, 278*, 792–793.

Levine, R.L., & Levy, L.A. (2006). Relationship between self-reported intensity of headache and magnitude of surface EMG. *Psychological Reports, 1,* 91–94.

Levinson, W. (1994). Physician-patient communication. A key to malpractice prevention. *Journal of the American Medical Association, 272,* 1619–1620.

Levinson, W., & Lurie, N. (2004). When most doctors are women: What lies ahead? *Annals of Internal Medicine, 141,* 471–474.

Levinson, W., Roter, D.L., Mullooly, J.P., Dull, V.T., & Frankel, R.M. (1997). Physician-patient communication. The relationship with malpractice claims among primary care physicians and surgeons. *Journal of the American Medical Association, 277,* 553–559.

Levy, S.S., Macera, C.A., Hootman, J.M., Coleman, K.J., Lopez, R., Nichols, J.F., et al. (2012). Evaluation of a multi-component group exercise program for adults with arthritis: Fitness and exercise for people with arthritis (FEPA). *Disability and Health Journal, 5*(4), 305–311.

Lewin, A.B., Heidgerken, A.D., Geffken, G.R., Williams, L.B., Storch, E.A., Gelfand, K.M., et al. (2006). The relation between family factors and metabolic control: The role of diabetes adherence. *Journal of Pediatric Psychology, 31*(2), 174–183.

Lewis, C.C., Matheson, D.H., & Brimacombe, C.A.E. (2011). Factors influencing patient disclosure to physicians in birth control clinics: An application of the Communication Privacy Management Theory. *Health Communication, 26,* 502–511.

Lewis, S.D. (2013). *The hypnosis treatment option: Proven solutions for pain, insomnia, stress, obesity, and other common health problems.* Las Vegas: Copper Ridge Press.

Ley, P. (1977). Psychological studies of doctor-patient communication. In S. Rachman (Ed.), *Contributions to medical psychology,* 1. Oxford: Pergamon.

Ley, P. (1982). Satisfaction, compliance, and communication. *British Journal of Clinical Psychology, 21,* 241–254.

Ley, P. (1988). *Communicating with the patient: Improving communication, satisfaction and compliance.* London, England: Chapman & Hall.

Li, C., Unger, J.B., Schuster, D., Rohrbach, L.A., Howard-Pitney, B., & Norman, G. (2003). Youths' exposure to environmental tobacco smoke (ETS) associations with health beliefs and social pressure. *Addictive Behaviors, 28,* 39–53.

Lieberman, A. (2006). Depression in Parkinson's disease—A review. *Acta Neurologica Scandinavica, 113*(1), 1–8.

Lin, L., Halgin, R.P., Well, A.D., & Ockene, I. (2008). The relationship between depression and occupational, household, and leisure-time physical activity. *Journal of Clinical Sport Psychology, 2,* 95–107.

Ling, D., Niu, T., Feng, Y., Xing, H., & Xu, X. (2004). Association between polymorphism of the dopamine transporter gene and early smoking onset: An interaction risk on nicotine dependence. *Journal of Human Genetics, 49,* 35–39.

Liossi, C., & Hatira, P. (2003). Clinical hypnosis in the alleviation of procedure-related pain in pediatric oncology patients. *International Journal of Clinical and Experimental Hypnosis, 51*(1), 4–28.

Lipsman, N., Woodside, D.B., Giacobbe, P., Hamani, C., Carter, J.C., Norwood, S.J., et al. (2013). Subcallosal cingulate deep brain stimulation for treatment-refractory anorexia nervosa: A phase 1 pilot trial. *Lancet, 381*(9875), 1361–1370.

Liu, H., Golin, C.E., Miller, L.G., Hays, R.D., Beck, C.K., Sanadji, S., et al. (2001). A comparison study of multiple measures of adherence to HIV protease inhibitors. *Annals of Internal Medicine, 134,* 968–977.

Literature review: Evaluation strategies in Aboriginal substance abuse programs: A discussion. (2002). Ottawa, ON: Health Canada.

Lloyd, C., Joyce, R., Hurry, J., & Ashton, M. (2000). The effectiveness of primary school drug education. *Drugs: Education, Prevention & Policy, 7*(2), 109–126.

Lloyd, E.C., Mathews, K.A., Wing, R.R., & Orchard, T.I. (1992). Psychosocial factors and complications of IDDM. The Pittsburgh Epidemiology of Diabetes Complications Study VIII. *Diabetes Care, 15,* 166–172.

Lobo, A., Dugouil, C., Marcos, G., Quetglas, B., Saz, P., & Guallar, E. (2010). Is there an association between low-to-moderate alcohol consumption and risk of cognitive decline? *American Journal of Epidemiology, 172*(6), 708–716.

Locke, E.A. (1968). Toward a theory of task motivation and incentives. *Organizational Behaviour and Human Performance, 3,* 157–189.

Locke, E.A., & Latham, G.P. (1985). The application of goal setting to sports. *Journal of Sports Psychology, 7,* 205–222.

Locke, E.A., & Latham, G.P. (1990). *A theory of goal-setting and task performance.* Englewood Cliffs, NJ: Prentice-Hall.

Lollis, C.M., Johnson, E.H., & Antoni, M.H. (1997). The efficacy of the health belief model for predicting condom usage and risky sexual practices in university students. *AIDS Education and Prevention, 9,* 551–563.

Lorber, J. (1975). Good patients and problem patients: Conformity and deviance in a general hospital. *Journal of Health and Social Behavior, 16,* 213–225.

Lower, J.S., Bonsack, C., & Guion, J. (2003). Peace and quiet. *Nursing Management, 34*(4), 40A–40D.

Lowery, D., Fillingim, R.B., & Wright, R.A. (2003). Sex differences and incentive effects on perceptual and cardiovascular responses to cold pressor pain. *Psychosomatic Medicine, 65,* 284–291.

Lu, D.P., Lu, G.P., & Kleinman, L. (2001). Acupuncture and clinical hypnosis for facial and head and neck pain: A single crossover comparison. *The American Journal of Clinical Hypnosis, 44,* 141–148.

Luce, G., & Peper, E. (1971). Mind over body, mind over mind. *New York Times Magazine,* September.

Luppino, F.S., de Wit, L.M., Bouvy, P.F., Stijnen, T., Cuijpers, P., Penninx, B.W., et al. (2010). Overweight, obesity, and depression: A systematic review and meta-analysis of longitudinal studies. *Archives of General Psychiatry, 67*(3), 220–229.

Lurie, J.D., & Sox, H.C. (1999). Principles of medical decision making. *Spine, 24,* 493–498.

Luschen, G., Cockerham, W., & Kunz, G. (1996). The sociocultural context of sport and health problems of causal relations and structural interdependence. *Sociology of Sport Journal, 13,* 197–213.

Lussier, M.-T., & Richard, C. (2006). Complaints and legal actions: Role of doctor-patient communication. *Canadian Family Physician, 51,* 37–39.

Lustman, P.J., Freedland, K.E., Griffith, L.S., & Clouse, R.E. (1998). Predicting response to cognitive behavior therapy of depression in type 2 diabetes. *General Hospital Psychiatry, 20,* 302–306.

Lustman, P.J., Griffith, L.S., Freedland, K.E., & Clouse, R.E. (1998). Cognitive behavior therapy for depression in type 2 diabetes mellitus. A randomized, controlled trial. *Annals of Internal Medicine, 129,* 613–621.

Lynch, G.P. (1988). Athletic injuries and the practicing sport psychologist: Practical guidelines for assisting athletes. *The Sport Psychologist, 2,* 161–167.

Lynch, M.E., & Watson, C.P.N. (2006). The pharmacotherapy of chronic pain: A review. *Pain Research and Management, 11,* 11–38.

Lynge, E., Olsen, A.H., Fracheboud, J., & Patnick, J. (2003). Reporting of performance indicators of mammography screening in Europe. *European Journal of Cancer Prevention, 12*(3), 213–222.

Lyubomirsky, S. (2001). Why are some people happier than others? The role of cognitive and motivational processes in well-being. *American Psychologist, 56,* 239–249.

Lyubomirsky, S., King, L., & Diener, E. (2005). The benefits of frequent positive affect: Does happiness lead to success. *Psychological Bulletin, 131,* 803–855.

M

Macciocchi, S.N., Barth, J.T., Alves, W.A., Rimel, R.W., & Jane, J.J. (1996). Neuropsychological functioning and recovery after mild head injury in collegiate athletes. *Neurosurgery, 39,* 510–514.

MacDonald, T.K., Fong, G.T., Zanna, M.P., & Martineau, A.M. (2000). Alcohol myopia and condom use: Can alcohol intoxication be associated with more prudent behavior? *Journal of Personality and Social Psychology, 78*(4), 605–619.

MacDonald, T.K., Zanna, M.P., & Fong, G.T. (1996). Why common sense goes out the window: Effects of alcohol on intentions to use condoms. *Personality and Social Psychology Bulletin, 22,* 763–775.

MacDonald, T.K., Zanna, M.P., & Fong, G.T. (1998). Alcohol and intentions to engage in risky behaviors: Experimental evidence for a causal relationship. In J.G. Adair, D. Belanger, & K. Dion (Eds.), *Advances in psychological science: Vol. 1. Social, personal, and cultural aspects* (pp. 407–428). East Sussex, UK: Psychology Press.

MacDonald, T.K., Zanna, M.P., & Fong, G.T. (1995). Decision making in altered states: Effects of alcohol on attitudes toward drinking and driving. *Journal of Personality and Social Psychology, 68,* 973–985.

MacKean, P., & Gutkin, C. (2003). Fewer medical students selecting family medicine. Can family practice survive? *Canadian Family Physician, 49,* 408–409, 415–407.

Macleod, U., Mitchell, E.D., Burgess, C., Macdonald, S., & Ramirez, A.J. (2009). Risk factors for delayed presentation and referral of symptomatic cancer: Evidence for common cancers. *British Journal of Cancer, 101,* S92–S101.

MacNeil, J., & Pauly, B. (2010). Impact: A case study examining the closure of a large urban fixed site needle exchange in Canada. *Harm Reduction Journal, 7.* http://www.harmreductionjournal.com/content/7/1/11. Accessed November 6, 2012).

Madsen, M.V., Gotzsche, P.C., & Hrobjartsson, A. (2009). Acupuncture treatment for pain: Systematic review of randomized clinical trials with acupuncture, placebo acupuncture, and no acupuncture groups. *British Medical Journal, 338,* 1–8.

Maes, M. (1995). Evidence for an immune response in major depression: A review and hypothesis. *Progress in Neuro-Psychopharmacology & Biological Psychiatry, 19,* 11–38.

Maes, M., Christophe, A., Bosmans, E., Lin, A., & Neels, H. (2000). In humans, serum polyunsaturated fatty acid levels predict the response of proinflammatory cytokines to psychologic stress. *Biological Psychiatry, 47,* 910–920.

Maes, H.H., Neale, M.C., & Eaves, L.J. (1997). Genetic and environmental factors in relative body weight and human adiposity. *Behavior Genetics, 27,* 325–351.

Magarey, J.M., & McCutcheon, H.H. (2005). "Fishing with the dead"—Recall of memories from the ICU. *Intensive and Critical Care Nursing, 21*(6), 344–354.

Mahoney, M. (1996). Foreword. In J.L. Van Raalte & B.W. Brewer (Eds.), *Exploring sport and exercise psychology* (pp. xiii–xvii) Washington, DC: American Psychological Association.

Mahoney, M.J., Gabriel, T.J., & Perkins, T.S. (1987). Psychological skills and exceptional athletic performance. *The Sport Psychologist, 1,* 181–199.

Maier, S.F., Watkins, L.R., & Fleshner, M. (1994). Psychoneuroimmunology: The interface between behaviour, brain, and immunity. *American Psychologist, 49,* 1004–1017.

Malina, D. (2005). Compliance, caricature, and culturally aware care. *New England Journal of Medicine, 353*(13), 1317–1318.

Malinauskas, B.M., Aeby, V.G., Overton, R.F., Carpenter-Aeby, T., & Barber-Heidal, K. (2007). A survey of energy drink consumption patterns among college students. *Nutrition Journal, 6,* 35.

Maloney, E.K., Lapinski, M.K., & Witte, K. (2011). Fear appeals and persuasion: A review and update of the Extended Parallel Process Model. *Social and Personality Psychology Compass, 5*(4), 206–219.

Mangelli, L., Gribbin, N., Buchi, S., Allard, S., & Sensky, T. (2002). Psychological well-being in rheumatoid arthritis: Relationship to "disease" variables and affective disturbance. *Psychotherapy and Psychosomatics, 71*(2), 112–116.

Manne, S.L., Jacobsen, P.B., Gorfinkle, K., Gerstein, F., & Redd, W.H. (1993). Treatment adherence difficulties among children with cancer: The role of parenting style. *Journal of Pediatric Psychology, 18,* 47–62.

Marentette T., & El-Masri, M.M. (2011). Predicting seasonal influenza vaccination among hospital-based nurses. *Clinical Nursing Research, 20*(4), 422–438.

Marks, D.F., Murray, M., Evans, B., & Estacio, E.V. (2011). *Health psychology: Theory, research and practice.* London: Sage.

Margolis, R.D., & Zweben, J.E. (2011). *Treating patients with alcohol and other drug problems: An integrated approach* (2nd ed.). Washington, DC: American Psychological Association.

Marlatt, G.A., & Gordon, J.R. (1980). Determinants of relapse: Implications for the maintenance of behavior change. In P.O. Davidson & S.M. Davidson (Eds.), *Behavioral medicine: Changing health lifestyles* (pp. 410–452). New York: Brunner/Mazel.

Marrero, D.G., Guare, J.C., Vandagriff, J.L., & Fineberg, N.S. (1997). Fear of hypoglycemia in the parents of children and adolescents with diabetes: Maladaptive or health response? *Diabetes Education, 23,* 281–286.

Marrett, L.D., De, P., Airia, P., Dryer, D. (2008). Cancer in Canada in 2008. *Canadian Medical Association Journal, 179*(11), 1163.

Marsland, A.L., Cohen, S., Rabin, B.S., & Manuck, S.B. (2006). Trait positive affect and antibody response to hepatitis B vaccination. *Brain, Behavior, and Immunity, 20,* 261–269.

Martel, M.O., Thibault, P., Roby, C., Catchlove, R., & Sullivan, M.J. (2008). Contextual determinants of pain judgments. *Pain, 139*(3), 562–568.

Martens, P., Bond, R., Jebamani, L., Brurchill, C., Noralou, R., Derksen, S., et al. (2002). *The health and health care use of registered First Nations people living in Manitoba: A population-based study.* Winnipeg: Manitoba Centre for Health Policy, University of Manitoba.

Martin, D.P., Diehr, P., Conrad, D.A., Davis, J.H., Leickly, R., & Perrin, E.B. (1998). Randomized trial of a patient-centered hospital unit. *Patient Education and Counseling, 34,* 125–133.

Martin, J.J., & Cutler, K. (2002). An exploratory study of flow and motivation in theater actors. *Journal of Applied Sport Psychology, 14,* 344–352.

Martin, P.D., & Brantley, P.J. (2004). Stress, coping, and social support in health and behavior. In J.M. Raczynsky & L.C. Leviton (Eds.), *Handbook of clinical health psychology* (Vol. 2, pp. 233–267). Washington, DC: American Psychological Association.

Martin, R., Lemos, K., Rothrock, N., Bellman, S.B., Russell, D. Trip-Reimer, T., et al. (2004). Gender disparities in common sense models of illness among myocardial infarction victims. *Health Psychology, 23,* 345–353.

Martinsen, E.W. (1990). Benefits of exercise for the treatment of depression. *Sports Medicine, 9,* 380–389.

Martinsen, E.W. (1993). Therapeutic implications of exercise for clinically anxious and depressed patients. *International Journal of Sport Psychology, 24,* 185–199.

Martinsen, E.W. (1994). Physical activity and depression: Clinical experience. *Acta Psychiatrica Scandinavica, 377,* 23–27.

Martinson, E.W., & Morgan, W.P. (1997). Antidepressant effects of physical activity. In W.P. Morgan (Ed.), *Physical activity and mental status* (pp. 93–106). Washington, DC: Taylor & Francis.

Marvel, M.K., Epstein, R.M., Flowers, K., & Beckman, H.B. (1999). Soliciting the patient's agenda: Have we improved? *Journal of the American Medical Association, 281*, 283–287.

Maslach, C., & Leiter, M.P. (1997). *The truth about burnout.* San Francisco: Jossey-Bass.

Massie, M.J. (2004). Prevalence of depression in patients with cancer. *Journal of the National Cancer Institute. Monographs, 32*, 57–71.

Masten, A.S. (2001). Ordinary magic: Resilience processes in development. *American Psychologist, 56*, 227–238.

Matarazzo, J.D. (1980). Behavioral health and behavioral medicine. *American Psychologist, 35*, 807–817.

Matarazzo, J.D., Weiss, S.M., Herd, J.A., Miller, N.E., & Weiss, S. (Eds.). (1984). *Behavioral health: A handbook of health enhancement and disease prevention.* New York: Wiley.

Matheson, D.H. (1997). The painful truth: Interpretation of facial expressions of pain in older adults. *Journal of Nonverbal Behaviour, 21*, 223–238.

Matsunaga, H., Kiriike, N., Iwasaki, Y., Miyata, A., & Matsui, T. (2000). Multi-impulsivity among bulimic patients in Japan. *International Journal of Eating Disorders, 27*, 348–352.

Mauksch, L.B., Dugdale, D.C., Dodson, S., & Epstein, R. (2008). Relationship, communication, and efficiency in the medical encounter: Creating a clinical model from a literature review. *Archives of Internal Medicine, 168*(13), 1387–1395.

Mayne, T.J., & Ambrose, T.K. (1999). Research review on anger in psychotherapy. *Journal of Clinical Psychology, 55*, 353–363.

Mazullo, J.M., Lasagna, L., & Griner, P.F. (1974). Variations in interpretation of prescription instructions. *Journal of the American Medical Association, 227*, 929–931.

McCarthy, P.J., Jones, M.V., Harwood, C.G., & Olivier, S. (2010). What do young athletes implicitly understand about psychological skills? *Journal of Clinical Sport Psychology, 4*, 158–172.

McAuley, E., & Courneya, K.S. (1992). Self-efficacy relationships with affective and exertion responses to exercise. *Journal of Applied Social Psychology, 22*, 312–326.

McAuley, E., Mihalko, S.L., & Bane, S.M. (1996). Acute exercise and anxiety reduction: Does the environment matter? *Journal of Sport and Exercise Psychology, 18*, 408–419.

McAuley, E., Schaffer, S.M., & Rudolph, D. (1995). Affective responses to acute exercise in elderly impaired males: The moderating effects of self-efficacy and age. *International Journal of Aging and Human Development, 41*, 13–35.

McCorkle, R., Tang, S.T., Greenwald, H., Holcombe, G., & Lavery, M. (2006). Factors related to depressive symptoms among long-term survivors of cervical cancer. *Health Care for Women International, 27*, 45–58.

McDonald, D.D., & Fedo, J. (2009). Older adults' pain communication: the effect of interruption. *Pain Management Nursing, 10*(3), 149–53.

McDonald, H.P., Garg, A.X., & Haynes, R.B. (2002). Interventions to enhance patient adherence to medication prescriptions: Scientific review. *Journal of the American Medical Association, 288*, 2868–2879.

McDonald, T.D., & Kennedy, S. (2004). Insights into the "healthy immigrant effect": Health status and health services use of immigrants to Canada. *Social Science & Medicine, 59*, 1613–1627.

McDonald, J.T., & Kennedy, S. (2005). Is migration to Canada associated with unhealthy weight gain? Overweight and obesity among Canada's immigrants. *Social Science & Medicine, 61*, 2469–2481.

McEwen, B.S. (1998). Protective and damaging effects of stress mediators. *New England Journal of Medicine, 338*, 171–1179.

McEwen, B.S. (2000). Allostasis and allostatic load: Implications for neuropsychopharmacology. *Neuropsychopharmacology, 22*, 108–124.

McEwen, B.S., & Stellar, E. (1993). Stress and the individual: Mechanisms leading to disease. *Archives of General Medicine, 153*, 2093–2101.

McFarland, K.F., & Rhoades, D.R. (1998). Gender-related values and medical specialty choice. *Academic Psychiatry, 22*, 236–239.

McFarlane, T., Polivy, J., & Herman, C.P. (1998). Effects of false weight feedback on mood, self-evaluation, and food intake in restrained and unrestrained eaters. *Journal of Abnormal Psychology, 107*, 312–318.

McFarlane, T., Polivy, J., & McCabe, R.E. (1999). Help, not harm: Psychological foundation for a nondieting approach toward health. *Journal of Social Issues, 55*, 261–276.

McGovern, R.J., Heyman, E.N., & Resnick, M.I. (2002). An examination of coping style and quality of life of cancer patients who attend a prostate cancer support group. *Journal of Psychosocial Oncology, 20*(3), 57–68.

McGrath, P.A. (1987). An assessment of children's pain: A review of behavioral, physiological and direct scaling techniques. *Pain, 31*, 147–176.

McGrath, P.A., & Gillespie, J. (2001). Pain assessment in children and adolescents. In D.C. Turk & R. Melzack (Eds.), *Handbook of pain assessment* (2nd ed., pp. 97–118). New York: Guilford.

McGrath, P.J., Latimer, M., Finley, G.A., & Chambers, C.T. (2009). Measurement of pain in children. *Pain Research and Management, 14*, 11–12.

McKinstry, B. (2000). Do patients wish to be involved in decision making in the consultation? A cross sectional survey with video vignettes. *British Medical Journal, 321*, 867–871.

McMurran, M. (1994). *The psychology of addiction*. London: Taylor & Francis.

McNaughton-Dunn, A. (2002). Cultural competence and the primary care provider. *Journal of Pediatric Health Care, 16*(3), 151–155.

McNeil, J., Doucet, E., & Chaput, J.-P. (2013). Inadequate sleep as a contributor to obesity and type 2 diabetes. *Canadian Journal of Diabetes, 37*(2), 103–108.

McPherson, A. (2005). Sustainability of family medicine. *Canadian Medical Association Journal, 172*(2), 157.

McWilliam, C.L., Brown, J.B., & Stewart, M. (2000). Breast cancer patients' experiences of patient-doctor communication: A working relationship. *Patient Education and Counseling, 39*, 191–204.

Meadows, B. (2009). Drug abuse sparks crisis. *Canadian Journal of Public Health, 100*(2), 104–108.

Meechan, G., Colins, J., & Petrie, K.J. (2003). The relationship of symptoms and psychological factors to delay in seeking medical care for breast symptoms. *Preventive Medicine, 36*, 374–378.

Mehler, P.S. (2003). Osteoporosis in anorexia nervosa: Prevention and treatment. *International Journal of Eating Disorders, 33*(2), 113–126.

Mehler, P.S. (2011). Medical complications of bulimia nervosa and their treatments. *International Journal of Eating Disorders, 44*(2), 95–104.

Meichenbaum, D. (1975). Enhancing creativity by modifying what subjects say to themselves. *American Educational Research Journal, 12*, 129–145.

Meichenbaum, D. (1977). *Cognitive-behavior modification: An integrative approach*. New York: Plenum Press.

Meichenbaum, D.H. (1985). *Stress inoculation training*. New York: Pergamon Press.

Melamed, B.G., & Siegal, L.J. (1975). Reduction of anxiety in children facing surgery by modeling. *Journal of Consulting and Clinical Psychology, 43*, 511–521.

Melzack, R. (1975). The McGill Pain Questionnaire: Major properties and scoring methods. *Pain, 1*, 277–299.

Melzack, R. (1987). The short-form McGill Pain Questionnaire. *Pain, 30*, 191–197.

Melzack, R. (1992). Phantom limbs. *Scientific American, 266*, 120–126.

Melzack, R. (2001). Pain and the neuromatrix in the brain. *Journal of Dental Education, 65*, 1378–1382.

Melzack, R., Israel, R., Laxroix, R., & Schultz, G. (1997). Phantom limbs in people with congenital limb deficiency or amputation in early childhood. *Brain, 120*, 1603–1620.

Melzack, R., & Katz, J. (2001). The McGill pain questionnaire: Appraisal and current status. In D.C. Turk & R. Melzack (Eds.), *Handbook of pain assessment* (2nd ed., pp. 35–52). New York: Guilford.

Melzack, R., & Katz, J. (2004). The gate control theory: Reaching for the brain. In T. Hadjistavropoulos & K.D. Craig (Eds.), *Pain: Psychological perspectives* (pp. 13–34). Mahwah, NJ: Erlbaum.

Melzack, R., & Wall, P.D. (1965). Pain mechanisms: A new theory. *Science, 150*, 971–979.

Melzack, R., & Wall, P.D. (1996). *The challenge of pain* (2nd ed.). New York: Basic Books.

Mercado, A.M., Quan, N., Padgett, D.A., Sheridan, J.F., & Marucha, P.T. (2002). Restraint stress alters the expression of interleukin-1 and keratinocyte growth factor at wound site: An in situ hybridization study. *Journal of Neuroimmunology, 129*, 74–83.

Mercken, L., Candel, M., Willems, P., & de Vries, H. (2007). Disentangling social selection and social influence effects on adolescent *smoking*: The importance of reciprocity in friendships. *Addiction, 102*(9), 1483–1492.

Merskey, H. (1986). Psychiatry and pain. In R.A. Sternbach (Ed.), *The psychology of pain* (2nd ed., pp. 97–120). New York: Raven Press.

Myers, C.D., Riley, J.L., & Robinson, M.E. (2003). Psychosocial contributions to sex-correlated differences in pain. *The Clinical Journal of Pain, 19*, 225–232.

Michalko, S.L., McAuley, E., & Bane, S. (1996). Self-efficacy and affective responses to acute exercise in middle-aged adults. *Journal of Social Behavior and Personality, 11*, 375–385.

Miles, F., & Meehan, J.W. (1995). Visual discrimination of pigmented skin lesions. *Health Psychology, 14*, 171–177.

Miller, B.M., Bartholomew, J.B., & Springer, B.A. (2005). Post-exercise affect: The effect of mode preference. *Journal of Applied Sport Psychology, 17*, 263–272.

Millar, M.G. (1997). The effects of emotion on breast self-examination: Another look at the Health Belief Model. *Social Behavior and Personality, 25*, 223–232.

Miller, D.L., & Stark, L.J. (1994). Contingency contracting for improving adherence in pediatric populations. *Journal of the American Medical Association, 271*, 81–83.

Miller, G.E., Chen, E., & Parker, K.J. (2011). Psychological stress in childhood and susceptibility to the chronic diseases of aging: Moving toward a model of behavioral and biological mechanisms. *Psychological Bulletin, 137*(6), 959–997.

Miller, G.E., & Cohen, S. (2001). Psychological interventions and the immune system: A meta-analytic review and critique. *Health Psychology, 20*(1), 47–63.

Miller, G.E., Cohen, S., Pressman, S., Barkin, A., Rabin, B.S., & Treanor, J.J. (2004). Psychological stress and antibody response to influenza vaccination: When is the critical period for stress, and how does it get inside the body? *Psychosomatic Medicine, 66*(2), 215–223.

Miller, L.G., Liu, H., Hays, R.D., Golin, C.W., Beck, C.K., Asch, S.M., et al. (2002). How well do clinicians estimate patients' adherence to combination antiretroviral therapy? *Journal of General Internal Medicine, 17,* 1–11.

Miller, N.E. (1983). Behavioral medicine: Symbiosis between laboratory and clinic. *Annual Review of Psychology, 34,* 1–31.

Miller, P.S., & Kerr, G.A. (2002). Conceptualizing excellence: Past, present, and future. *Journal of Applied Sport Psychology, 14,* 140–153.

Miller, S.M. (1980). When is a little information a dangerous thing? Coping with stressful life-events by monitoring vs. blunting. In S. Levine & H. Ursin (Eds.), *Coping and health* (pp. 145–170). New York: Plenum Press.

Miller, S.M. (1996). Monitoring/blunting of threatening information: Cognitive interference and facilitation in the coping process. In I.G. Sarison, G.R. Pierce, & S.B.R. (Eds.), *Cognitive interference: Theories, methods and findings* (pp. 175–190). Mahwah, NJ: Lawrence Erlbaum.

Miller, S.M., & Mangan, C.E. (1983). Interacting effects of information and coping style in adapting to gynecologic stress: Should the doctor tell all? *Journal of Personality and Social Psychology, 45,* 223–236.

Miller, T.D., Balady, G.J., & Fletcher, G.F. (1997). Exercise and its role in the prevention and rehabilitation of cardiovascular disease. *Annals of Behavioral Medicine, 19,* 220–229.

Miller, V.A., & Drotar, D. (2003). Discrepancies between mother and adolescent perceptions of diabetes-related decision-making autonomy and their relationship to diabetes-related conflict and adherence to treatment. *Journal of Pediatric Psychology, 28,* 265–274.

Millett, C., & Glantz, S.A. (2010). Assigning an "18" rating to movies with tobacco imagery is essential to reduce youth smoking. *Thorax, 65,* 377–378.

Millstein, S.G. (1996). Utility of the theories of reasoned action and planned behavior for predicting physician behavior: A prospective analysis. *Health Psychology, 15,* 398–402.

Milton, B., Cook, P.A., Dugdill, L., Porcellato, L., Spsringett, J., & Woods, S.W. (2004). Why do primary school children smoke? A longitudinal analysis of predictors of smoking uptake during pre-adolescence. *Public Health, 118,* 247–255.

Minor, M.A., & Sanford, M.K. (1993). Physical interventions in the management of pain in arthritis. *Arthritis Care and Research, 6,* 197–206.

Minore, B., & Boone, M. (2002). Realizing potential: Improving interdisciplinary professional/paraprofessional health care teams in Canada's northern aboriginal communities through education. *Journal of Interprofessional Care, 16*(2), 139–147.

Minore, B., Jacklin, K., Boon, M., & Cromarty, H. (2009). Realistic expectations: The changing role of paraprofessional health workers in the First Nation communities in Canada. *Education for Health, 22*(2), 1–9.

Minton, C., & Carryer, J. (2005). Memories of former intensive care patients six months following discharge. *Contemporary Nurse, 20*(2), 152–158.

Miró, J., Turk, D.C., & Rudy, T.E. (1991). *Chronic pain management. Against the uniformity myth.* Paper presented at the II congr's Internacional Latini Dies, Sitges, Spain.

Miró, J.R., & Rosa, M. (1999). Preoperative preparation for surgery: An analysis of the effects of relaxation and information provision. *Clinical Psychology & Psychotherapy, 6*(3), 202–209.

Miyazaki, T., Ishikawa, T., Iimori, H., Miki, A., Wenner, M., Fukunishi, I., et al. (2003). Relationship between perceived social support and immune function. *Stress & Health: Journal of the International Society for the Investigation of Stress, 19,* 3–7.

Mkanta, W.N., Mejia, M.C., & Duncan, R.P. (2010). Race, outpatient mental health service use, and survival after an AIDS diagnosis in the highly active antiretroviral therapy era. *AIDS Patient Care and STDS, 24*(1), 31–37.

Moayedi, M., & Davis, K.D. (2013). Theories of pain: From specificity to gate control. *Journal of Neurophysiology, 109*(1), 5–12.

Mock, V., Frangakis, C., Davidson, N.E., Ropka, M.E., Pickett, M., Poniatowski, B., et al. (2005). Exercise manages fatigue during breast cancer treatment: A randomized controlled trial. *Psycho-Oncology, 14*(6), 464–477.

Moffett, J.K., Torgerson, D., Bell-Syer, S., Jackson, D., Llewlyn-Phillips, H., Farrin, A., et al. (1999). Randomized controlled trial of exercises for low back pain: Clinical outcomes, costs, and preferences. *British Medical Journal, 319,* 279–283.

Moldovan, A.R., & David, D. (2011). Effect of obesity treatments on eating behavior: Psychosocial interventions versus surgical interventions: A systematic review. *Eating Behaviors, 12*(3), 161–167.

Mollema, E.D., Snoek, F.J., Ader, H.J., Heine, R.J., & van der Ploeg, H.M. (2001). Insulin-treated diabetes patients with fear of self-injecting or fear of self-testing: Psychological comorbidity and general well-being. *Journal of Psychosomatic Research, 51*(5), 665–672.

Montgomery, C., Pocock, M., Titley, K., & Lloyd, K. (2003). Predicting psychological distress in patients with leukaemia and lymphoma. *Journal of Psychosomatic Research, 54*(4), 289–292.

Montgomery, G.H. (2004). Cognitive factors in health psychology and behavioral medicine. *Journal of Clinical Psychology, 60*(4), 405–413.

Montgomery, G.H., & Bovbjerg, D.H. (2003). Expectations of chemotherapy-related nausea: Emotional and experiential predictors. *Annals of Behavioral Medicine, 25*, 48–54.

Monti, D.A., Mago, R., & Kunkel, E.J.S. (2005). Depression, cognition, and anxiety among postmenopausal women with breast cancer. *Psychiatric Services, 56*(11), 1353–1355.

Moore, S.M., Barling, N.R., & Hood, B. (1998). Predicting testicular and breast self-examination behaviour: A test of the theory of reasoned action. *Behaviour Change, 15*, 41–49.

Moore, Z. (2009). Theoretical and empirical developments of the mindfulness-acceptance-commitment (MAC) approach to performance enhancement. *Journal of Clinical Sports Psychology, 4*, 291–302.

Moore, Z.E., & Gardner, F.L. (2001, October). *Taking applied sport psychology from research to practice: Integrating empirically supported interventions into a self-regulatory model of athletic performance.* Workshop presented at the meeting of the Annual Conference of the Association for the Advancement of Applied Sport Psychology, Orlando, FL.

Moos, R.H., & Moos, B.S. (2006). Rates and predictors of relapse after natural and treated remission from alcohol use disorders. *Addiction, 101*(2), 212–222.

Moran, A. (2009). Attention in sport. In S.D. Mellalieu & S. Hanton (Eds.), *Advances in applied sport psychology: A review* (pp. 195–220). London: Routledge.

Moraska, A., Campisi, J., Nguyen, K.T., Maier, S.F., Watkins, L.R., & Fleshner, M. (2002). Elevated IL-1beta contributes to antibody suppression produced by stress. *Journal of Applied Physiology, 93*, 207–215.

Morgenstern, M., Poelen, E.A.P., Scholte, R., Karlsdottir, S., Jonsson, S.H, Mathis, F., et al. (2011). Smoking in movies and adolescent smoking: Cross-cultural study in six European countries. *Thorax, 66*, 875–883.

Morgan, W.P. (Ed.). (1997). *Physical activity in mental health.* Washington, DC: Taylor & Francis.

Morgan, W.P., & Ellickson, K.A. (1989). Health, anxiety and physical exercise. In D. Hackfort & C. Spielberger (Eds.), *Anxiety in sports: An international perspective* (pp. 165–182). New York: Hemisphere Publishing.

Morrison, D.M., Baker, S.A., & Gillmore, M.R. (2000). Using the Theory of Reasoned Action to predict condom use among high-risk heterosexual teens. In P. Norman, C. Abraham, & M. Conner (Eds.), *Understanding and changing health behaviour: From health beliefs to self-regulation* (pp. 27–49). Amsterdam: Overseas Publishers Association.

Morrison, T.G., & Halton, M. (2009). Buff, tough, and rough: Representations of muscularity in action motion pictures. *Journal of Men's Studies, 17*(1), 57–74.

Moulin, D.W., Clark, A.H., Speechley, M., & Morley-Forster, P.K. (2002). Chronic pain in Canada—Prevalence, treatment, impact and the role of opioid analgesia. *Pain Research and Management, 7*, 179–184

Moyer, A. (1997). Psychosocial outcomes of breast-conserving surgery versus mastectomy: A meta-analytic review. *Health Psychology, 16*, 284–298.

Mpofu, E., & Houston, E. (1998). Assessment of value change in persons with acquired physical disabilities: Current and prospective applications for rehabilitation counselors. *Canadian Journal of Rehabilitation, 12*, 53–61.

Mulvihill, C.K. (1996). AIDS education for college students: Review and proposal for a research-based curriculum. *AIDS Education and Prevention, 8*, 11–25.

Mulvihill, D. (2005). The health impact of childhood trauma: An interdisciplinary review, 1997–2003. *Issues in Comprehensive Pediatric Nursing, 28*, 115–136.

Murgraff, V., Walsh, J., & McDermott, M.R. (2000). The application of Batozzi and Edwards' theory of self-regulation to the prediction of low-risk single-occasion drinking. *Psychology, Health & Medicine, 5*(4), 451–466.

Murphy, H., Dickens, C., Creed, F., & Bernstein, R. (1999). Depression, illness perception and coping in rheumatoid arthritis. *Journal of Psychosomatic Research, 46*, 155–164.

Murphy, S., Nordin, S., & Cumming, J. (2008). Imagery in sport, exercise and dance. In T.S. Horn (Ed.), *Advances in sport psychology* (3rd ed., pp. 297–324). Champaign, IL: Human Kinetics.

Murray, M. (1980). *Seeking the master.* London: Neville Spearman.

Murthy, P., Kudlur, S., George, S., & Mathew, G. (2009). A clinical overview of fetal alcohol syndrome. *Addictive Disorders and Their Treatment, 8*(1), 1–12.

Musclow, S.L., Sawhney, M., & Watt-Watson, J. (2002). The emerging role of advanced nursing practice in acute pain management throughout Canada. *Clinical Nurse Specialist, 16*(2), 63–67.

Muustedt, K., Muller, H., Blauth-Eckmeyer, E., Stenger, K., Zygmunt, M., & Vahrson, H. (1999). Role of dexamethoasone dosage in combination with 5-HT3 antagonists for prophylaxis of acute chemotherapy-induced nausea and vomiting. *British Journal of Cancer, 79*, 637–639.

N

Nachamkin, I., Allos, B.M., & Ho, T. (1998). *Campylobacter* species and Guillain–Barré syndrome. *Clinical Microbiology Review, 11,* 555–567.

Nakamura, M., Tanaka, M., Kinukawa, N., Abe, S., Itoh, K., Imai, K., et al. (2000). Association between basal serum and leptin levels and changes in abdominal fat distribution during weight loss. *Journal of Atherosclerosis and Thrombosis, 6,* 28–32.

Naqvi, T.Z., Naqvi, S.S.A., & Marz, C.N.B. (2005). Gender differences in the link between depression and cardiovascular disease. *Psychosomatic Medicine, 67*(Suppl. 1), S15–S18.

National Cancer Institute. (2012). Flavored cigar use common among young adult cigar smokers. *National Cancer Institute Bulletin, 9*(17), 2.

Nedeltcheva, A.V., Kilkus, J.M., Imperial, J., Kasza, K., Schoeller, D.A., & Penev, P.D. (2009). Sleep curtailment is accompanied by increased intake of calories from snacks. *American Journal of Clinical Nutrition, 89,* 126–133.

Newbold, K.B. (2005). Self-rated health within the Canadian immigrant population: Risk and the healthy immigrant effect. *Social Science and Medicine, 60,* 1359–1370.

Newman, M.G., Hofmann, S.G, Trabert, W., Roth, W.T., & Taylor, C.B. (1994). Does behavioral treatment of social phobia lead to cognitive changes? *Behavior Therapy, 25,* 503–517.

Ng, E., Wilkins, R., Gendron, F., & Berthelot, J.-M. (2005). Health today, health tomorrow? Findings from the National Population Health Survey. Dynamics of immigrants' health in Canada: Evidence from the National Population Health Survey. Statistics Canada Catalogue no. 82-618-MWE2005002

Nguyen, N., & Achusim, L.E. (2002). Medical adherence in an immigrant population. Vietnamese Americans. *Drug Benefit Trends, 14*(4), 34–48.

Nguyen, H.L., Saczynski, J.S., Gore, J.M., & Goldberg, R.J. (2010). Age and sex differences in duration of prehospital delay in patients with acute myocardial infarction: A systematic review. *Circulation: Cardiovascular Quality and Outcomes, 3,* 82–92.

Niaura R., & Abrams, D.B. (2002). Smoking cessation: Progress, priorities, and prospectus. *Journal of Consulting and Clinical Psychology, 70,* 494–509.

Nicholas, D.R. (2000). Men, masculinity, and cancer: Risk-factor behaviors, early detection, and psychosocial adaptation. *Journal of American College Health, 49,* 27–33.

Nickel, C., Widermann, C., Harms, D., Leiberich, P.L., Tritt, K., Kettler, C., et al. (2005). Patients with extreme obesity: Change in mental symptoms three years after gastric banding. *International Journal of Psychiatry in Medicine, 35,* 109–122.

Nieuwoudt, J.E., Zhou, S., Coutts, R.A., & Booker, R. (2012). Muscle dysmorphia: Current research and potential classification as a disorder. *Psychology of Sport and Exercise, 13,* 569–577.

Nimbarte, A., Aghazadeh, F., & Harvey, C. (2006). Comparison of current U.S. and Canadian cigarette pack warnings. *International Quarterly of Community Health Education, 24*(1), 3–27.

North, T.C., McCullagh, P., & Tran, Z.V. (1990). Effects of exercise on depression. *Exercise and Sport Science Reviews, 18,* 379–415.

Norton, G.R., Norton, P.J., Asmundson, G.J.G., Thompson, L.A., & Larsen, M.A. (1999). Neurotic butterflies in my stomach: The role of anxiety, anxiety sensitivity and depression in functional gastrointestinal disorders. *Journal of Psychosomatic Research, 47*(3), 233–240.

Nova, E., Baccan, G.C., Veses, A.M., Zapatera, B., & Marcos, A. (2012). Potential health benefits of moderate alcohol consumption: Current perspectives in research. *Proceedings of the Nutrition Society, 71,* 307–315.

Novins, D.K., Beals, J., Moore, L.A., Spicer, P., & Manson, S.M. (2004). Use of biomedical services and traditional healing options among American Indians: Sociodemographic correlates, spirituality and ethnic identity. *Medical Care, 42,* 670–679.

O

O'Brien, M.C., McCoy, T.P., Rhodes, S.D., Wagoner, A., & Wlfson, M. (2008). Caffeinated cocktails: Energy drink consumption, high-risk drinking, and alcohol-related consequences among college students. *Academic Emergency Medicine, 15*(5), 453–460.

O'Brien-Pallas, L., Alksnis, C., & Wang, S. (2003). *Bringing the future into focus: Projecting RN retirement in Canada.* Ottawa, ON: Canadian Institute for Health Information.

Ockene, J.K. (2001). Strategies to increase adherence to treatment. In L.E. Burke & I.S. Ockene (Eds.), *Compliance in healthcare and research* (pp. 43–55). Armonk, NY: Futura.

Ockene, J.K., Emmons, K.M., Mermelstein, R.J., Perkins, K.A., Bonollo, D.S., Voorhees, C.C., et al. (2000). Relapse and maintenance issues for smoking cessation. *Health Psychology, 19,* 17–31.

O'Connor, D.B., Jones, F., & Conner, M. (2011). Psychological stress, diary methods, and eating behavior. In Richard J. Contrada & Andrew Baum (Eds.), *The handbook of stress science: Biology, psychology and health* (pp. 1619–1633). Springer: New York.

O'Connor, D.B., Jones, F., Conner, M., McMillan, B., & Ferguson, E. (2008). Effects of daily hassles and eating style on eating behavior. *Health Psychology, 27*(1, Suppl.), S20–S31.

O'Connor, D.B., & O'Connor, R.C. (2004). Perceived changes in food intake in response to stress: The role of conscientiousness. *Journal of the International Society for the Investigation of Stress, 20*(5), 279–291.

O'Connor, P.G., & Spickard, A., Jr. (1997). Physician impairment by substance abuse. *Medical Clinics of North America, 81*, 1037–1052.

OECD. (2011). *Health at a Glance 2011: OECD Indicators*, OECD Publishing. Doi: 10.1787/health_glance-2011-en

Oenema, A., Brug, J., Dijkstra, A., De Weerdt, I., & De Vries, H. (2008). Efficacy and use of an Internet-delivered computer-tailored lifestyle intervention, targeting saturated fat intake, physical activity and smoking cessation: A randomized controlled trial. *Annals of Behavioral Medicine, 35*, 125–135.

Ogden, J. (2010). *The psychology of eating: From healthy to disordered behavior*. Malden, MA: Wiley.

Oggins, J. (2003). Notions of HIV and medication among multiethnic people living with HIV. *Health and Social Work, 28*, 53–62.

Oliver, L.N., & Hayes, M.V. (2008). Effects of neighbourhood income on reported body mass index: An eight-year longitudinal study of Canadian children. *BMC Public Health, 8*, 16.

Olivardia, R. (2001). Mirror, mirror on the wall, who's the largest of them all? The features and phenomenology of muscle dysmorphia. *Harvard Review of Psychiatry, 9*, 254–259.

Olivardia, R., Pope, H.G., Jr., & Hudson, J.I. (2000). Muscle dysmorphia in male weightlifters: A case-control study. *American Journal of Psychiatry, 157*(8), 1291–1296.

O'Loughlin, J., Karp, I., Koulis, T., Paradis, G., & DiFranza, J. (2009). Determinants of first puff and daily cigarette smoking in adolescents. *American Journal of Epidemiology, 170*(5), 585–597.

Olson, J.M., & Maio, G.R. (2003). Attitudes in social behavior. In T. Millon & M.J. Lerner (Eds.), *Handbook of psychology: Personality and social psychology* (Vol. 5, pp. 299–325). New York: Wiley & Sons.

O'Neill, M., Rootman, I., & Pederson, A. (1994). Beyond Lalonde: Two decades of Canadian health. In A. Pederson, M. O'Neill, & I. Rootman (Eds.), *Health promotion in Canada: Provincial, national and international perspectives* (pp. 374–386). Toronto: Saunders.

Ong, L.M.L., Visser, M.R.M., Lammes, F.B., & de Haes, J.M. (2000). Doctor-patient communication and cancer patients' quality of life and satisfaction. *Patient Education and Counselling, 41*, 145–156.

Ontario Health Promotion e-Bulletin, No. 453, Volume 2006. Retrieved March 1, 2010, from www.ohpe.ca/node/7231

Ontario, Ministry of Transportation. (2009). Impaired driving. Retrieved July 1, 2010, from www.mto.gov.on.ca/english/safety/impaired/interlock.shtml

Orlick, T., & Partington, J. (1988). Mental links to excellence. *The Sport Psychologist, 2*, 105–130.

Orne, M.T. (1980). On the construct of hypnosis: How its definition affects research and its clinical application. In G.D. Burrows & L. Dennerstein (Eds.), *Handbook of hypnosis and psychosomatic medicine* (pp. 29–51). Amsterdam: Elsevier.

Orne, M.T., & Dinges, D.F. (1989). Hypnosis. In P.D. Wall & R. Melzack (Eds.), *Textbook of pain* (2nd ed., pp. 1021–1031). Edinburgh: Churchill Livingstone.

Ortner, C.N.M., MacDonald, T.K., & Olmstead, M.C. (2003). Alcohol intoxication reduces impulsivity in the delay-discounting paradigm. *Alcohol & Alcoholism, 38*, 151–156.

Out, J.W., & Lafreniere, K.D. (2001). Baby Think It Over®: Using role-play to prevent teen pregnancy. *Adolescence, 36*(143), 571–582.

P

Pabst, A., Baumeister, S.E., & Kraus, L. (2010). Alcohol-expectancy dimensions and alcohol consumption at different ages in the general population. *Journal of Studies on Alcohol & Drugs, 71*(1), 46–53.

Paffenbarger, R.S., Wing, A.L., & Hyde, R.T. (1978). Physical activity as an index of heart attack risk in college alumni. *American Journal of Epidemiology, 108*, 161–175.

Pallavicini-Gonzalez, J., Venegas-Ramirez, L., & Espinoza, M.A. (1995). The experience of intensive care patients of J.J. Aguirre Hospital: 1989–1992. *Revista de Psiquiatria Clinica, 32*(1–2), 25–36.

Papacharisis, V., Goudas, M., Danish, S., & Theodorakis, Y. (2005). The effectiveness of teaching a life skills program in a sport context. *Journal of Applied Sport Psychology, 17*, 247–254.

Paparizos, A.L., Tripp, D.A., Sullivan, M.J.L., & Rubenstein, M.L. (2005). Catastrophizing and pain perception in recreational ballet dancers. *Journal of Sport Behavior*, 28(1), 35–50.

Pargman, D. (1998). *Understanding sport behavior*. Upper Saddle River, NJ: Prentice-Hall.

Park, D.C., Hertzog, C., Leventhal, H., Morrell, R.W., Leventhal, E., Birchmore, D., et al. (1999). Medication adherence in rheumatoid arthritis patients: Older is wiser. *Journal of the American Geriatric Society*, 47(2), 172–183.

Parker, G., Heruc, G., Hilton, T., Oiley, A., Brotchie, H., Hadzi-Pavlovic, D., et al. (2006). Explicating links between acute coronary syndrome and depression: Study design and methods. *Australian and New Zealand Journal of Psychiatry*, 40(3), 245–252.

Parker, P.A., & Kulik, J.A. (1995). Burnout, self- and supervisor-related job performance, and absenteeism among nurses. *Journal of Behavioral Medicine*, 18, 581–599.

Parrish, J.M. (1986). Parent compliance with medical and behavioral recommendations. In N.A. Krasnegor, J.D. Arasteh, & M.F. Cataldo (Eds.), *Child health behavior: A behavioral pediatrics perspective* (pp. 453–501). New York: Wiley.

Paskett, E.D., & Rimer, B.K. (1995). Psychosocial effects of abnormal Pap tests and mammograms: A review. *Journal of Women's Health*, 4, 73–82.

Passik, S.D., & Weinreb, H.J. (2000). Managing chronic nonmalignant pain: Overcoming obstacles to the use of opioids. *Advances in Therapy*, 17, 70–83.

Passyn, K., & Sujan, M. (2006). Self-accountability emotions and fear appeals: Motivating behaviour. *Journal of Consumer Research*, 32, 583–589.

Pate, R.R., Pratt, M., Blair, S.N., Haskell, W.L., Macera, C.A., Bouchard, C., et al. (1995). Physical activity and public health: A recommendation from the Centers for Disease Control and Prevention and the American College of Sports Medicine. *Journal of the American Medical Association*, 273, 402–407.

Patodia, R. (2010). *Optimizing medication adherence*. Retrieved November 18, 2014, from www.tevacanada.com/Pdfs?jun-Jul-2010-CE-(Eng).aspx

Patrick, D.M., Tyndall, M.W., Cornelisse, P.G., Li, K., Sherlock, C.W., Rekart, M.L., et al. (2001). Incidence of hepatitis C virus infection among injection drug users during an outbreak of HIV infection. *Canadian Medical Association Journal*, 165(7), 889–895.

Patterson, D.R. (2004). Treating pain with hypnosis. *Current Directions in Psychological Science*, 13(6), 252–255.

Patterson, D.R. (2005). Behavioral methods for chronic pain and illness: A reconsideration and appreciation. *Rehabilitation Psychology*, 50(3), 312–315.

Patterson, D.R., Hoffman, H.G., Weichman, S.A., Jensen, M.P., & Shara, S.R. (2004). Optimizing control of pain from severe burns: A literature review. *American Journal of Clinical Hypnosis*, 47(1), 43–54.

Patterson, D.R., & Jensen, M.P. (2003). Hypnosis and clinical pain. *Psychological Bulletin*, 129(4), 495–521.

Pavlin, D.J., Sullivan, M.J.L., Freund, P.R., & Roesen, K. (2005). Catastrophizing: A risk factor for postsurgical pain. *Clinical Journal of Pain*, 21(1), 83–90.

Payne, S.A., Dean, S.J., & Kalus, C. (1998). A comparative study of death anxiety in hospice and emergency nurses. *Journal of Advanced Nursing*, 28, 700–706.

Pearlin, L.I. (1993). The social contexts of stress. In L. Goldberger & S. Breznitz (Eds.), *Handbook of stress: Theoretical and clinical aspects* (2nd ed., pp. 303–315). New York: Free Press.

Peng, P., Choiniere, M., Dion, D., Intrater, H., LeFort, S., Lynch, M., et al. (2007). Challenges in accessing multidisciplinary pain treatment facilities in Canada. *Canadian Journal of Anesthesia*, 54, 977–984.

Peng, P., Stinson, J.N., Choiniere, M., Dion, D., Intrater, H., LeFort, S., et al. (2008). Role of health care professionals in multidisciplinary pain treatment facilities in Canada. *Pain Research and Management*, 13(6), 484–488.

Pennebaker, J.W. (2000). Psychological factors influencing the reporting of physical symptoms. In A.A. Stone, J.S. Turkkan, C.A. Bachrach, J.B. Jobe, H.S. Kurtzman, & V.S. Cain (Eds.), *The science of self-report: Implications for research and practice* (pp. 299–362). Mahwah, NJ: Lawrence Erlbaum.

Penninx, B.W., Guralnik, J.M., Mendes de Leon, C.F., Pahor, M., Visser, M., Corti, M.C., et al. (1998). Cardiovascular events and mortality in newly and chronically depressed persons >70 years of age. *American Journal of Cardiology*, 81, 988–994.

Perneger, T.V., Charvet-Bérard, A., & Perrier, A. (2008). Patient assessments of the most important medical *decision* during a hospitalization. *Journal of General Internal Medicine*, 23(10), 1659–1665.

Persky, V.W., Kempthorne-Rawson, J., & Shekelle, R.B. (1987). Personality and risk of cancer: 20-year follow-up of the Western Electric Study. *Psychosomatic Medicine*, 49, 435–449.

Peterson, C.M., & Fischer, S. (2012). A prospective study of the influence of the UPPS model of impulsivity on the co-occurrence of bulimic symptoms and non-suicidal self-injury. *Eating Behaviors*, 13(4), 335–341.

Petticrew, M., Bell, R., & Hunter, D. (2002). Influence of psychological coping on survival and recurrence in people with cancer: Systematic review. *British Medical Journal*, 325(7372), 1066–1069.

Petty, R.E., & Cacioppo, J.T. (1981). *Attitudes and persuasion: Classic and contemporary approaches*. Dubuque, IA: Brown.

Phillips, A.C., Carroll, D., Evans, P., Bosch, J.A., Clow, A., Hucklebridge, F., et al. (2006). Stressful life events are associated with low secretion rates of immunoglobulin A in saliva in the middle aged and elderly. *Brain, Behavior, and Immunity, 20*(2), 191–197.

Phillips, K.D., & Morrow, J.H. (1998). Nursing management of anxiety in HIV infection. *Issues in Mental Health Nursing, 19*, 375–397.

Phillips, S. (1996). Sexual harassment of female physicians by patients. What is to be done? *Canadian Family Physician, 42*, 73–76.

Physicians for a Smoke-Free Canada. (2012). Frequent exposure to second-hand smoke in public places in Canada, 2011. Ottawa, ON. Retrieved June 6, 2013, from www.smoke-free.ca/factsheets/pdf/cchs/Canada-shs-public.pdf

Pierce, J.P. (2005). Influence of movie stars on the initiation of adolescent smoking. *Pediatric Dentistry, 27*, 149.

Pietrzak, R.H., Goldstein, R.B., Southwick, S.M., & Grant, B.F. (2012). Physical health conditions associated with posttraumatic stress disorder in U.S. older adults: Results from Wave 2 of the National Epidemiologic Survey on Alcohol and Related Conditions. *Journal of the American Geriatrics Society, 60*, 296–303.

Pike, K.M., Walsh, B.T., Vitousek, K., Wilson, G.T., & Bauer, J. (2003). Cognitive behavior therapy in the posthospitalization treatment of anorexia nervosa. *American Journal of Psychiatry, 160*, 2046–2049.

Pinder, R. (1990). *The management of chronic disease: Patient and doctor perspectives on Parkinson's disease*. London: MacMillan Press.

Pinquart, M., & Frohlich, C. (2009). Psychosocial resources and subjective well-being of cancer patients. *Psychology & Health, 24*(4), 407–421.

Pistrang, N., Barker, C., & Rutter, C. (1997). Social support as conversation: Analysing breast cancer patients' interactions with their partners. *Social Science and Medicine, 45*, 773–782.

Pi-Sunyer, X. (2003). A clinical view of the obesity problem. *Science, 299*, 859–860.

Pitts, M.K., Wooliscroft, J., Cannon, S., Johnson, I., & Singh, G. (2000). Factors influencing delay in treatment seeking by first-time attenders at a genitourinary clinic. *International Journal of STD & AIDS, 11*, 375–378.

Playford, E.D., Dawson, L., Limbert, V., Smith, M., Ward, C.D., & Wells, R. (2000). Goal-setting in rehabilitation: Report of a workshop to explore professionals' perceptions of goal-setting. *Clinical Rehabilitation, 14*, 491–496.

Plotkin, S.A. (2001). Immunologic correlates of protection induced by vaccination. *Pediatric Infectious Disease, 20*, 73–75.

Poczwarsdowski, A., & Conroy, D.E. (2002). Coping responses to failure and success among elite athletes and performing artists. *Journal of Applied Sport Psychology, 14*, 313–329.

Polimeni, A.-M., & Moore, S. (2002). Insights into women's experiences of hospital stays: Perceived control, powerlessness and satisfaction. *Behaviour Change, 19*(1), 52–64.

Polivy, J. (1996). Psychological consequences of food restriction. *Journal of the American Dietetic Association, 96*, 859–592.

Polivy, J., & Herman, C.P. (2002). Causes of eating disorders. *Annual Review of Psychology, 53*, 187–213.

Polivy, J., & Herman, C.P. (2004). Sociocultural idealization of thin female body shapes: An introduction to the special issue on body image and eating disorders. *Journal of Social and Clinical Psychology, 23*, 1–6.

Polivy, J., & Herman, C.P. (2006). An evolutionary perspective on dieting. *Appetite, 47*, 30–35.

Polivy, J., Herman, C.P., & Boivin, M. (2005). Eating disorders. In J.E. Maddux & B.A. Winstead (Eds.), *Psychopathology: Foundations for a contemporary understanding* (pp. 229–254). Mahwah, NJ: Erlbaum.

Pomerleau, O.F. (1979). Behavioral factors in the establishment, maintenance, and cessation of smoking. In *Smoking and health: A report of the Surgeon General* (pp. 16–31). Washington, DC: GPO.

Ponte, P.R., Conlin, G., Conway, J.B., Grant, S., Medeiros, C., Nies, J., et al. (2003). Making patient-centered care come alive: Achieving full integration of the patient's perspective. *Journal of Nursing Administration, 33*(2), 82–90.

Poole, G.D., Poon, C., Achille, M., White, K., Franz, N., Jittler, S., et al. (2001). Social support for prostate cancer patients: The effect of support groups. *Journal of Psychosocial Oncology, 19*(2), 1–16.

Poole, G.D., & Ting, K. (1995). Cultural differences between Euro-Canadian and Indo-Canadian maternity patients. *Journal of Social Psychology, 135*, 631–644.

Pope, H.G., Jr. (2001). Unraveling the Adonis complex. *Psychiatric Times, 18*(3), 22–26.

Pope, H.G., Jr., Olivardia, R., Gruber, A.J., & Borowiecki, J. (1999). Evolving ideals of male body image as seen through action toys. *International Journal of Eating Disorders, 26*, 65–72.

Pope, C.G., Pope, H.G., Jr., Menard, W., Fay, C., Olivardia, R., & Phillips, K.A. (2005). Clinical features of muscle dysmorphia among males with body dysmorphic disorder. *Body Image, 2*, 395–400.

Porteous, A., & Tyndall, J. (1994). Yes, I want to walk to the OR. *Canadian Operating Room Nursing Journal, 12*, 15–25.

Posadzki, P., & Ernst, E. (2011). Guided imagery for musculoskeletal pain: A systematic review of randomized clinical trials. *Clinical Journal of Pain, 27*(7), 648–653.

Powell, A.G., Apovian, C.M., & Aronne, L.J. (2011). New drug targets for the treatment of obesity. *Clinical Pharmacology and Therapeutics, 90*(1), 40–51.

Powell, L.H., Calvin, J.E., III., & Calvin, J.E., Jr. (2007). Effective obesity treatments. *American Psychologist, 62*, 234–246.

Powers, P.S., & Bruty, H. (2009). Pharmacotherapy for eating disorders and obesity. *Child and Adolescent Psychiatric Clinics of North America, 18*, 175–187.

Prapavessis, H., Maddison, R., Ruygrok, P.N., Bassett, S., Harper, T., & Gillanders, L. (2005). Using Theory of Planned Behavior to understand exercise motivation in patients with congenital heart disease. *Psychology, Health & Medicine, 10*(4), 335–343.

Pratt, L.A., Ford, D.E., Crum, R.M., Armenian, H.K., Gallo, J.J., & Eaton, W.W. (1996). Depression, psychotropic medication, and risk of myocardial Infarction. *Circulation, 94*, 3123–3129.

Pressman, S.D., & Cohen, S. (2005). Does positive affect influence health? *Psychological Bulletin, 131*(6), 925–971.

Preti, A., Rocchi, M. Sisti, D. Camboni, M., & Miotto, P. (2011). A comprehensive meta-analysis of the risk of suicide in eating disorders. *Acta Psychiatrica Scandinavica, 124*, 6–17.

Price, R.A. (2002). Genetics and common obesities: Background, current status, strategies and future prospects. In T.A. Wadden & A.J. Stunkard (Eds.), *Handbook of obesity treatment* (pp. 73–94). New York: Guilford Press.

Prickett, C., Lister, E.C., Trevithick-Sutton, C., Hirst, M., Vinson, J., Noble, E., & Trevithick, R. (2004). Alcohol: Friend or foe? Alcoholic beverage hormesis for cataract and atherosclerosis is related to plasma antioxidant activity. *Nonlinearity in Biology, Toxicology and Medicine, 2*(4), 353–370.

Prkachin, K.D. (2007). The coming of age of pain expression. *Pain, 133*, 3–4.

Prkachin, K.D., Hughes, E.A., Schultz, I., Joy, P., & Hunt, D. (2002). Real-time assessment of pain behavior during clinical assessment of low-back pain patients. *Pain, 95*, 23–30.

Prkachin, K.M., Solomon, P.E., & Ross, J. (2007). Underestimation of pain by health-care providers: Towards a model of the process of inferring pain in others. *Canadian Journal of Nursing Research, 39*, 88–106

Prochaska, J.O., & DiClemente, C.C. (1983). Stages and processes of self-change of smoking: Toward an integrative model of change. *Journal of Consulting and Clinical Psychology, 51*, 390–395.

Prochaska, J.O., & DiClemente, C.C. (1986). Toward a comprehensive model of change. In W.R. Miller, N. Heather, et al. (Eds.), *Treating addictive behaviors: Processes of change. Applied clinical psychology* (pp. 3–27). New York: Plenum Press.

Prochaska, J.O., & Velicer, W.F. (1997). The transtheoretical model of health behavior change. *American Journal of Health Promotion, 12*, 38–48.

Proctor, S.L., & Boan-Lenzo, C. (2010). Prevalence of depressive symptoms in male intercollegiate student-athletes and nonathletes. *Journal of Clinical Sport Psychology, 4*, 204–220.

Pruzinsky, T., Levine, E., Persing, J.A., Barth, J.T., & Obrecht, R. (2006). Facial trauma and facial cancer. In D.B. Sarwer, T. Pruzinsky, T.F. Cash, R.M. Goldwyn, J.A. Persing, & L.A. Whitaker (Eds.), *Psychological aspects of reconstructive and cosmetic plastic surgery: Clinical empirical and ethical perspectives* (pp. 125–143). Philadelphia: Lippincott Williams & Wilkins.

Pryse-Phillips, W., Findlay, H., Tugwell, P., Edmeads, J., Murray, T.J., & Nelson, R.F. (1992). A Canadian population survey on the clinical, epidemiological and societal impact of migraine and tension-type headache. *Canadian Journal of Neurological Sciences, 19*, 333–339.

Ptacek, J.T., Fries, E.A., Eberhardt, T.L., & Ptacek, J.J. (1999). Breaking bad news to patients: Physicians' perceptions of the process. *Support and Care for Cancer, 7*(3), 113–120.

Public Health Agency of Canada. (2002). Environmental tobacco smoke and deaths from coronary heart disease in Canada. *Chronic Diseases in Canada, 23*(1). Retrieved September 1, 2006, from www.phac-aspc.gc.ca/publicat/cdic-mcc/23-1/b_e.html

Public Health Agency of Canada. (2006). *HIV and AIDS in Canada: Surveillance report to December 31, 2005.* Surveillance and Risk Assessment Division, Centre for Infectious Disease Prevention and Control.

Public Health Agency of Canada. (2010a). *HIV/AIDS Epi Updates–July, 2010.* http://www.phac-aspc.gc.ca/aids-sida/publication/epi/2010/1-eng.php

Public Health Agency of Canada. (2010b). *Information on Mammography for Women Aged 40 and Older*. Retrieved on October 16, 2014, from http://www.phac-aspc.gc.ca/cd-mc/mammography-mammographie-eng.php#chap8

Public Health Agency of Canada. (2011a). *Diabetes in Canada: Facts and figures from a public health perspective*. Retrieved October 14, 2014, from http://www.phac-aspc.gc.ca/cd-mc/publications/diabetes-diabete/facts-figures-faits-chiffres-2011/highlights-saillants-eng.php#chp1

Public Health Agency of Canada. (2011b). *Diabetes among First Nations, Inuit, and Métis populations*. Retrieved October 14, 2014, from http://www.phac-aspc.gc.ca/cd-mc/publications/diabetes-diabete/facts-figures-faits-chiffres-2011/chap6-eng.php

Public Health Agency of Canada. (2011c). *AIDS among Aboriginal people in Canada*. Retrieved November 12, 2014, from http://www.phac-aspc.gc.ca/aids-sida/publication/epi/2010/8-eng.php

Puhl, R.M., & Heuer, C.A. (2009). The stigma of obesity: A review and update. *Obesity, 17*, 941–964.

Puro, H., Pakarinen, P., Korttila, K., & Tallgren, M. (2013). Verbal information about anesthesia before scheduled surgery—Contents and patient satisfaction. *Patient Education and Counseling, 90*, 367–371.

Q

Quinn, J.F., Bodenhamer-Davis, E., & Koch, D.S. (2004). Ideology and the stagnation of AODA treatment modalities in America. *Deviant Behavior, 25*(2), 109–131.

R

Raglan, J.S., & Morgan, W.P. (1987). Influence of exercise and "distraction therapy" on state anxiety and blood pressure. *Medicine and Science in Sport and Exercise, 19*, 456–463.

Raedeke, T.D. (2007). The relationship between enjoyment and affective responses to exercise. *Journal of Applied Sport Psychology, 19*, 105–115.

Rahim-Williams, F.B., Riley, J.L., III, Herrera, D., Campbell, C.M., Hastie, B.A., & Fillingim, R.B. (2007). Ethnic identity predicts experimental pain sensitivity in African Americans and Hispanics. *Pain, 129*, 177–184.

Rahim-Williams, B., Riley, J.L., III, & Fillingim, R.B. (2012). A quantitative review of ethnic differences and experimental pain response. Do biology, psychology and culture matter? *Pain Medicine, 13*, 522–540.

Ramage-Morin, P.L., & Gilmour, H. (2010). Chronic pain at ages 12 to 44. *Health Reports, 21*(4), 53–60.

Ramirez, A., Bravo, I.M., & Katsikas, S. (2005). Infant feeding decisions and practices in the U.S. and Colombia. *Journal of Prenatal & Perinatal Psychology & Health, 19*(3), 237–249.

Ramirez, A.J., Westcombe, A.M., Burgess, C.C., Sutton, S., Littlejohns, P., & Richards, M.A. (1999). Factors predicting delayed presentation of symptomatic breast cancer: A systematic review. *The Lancet, 353*, 1127–1131.

Rando, T. (1996). Complications in mourning traumatic death. In K. Doka (Ed.), *Living with grief after sudden loss: Suicide, homicide, accident, heart attack, stroke* (pp. 134–159). Washington, DC: Hospice Foundation of America.

Ranney, L., Melvin, C., Lux, L., McClain, E., & Lohr, K.N. (2006). Systematic review: Smoking cessation intervention strategies for adults and adults in special populations. *Annals of Internal Medicine, 145*(11), 845–856.

Raphael, D. (2004). *Social determinants of health: Canadian perspectives*. Toronto: Canadian Scholars Press.

Rathmore, S.S., Lenert, L.A., Weinfurt, K.P., Tinoco, A., Taleghani, C.K., Harless, W., & Schulman, K.A. (2000). The effects of patient sex and race on medical students' rating of quality of life. *American Journal of Medicine, 108*, 561–566.

Ratanawongsa, N., Haywood, C., Jr., Bediako, S.M., Lattimer, L., Lanzkron, S., Hill, P.M., et al. (2009). Health care provider attitudes toward patients with acute vaso-occlusive crisis due to sickle cell disease: Development of a scale. *Patient Education and Counseling, 76*, 272–278.

Rattray, J.E., Johnston, M., & Wildsmith, J.A.W. (2005). Predictors of emotional outcomes of intensive care. *Anesthesia, 60*(11), 1985–1092.

Ravaldi, C., Vannacci, A., & Zucchi, T. (2003). Eating disorders and body image disturbances among ballet dancers, gymnasium users and body builders. *Psychopathology, 36*(5), 247–254.

Rehm, J., Baliunas, D., Borges, G.L.G., Graham, K., Irving, H., Kehoe, T., et al. (2010). The relation between different dimensions of alcohol consumption and burden of disease: An overview. *Addiction, 105*(5), 817–843.

Rehm, J., Patra, J., & Taylor, B. (2007). Harm, benefits, and net effects on mortality of moderate drinking of alcohol among adults in Canada in 2002. *Annals of Epidemiology, 17*(5S), S81–S86.

Reiche, E.M.V., Morimoto, H.K., & Nunes, S.O.V. (2005). Stress and depression-induced immune dysfunction: Implications for the development and progression of cancer. *International Review of Psychiatry, 17*(6), 515–527.

Reiche, E.M.V., & Nunes, S.O.V. (2005). Stress and depression—Induced immune dysfunction: Implications for the development and progression of cancer. *International Review of Psychiatry, 17*(6), 515–527.

Reid, J.L., & Hammond, D. (2009). *Tobacco use in Canada: Patterns and trends*, 2009 edition. Waterloo, ON: Propel Centre for Population Health Impact, University of Waterloo.

Reid, J., Hammond D., Burkhalter, R., Rynard, V.L., & Ahmed, R. (2013). *Tobacco use in Canada: Patterns and trends* (4th ed.). Waterloo, ON: Propel Centre for Population Health Impact, University of Waterloo.

Reid, J.L., Hammond, D., & Driezen, P. (2010). Socioeconomic status and smoking in Canada, 1999–2006: Has there been any progress on disparities in tobacco use? *Canadian Journal of Public Health, 101*(1), 73–78.

Rejeski, W.J., Hardy, C.H., & Shaw, J. (1991). Psychometric confounds of assessing state anxiety in conjunction with acute bouts of vigorous exercise. *Journal of Sport and Exercise Psychology, 13*, 65–74.

Remick, A.K., Polivy, J., & Pliner, P. (2009). Internal and external moderators of the effect of variety on food intake. *Psychological Bulletin, (3)*, 434–451.

Rentsch, D., Luthy, C., Perneger, T.V., & Allaz, A.F. (2003). Hospitalisation process seen by patients and health care professionals. *Social Science & Medicine, 57*(3), 571–576.

Research Quarterly for Exercise and Sport. (1995). Physical Activity, Health and Well-being. *Research Quarterly for Exercise and Sport Science*, special issue: Proceedings of the International Scientific Consensus Conference, 66(4), whole.

Reynolds, D.V. (1969). Surgery in the rat during electrical anesthesia induced by focal brain stimulation. *Science, 164*, 444–445.

Reynolds, F. (2001). Strategies for facilitating physical activity and wellbeing: A health promotion perspective. *British Journal of Occupational Therapy, 64*, 330–336.

Rhymes, J., & Brown, D.C. (2005). Cultural competency in Primary Health Care: Perspectives, tools and resources. Summary report for Capital District Health.

Rice, P.R. (1999). *Stress and health* (3rd ed.). Pacific Grove, CA: Brooks/Cole.

Richards, J.S., Nepomuceno, C., Riles, M., & Suer, Z. (1982). Assessing pain behavior: The UAB Pain Behavior Scale. *Pain, 14*, 393–398.

Richards, M.A., Westcombe, A.M., Love, S.B., Littlejohns, P., & Ramirez, A.J. (1999). Influence of delay on survival in patients with breast cancer: A systematic review. *The Lancet, 353*, 1119–1126.

Richards, T. (1990). Chasms in communication. *British Medical Journal, 301*, 1407–1408.

Richardsen, A.M., & Burke, R.J. (1991). Occupational stress and job satisfaction among Canadian physicians. *Work and Stress, 5*, 301–313.

Richardson, C., Glenn, S., Nurmikko, T., & Horgan, M. (2006). A prospective study of factors associated with the presence of phantom limb pain six months after major lower limb amputation in patients with peripheral vascular disease. *The Clinical Journal of Pain, 22*(4), 353–358.

Richman, L.S., Kubzansky, L., Maselko, J., Kawachi, I., Choo, P., & Bauer, M. (2005). Positive emotion and health: Going beyond the negative. *Health Psychology, 24*, 422–429.

Riegel, B.J., Dracup, K.A., & Glaser, D. (1998). A longitudinal causal model of cardiac invalidism following myocardial infarction. *Nursing Research, 47*(5), 285–292.

Rintamaki, L.S., & Brashers, D.E. (2005). Social identity and stigma management for people living with HIV. In E.B. Ray (Ed.), *Health communication in practice: A case study approach* (pp. 145–156). Mahwah, NJ: Lawrence Erlbaum Associates Publishers.

Ritholz, M.D., & Jacobson, A.M. (1998). Living with hypoglycemia. *Journal of General Internal Medicine, 13*, 799–804.

Ritter, B. (1968). The group desensitization of children's snake phobias using vicarious and contact desensitization procedures. *Behaviour Research and Therapy, 6*, 1–6.

Roberts, K.C., Shields, M., de Groh, M., Aziz, A., & Gilbert, J. (2012). Overweight and obesity in children and adolescents: Results from the 2009–2011 Canadian Health Measures Survey, *Health Reports, 23*(5), 37–42.

Robinson, D. (1973, July 15). Ten noted doctors answer ten tough questions. *Parade.*

Robinson, G.E. (2003). Stresses on women physicians: Consequences and coping techniques. *Depression and Anxiety, 17*(3), 180–189.

Robinson, M.E., Riley, J.L., III, Myers, C.D., Papas, R.K., Wise, E.A., Waxenberg, L.B., et al. (2001). Gender role expectations of pain: Relationship to sex differences in pain. *The Journal of Pain, 2*(5), 251–257.

Robinson, M.E., Wise, E.A., Gagnon, C., Fillingim, R.B., & Price, D.D. (2004). Influences of gender role and anxiety on sex differences in temporal summation of pain. *The Journal of Pain, 5*(2), 77–82.

Robles, T.F., & Kiecolt-Glaser, J.K. (2003). The physiology of marriage. Pathways to health. *Physiology & Behavior, 79*(3), 409–416.

Rodin, J. (1981). Current status of the internal-external hypothesis for obesity: What went wrong? *American Psychologist, 36*, 361–372.

Rodin, J., & Salovey, P. (1989). Health psychology. *Annual Review of Psychology, 40*, 533–579.

Roesch, S.C., Adams, L., Hines, A., Palmores, A., Vyas, P., Tran, C., et al. (2005). Coping with prostate cancer: A meta-analytic review. *Journal of Behavioral Medicine, 38*(3), 281–293.

Rogg, L., Loge, J.H., Aasland, O.G., & Graugaard, P.K. (2009). Physicians' attitudes towards disclosure of prognostic information: A survey among a representative cross-section of 1605 Norwegian physicians. *Patient Education and Counseling, 77*(2), 242–247.

Rohman, L. (2009). The relationship between anabolic androgenic steroids and muscle dysmorphia: A review. *Eating Disorders, 17*, 187–199.

Rollman, G.B. (2004). Ethnocultural variations in the experience of pain. In T. Hadjistavropoulos & K.D. Craig (Eds.), *Pain: Psychological perspectives* (pp. 155–178). Mahwah, NJ: Erlbaum.

Rollman, G.B., Abdel-Shaheed, J., Gillespie, J.M., & Jones, K.S. (2004). Does past pain influence current pain: Biological and psychosocial models of sex differences. *European Journal of Pain, 8*(5), 427–433.

Romas, J.A., & Sharma, M. (2004). *Practical stress management* (3rd ed.). San Francisco: Pearson Education.

Rootman, I., Godstadt, M., Polvin, L., & Springett, J. (2001). A framework for health promotion evaluation. In Rootman, I., et al. (Eds.), *Evaluation in health promotion: Principles and perspectives*. Copenhagen: WHO Regional Office for Europe, 2001 (WHO Regional Publications, European Sewries, No. 92, pp. 7–38).

Rosengard, C., Chambers, D.B., Tulsky, J.P., Long, H.L., & Chesney, M. (2001). Value on health, health concerns and practices of women who are homeless. *Women & Health, 34*, 29–44.

Rosenstock, I.M. (1974). Historical origins of the health belief model. *Health Education Monographs, 2*, 328–335.

Rosenstock, I.M., Strecher, V.J., & Becker, M.H. (1994). The Health Belief Model and HIV risk behavior change. In R.J. DiClemente & J.L. Peterson (Eds.), *Preventing AIDS: Theories and methods of behavioral interventions* (pp. 5–25). New York: Plenum.

Roseveare, C., Seavell, C., Patel, P., Criswell, J., Kimble, J., Jones, C., & Shepherd, H. (1998). Patient-controlled sedation and analgesia, using propofol and alfentanil, during colonoscopy: A prospective randomized controlled trail. *Endoscopy, 30*, 768–773.

Rosier, E.M., Iadarola, M.J., & Cognill, R.C. (2002). Reproducibility of pain measurement and pain perception. *Pain, 98*, 205–216.

Ross, C.E., & Mirowsky, J. (2002). Family relationships, social support and subjective life expectancy. *Journal of Health & Social Behavior, 43*, 469–489.

Roter, D.L. (2000). The enduring and evolving nature of the patient-physician relationship. *Patient Education and Counseling, 39*, 5–15.

Roter, D.L., Frankel, R.M., Hall, J.A., & Sluyter, D. (2006). The expression of emotion through nonverbal behavior in medical visits. *Journal of Internal Medicine, 21*, S28.

Roter, D.L., & Hall, J.A. (2006). *Doctors talking with patients/patients talking with doctors: Improving communication in medical visits* (2nd ed.). Westport, CT: Greenwood Publishing Group.

Roter, D.L., Hall, J.A., Merisca, R., Nordstrom, B., Cretin, D., & Svarstad, B. (1998). Effectiveness of interventions to improve patient compliance: A meta-analysis. *Medical Care, 36*, 1138–1161.

Roter, D.L., Hall, J.A., & Aoki, Y. (2002). Physician gender effects in medical communication: A meta-analytic review. *Journal of the American Medical Association, 288*, 756–764.

Roter, D.L., Larson, S., Sands, D.Z., Ford, D.E., & Houston, T. (2008). Can e-mail messages between patients and physicians be patient-centered? *Health Communication, 23*(1), 80–86.

Roter, D.L., Stewart, M., Putnam, S.M., Lipkin, M., Jr., Stiles, W., & Inui, T.S. (1997). Communication patterns of primary care physicians. *Journal of the American Medical Association, 277*, 350–356.

Rotstein, J., Barber, J., Strowbridge, C., Hayward, S., Huang, R., & Godefroy, S.B. (2013). Energy drinks: An assessment of the potential health risks in the Canadian context. *International Food Risk Analysis Journal, 3*(4), 1–29.

Rotton, J., & Dubitsky, S.S. (2002). Immune function and affective states following a natural disaster. *Psychological Reports, 90*, 521–524.

Rouse, B.A. (Ed.). (1998). *Substance abuse and mental health statistics source book*. Rockville, MD: Department of Health and Human Services: Substance Abuse and Mental Health Services Administration.

Rozanski, A., Blumenthal, J.A., & Kaplan, J. (1999). Impact of psychological factors on the pathogenesis of cardiovascular disease and implications for therapy. *Circulation, 99,* 2192–2217.

Rubin, G.J., Potts, H.W.W., & Michie, S. (2010). The impact of communications about swine flu (influenza A H1N1v) on public responses to the outbreak: Results from 36 national telephone surveys in the UK. *Health Technology Assessment, 14*(34), 183–266.

Ruby, M.B., Dunn, E.W., Perrino, A., Gillis, R., & Viel, S. (2011). The invisible benefits of exercise. *Health Psychology, 30*(1), 67–74.

Rudolph, D.L., & Butki, B.D. (1998). Self-efficacy and affective responses to short bouts of exercise. *Journal of Applied Sport Psychology, 10,* 268–280.

Rudolph, K.D., Dennig, M.D., & Weisz, J.R. (1995). Determinants and consequences of children's coping in the medical setting: Conceptualization, review and critique. *Psychological Bulletin, 118,* 328–357.

Russell, S. (1999). An exploratory study of patients' perceptions, memories and experiences in an intensive care unit. *Journal of Advanced Nursing, 29,* 783–791.

Ryan, C.J., & Zerwic, J.J. (2003). Perceptions of symptoms of myocardial infarction related to health care seeking behaviors in the elderly. *Journal of Cardiovascular Nursing, 18,* 184–196.

Ryan, K.K., MacKillop, J., & Carpenter, M.J. (2013). The relationship between impulsivity, risk-taking propensity and nicotine dependence among older adolescent smokers. *Addictive Behaviors, 38*(1), 1431–1434.

Rydahl-Hansen, S. (2005). Hospitalized patients experienced suffering in life with incurable cancer. *Scandinavian Journal of Caring Sciences, 19*(3), 213–222.

S

Saelens, B.E., Sallis, J.F., & Frank, L.D. (2003). Environmental correlates of walking and cycling: Findings from the transportation, urban design, and planning literatures. *Annals of Behavioral Medicine, 25*(3), 80–91.

Salmon, P. (2000). Effects of physical exercise on anxiety, depression, and sensitivity to stress: A unifying theory. *Clinical Exercise Review, 21,* 33–61.

Salovey, P., Rothman, A.J., Detweiler, J.B., & Steward, W.T. (2000). Emotional states and physical health. *American Psychologist, 55,* 110–121

Saltz, R. (2004–2005). Preventing alcohol-related problems on college campuses. *Alcohol Research and Health, 28*(4), 249–251.

Saltz, R. (2005). Prevention of college student drinking problems. In B. Galanter (Ed.), *Recent developments in alcoholism: Volume 17. Alcohol problems in adolescents and young adults* (pp. 255–274). New York: Kluwer Academic/Plenum Publishers.

Samson, A., & Solmon, M.A. (2011). Examining the sources of self-efficacy for physical activity within the sport and exercise domains. *International Review of Sport and Exercise Psychology, 4,* 70–89.

Sands, L.P., Yaffe, K., Covinsky, K., Chren, M.-M., Counsell, S., Palmer, R., et al. (2003). Cognitive screening predicts magnitude of functional recovery from admission to 3 months after discharge in hospitalized elders. *Journals of Gerontology: Series A: Biological Sciences & Medical Sciences, 58*(1), 37–45.

Santavirta, N., Bjorvell, H., Solovieva, S., Alaranta, H., Hurskainen, K., & Konttinen, Y.T. (2001). Coping strategies, pain and disability in patients with hemophilia and related disorders. *Arthritis and Rheumatism, 45,* 48–55.

Santos, S.R., Carroll, C.A., Cox, K.S., Teasley, S.L., Simon, S.D., Bainbridge, L., et al. (2003). Baby boomer nurses bearing the burden of care: A four-site study of stress, strain, and coping for inpatient registered nurses. *Journal of Nursing Administration, 33*(4), 243–250.

Sarafino, E.P. (1998). *Health psychology: Biopsychosocial interactions*. New York: John Wiley and Sons.

Sareen, J., Cox, B.J., Stein, M.B., Afifi, T.O., Fleet, C., & Asmundson, G.J. (2007). Physical and mental comorbidity, disability, and suicidal behavior associated with posttraumatic stress disorder in a large community sample. *Psychosomatic Medicine, 69,* 242–248.

Sarna, L., Padilla, G., Holmes, C., Tashkin, D., Brecht, M.L., & Evangelista, L. (2002). Quality of life of long-term survivors of non-small cell lung cancer. *Journal of Clinical Oncology, 20,* 2920–2929.

Sasieni, P., Adams, J., & Cuzick, J. (2003). Benefit of cervical screening at different ages: Evidence from the UK audit of screening histories. *British Journal of Cancer, 89*(1), 88–93.

Savard, M., Miller, S., Mills, M., O'Leary, A., Harding, H., Douglas, S.D., et al. (1999). Association between subjective sleep quality and depression on immunocompetence in low-income women at risk for cervical cancer. *Psychosomatic Medicine, 61,* 496–507.

Say, R., Murtagh, M., & Thomson, R. (2006). Patients' preference for involvement in medical decision making: A narrative review. *Patient Education and Counseling,* 60(2), 102–114.

Scascighini, L., Toma, V., Dober-Spielmann, S., & Sprott, H. (2008). Multidisciplinary treatment for chronic pain: A systematic review of interventions and outcomes. *Rheumatology, 47*(5), 670–678.

Schackman, B.R., Finkelstein, R., Neukermans, C.P., Lewis, L., & Eldred, L. (2005). The cost of HIV medication adherence support interventions: Results of a cross-site evaluation. *AIDS Care, 17,* 927–937.

Schachter, S. (1971). Some extraordinary facts about obese humans and rats. *American Psychologist, 26,* 129–144.

Schachter, S. (1982). Recidivism and self-cure of smoking and obesity. *American Psychologist, 37,* 436–444.

Schleifer, S.J., Keller, S.E., & Bartlett, J.A. (1999). Depression and immunity clinical factors and therapeutic course. *Psychiatric Research, 85,* 63–69.

Schleifer, S.J., Keller, S.E., Camerino, M., Thornton, J.C., & Stein, M. (1983). Suppression of lymphocyte stimulation following bereavement. *Journal of the American Medical Association, 250*(3), 374–377.

Schmale, A.H., Jr., & Engel, G.L. (1967). The giving up-given up complex illustrated on film. *Archives of General Psychiatry, 17,* 135–145.

Schmid-Büchi, S., Halfens, R.J.G., Dassen, T., & van den Borne. (2011). Psychosocial problems and needs of posttreatment patients with breast cancer and their relatives. *European Journal of Oncology Nursing, 15*(3), 260–266.

Schmid, S.M., Hallschmid, M., Jauch-Chara, K., Wilms, B., Benedict, C., Lehnert, H., et al. (2009). Short-term sleep loss decreases physical activity under free-living conditions but does not increase food intake under time-deprived laboratory conditions in healthy men. *American Journal of Clinical Nutrition, 90,* 1476–1482.

Schmidt, H. (2009). Personal responsibility in the NHS constitution and the social determinants of health approach: Competitive or complementary? *Health Economics, Policy and Law, 4,* 129–138.

Schmitz, M.F., & Crystal, S. (2000). Social relations, coping, and psychological distress among persons with HIV/AIDS. *Journal of Applied Social Psychology, 30*(4), 665–683.

Schneider, M., Dunn, A., & Cooper, D. (2009). Affect exercise, and physical activity among healthy adolescents. *Journal of Sport and Exercise Psychology, 31,* 706–723.

Schneiderman, N., Antoni, M.H., Saab, P.G., & Ironson, G. (2001). Health psychology: Psychosocial and biobehavioural aspects of chronic disease management. *Annual Review of Psychology, 52,* 555–580.

Schopflocher, D., Taenzer, P., & Jovey, R. (2011). The prevalence of chronic pain in Canada. *Pain Research and Management, 16*(6), 445–450.

Schröder-Butterfil, E., & Marianti, R. (2006). A framework for understanding old-age vulnerabilities. *Aging and Society, 26*(1), 9–35.

Schulz, R., Bookwalla, J., Knapp, J.E., Scheier, M., & Williamson, G.M. (1996). Pessimism, age, and cancer mortality. *Psychology and Aging, 11,* 304–309.

Schutz, J., & Luthe, W. (1959). *Autogenic training: A psychophysiological approach to psychotherapy.* New York: Grune and Stratton.

Schwam, K. (1998). The phenomenon of compassion fatigue in perioperative nursing. *AORN Journal, 68,* 642–645, 647–648.

Schwarzer, R. (1992). Self-efficacy in the adoption and maintenance of health behaviors: Theoretical approaches and a new model. In R. Schwarzer (Ed.), *Self-efficacy: Thought control of action* (pp. 217–243). Washington, DC: Hemisphere.

Schwarzer, R., & Luszczynska, A. (2013). Stressful life events. In I.B. Weiner (Ed.-in-Chief) & A.M. Nezu, C.M. Nezu, & P.A. Geller (Vol. Eds.), *Handbook of psychology: Vol. 9. Health psychology* (2nd rev. ed., pp. 29–56). New York: Wiley.

Schwartzberg, J.G., Cowett, A., VanGeest, J., & Wolf, M.S. (2007). Communication techniques for patients with low health literacy: A survey of physicians, nurses, and pharmacists. *American Journal of Health Behavior, 31*(Suppl. 1), S96–S104.

Schwitzer, G. (2002). A review of features in Internet consumer health decision-support tools. *Journal of Medical Internet Research, 4*(2), E11.

Sebire, S.J., Standage, M., & Vansteenkiste, M. (2009). Examining intrinsic versus extrinsic exercise goals: Cognitive, affective, and behavioural outcomes. *Journal of Sport and Exercise Psychology, 31,* 189–210.

Segerstrom, S.C., & Miler, G.E. (2004). Psychological stress and the human immune system: A meta-analytic study of 30 years of inquiry. *Psychological Bulletin, 130*(4), 601–630.

Sellwood, W., & Tarrier, N. (1994). Demographic factors associated with extreme non-compliance in schizophrenia. *Social Psychiatry and Psychiatric Epidemiology, 29,* 172–177.

Selye, H. (1956). *The stress of life.* New York: McGraw-Hill.

Selye, H. (1974). *Stress without distress.* Philadelphia: Lippincott.

Serpell, L., & Treasure, J. (2002). Bulimia nervosa: Friend or foe? The pros and cons of bulimia nervosa. *International Journal of Eating Disorders, 32*(2), 164–170.

Sexton, M.M. (1979). Behavioral epidemiology. In O.F. Pomerleau & J.P. Brady (Eds.), *Behavioral medicine: Theory and practice* (pp. 3–22). Baltimore, MD: Williams & Wilkins.

Shadel, W.G., Shiffman, S., Niaura, R., Nichter, R., Nichter, M., & Abrams, D.B. (2000). Current models of nicotine dependence: What is known and what is needed to advance understanding of tobacco etiology among youth. *Drug and Alcohol Dependence, 59*(Suppl.), S9–S22.

Sheffield, D., Biles, P.L., Orom, H., Maixner, W., & Sheps, D.S. (2000). Race and sex differences in cutaneous pain perception. *Psychosomatic Medicine, 62,* 517–523.

Shekelle, R.B., Raynor, W.J., Ostfeld, A.M., Garron, D.C., Bieliauskas, L.A., Liu, S.C., et al. (1981). Psychological depression and 17-year risk of death from cancer. *Psychosomatic Medicine, 43,* 117–125.

Sheldon, K.M., & King, L. (2001). Why positive psychology is necessary. *American Psychologist, 56,* 216–217.

Sheps, D.S., & Rozanski, A. (2005). From feeling blue to clinical depression: Exploring the pathogenicity of depressive symptoms and their management in cardiac practice. *Psychosomatic Medicine, 67*(Suppl. 1), S2–S5.

Sher, K.J., & Levenson, R.W. (1982). Risk for alcoholism and individual differences in the stress-response-dampening effect of alcohol. *Journal of Abnormal Psychology, 91,* 350–367.

Sherwood, P.R., Given, B.A., Given, C.W., Schiffman, R.F., Murman, D.L., Lovely, M., et al. (2006). Predictors of distress in caregivers of persons with a primary malignant brain tumor. *Research in Nursing & Health, 29*(2), 105–120.

Shields M. (2006). Overweight and obesity among children and youth. *Health Reports, 17,* 27–42.

Shields, M., Carooll, M.D., & Ogden, C.L. (2011). Adult obesity prevalence in Canada and the United States. *NCHS data brief, no 56.* Hyattsville, MD: National Center for Health Statistics.

Shields, M., & Tremblay, M.S. (2008). Sedentary behaviour and obesity. *Health Reports, 19,* pp. 19–30.

Shine, K.I. (2002). Health care quality and how to achieve it. *Academic Medicine, 77,* 91–99.

Shi, Y., de Groh, M., & Morrison, H. (2013). Perinatal and early childhood factors for overweight and obesity in young Canadian children. *Canadian Journal of Public Health, 104*(1), 69–74.

Shoham-Yakubovich, I., Ragland, D.R., Brand, R.J., & Syme, S.L. (1988). Type A behavior patterns and health status after 22 years of follow-up in the Western Collaborative Group Study. *American Journal of Epidemiology, 128,* 579–588.

Shopland, D.R., & Burns, D.M. (1993). Medical and public health implications of tobacco addiction. In C.T. Orleans & J. Slade (Eds.), *Nicotine addiction: Principles and management* (pp. 105–142). New York: Oxford University Press.

Short, S.E., & Ross-Stewart, L. (2008). A review of self-efficacy based interventions. In S. Mellalieu & S. Hanton (Eds.), *Applied sport psychology advances: A review* (pp. 221–280). London: Routledge.

Shrier, D.K., & Shrier, L.A. (2005). An exploratory study of mother-daughter physicians: An intergenerational comparison of professional and personal experiences. *Journal of Women's Health, 14*(10), 946–957.

Siegert, R.J., & Taylor, W.J. (2004). Theoretical aspects of goal-setting and motivation in rehabilitation. *Disability and Rehabilitation, 26*(1), 1–8.

Silverman, J., Kurtz, S., & Draper, J. (2005). *Skills for communicating with patients* (2nd ed.). Oxford: Radcliffe Medical Press.

Siminoff, L.A., Graham, G.C., & Gordon, N.H. (2006). Cancer communication patterns and the influence of patient characteristics: Disparities in information-giving and affective behaviors. *Patient Education and Counseling, 62*(3), 355–360.

Simoni, J.M., Franks, J.C., Lehavot, K., & Yard, S.S. (2011). Peer interventions to promote health: Conceptual considerations. *American Journal of Orthopsychiatry, 8*(3), 351–359.

Simpson, M., Buckman, R., Stewart, M., Maguire, P., Lipkin, M., Novack, D., & Till, J. (1991). Doctor-patient communication: The Toronto consensus statement. *British Medical Journal, 303,* 1385–1367.

Simpson, S., Eurich, D.T., Majumdar, S.R., Padwal, R.S., Tsuyuki, R.T., Varney, J., et al. (2006). A meta-analysis of the association between adherence to drug therapy and mortality. *British Medical Journal, 332,* 7557.

Singh, A.N. (2005). Multidisciplinary management of chronic pain. *International Medical Journal, 12*(2), 111–116.

Single, E. (1995). Defining harm reduction. *Drug and Alcohol Review, 14,* 287–290.

Single, E. (2005). New directions in alcohol policy. In *Substance abuse in Canada: Current challenges and choices.* Ottawa, ON: Canadian Centre on Substance Abuse.

Sist, T.C., Florio, G.A., Miner, M.F., Lema, M.J., & Zevon, M.A. (1998). The relationship between depression and pain language in cancer and chronic non-cancer pain patients. *Journal of Pain and Symptom Management, 15,* 350–358.

Sivadon-Tardy, V., Orlikowski, D., Porcher, R., Sharshar, T., Durand, M.-C., Enouf, V., et al. (2009). Guillain-Barre syndrome and influenza virus infection. *Clinical Infectious Disease, 48,* 48–56.

Skevington, S.M. (2004). Pain and symptom perception. In A. Kaptein & J. Weinman (Eds.), *Health psychology* (pp. 182–206). Malden, MA: Blackwell.

Skinner, H.H., Haines, J., Austin, S.B., & Field, A.E. (2012). A prospective study of overeating, binge eating, and depressive symptoms among adolescent and young adult women. *Journal of Adolescent Health, 50*(5), 478–483.

Slomkowski, C., Rende, R., Novak, S., Lloyd-Richardson, E., & Niaura, R. (2005). Sibling effects on smoking in adolescence: Evidence for social influence from a genetically informative design. *Addiction, 100,* 430–438.

Sluijs, E.M., Kerssens, J.J., van der Zee, J., & Myers, L.B. (1998). Adherence to physiotherapy. In L.B. Meyers, K. Midence, et al. (Eds.), *Adherence to treatment in medical conditions* (pp. 363–382). Amsterdam: Harwood Academic.

Sluka, K.A., & Walsh, D. (2003). Transcutaneous electric nerve stimulation: Basic science mechanisms and clinical effectiveness. *Journal of Pain, 4*(3), 109–121.

Smiley, K.A. (2004). A structured group for gay men newly diagnosed with HIV/AIDS. *The Journal for Specialists in Group Work, 29*(2), 207–224.

Smith, A., & Cook-Cottone, C. (2011). A review of family therapy as an effective intervention for anorexia nervosa in adolescents. *Journal of Clinical Psychology in Medical Settings, 18*(4), 323–334.

Smith, A., Vollmer-Conna, U., Bennett, B., Wakefield, D., Kickie, I., & Lloyd, A. (2004). The relationship between distress and the development of a primary immune response to a novel antigen. *Brain, Behavior, and Immunity, 18,* 65–75.

Smith, J.C. (1993). *Understanding stress and coping.* New York: MacMillan.

Smith, R.E. (1980). Development of an integrated coping response through cognitive-affective stress management training. In I.G. Sarason & C.D. Spielberger (Eds.), *Stress and anxiety* (Vol. 7, pp. 265–280). Washington, DC: Hemisphere Publishing Corporation.

Smith, R.E. (1999). Generalization effects in coping skills training. *Journal of Sport and Exercise Psychology, 21,* 189–204.

Smith, T.P., Kennedy, S.L., & Fleshner, M. (2004). Influence of age and physical activity on the primary in vivo antibody and T cell-mediated responses in men. *Journal of Applied Physiology, 97,* 491–498.

Smith, T.W., & Ruiz, J.M. (2002). Psychosocial influences on the development and course of coronary heart disease: Current status and implications for research and practice. *Journal of Consulting and Clinical Psychology, 70,* 548–568.

Solomon, G.F., Segerstrom, S.C., Grohr, P., Kemeny, M., & Fahey, J. (1997). Shaking up immunity: Psychological and immunologic changes after a natural disaster. *Psychosomatic Medicine, 59,* 114–127.

Song, C., & Leonard, B. (2000). *Fundamentals of psychoneuroimmunology.* New York: John Wiley and Sons Ltd.

Sonstroem, R.J. (1997). Physical activity and self-esteem. In W.P. Morgan (Ed.), *Physical activity and mental health* (pp. 127–143). Washington, DC: Taylor & Francis.

Sotero, M.M. (2006). A conceptual model of historical trauma: Implications for public health practice and research. *Journal of Health Disparities Research and Practice, 1*(1), 93–108.

Spence, J.C., McGannon, K.R., & Poon, P. (2005). The effect of exercise on global self-esteem: A quantitative review. *Journal of Sport and Exercise Psychology, 27,* 311–334.

Spencer, J., Young, M.E., Rintala, D., & Bates, S. (1995). Socialization to the culture of a rehabilitation hospital: An ethnographic study. *Journal of Occupational Therapy, 49,* 53–62.

Spickard, A., Gabbe, S.G., & Christensen, J.F. (2002). Mid-career burnout in generalist and specialist physicians. *Journal of the American Medical Association, 288*(12), 1447–1450.

Spiegel, D., & Bloom, J.R. (1983). Group therapy and hypnosis reduce metastatic breast carcinoma pain. *Psychosomatic Medicine, 45,* 333–339.

Spiegel, D., Sephton, S.E., Terr, A.I., & Stites, D.P. (1998). Effects of psychosocial treatment in prolonging cancer survival may be mediated by neuroimmune pathways. *Annals of the New York Academy of Sciences, 840,* 674–683.

Spielmans, G.I., Benish, S.G., Marin, C., Bowman, W.M., Menster, M., & Wheeler, A. (2013). Specificity of psychological treatments for bulimia nervosa and binge eating disorder? A meta-analysis of direct comparisons. *Clinical Psychology Review, 33*(3), 460–469.

Springer, S.A., Chen, S., & Altice, F. (2009). Depression and symptomatic response among HIV-infected drug users enrolled in a randomized controlled trial of directly administered antiretroviral therapy. *AIDS Care, 21*(8), 976–983.

Stack, A.G., & Martin, D.R. (2005). Association of patient autonomy with increased transplantation and survival among new dialysis patients in the United States. *American Journal of Kidney Disease, 45*(4), 730–742.

Stainer, U.M., Grond, S., & Maier, C. (1999). Responders and non-responders to post-operative pain treatment: The loading dose predicts analgesic needs. *European Journal of Anaesthesiology, 16*, 103–110.

Starkweather, A.R. (2007). The effects of exercise on perceived stress and IL-6 levels among older adults. *Biological Research for Nursing, 8*(3), 186–194.

Standaert, C.J., Friedly, J., Erwin, M.W., Lee, M.J., Rechtine, G., Henrikson, N.B., et al. (2011). Comparative effectiveness of exercise, acupuncture, and spinal manipulation for low back pain. *Spine, 36*(21, Suppl.), S120–S130.

Standl, T., Burmeister, M.A., Ohnesorge, H., Wilhelm, S., Striepke, M., Gottschalk, A., et al. (2003). Patient-controlled epidural analgesia reduces analgesic requirements compared to continuous epidural infusion after major abdominal surgery. *Canadian Journal of Anaesthesia, 50*(3), 258–264.

Stanford, E.A., Chambers, C.T., Biesanz, J.C., & Chen, E. (2008). The frequency, trajectories and predictors of adolescent recurrent pain: A population based approach. *Pain, 138*, 11–21.

Stanton, W.R., Flay, B.R., Colder, C.R., & Mehta, P. (2004). Identifying and predicting adolescent smokers' developmental trajectories. *Nicotine & Tobacco Research, 6*(5), 843–852.

Stanton, W.R., Mahalski, P.A., McGee, R., & Silva, P.A. (1993). Reasons for smoking or not smoking in early adolescence. *Addictive Behaviors, 18*, 321–329.

Starfield, B. (1994). Is primary care essential? *Lancet, 344*, 1129.

Starfield, B., Wray, C., Hess, K., Gross, R., Birk, P.S., & D'Lugoff, B.C. (1981). The influence of patient-practitioner agreement on outcome of care. *American Journal of Public Health, 71*, 127–131.

Starkes, J.L., Helson, W., & Jack, R. (2001). Expert performance in sport and dance. In R.N. Singer, H.A. Hausenblas, & C.M. Janelle (Eds.), *Handbook of Sport Psychology* (2nd ed., pp. 174–204). New York: Wiley.

Statistics Canada. (2001, June 22). Impact of smoking on life expectancy and disability. *The Daily*. Ottawa, ON: Author.

Statistics Canada. (2002). Canadian community health survey: A first look. *The Daily*. Retrieved July 9, 2003, from www.statcan.ca/Daily/English/020508/d020508a.htm

Statistics Canada. (2002, May 8). Canadian community health survey: A first look. *The Daily*. Ottawa, ON: Author.

Statistics Canada. (2004a). Alcohol and illicit drug dependence. *Health Reports, 9*(Suppl.), 9–19.

Statistics Canada. (2004b). Use of cannabis and other illicit drugs. *Health Reports, 15*, 43–47.

Statistics Canada. (2005c). Adult obesity in Canada: Measured height and weight. Retrieved June 2, 2010, from www.statcan.gc.ca/pub/82-620-m/2005001/article/adults-adultes/8060-eng.htm

Statistics Canada. (2007). Physically active Canadians. *The Daily*. Ottawa, ON: Author.

Statistics Canada. (2008a). Organized sports participation among children. *The Daily*. Retrieved April 4, 2010, from www.statcan.gc.ca/daily-quotidien/080603/dq080603a-eng.htm

Statistics Canada. (2008b). Participation in sports. *The Daily*. Retrieved April 14, 2010, from www.statcan.gc.ca/daily-quotidien/080207/dq080207b-eng.htm

Statistics Canada. (2010, June 15). Canadian Community Health Survey. *The Daily*. Retrieved June 24, 2010, from www.statcan.gc.ca/daily-quotidien/100615/dq100615b-eng.htm

Statistics Canada. (2011a). Canadian Community Health Survey. June 21, 2011 www.statcan.gc.ca/daily-quotidien/110621/dq110621b-eng.htm. Accessed December 6, 2012.

Statistics Canada. (2011b, January). *Canadian Health Measures Survey: Physical activity of youth and adults*. Ottawa, ON: Author.

Statistics Canada. (2011b). Mortality, summary list of causes 2008. Ottawa, ON: Author.

Statistics Canada. (2012a). Leading causes of death in Canada, 2009. Retrieved July 15, 2013, from www.statcan.gc.ca/pub/84-215-x/2012001/hl-fs-eng.htm

Statistics Canada. (2012b). Leading causes of death, by sex. CANSIM table 102-0561 and Catalogue no. 84-215-X. Last modified: 2012-07-25.

Statistics Canada. (2013). Access to a regular medical doctor, 2010. Retrieved October 19, 2014, from http://www.statcan.gc.ca/pub/82-625-x/2011001/article/11456-eng.htm

Stead, L.F., Perera, R., Bullen, C., Mant, D., Harmann-Boyce, J., Cahill, K., & Lancaster, T. (2012). Nicotine replacement therapy for smoking cessation. *Cochrane Database System Review, 14,* 11.

Steele, C.M., & Josephs, R.A. (1990). Alcohol myopia: Its prized and dangerous effects. *American Psychologist, 45,* 921–933.

Steffens, D.C., O'Connor, C.M., Jiang, W.J., Pieper, C.F., Kuchibhatla, M.N., Arias, R.M., et al. (1999). The effect of major depression on functional status in patients with coronary artery disease. *Journal of the American Geriatric Society, 47,* 319–322.

Stein, P.N., & Motta, R.W. (1992). Effects of aerobic and nonaerobic exercise on depression and self-concept. *Perceptual Motor Skills, 74,* 79–89.

Stein, R.I., Saelens, B.E., Dounchis, J.Z., Lewczyk, C.M., Swenson, A.K., & Wilfley, D.E. (2001). Treatment of eating disorders in women. *The Counseling Psychologist, 29*(5), 695–732.

Steinbach, J.P., Blaicher, H.-P., Herrlinger, U., Wick, W., Nägele, T., Meyermann, R., et al. (2006). Surviving gliobastoma for more than 5 years: The patient's perspective. *Neurology, 66,* 239–242.

Stelfox, H.T., Hemmelgarn, B.R., Bagshaw, S.M., Gao, S., Doig, C.J., Nijssen-Jordan, C., et al. (2012). Intensive care unit bed availability and outcomes for hospitalized patients with sudden clinical deterioration. *Archives of Internal Medicine, 172*(6), 467–474.

Stephen, E., Foote, K., Hendershot, G., & Schoenborn, C. (1994). Health of the foreign-born population. *Advance Data from Vital and Health Statistics, 241,* 1–10.

Stevens, B. (2001). Acute pain management in infants in the neonatal intensive care unit. In G.A. Finley & P.J. McGrath (Eds.), *Acute and procedure pain in infants and children* Progress in pain research and management, Vol. 20. (pp. 101–128). Seattle: IASP Press.

Stevens, B.J., & Franck, L.S. (2001). Assessment and management of pain in neonates. *Paediatric Drugs, 3,* 539–558.

Stevens, S.L., Colwell, B., Smith, D.W., Robinson, J., & McMillan, C. (2005). An exploration of self-reported negative affect by adolescence as a reason for smoking: Implications for tobacco prevention and intervention programs. *Preventive Medicine, 41,* 589–596.

Stevens, B.J., & Franck, L.S. (2001). Assessment and management of pain in neonates. *Paediatric Drugs, 3,* 539–558.

Stewart, L., Reilly, J.J., & Hughes, A.R. (2009). Evidence-based behavioral treatment of obesity in children and adolescents. *Child and Adolescent Psychiatric Clinics of North America, 18,* 189–198.

Stewart, M.A. (1995). Effective physician-patient communication and health outcomes: A review. *Canadian Medical Association Journal, 152,* 1423–1433.

Stewart, M., Brown, J.B., Donner, A., McWhinney, I.R., Oates, J., Weston, W.W., et al. (2000). The impact of patient-centered care on outcomes. *The Journal of Family Practice, 49,* 796–804.

Stewart, M.A., Brown, J.B., Levenstein, J.H., McCracken, E., & McWhinney, I.R. (1986). The patient-centered clinical method: Changes in residents' performance over two months of training. *Family Practice, 3,* 164–167.

Stewart, M.A., Brown, J.B., Weston, W.W., McWhinney, I.R., McWilliam, C.L., & Freeman, T.R. (1999). *Patient-centred medicine: Transforming the clinical method.* Thousand Oaks, CA: Sage.

Stewart, M.A., McWhinney, I.R., & Buck, C.W. (1979). The doctor-patient relationship and its effect upon outcome. *Journal of the Royal College of General Practice, 29,* 77–82.

Stice, E., Marti, C.N., & Rohde, P. (2013). Prevalence, incidence, impairment, and course of the proposed DSM-5 eating disorder diagnoses in an 8 year prospective community study of young women. *Journal of Abnormal Psychology, 122*(2), 445–457.

St. Leger, L. (2005). Questioning sustainability in health promotion projects and programs. *Health Promotion International, 20*(4), 317–319.

Stock Keister, M.C., Green, L.A., Kahn, N.B., Phillips, R.L., McCann, J., & Fryer, G.D. (2004). What people want from their family physician. *American Family Physician, 69*(10), 2310.

Stokols, D. (1996). Translating social ecological theory into guidelines for community health promotion. *American Journal of Health Promotion, 10*(4), 282–298.

Stone, A.A., Cox, D.S., Valdimarsdottir, H., Jandorf, L., & Neale, J.M. (1987). Evidence that secretory IgA antibody is associated with daily mood. *Journal of Personality and Social Psychology, 52,* 988–993.

Story, M., French, S.A., Resnick, M.D., & Blum, R.W. (1995). Ethnic/racial and socioeconomic differences in dieting behaviors and body image perceptions in adolescents. *International Journal of Eating Disorders, 18,* 173–179.

Stowe, J., Andrews, N., Wise, L., & Miller, E. (2009). Investigation of the temporal association of Guillain-Barre syndrome with influenza vaccine and influenza like illness using the United Kingdom General Practice Research Database. *American Journal of Epidemiology, 169,* 382–388.

Stowell, J.R., Robles, T.F., & Kane, H.S. (2013). Psycho-neuroimmunology: Mechanisms, individual differences, and interventions. In C.M. Nezu, P.A. Geller, & I.B. Weiner (Eds.), *Handbook of psychology, Volume 9* (2nd ed., pp. 79–101). Hoboken, NJ: Wiley and Sons.

Strahan, E.H.E., & Brown, R.J. (2004). A qualitative study of the experiences of patients following transfer from intensive care. *Intensive and Critical Care Nursing, 21,* 160–171.

Strasser, F., Walker, P., & Bruera, E. (2005). Palliative pain management: When both pain and suffering hurt. *Journal of Palliative Care, 21*(2), 69–79.

Straub, R.O. (2007). *Health psychology* (2nd ed.). New York: Worth.

Streltzer, J. (1997). Pain. In W.S. Tseng & J. Streltzer (Eds.), *Culture and psychopathology: A guide to clinical assessment* (pp. 87–100). New York: Brunner/Mazel.

Striegel-Moore, R.S., & Bulik, C.M. (2007). Risk factors for eating disorders. *American Psychologist, 62*(3), 181–198.

Stuber, M.L. (1995). Stress responses to pediatric cancer: A family phenomenon. *Family Systems Medicine, 13,* 163–172.

Suarez, E.C., & Goforth, H. (2010). Sleep and inflammation: A potential link to chronic disease. In K. Kendall-Tackett (Ed.), *The psychoneuroimmunology of chronic disease: Exploring the links between inflammation, stress, and illness* (pp. 53–75). Washington, DC: American Psychological Association.

Sui, Z., Turnbull, D.A., & Dodd, J.M. (2013). Overweight and obese women's perceptions about making healthy change during pregnancy: A mixed method study. *Maternal and Child Health Journal, 17*(10), 1879–1887.

Suinn, R. (1972). Behavioral rehearsal training for ski racers. *Behavior Therapy, 3,* 519.

Sullivan, M.D., LaCroix, A.Z., Spertus, J.A., Hecht, J., & Russo, J. (2003). Depression predicts revascularization for 5 years after coronary angiography. *Psychosomatic Medicine, 65*(2), 229–236.

Sullivan, M.J.L., Adams, H., & Sullivan, M.E. (2004). Communicative dimensions of pain catastrophizing: Social cueing effects on pain behaviour and coping. *Pain, 107*(3), 220–226.

Sullivan, M.J.L., Bishop, S.R., & Pivik, J. (1995). The Pain Catastrophizing Scale: Development and validation. *Psychological Assessment, 7,* 524–532.

Sullivan, M.J.L., Lynch, M.E., & Clark, A.J. (2005). Dimensions of catastrophic thinking associated with pain experience and disability in patients with neuropathic pain conditions. *Pain, 113*(3), 310–315.

Sullivan, M.J.L., Martel, M.O., Tripp, D.A., Savard, A., & Crombez, G. (2006). Catastrophic thinking and heightened perception of pain in others. *Pain, 123*(1), 37–44.

Sullivan, M.J.L., Thorn, B., Haythornthwaite, J.A., Keefe, F.J., Martin, M., Bradley, L.A., et al. (2001). Theoretical perspectives on the relation between catastrophizing and pain. *Clinical Journal of Pain, 17,* 52–64.

Sullivan, M.J.L., Tripp, D.A., & Santor, D. (2000). Gender differences in pain and pain behavior: The role of catastrophizing. *Cognitive Therapy and Research, 24,* 121–134.

Sullivan, P., & Buske, L. (1998). Results from CMA's huge 1998 physician survey point to a dispirited profession. *Canadian Medical Association Journal, 159*(5), 525–528.

Suls, J., Martin, R., & Leventhal, H. (1997). Social comparison, lay referral, and the decision to seek medical care. In B.P. Buunk & F.X. Gibbons (Eds.), *Health, coping, and well-being: Perspectives from social comparison theory* (pp. 195–226). Mahwah, NJ: Erlbaum.

Suls, J., & Wallston, K.A. (Eds.). (2003). *Social psychological foundations of health and illness*. Maiden, MA: Blackwell.

Surtees, P.G., Wainwright, N.W.J., Bockholdt, S.M., Luben, R.N., Warcham, N.J., & Khaw, K.-T. (2008). Major depression, C-reactive protein, and incident ischemic heart disease in healthy men and women. *Psychosomatic Medicine, 70,* 850–855.

Surtees, P.G., Wainwright, N.W.J., Luben, R., Khaw, K.-T., & Day, N.E. (2006). Mastery, sense of coherence, and mortality: Evidence of independent associations from the EPIC-Norfolk Prospective Cohort Study. *Health Psychology, 25*(1), 102–110.

Suskin, N., MacDonald, S., Swabey, T., Arthur, H., Vimr, M.A., & Tihaliani, R. (2003). Cardiac rehabilitation and secondary prevention services in Ontario: Recommendations from a consensus panel. *Canadian Journal of Cardiology, 19,* 833–838.

Sutton, S.R., & Eiser, J.R. (1984). The effect of fear-arousing communications on cigarette smoking: An expectancy-value approach. *Journal of Behavioral Medicine, 7,* 13–34.

Szasz, T.S., & Hollender, M.H. (1956). A contribution to the philosophy of medicine. The basic models of the doctor-patient relationship. *Archives of Internal Medicine, 97,* 585–592.

T

Taddio, A., Appleton, M., Bortolussi, R., Chambers, C.T., Dubey, V., Halperin, S., et al. (2010). Reducing the pain of childhood vaccination: An evidence–based clinical practice guideline. *Canadian Medical Association Journal, 182*, 1989–1995.

Tate, A.K., & Petruzzello, S.J. (1995). Varying the intensity of acute exercise: Implications for changes in affect. *Journal of Sports Medicine and Physical Fitness, 35*, 1–8.

Taylor, A.H., Cable, N.T., Faulkner, G., Hillsdon, M., Narici, M., & Van Der Bij, A.K. (2004, August). Physical activity and older adults: A review of health benefits and the effectiveness of interventions. *Journal of Sports Sciences, 22*(8), 703–725.

Taylor, C.B., Bryson, S., Luce, K.H., Cunning, D., Doyle, A., Abascal, L.B., et al. (2006). Prevention of eating disorders in at-risk college-age women. *Archives of General Psychiatry, 63*(8), 881–888.

Taylor, C.B., Conrad, A., Wilhelm, F.H., Neri, E., DeLorenzo, A., Kramer, M.A., et al. (2006). Psychophysiological and cortisol responses to psychological stress in depressed and nondepressed older men and women with elevated cardiovascular disease risk. *Psychosomatic Medicine, 68*, 538–546.

Taylor, J. (1994). On exercise and sport avoidance: A reply to Dr. Albert Ellis. *The Sport Psychologist, 8*, 262–271.

Taylor, J. (1996). Intensity regulation and athletic performance. In J.L. Van Raalte & B.W. Brewer (Eds.), *Exploring sport and exercise psychology* (pp. 75–106). Washington, DC: American Psychological Association.

Taylor, N., Hall, G.M., & Salmon, P. (1996). Is patient-controlled analgesia controlled by the patient? *Social Science and Medicine, 43*, 1137–1143.

Taylor, S.E., Klein, L.C., Lewis, B.P., Gruenewald, T.L., Gurung, R.A.R., & Updegraff, J.A. (2000). Biobehavioral responses to stress in females: Tend-and-befriend, not fight-or-flight. *Psychological Review, 107*, 411–429.

Taylor, S.E., & Sirois, F.M. (2012). *Health psychology.* Toronto: McGraw-Hill Ryerson.

Teasdale, E., & Yardley, L. (2011). Understanding responses to government health recommendations: Public perceptions of government advice for managing the H1N1 (swine flu) influenza pandemic. *Patient Education and Counselling, 85*(3), 413–418.

Tedeschi, R.G., & Calhoun, L.G. (1995). *Trauma and transformation: Growing in the aftermath of suffering.* Thousand Oaks, CA: Sage.

Tedeschi, R.G., & Kilmer, R.P. (2005). Assessing strengths, resilience and growth to guide clinical interventions. *Professional Psychology: Research and Practice, 36*, 230–237.

Tennen, H., Affleck, G., & Zautra, A. (2006). Depression history and coping with chronic pain: A daily process analysis. *Health Psychology, 25*(3), 370–379.

Tennier, L.D. (1997). Discharge planning: An examination of the perceptions and recommendations for improved discharge planning at the Montreal General Hospital. *Social Work in Health Care, 26*(1), 41–60.

Teno, J.M., & Coppola, K.M. (1999). For every numerator, you need a denominator: A simple statement but key to measuring the quality of care of the "dying." *Journal of Pain and Symptom Management, 17*, 109–113.

Teo, K.K., Ounpuss, S., Hawken, S., Pandey, M.R., Valentin, V., Hunt, D., et al. (2006). Tobacco use and risk of myocardial infarction in 52 countries in the INTERHEART study: A case-control study. *The Lancet, 368*, 647–658.

Thoburn, J., & Hammond-Meyer, A. (2004). Eating disorders. In F.M. Kline & L.B. Silver (Eds.), *The educator's guide to mental health issues in the classroom* (pp. 141–170). Baltimore, MD: Brookes Publishing.

Thomas, I.L., Tyle, V., Webster, J., & Neilson, A. (2008). An evaluation of transcutaneous electric nerve stimulation for pain relief in labour. *Australian and New Zealand Journal of Obstetrics and Gynaecology, 28*, 182–189.

Thomas, N.K. (2004). Resident burnout. *Journal of the American Medical Association, 292*(23), 2880–2889.

Thomas, O., Mellalieu, S.D., & Hanton, S. (2009). Stress management in sport: A critical review and synthesis. In S.D. Mellalieu & S. Hanton (Eds.), *Advances in applied sport psychology: A review* (pp. 124, 161). London: Routledge.

Thomas, W., White, C.M., Mah, J., Geisser, M.S., Church, T.R., & Mandel, J.S. (1995). Longitudinal compliance with annual screening for fecal occult blood. *American Journal of Epidemiology, 142*, 176–182.

Thomason, T.E., McCune, J.S., Bernard, S.A., Winer, E.P., Tremont, S., & Lindley, C.M. (1998). Cancer pain survey: Patient-centered issues in control. *Journal of Pain Symptom Management, 15*, 275–284.

Thombs, D.L., O'Mara, R.J., Tsukamoto, M., Rossheim, M.E., Weiler, R.M., Mervews, M.L., et al. (2010). Event level analyses of energy drink consumption and alcohol intoxication in bar patrons. *Addictive Behavior, 35*(4), 325–330.

Tompkins, M.A. (2013). *Anxiety and avoidance: A universal treatment for anxiety, panic, and fear.* Oakland, CA: New Harbinger Publications.

Thompson, C.L., & Pledger, L.M. (1993). Doctor-patient communication: Is patient knowledge of medical terminology improving? *Health Communication, 5,* 89–97.

Thompson, J.K. (1986, April). Larger than life. *Psychology Today,* pp. 38–44.

Thompson, T.L. (2000). The nature and language of illness explanations. In B.B. Whaley (Ed.), *Explaining illness: Research theory and strategies* (pp. 3–40). Mahwah, NJ: Lawrence Erlbaum.

Thornton, L.M., Andersen, B.L., Crespin, T.R., & Carson, W.E. (2007). Individual trajectories in stress covary with immunity during recovery from cancer diagnosis and treatments. *Brain, Behavior, and Immunity, 21,* 185–194.

Tierney, A.J., Taylor, J., & Closs, S.J. (1992). Knowledge, expectations and experiences of patients receiving chemotherapy for breast cancer. *Scandinavian Journal of Caring Sciences, 6*(2), 75–80.

Tjepkema, M. (2002). The health of the off-reserve Aboriginal population. *Health Reports: How Healthy Are Canadians,* Supplement to Volume 13, 73–88.

Tod, D., Hardy, J., & Oliver E. (2011, October). Effects of self-talk: A systematic review. *Journal of Sport and Exercise Psychology, 33*(5), 666–687.

Tomasi, T.B., Jr. (1971). *The immune system of secretions.* Englewood Cliffs, NJ: Prentice-Hall.

Tomkins, S.S. (1966). Psychological model for smoking behavior. *American Journal of Public Health, 56*(Suppl. 12), 17–20.

Tomkins, S.S. (1968). A modified model of smoking behavior. In E.F. Borgatta & R.R. Evans (Eds.), *Smoking, health and behavior* (pp. 165–188). Chicago: Aldine.

Tompkins, J.M. (2005). Two decades have passed . . . and still it is her eyes that I remember: Reflections of a pediatric nurse. *Pediatric Nursing, 31*(5), 426, 424–425.

Tomporowski, P.D., & Ellis, N.R. (1986). Effects of exercise on cognitive process: A review. *Psychological Bulletin, 99,* 338–346.

Topaz, O., Minisi, A.J., Bernardo, N., Alimar, R., Ereso, A., & Shah, R. (2003). Comparison of effectiveness of excimer laser angioplasty in patients with acute coronary syndromes in those with versus those without normal left ventricular function. *American Journal of Cardiology, 91*(7), 797–802.

Toynbee, P. (1977). *Patients.* New York: Harcourt Brace.

Tremblay, S., Ross, N.A., & Berthelot, J.-M. (2002). Regional socio-economic context and health. *Health Reports: How Healthy Are Canadians,* Supplement to Volume 13, 33–44.

Triandis, H.C., Bontempo, R., Villareal, M.J., Asai, M., & Lucca, N. (1988). Individualism and collectivism: Cross-cultural perspectives on self-ingroup relationships. *Journal of Personality and Social Psychology, 54,* 323–338.

Tremblay, M.S., Shields, M., Laviolette, M., Craig, C.L., Janssen, I., & Gorber, S.C. (2010). Fitness of Canadian children and youth: Results from the 2007-2009 Canadian Health Measures Survey. *Statistics Canada, Health Reports, 21*(1), Catalogue no. 82-003-XPE.

Tremblay, L., Boudreau-Larivière, C., & Cimon-Lambert, K. (2012, November). Promoting physical activity in preschoolers: A review of the guidelines, barriers, and facilitators for implementation of policies and practices. *Canadian Psychology, 53*(4), 280–290.

Trifiletti, L.B., Gielen, A.C., Sleet, D.A., & Hopkins, K. (2005). Behavioral and social sciences theories and models: Are they used in unintentional injury prevention research. *Health Education Research, 20*(3), 298–307.

Tsai, P.F. (2011). Assessing pain in older adults: What to do when the gold standard isn't applicable. *Journal of Gerontological Nursing, 37*(5), 3–4.

Tucker, O.N., Szomstein, S., & Rosenthal, R.J. (2007). Nutritional consequences of weight loss surgery. *Medical Clinics of North America, 91,* 499–513.

Tuckett, D., Boulton, M., Olson, C., & Williams, A. (1985). *Meetings between experts: An approach to sharing ideas in medical consultations.* New York: Taylor & Francis.

Turk, D.C. (2001). Physiological and psychological bases of pain. In A. Baum, T.A. Revenson, & J.E. Singer (Eds.), *Handbook of health psychology* (pp. 117–131). Mahwah, NJ: Erlbaum.

Turk, D.C., & Meichenbaum, D. (1991). Adherence to self-care regimens: The patient's perspective. In R.H. Rozensky, J.J. Sweet, & S.M. Tovian (Eds.), *Handbook of clinical psychology. I. Medical settings* (pp. 249–266). New York: Plenum.

Turk, D.C., Meichenbaum, D., & Genest, M. (1983). *Pain and behavioral medicine: A cognitive-behavioral perspective.* New York: Guilford Press.

Turk, D.C., & Melzack, R. (Eds.). (2001). *Handbook of pain assessment* (2nd ed.). New York: Guilford.

Turk, D.C., Monarch, E.S., & Williams, A.D. (2004). Assessment of pain sufferers. In T. Hadjistavropoulos & K.D. Craig (Eds.), *Pain: Psychological perspectives* (pp. 209–243). Mahwah, NJ: Erlbaum.

Turk, D.C., & Okifuji, A. (1996). Perception of traumatic onset, compensation status, and physical findings: Impact on pain severity, emotional distress, and disability in chronic pain patients. *Journal of Behavioral Medicine, 19*, 435–454.

Turk, D.C., & Stacey, B.R. (2000). Multidisciplinary pain centers in the treatment of chronic back pain. In J.W. Frymoyer, T.B. Ducker, N.M. Hadler, J.P. Kostuik, J.N. Weinstein, & T.S. Whitcloud (Eds.), *The adult spine: Principles and practice* (2nd ed., pp. 253–274). Philadelphia: Lippincott Williams & Wilkins.

Turk, D.C., & Winter, F. (2006). *The pain survival guide: How to reclaim your life.* Washington, DC: American Psychological Association.

Turncock, C. (1991). Communicating with patients in the ICU. *Nursing Standard, 5*(15), 38–40.

Tversky, A., & Kahneman, D. (1981). The framing of decisions and the psychology of choice. *Science, 211*, 453–458.

Tzamazis, K., & Stough, C. (2000). Alcohol impairs reaction time and differentially impairs higher order cognitive abilities. *Alcohol and Alcoholism, 35*(2), 197–201.

U

Udry, E., & Anderson, M.B. (2008). Athletic injury and sport behaviour. In T.S. Horn (Ed.), *Advances in sport psychology* (3rd ed., pp. 401–422). Champaign, IL: Human Kinetics.

Unruh, A.M. (1996). Gender variations in clinical pain experience. *Pain, 65*, 123–167.

U.S. Department of Health and Human Services. (2000). *Health people 2010: Volume 1. Understanding and improving health and objectives for improving health.* Washington, DC: Government Printing Office.

U.S. Department of Health and Human Services. (2010). The biology and behavioral basis for smoking-attributable disease: A report of the Surgeon General. Atlanta, GA: Centers for Disease Control and Prevention. Washington, DC: Government Printing Office.

V

van den Berg, M.H., Schoones, J.W., & Vliet Vlieland, T.P. (2007). Internet-based physical activity interventions: A systematic review of the literature. *Journal of Medical Internet Research, 9*(3), e26.

Van Wieringen, J.C., Harmsen, J.A., & Brujnzeels, M.A. (2002). Intercultural communication in general practice. *European Journal of Public Health, 12*, 63–68.

Van Dorsten, B. (2006). Psychological considerations in preparing patients for implantation procedures. *Pain Medicine, 7*(S1), S47–S57.

Van Kleef, E., Shimizu, M., & Wansink, B. (2013). Just a bite: Considerably smaller snack portions satisfy delayed hunger and craving. *Food Quality and Preference, 27*(1), 96–100.

VanIneveld, C.H., Cook, D.J., Kane, S.L., & King, D. (1996). Discrimination and abuse in internal medicine residency. The Internal Medicine Program Directors of Canada. *Journal of General Internal Medicine, 11*, 401–405.

Vealey, R. (1988). Future directions in psychological skills training. *The Sports Psychologist, 2*, 318–336.

Verberne, T.J.P. (2002). Suicide in doctors. *Journal of Epidemiology & Community Health, 56*(3), 237.

Veronin, M.A. (2002). Where are they now? A case study of health-related Web site attrition. *Journal of Medical Internet Research, 4*(2), E10.

Verplanken, B., & Faes, S. (1999). Good intentions, bad habits and effects of forming implementations in healthy eating. *European Journal of Social Psychology, 29*(5–6), 591–604.

Videon, T.M., & Manning, C.K. (2003). Influences on adolescent eating patterns: The importance of family meals. *Journal of Adolescent Health, 32*, 365–373.

Vidic, Z., & Burton, D. (2010). The roadmap: Examining the impact of a systematic goal-setting program for collegiate women. *The Sport Psychologist, 24*(4), 427–447.

Vidrine, J.I., Anderson, C.B., Pollak, K.I., & Wetter, D.W. (2006). Gender differences in adolescent smoking: Mediator and moderator effects of self-generated expected smoking outcomes. *American Journal of Health Promotion, 20*(6), 383–387.

Viemeroe, V., & Krause, C. (1998). Quality of life in individuals with physical disabilities. *Psychotherapy and Psychosomatics, 67*, 317–322.

Vilhauer, R. (2011). "Them" and "us": The experiences of women with metastatic disease in mixed-stage versus stage-specific breast cancer support groups. *Psychology and Health, 26*(6), 781–797.

Vocks, S., Ockenfels, M., Jurgensen, R., Mussgay, L., & Ruddel, H. (2004). Blood pressure reactivity can be reduced by a cognitive behavioral stress management program. *International Journal of Behavioral Medicine, 11*, 63–70.

Vogel, L. (2011). BC First Nations to run own health system. *Canadian Medical Association Journal, 183*(7), E1227–E1228.

Ottawa: Royal Commission on Aboriginal Peoples. (1996). *Volume III: Gathering strength.*

von Baeyer, C.L., Baskerville, S., & McGrath, P.J. (1998). Everyday pain in three- to five-year-old children in day care. *Pain Research and Management, 3*(2), 111–116.

W

Wadden, T.A., Brownell, K.D., & Foster, G.D. (2002). Obesity: Responding to the global epidemic. *Journal of Consulting and Clinical Psychology, 70*, 510–525.

Wadden, T.A., Womble, L.G., Stunkard, A.J., & Anderson, D.A. (2002). Psychosocial consequences of obesity and weight loss. In T.A. Wadden & A.J. Stunkard (Eds.), *Handbook of obesity treatment* (pp. 144–169). New York: Guilford Press.

Wadee, A.A., Kuschke, R.H., Kometz, S., & Berk, M. (2001). Personality factors, stress and immunity. *Stress & Health: Journal of the International Society for the Investigation of Stress, 17*, 25–40.

Wagner, C.C., & McMahon, B.T. (2004). Motivational interviewing and rehabilitation counseling practice. *Rehabilitation Counseling Bulletin, 47*(3), 152–161.

Wahl, C., Gregoire, J.-P., Teo, K., Beaulieu, M., Labelle, S., Leduc, B., et al. (2005). Concordance, compliance and adherence in healthcare: Closing gaps and improving outcomes. *Healthcare Quarterly,* 8(1), Retrieved April 20, 2006, from www.longwoods.com/product.php?productid=16941&cat=&page=1

Waitzkin, H. (1984). Doctor-patient communication: Clinical implications of social scientific research. *Journal of the American Medical Association, 252*, 2441–2446.

Waitzkin, H. (1985). Information giving in medical care. *Journal of Health and Social Behavior, 26*, 81–101.

Walcher, T., Haenle, M.M., Mason, R.A., Koenig, W., Imhof, A., & Kratzer, W. (2010). The effect of alcohol, tobacco and caffeine consumption and vegetarian diet on gallstone prevalence. *European Journal of Gastroenterology & Hepatology, 22*(11), 1345–1351.

Walker, L.G. (2004). Hypnotherapeutic insights and interventions: A cancer odyssey. *Contemporary Hypnosis, 21*, 35–45.

Walsh, B.T., Kaplan, A.S., Attia, E., Olmstead, M., Parides, M., Carter, J.C., et al. (2006). Fluoxetine after weight restoration in anorexia nervosa: A randomized controlled trial. *Journal of the American Medical Association, 295*, 2605–2612.

Walsh, J.D., Blanchard, E.B., Kremer, J.M., & Blancard, C.G. (1999). The psychosocial effects of rheumatoid arthritis on the patient and the well partner. *Behaviour Research and Therapy, 37*, 259–271.

Walsh-Burke, K. (2000). Matching bereavement services to level of need. *Hospice Journal, 15*(1), 77–86.

Walsh, T. (2013). The enigmatic persistence of anorexia nervosa. *American Journal of Psychiatry, 170*, 477–484.

Wang, M.-Y., Tsai, P.-S., Chou, K.-R., & Chen, C.-M. (2008). A systematic review of the efficacy of non-pharmacological treatments for depression on glycaemic control in type 2 diabetics. *Journal of Clinical Nursing, 17*, 2524–2530.

Wann, D.L. (1997). *Sport psychology.* Upper Saddle River, NJ: Wadsworth.

Wansink, B. (2004). Environmental factors that increase the food intake and consumption volume of unknowing consumers. *Annual Review of Nutrition, 24*, 455–479.

Wansink, B. (2006). *Mindless eating: Why we eat more than we think.* New York: Random House.

Wansink, B. (2013). Turning mindless eating into healthy eating. In Eldar Shafir (Ed.), *The behavioral foundations of public policy* (pp. 310–328). Princeton, NJ: Princeton University Press.

Ward, A., Ramsay, R., & Treasure, J.L. (2000). Attachment research in eating disorders. *British Journal of Medical Psychology, 73*, 35–51.

Ward, A., Ramsay, R., Turnbull, S., Benedettini, M., & Treasure, J. (2000). Attachment patterns in eating disorders: Past in the present. *International Journal of Eating Disorders, 28*, 370–376.

Ward, C.F. (2005). Physicians with opioid dependence. *Journal of the American Medical Association, 293*(3), 294.

Ward, H.E., Tueth, M., & Sheps, D. (2003). Depression and cardiovascular disease. *Current Opinion in Psychiatry, 16*(2), 221–225.

Wardle, J., & Pope, R. (1992). The psychological costs of screening for cancer. *Journal of Psychosomatic Research, 36*, 609–624.

Ware, M.A., Doyle, C.R., Woods, R., Lynch, M.E., & Clark, A.J. (2003). Cannabis use for chronic non-cancer pain: Results of a prospective study. *Pain, 102*, 211–216.

Warner, L., Gallo, M.F., & Macaluso, M. (2012). Condom use around the globe: How can we fulfill the prevention potential of male condoms? *Sexual Health, 9*, 4–9.

Wartella, J.E., Auerbach, S.M., & Ward, K.R. (2009). Emotional distress, coping and adjustment in family members of neuroscience intensive care unit patients. *Journal of Psychosomatic Research, 66*, 503–509.

Watkins, L.R., & Maier, S.F. (2000). The pain of being sick: Implications of immune-to-brain communication for understanding pain. *Annual Review of Psychology, 51*, 29–57.

Watson, P.J., Latif, K.R., & Rowbotham, D.J. (2005). Ethnic differences in thermal pain responses: A comparison of South Asian and White British healthy males. *Pain, 118*, 194–200.

Weidong, L., & Rosenthal, D.S. (2013). Acupuncture for cancer pain and related symptoms. *Current Pain and Headache Reports, 17*, 321–328.

Weiger, W.A., Smith, M., Boon, H., Richardson, M.A., Kaptchuk, T.J., & Eisenberg, D.M. (2002). Advising patients who seek complementary and alternative medical therapies for cancer. *Annals of Internal Medicine, 137*(11), 889–903.

Weinberg, R., & McDermott, M. (2002). A comparative analysis of sport and business organizations: Factors perceived critical for organizational success. *Journal of Applied Sport Psychology, 14*, 282–298.

Weinberg, R.S. (1996). Goal setting in sport and exercise: Research to practice. In J.L. Van Raalte & B.W. Brewer (Eds.), *Exploring sport and exercise psychology* (pp. 3–24). Washington, DC: American Psychological Association.

Weinberg, R.S., & Gould, D. (2003). *Foundations of sport and exercise psychology* (3rd ed.). Champaign, IL: Human Kinetics.

Weiner, D., Peiper, C., McConnell, E., Martinez, S., & Keefe, F.J. (1996). Pain measurement in elders with chronic low back pain: Traditional and alternative approaches. *Pain, 67*, 461–467.

Weiner, E.L., Swain, G.R., Wolf, B., & Gottlieb, M. (2001). A qualitative study of physician's own wellness promotion practices. *Western Journal of Medicine, 174*, 19–23.

Weir, E. (2000). Substance abuse among physicians. *CMAJ, 162*(12), 1730.

Weiss, M.R., Wiese, D.M., & Klint, K.A. (1989). Head over heels with success: The relationship between self-efficacy and performance in competitive youth gymnastics. *Journal of Sport and Exercise Psychology, 11*, 444–451.

Weisse, C.S., Sorum, P.C., Sanders, K.N., & Syat, B.L. (2001). Do gender and race affect decisions about pain management? *Journal of General Internal Medicine, 16*, 211–217.

Weller, A., & Hener, T. (1993). Invasiveness of medical procedures and state anxiety in women. *Behavioral Medicine, 19*, 60–65.

Wells, D. (1997). A critical ethnography of the process of discharge decision-making for elderly patients. *Canadian Journal on Aging, 16*, 682–699.

Wells, K.J., Battaglia, T.A., Dudley, D.J., Garcia, R., Greene, A., Calhoun, E., et al. (2008). Patient navigation: State of the art or is it science? *Cancer, 113*(8), 1999–2010.

Wenger, M., Bagchi, B., & Anand, B. (1961). Experiments in India on "voluntary" control of the heart and pulse. *Circulation, 24*, 1319–1325.

Wenzel, L.B., Donnelly, J.P., Fowler, J.M., Habbal, R., Taylor, T.H., Aziz, N., et al. (2002). Resilience, reflection and residual stress in ovarian cancer survivorship: A gynecologic oncology group study. *Psycho-Oncology, 11*, 142–153.

Weston, W.W., & Brown, J.B. (1995). Overview of the patient-centered clinical model. In M. Stewart, J.B. Brown, W.W. Weston, I.R. McWhinney, C.L. McWilliam, & T.R. Freeman. *Patient-centered medicine: Transforming the clinical method* (pp. 21–30). Thousand Oaks, CA: Sage.

Whitaker, K.L., Brewin, C.R., & Watson, M. (2008). Intrusive cognitions and anxiety in cancer patients. *Journal of Psychosomatic Research, 64*, 509–517.

Whitaker, K.L., Watson, M., & Brewin, C.R. (2009). Intrusive cognitions and their appraisal in anxious cancer patients. *Psycho-Oncology, 18*, 1147–1155.

Whyte, A., & Niven, C.A. (2004). The illusive phantom: Does primary care meet patient need following limb loss? *Disability and Rehabilitation, 26*(14–15), 894–900.

Wiegmann, S.M., & Berven, N.L. (1998). Health locus-of-control beliefs and improvement in physical functioning in a work-hardening, return-to-work program. *Rehabilitation Psychology, 43*, 83–100.

Wilkins, K. (1995). Causes of death: How the sexes differ. *Health Reports, 7*(2), 33–43.

Wilkins, K., & Beaudet, M.P. (1998). Work stress and health. *Health Reports, 10*(3), 47–62.

Wilkins, R., Berthelot, J.-M., & Ng, E. (2002). Trends in mortality by neighbourhood income in urban Canada from 1971 to 1996. *Health Reports: How Healthy Are Canadians*, Supplement to Volume 13, 45–71.

Willenbring, M.L., Levine, A.S., & Morley, J.E. (1986). Stress induced eating: A pilot study. *International Journal of Eating Disorders, 5*, 855.

Williams, D.M. (2008). Exercise, affect, and adherence: An integrated model and a case for self-paced exercise. *Journal of Sport and Exercise Psychology, 30*, 471–496.

Williams, J. (2001). Psychology of injury risk and prevention. In R.N. Singer, H.A. Hausenblas, & C.M. Janelle (Eds.), *Handbook of sport psychology* (2nd ed., pp. 766–786). New York: John Wiley and Sons.

Williams, J.E., Paton, C.C., Siegler, I.C., Eigenbrot, M.I., Nieto, F.J., & Tyroler, H.A. (2000). Clinical investigation and reports: Anger proneness predicts coronary heart disease risk: Prospective analysis from the Atherosclerosis Risk in Communities (ARIC) Study. *Circulation, 101*, 2034–2039.

Williams, J.M., & Leffingwell, T.R. (1996). Cognitive strategies in sport and exercise psychology. In J.L. Van Raalte & B.W. Brewer (Eds.), *Exploring sport and exercise psychology* (pp. 51–74). Washington, DC: American Psychological Association.

Williams, P., Narcisco, L., Browne, G., Roberts, J., Weir, R., & Gafni, A. (2005). The prevalence, correlates, and costs of depression in people living with HIV/AIDS in Ontario: Implications for service directions. *AIDS Education and Prevention, 17*(2), 119–130.

Williams, M., & Leichner, P. (2006). More training needed in eating disorders: A time cohort comparison study of Canadian psychiatry residents. *The Journal of Treatment and Prevention, 14*(4), 323–334.

Williams, S.E., & Cumming, J. (2011). Measuring athlete imagery ability: The Sport Imagery Ability Questionnaire. *Journal of Sport & Exercise Psychology, 33,* 416–440.

Williams, S.E., Cumming, J., & Balanos, G.M. (2010, January). The use of imagery to manipulate challenge and threat appraisal States in athletes. *Journal of Sport and Exercise Psychology, 32*(3), 339–358.

Wilson, G.T., Grilo, C.M., & Vitousek, K.M. (2007). Psychological treatment of eating disorders. *American Psychologist, 62*(3), 199–216.

Winkley, K., Landau, S., Eisler, I., & Ismail, K. (2006). Psychological interventions to improve glycaemic control in patients with type 1 diabetes: Systematic review and meta-analysis of randomised controlled trials. *British Medical Journal, 333*(7558), 65.

Wing, R.R. (2002). Behavioral weight control. In T.A. Wadden & A.J. Stunkard (Eds.), *Handbook of obesity treatment* (pp. 301–316). New York: Guilford Press.

Winters, R. (1985). Behavioral approaches to pain. In N. Schneiderman & J.T. Tapp (Eds.), *Behavioral medicine: The biopsychosocial approach* (pp. 24–59). Hillsdale, NJ: Erlbaum.

Wipfli, B.M., Rethorst, C.D., & Landers, D. (2008). The anxiolytic effects of exercise: A meta-analysis of randomized trials and dose-response analysis. *Journal of Sport and Exercise Psychology, 30,* 392–410.

Wisenfeld, H.Z. (2005). Sex differences in pain perception. *Gender Medicine, 2*(3), 137–145.

Witek-Janusek, L, Gabram., S., & Mathews, H.L. (2007). Psychologic stress, reduced NK cell activity, and cytokine dysregulation in women experiencing diagnostic breast biopsy. *Psychoneuroendocrinology, 32,* 22–35.

Witkiewitz, K., & Marlatt, G.A. (2011). Behavioral therapy across the spectrum. *Alcohol Research and Health, 33*(4).

Retrieved July 17, 2013, from http://pubs.niaaa.nih.gov/publications/arh334/313-319.htm

Witte, K., (1992). Putting the fear back into fear appeals: Reconciling the literature. *Communication Monographs, 59,* 329–349.

Wolpe, J. (1958). *Psychotherapy by reciprocal inhibition.* Stanford, CA: Stanford University Press.

Woodhouse, A. (2005). Phantom limb sensation. *Clinical and Experimental Pharmacology and Physiology, 32,* 132–134.

World Health Organization. (1946). Preamble to the Constitution of the World Health Organization as adopted by the International Health Conference, New York, 19–22 June, 1946; signed on 22 July 1946 by the representatives of 61 States (Official Records of the World Health Organization, no. 2, p. 100) and entered into force on 7 April 1948.

World Health Organization. (1986). *Ottawa Charter for Health Promotion.* Ottawa, ON: Canadian Public Health Association.

World Health Organization. (2004). *World Health Organization supports global effort to relieve chronic pain.* Retrieved May 5, 2010, from www.who.int/mediacentre/news/releases/2004/pr70/en/

World Health Organization. (2005). *WHO Framework Convention on Tobacco Control.* Retrieved September 1, 2006, from www.who.int/tobacco/framework/WHO_FCTC_english.pdf

World Health Organization. (2006). *Management of substance abuse: Cannabis.* Retrieved September 1, 2006, from www.who.int/substance_abuse/facts/cannabis/en/

World Health Organization. (2013). *Obesity and overweight. Fact Sheet No. 311.* Retrieved November 18, 2014, from www.who.int/mediacentre/factsheets/fs311/en/

Wressle, E.B., Oberg, B., & Henriksson, C. (1999). The rehabilitation process for the geriatric stroke patient—An exploratory study of goal setting and interventions. *Disability and Rehabilitation, 21*(2), 80–87.

Wright, B., Scott, I., Woloschuk, W., & Brenneis, F. (2004). Career choice of new medical students at three Canadian universities: Family medicine versus specialty medicine. *Canadian Medical Association Journal, 170*(13), 1920–1924.

Wright, K.B., & Bell, S.B. (2003). Health-related support groups on the Internet: Linking empirical findings to social support and computer-mediated communication theory. *Journal of Health Psychology, 8*(1), 39–54.

Wright, L. (1988). The Type A behavior pattern and coronary heart disease. *American Psychologist, 43,* 2–14.

Wroth, T.H., & Pathman, D.E. (2006). Primary medication adherence in a rural population: The role of the patient physician relationship and satisfaction with care. *Journal of the American Board of Family Medicine, 19,* 478–486.

Wu, Z.H., Freeman, J.L., Greer, A.L., Freeman, D.H., & Goodwin, J.S. (2001). The influence of patients' concerns on surgeons' recommendations for early breast cancer. *European Journal of Cancer Care, 10*(2), 100–106.

Wulsin, L.R., & Singal, B.M. (2003). Do depressive symptoms increase the risk for the onset of coronary disease? A systematic quantitative review. *Psychosomatic Medicine, 65,* 201–210.

Wysocki, T. (2006). Behavioral assessment and intervention in pediatric diabetes. *Behavior Modification, 20*(1), 72–92.

X

Xanthopoulos, M.S., & Daniel, L.C. (2013). Coping and social support. In I.B. Weiner (Ed.-in-Chief) & A.M. Nezu, C.M. Nezu, & P.A. Geller (Vol. Eds.), *Handbook of psychology: Vol. 9. Health psychology* (2nd rev. ed., pp. 57–78). New York: Wiley.

Y

Yanovski, S.Z., & Yanovski, J.A. (2014). Long-term drug treatment for obesity: A systematic and clinical review. *Journal of the American Medical Association, 311*(1), 74–86.

Ye, J., Rust, G., Fry-Johnson, Y., & Strothers, H. (2010). E-mail in patient–provider communication: A systematic review. *Patient Education and Counseling, 80*(2), 266–273.

Ylinen, E.-R., Vehviläinen-Julkunen, K., & Pietilä, A.-M. (2009). Effects of patients' anxiety, previous pain experience and non-drug interventions on the pain experience during colonoscopy. *Journal of Clinical Nursing, 18,* 1937–1944.

Yogananda, P. (1969). *Autobiography of a yogi.* Bombay, India: Jaico Publishing House.

Young-Hoon, K.-N. (2012). A longitudinal study on the impact of income change and poverty on smoking cessation. *Canadian Journal of Public Health, 103*(3), 189–194.

Z

Zabora, J., Brintzenhofeszoc, K., Curbow, B., Hooker, C., & Piantadosi, S. (2001). The prevalence of psychological distress by cancer site. *Psycho-Oncology, 10*(1), 19–28.

Zachariae, R., Pedersen, C.G., Jensen, A.B., Ehrnrooth, E., Rossen, P.B., & von der Maase, H. (2003). Association of perceived physician communication style with patient satisfaction, distress, cancer-related self-efficacy, and perceived control over the disease. *British Journal of Cancer, 88,* 658–665.

Zajonc, R.B. (1968). Attitudinal effects of mere exposure. *Journal of Personality and Social Psychology Monograph Supplements, 9,* 1–27.

Zautra, A., Arewasikporn, A., & Davis, M.C. (2010). Resilience: Promoting well-being through recovery, sustainability, and growth. *Research in Human Development, 7*(3), 221–238.

Zhang, Y., Proenca, R., Maffei, M., Barone, M., Leopold, L., & Friedman, J.M. (1994). Positional cloning of the mouse obese gene and its human homologue. *Nature, 372,* 425–432.

Zeitlin, D., Keller, S.E., Shiflett, S.C., Schleifer, S.J., & Bartlett, J.A. (2000). Immunological effects of massage therapy during acute academic stress. *Psychosomatic Medicine, 62,* 83–84.

Zhuk, M., Hart, T.A., & James, C.A. (2006, August). HIV-knowledge, sexual activity and HIV-testing attitudes and behaviour among immigrant and non-immigrant Canadian university students. Poster session presented at the International AIDS conference. Toronto.

Zifferblatt, S.M. (1975). Increasing patient compliance through applied analysis of behavior. *Preventive Medicine, 4,* 173–182.

Zimlichman, E., Kochba, I., Mimouni, F.B., Chochat, T., Grott, I., Kreiss, Y., & Mandel, D. (2005). Smoking habits and obesity in young adults. *Addiction, 100,* 1021–1025.

Zimmerman, S., Gruber-Baldini, A.L., Hebel, J.R., Sloane, P.D., & Magaziner, J. (2002). Nursing home facility risk factors for infection and hospitalization: Importance of registered nurse turnover, administration, and social factors. *Journal of the American Geriatrics Society, 50*(12), 1987–1995.

Ziv, G., & Lidor, R. (2011). Music, exercise performance, and adherence in clinical populations and in the elderly: A review. *Journal of Clinical Sport Psychology, 5,* 1–23.

Zorilla, E.P., Luborsky, L., McKay, J.R., Rosenthal, R., Houldin, A., Tax, A., et al. (2001). The relationship of depression and stressors to immunological assays: A meta-analytic review. *Brain, Behavior, and Immunity, 15,* 199–226.

Zouridakis, E., Avanzas, P., Arroyo-Espliguero, R., Fredericks, S., & Kaski, J.C. (2004). Markers of inflammation and rapid coronary artery disease progression in patients with stable angina pectoris. *Circulation, 10*, 1747–1753.

Zucker, T.P., Flesche, C.W., Germing, U., Schroeter, S., Willers, R., Wolf, H.H., et al. (1998). Patient-controlled versus staff-controlled analgesia with pethidine after allogeneic bone marrow transplantation. *Pain, 75*, 305–312.

Zussman, R. (1993). Life in the hospital: A review. *Milbank Quarterly, 71*, 167–185.

Zywiak, W.H., Stout, R.L., Trefry, W.B., Glasser, I., Connors, G.J., Maisto, S.A., et al. (2006). Alcohol relapse repetition, gender, and predictive validity. Journal of Substance Abuse Treatment, 30(4), 349–353.

Zyzanski, S.J., Stange, K.C., Langa, D., & Flocke, S.A. (1998). Trade-offs in high-volume primary care practice. *Journal of Family Practice, 46*(5), 397–402.

Index

A

Aboriginal Head Start Program, 304
Aboriginal people
  AIDS and, 196
  definition, 291
  diabetes among, 191
  health challenges, 293–294
  smoking behavior, 138
  social determinants of health, 292–293
Aboriginal youth
  health challenges, 291
  smoking behaviours, 138
absolute thinking, 47, 129
absorption, 93, 148, 167, 173
acceleration-deceleration injury, 133
acceptance and commitment therapy (ACT), 47
acceptance-based interventions, 131–132
acceptance stage (of death), 203
accidental deaths, 38
Achieving Health for All: A Framework for Health Promotion,
  304
acquired immune deficiency syndrome (AIDS), 195–199
  effects of negative mood on, 72
  elaboration likelihood model to prevent, 312
  helping people cope with, 197–198
  psychological distress and, 197
acquired immunodeficiency syndrome (AIDS), 13–14, 16, 38
Active Canada 20/20, 114, 123
active leisure, 112
active-passive model, 78
acupuncture, 230
acute illness, 177
acute pain, 213
acute stressor, 56
adaptation, 41, 127, 248
Adderall, 156
addiction, 145, 156
addictive smokers, 140
A-delta fibres, 209
adherence
  to exercise programs, 115
  to physical activity, 124–126
  to physical therapy, 276
adherence to medical advice
  assessment of, 92–93
  behavioural strategies to improve, 97–98
  educational strategies to improve, 97

  factors predicting, 94–96
  frequency and cost of non-adherence, 93–94
  health outcomes and, 99
  improving patient, 96–100
  social and emotional support for pateint, 98–100
adjuvant therapy, 184
adrenal cortex, 32
adrenal gland, 32
adrenaline, 31
adrenal medulla, 30–31
adrenocorticotropic hormone (ACTH), 32
advanced illness, 260
advanced-practice nursing, 271
Adverse Childhood Experiences (ACE), 59
aerobic exercise, 114
afferent, 209
afferent neurons, 209–210
age, 58, 70–71, 80, 291, 296–297, 302
  adherence and, 95, 100
  alcohol use, 148
  being physically active and, 113
  body piercing/tattooing and, 219
  depression and, 121, 194
  diabetes and, 189–190
  discharge planning and, 259
  drinking and driving behaviour, 153
  illicit drug use and, 154–156
  obesity and, 8–9, 159
  pain assessment and, 226
  patient–physician interaction, 90–91
  as predictor of mortality, 65–66
  related health concerns, 306, 308
  relationship between cardiovascular fitness and cognitive
    aging, 120
  reporting of symptoms and willingness to seek care,
    243–244, 247
  smoking and, 136–137, 148
agency-provided support, 309
agents, 167
alarm, 32
alcohol dependency syndrome model, 151
Alcoholics Anonymous (AA), 152
alcohol myopia, 151
alcohol use
  age differences, 148
  binge drinking, 148
  blackouts and hangovers from, 149

alcohol use (*continued*)
  death from, 149
  driving and, 153
  effects of, 148–150
  explaining drinking behaviour, 150–152
  gender differences, 147
  mixing energy drinks, 148
  physician impairment and, 268
  preventing and treating alcohol abuse, 152–153
allostatic load, 33
alopecia, 184
alveoli, 141
Alzheimer's disease, 7, 102, 264
Alzheimer Society of Canada, 101
American Accreditation Health Care Commission, 102
American Psychological Association, 3, 129
anaerobic exercise, 141
analgesics, 180, 227
Anger, 202
angioplasty, 192
anorexia, 5
anorexia nervosa, 169
antibiotics, 3
antibodies (Ab), 55, 62, 68
anticipatory nausea, 184
antidepressants, 228
antiemetic medication, 185
antigens, 54–55
anxiety, 22, 118, 171, 173, 189, 193, 198, 210, 213, 228, 252, 256, 259–262, 272–273
  cancer and, 181–182, 186
  cardiovascular diseases and, 193–194
  distinction between state- and trait-negative affect, 67
  illicit drug use and, 155–156
  patients' inability to remember information and, 90
  physical activity and, 120–122
  provoking situation, 46
  relaxation and, 128
  smoking and, 140, 145
  social, 157
  stress and, 28, 31, 40, 47
  systematic desensitization for managing, 46
  threat and, 34
  trait, 56
  uncertainty about the future and, 197
anxiety disorder, 170
appraisal, 34
appraisal delay, 245
arbitrary standards, 320
arousal
  effect of sexual, 158
  emotional, 117–118

arrhythmia, 156, 168–169
arthritis, 199
assays, 54, 57
Assembly of First Nations Health and Social Secretariat, 293
asthma, 92
asymptomatic, 4
asymptomatic condition, 4
athletic performance, 117
Ativan, 156
attachment–caregiving response in females, 29
attitude, 311
attributions, 118, 276
autoimmune disease, 62
autonomic activity, 220
autonomic nervous system, 30, 32
aversion therapies, 147

B

Baby Think It Over®, 17
Bagozzi's goal theory, 20
bargaining, 202
B cells, 53
befriending, 29
behavioral proclivities, 60
behavioural contracting, 147
behavioural control of stressful events, 41
behavioural delay, 245
behavioural enaction models, 19
behavioural medicine, 2
behaviourism, 3–5
behaviour therapy, 46–47, 173
beliefs as person variables, 36
benefit finding, 188
benign breast biopsy, 262
benign-positive appraisal, 34
Bensonian relaxation, 232
benzodiazepine, 156
bereavement, 204
binge eating disorder (BED), 170
biofeedback, 43, 45, 232
Biological Embedding of Childhood Adversity Model, 60
biologic stress syndrome, 29
biomedical model, 11
biopsy, 262
biopsychosocial approach to health, 10–12, 280–282
  implications of, 11–12
  significance of, 10–11
  term biopsychosocial, meaning, 10
biopsychosocial communication, 79–80
bladder, 144
blood cells, 53

blunters, 6, 187, 250–251
body dysmorphic disorder, 171–172
body-mass index (BMI), 160
  Nomogram, 160
body systems
  adrenal cortex, 32
  adrenal medulla, 31
  endocrine system, 30, 32
  glucocorticoids and mineralocorticoids, 32
  homeostasis, 28
  hypothalamic-pituitaryadrenal (HPA) axis, 30–31
  hypothalamus, 31
  limbic system of the brain, 31
  pancreas, 32
  parasympathetic component of autonomic system, 32
  reticular formation, 31
  sympathetic adrenomedullary (SAM) system, 30
  sympathetic nervous system, 31
  thyroid gland, 32
Boehm, Peterson, Kivimaki, and Kubzansky (2011), 42
boredom, 169
box scale, 222
brain, 31
brain imaging studies, 233
brain stem, 31, 209
breast cancer, 16, 64–65, 82, 124, 150, 180, 182, 184,
    186–187, 237, 245–247, 263, 314
breastfeeding, 13, 22
bronchial asthma, 33
bronchial pneumonia, 7
Brousse, Therese, 43
built environment, 298–300
bulimia nervosa, 168–170
burnout, 265

C

cachexia, 5
cachexia (malnourishment), 5
Calgary-Cambridge observation guide, 97
Canada
  aging population in, 120
  alcohol-consumption, 147–148
  cases of GBS, 297–298
  colorectal cancer prevalence, 183
  diabetes prevalence, 189
  drinking and driving, 153
  Drug Strategy, 175
  general and family practitioners in, 266
  health promotion in, 304–310
  health status, 286
  HIV/AIDS in, 196
  hospitalized patients, 247

literacy rate, 316
multidisciplinary treatment for pain, 238
organ transplants, 248
percentage suffering from chronic pain, 214
SARS in, 282–283
shortage of nurses in, 271
social determinants of health, 283–284
study of vulnerability in, 285
unsafe sexual behaviours, 157
use of illicit drugs, 154–155
violence and accidents due to alcohol consumption, 149
Canadian Cancer Society, 179
Canadian Community Health Survey, 307
Canadian Fitness and Lifestyle Research Institute, 113
Canadian Health Network, 102
Canadian Human Mortality Data Base, 307
Canadian Institute for Health Information (CIHI), 9,
    101, 305
Canadian Medical Association Journal, 264
Canadian Nurses Association (CNA), 271
Canadian Psychological Association (CPA), 3
Canadian Tobacco Use Monitoring Survey, 137–138
Canadian Youth, Sexual Health and HIV/AIDS
    Study, 157
cancer, 38
  adolescents with, 179
  anticipatory nausea in, 184
  antiemetic medication for, 185
  colorectal, 183
  coping with, 181–182, 186–189
  depression and, 69–72, 181
  disfigurement in, 182
  family-oriented care for, 186
  growth of cells, 178
  illness burden for, 179
  impact of physical activity, 123–124
  metastasized, 178
  pain, 214, 219, 227, 230
  perception of symptoms, 243
  physical activity and, 122
  physical problems with, 179–180
  prostate, 182
  psychological reactions to a diagnosis of, 178, 180–182
  psychotropic medication and psychotherapy, 188–189
  radical surgery, 182
  reactions to a diagnosis of, 68–69
  screening for, 16, 18, 95, 262
  self-examinations, 313–314
  sites of, 178
  smoking and risk of, 143–144
  statistics in Canada, 178–179
  stress and, 63

cancer (*continued*)
  support networks for cancer-related treatments, 188
  surgery and radiation therapy, 183–184
  treatment, 182–185
cancerous cells, nature of, 74
cannabis, 155
Cannon, Walter, 28–29
cardiac arrest, 193
cardiac invalidism, 193
cardiopulmonary disease, 66
cardiovascular diseases, 38, 192–195, 319
  depression and, 195
  diabetes and, 190
  due to depression, 66, 72
  exposure to stress and, 30, 33
  helping people cope with, 194–195
  illicit drug use and, 38, 156
  inflammation and, 60
  neurological and hormonal changes, 33
  obesity and, 161, 168
  in people with PTSD, 59
  physical activity and, 122
  prevention and rehabilitation of, 123
  psychological distress and, 193–194
  as a result of ETS, 144
  risk factors for, 41, 59–60
  smoking and, 143
cardiovascular health
  low-fat diet and, 13
  relationship between behaviour and, 5
  relationship between positive emotions and, 42
caring, 270
catastrophization, 129
catecholamines, 31
CD4, 73
CD3+ cell, 70
CD8+ cell, 70
CD4 cells, 197
Centers for Disease Control, 295
central control trigger, 210
centrally acting analgesics, 227
central nervous system, 30
central route, 311
Centre for Health Evidence, 101
Centre for Rural and Northern Health
    Research, 293
cerebral cortex, 209
cerebrovascular disease, 7, 143
cervical cancer, 14, 18, 250, 262, 308, 315
C-fibres, 209
challenge appraisal, 34–35
challenge–skills (CS) balance, 117

Chaoulli vs. the Attorney General of Quebec, 306
chemotherapy, 180, 182, 184
Child Facial Coding System (CFCS), 225
childhood obesity, 8–9, 159, 165–166
children
  adherence to monitoring regimens, 95, 98, 190
  anxieties about hospitalization and medical procedures, 46
  assessment of pain, 225–226
  delay behaviour, 247
  diabetic, 190–191, 292
  eating behaviours, 164
  with eating disorders, 169
  illegal drug use and, 156–157
  pain in, 214
  pain management, 233–234
  physical activity, 113–114
  risk for ill health, 60
  smoking behavior, 139, 144
Children's Comprehensive Pain Questionnaire, 226
chronic bronchitis, 21, 144
chronic conditions, 177, 199
chronic illness
  arthritis, 199
  cancer, 178–189
  cardiovascular diseases, 192–195
  death and dying, 202–204
  diabetes, 189–192
  HIV and AIDS, 195–199
  Parkinson's disease, 199
  permanent physical disabilities, 199
  quality of life in context of, 199–202
  range of symptom-related experience, 177
chronic intractable benign pain, 214
chronic obstructive pulmonary disease
    (COPD), 175
Chronic Pain Coping Inventory, 225
chronic pain syndromes, 59
chronic progressive pain, 214
chronic recurrent pain, 214
chronic stressors, 56
circulatory disease, 7–8
clinical psychologists, 22–23
clinical significance, 56–57
closed head injury, 132–133
cocaine (stimulant drug), 156
cognition, 5–6
cognitive-affective stress management training, 127
cognitive appraisals, 34
cognitive behavioural stress management, 47, 64
cognitive behavioural therapy (CBT), 173–174, 192
cognitive control of stressful events, 41
cognitive interventions, 276

cognitive reappraisal, 194
cognitive reappraisal and restructuring, 194
cognitive restructuring, 5, 46–47
cognitive transactional models of stress, 34–37
colds, 11, 53, 60, 67
cold sores, 55
collective empiricism, 47
collectivist culture, 21
colonoscopy, 261–262
colorectal cancer, 95, 179, 183, 261
combative coping, 39
commitments, 36
communication
    biopsychosocial, 79–80
    consumerist, 80
    differences between helpful and unhelpful, 186
    effective, 77
    help-intended, 186
    in medical settings, 5
    physician-patient interaction, 78–91
Community Action Program for Children, 304
community capacity, 319
compassion fatigue, 265, 272
competent immune systems, 74
compliance, 6, 92, 124
compliance rates, 4
concanavalin A (Con A), 54
Concerta, 156
concussion, 133
condom usage, 13–14, 16
    beliefs related to, 14
confidence, 13–14, 34, 69, 95–96, 116–17,
    128–129
conflict, 28
confronting, 35
connectivity, 299
Conner, Mark, 12
conscientiousness, 38
conscientiousness-related traits, 38
consumerist communication, 80
contingency contracting, 98
control groups, 115
Coombs, Robert, 263
cooperation, 158, 192
coping
    behaviour therapy and cognitive therapy, 46–48
    combative, 39
    emotion-focused, 39–40
    issues in defining, 26–30
    personal resources for, 40
    proactive, 39
    problem- and emotion-focused, 181–182

problem-focused, 39
relaxation responses, 48–50
relaxation techniques, 42
role of personality in, 37–39
self-help manuals for, 48
social support and, 40
coping goal, 39
coping outcomes, 39
coping response, 39–40
coping styles, 6, 25, 50, 57
co-production process, 321
coronary artery bypass graft (CABG), 192
coronary heart disease (CHD), 37–38, 123, 149
    anger and, 194
    personality traits and, 37
    prevention and rehabilitation of, 123
    psychological distress and, 193–194
    rehabilitation programs for, 194
cortisol, 31–32, 58, 61, 63, 73
cost-gain belief, 13
counselling psychologists, 22–23
Cox, Harvey, 43
crack, 154
C-reactive protein, 74
creative non-adherence, 92
culture
    collectivist, 21
    culturally appropriate care, 290–291
    definition, 288–289
    health and, 287–291
    individualist, 21
    pain and, 219–220
    vulnerabilities and, 289
    Western, 43, 45, 244
curing, 270
cytokines, 73–74

D

Dalhousie Everyday Pain Scale, 224, 226
day care patients, 247–248
death and dying
    bereavement and grief, 204
    patients' reactions to, 202–203
DeBakey, Michael, 87
deception, 88
defensive reappraisal, 35
dehumanization, 252
delayed gratification, 4
delaying medical care, 245–247. *See also* seeking medical care
delta alcoholism, 151
dementia, 227, 282
Demerol, 156

denial, 202
density, 300
dependent variables, 53
depersonalization, 252
depression, 199
    cancer and, 69–72, 181
    cardiovascular disease and, 66, 72
    cardiovascular diseases and, 195
    as a common reaction to dying, 203
    diabetes and, 191
    effect on health, 65
    heart health and, 72
    HIV infection and, 72–73
    immune function and, 64–73
    NK cell counts, effect on, 66
    pain and, 216
    upper respiratory infection and, 66–69
desensitization, 46
Dexedrine, 156
diabetes, 189–192
    among Canada's Aboriginal population, 191
    cardiovascular disease and, 190–191
    depression and, 191
    fear and, 190–191
    gestational, 189
    helping people cope with, 192
    hypoglycemia, 190
    type I, 189–190
    type II, 189
Dialogue on Drinking, 304
diarrhea, 184, 197
diathesis-stress model, 34
digestion, 31
digestive tract, 168
DiMatteo, Robin, 11–12, 93
discharge planning from ICU, 259–260
    challenges, 259
    elderly patients, 259–260
disease model (of problem drinking), 150
diseases of adaptation, 33
disempowering care, 249
disfigurement, 182, 246
distraction, 233–234
divorce, 59, 136, 140
do-not-resuscitate order, 261
Do Not Resuscitate order (DNR), 261
dopamine, 140, 155
dose-response effect, 64
drinking and driving, 153
drive-reduction theory, 312
drug abuse, 156–157
DrugsNot4Me program, 156

duration, 36, 109, 200–201
dying, stages of, 202

E

Eastern philosophies, 43
eating disorders, 5
    anorexia nervosa, 169
    antidepressant for, 173
    binge eating disorder (BED), 170
    biological, cultural, and psychological factors, 170–171
    bulimia nervosa, 168–169
    cognitive behavioural therapy (CBT), 173–174
    deep brain stimulation therapy for, 174
    psychological treatments, 174
    selective serotonin reuptake inhibitors (SSRIs) for, 173
    treatment for, 171–174
Eat Well Central, 101
ecstasy, 110, 154–155
education level, 238, 271–272
    alcohol-consumption and, 148, 152
    diabetes and, 187, 192
    drug dependence and, 154
    educational strategies to improve adherence, 97, 100
    health challenges and, 292, 295–296, 303–306
    obesity and, 164, 166
    patient–physician interaction, 82, 90–91
    physical activity and, 125
    smoking behavior and, 137–138
effectiveness, 54
efficacy beliefs, 276, 314
effleurage, 231
ego orientation, 131
elaboration likelihood model of persuasion, 311–312
electric shock, 147
electrocardiogram (EKG), 44
electroencephalograph (EEG), 44, 220
electromyography (EMG), 45, 220
Ellis, Albert, 46–47, 129
embarrassment, 13, 88, 170, 246, 262
emergency department, 253–254
emotional-approach coping, 181
emotional arousal, 117–118
emotional distress, 28
emotional support, 40, 82, 98, 309
emotion-focused coping, 39–40, 50, 181
empathy, 187
emphysema, 143–144
empowering care, 249
endocrine system, 30–32
endogenous opioids, 21
Engel, George, 70
enumerative assay, 53

environmental factors
  interpretation of symptoms, 244–245
  perception of symptoms, 242–244
  stress, 30
environmental tobacco smoke (ETS), 144
Epictetus, 30
epilepsy, 289
epinephrine, 31
Epp, Jake, 304
Epstein–Barr virus, 55, 71
ethanol, 148
ethics, 320
ethyl alcohol, 148
eustress, 28
euthanasia, 261
event uncertainty, 36
evoked potentials, 220
exam-related effects on immune system, 52
exam stress, 53
exercise. *See also* physical activity
  adherence, 124–126
  definition, 108
  psychology, 108
exhaustion, 33
expanded biomedical communication, 79
expanded biomedical communication pattern, 79
experiential standards, 320
expertise model, 258
extended parallel process model, 312
external imagery, 130
external reinforcement, 276
extrinsic goals, 131

F

Faces Pain Scale Revised, 226
faecal occult blood test (FOBT), 261
false-positive results, 262
fear appeals, 312–314
fears, 3, 20, 31, 34, 46, 223, 283, 308–309
  about death, 261–262
  cancer and, 179–180, 186, 188, 246
  cardiovascular disease and, 193
  diagnosis of diabetes and, 177, 190–191
  of failing, 129
  feared event or situation, 46
  in hallucinogen users, 155
  of losing decision-making capacity, 203
  in negative-affect smokers, 140
  pain behaviours and, 215
  of sports or exercise injury, 133
  strategies to reduce, 46
  of weight gain, 169

feasibility standards, 320–321
feminization of medicine, 268–270
fentanyl, 156
fetal alcohol spectrum disorder (FASD), 149
field research, 56
fight-or-flight response, 28–31, 42
First Nations and Inuit Health Branch (FNIHB), 293
First Nations Health Authority (FNHA), 293–294
flexibility, 109
Framework Convention on Tobacco Control (FCTC), 143
Framingham Heart Study, 123
Frasure-Smith, Nancy, 15
Friedman, Meyer, 37
frustration, 28
Functional Assessment of Cancer Therapy (FACT) scales, 201–202
functional tests of immunity, 54

G

gamma alcoholism, 151
gastric banding, 168
gastric bypass, 168
gastrointestinal illnesses, 59
gate control theory, 210–211
gender differences
  alcohol use, 147
  in medical practice, 268–270
  pain and, 216–219
  physical activity, 113
  smoking, 136–137
general adaptation syndrome (GAS), 29, 32–34
generalized anxiety disorder, 61–62
germ theory, 3
gestational diabetes, 189
glucagon, 32
glucocorticoids, 32
goal setting, 130–131
Gollwitzer's implementation intentions model, 20
Google, 100
gradient of reinforcement, 4
grief, 204
Guerrouj, Hicham El, 117
guidance-cooperation model, 78
guided imagery, 233
Guillain–Barré Syndrome (GBS), 258, 297–298
Gulf War, 59

H

habits, 94
habitual smokers, 140
hair loss, 184
hallucinogens, 154–156

Hanson, Peter, 28
  The Joy of Stress, 28
happiness, 34, 41–42, 53, 110–111
harm/loss appraisal, 34
harm reduction strategies, 294–296
headache pain, 232
headaches, 45, 85, 133, 208, 214, 216, 220, 232–233, 237
head injury, 132–133
health action process approach (HAPA), 20
health advertising, 311
health belief model, 13–16, 318
  condom usage, beliefs related to, 14
  decision to have surgery, 16
  health values and, 14–15
  predicting health-related behaviour, 15–16
Health Canada, 9
health care providers
  nurses, 270–273
  physicians, 264–270
  physiotherapists, 274–276
health-compromising behaviours
  alcohol use, 147–153
  illicit drug use, 153–157
  smoking, 136–147
  unsafe sexual behaviour, 157–158
health–illness continuum, 112
health information on the Internet, 100–102
  assessment of quality of, 102–103
  health initiatives and health promotion, 101–102
  health surveys, 102
  implications for patient–physician relationships,
    103–104
  medical articles and reports, 100–101
  services, 101
  support services, 102
Health Locus of Control Scale, 248
Health on the Net Foundation (HON), 101–103
health promotion
  assessing the efectiveness of, 319–320
  audience's knowledge level and, 316
  Canada as a worldwide leader in, 304–310
  definition of, 303
  elaboration likelihood model of persuasion, 311–312
  fear appeals, 312–314
  loss-framed and gain-framed health promotion
    messages, 315
  mechanisms, 307–310
  political campaigns, 311
  precede-proceed model, 317–319
  social psychology of, 311–317
  social support for, 308–310
  standards, 320

strategies, 303
  using psychological principles, 310–311
health psychology
  biopsychosocial approach to health, 10–12
  career in, 22–23
  changes in health and illness patterns, 7–10
  clinical psychologists and counselling psychologists,
    role in, 22–23
  cognition and personality factors, 5–6
  coping styles, 6
  definition, 2–3
  early stages of, 3–5
  links between psychological and biological processes, 6–7
  Matarazzo's definition of, 3
  motivational models of health behaviour, 12–13
  psychoneuroimmunology (PNI), importance of, 6–7,
    52–53
  relationship between psychology and health, 2–3
  research careers in, 23
health-related vulnerability, 285
health status of populations, tracking of, 282–283
healthy adherer effect, 99
Healthy Heart program, 14
healthy immigrant effect, 287
heart disease, depression and risk of, 72
help-intended communication, 186
hemorrhagic stroke, 150
hepatitis B vaccination, 68
herpesvirus, 54
hierarchy, 46, 273
high-density lipoprotein (HDL), 149
high-fat diet, effect of, 4
highly active antiretroviral treatment (HAART), 198
historical standards, 320
HIV infection, 157
  effects of negative mood on, 72
  helping people cope with, 197–198
  psychological distress and, 197
  T-helper-cell activity in, 72
  therapies, 198
Hollender, Marc, 78–79
homeostasis, 28
hopelessness, 69
hormone therapy, 182
hospital palliative care, 260
hospitals, 247–261
  behaviours in, 249
  day care patients, 247–248
  decision-making process, 249
  depersonalization or dehumanization environments, 252
  discharge planning, 259–260
  emergency department, 253–254

intensive care unit (ICU), 255–259
mixed management model of care, 261
outpatients, 247
palliative care, 260–261
patient-centred care, 253
postoperative recovery, 254–255
preparation for surgery, 251–252
providing information to patients, 250–251
women's experiences in, 248–249
Human Early Learning Partnership (HELP), 59
human immunodeficiency virus (HIV). *See* HIV infection
Hutchings, Deanna, 260
hypermetabolic fight-or-flight response, 42
hypnosis, 236–238
hypochondriasis, 58
hypoglycemia, 190
hypometabolic response, 42
hypothalamic-pituitary-adrenal (HPA) axis, 30–31, 65, 73
hypothalamus, 31

I

illicit drug use, 153–155
cannabis or marijuana, 155
cocaine (stimulant drug), 156
hallucinogens, 155–156
harm reduction strategies for illicit drug injections, 295–296
LSD (lysergic acid diethylamide), 155
MDMA (3,4-methylenedioxymethylamphetamine), 155
PCP (phencyclidine), 155
prescription drug misuse, 156
prescription opioids, 156
preventing and treating, 156–157
psilocybin, 155
tranquilizers and sedatives, 156
illness delay, 245–246
imagery, role in sport and exercise, 129–130
immigrants, health status of, 287–288
imminence, 36
immune-cell activity, 54–55
immune functioning
depression and, 64–66
divorced women, 59
inflammatory response, 60
major negative life events and, 64
measuring, using vaccinations, 61
stress effect on, 58–59
veterans of Gulf War, 59
immune system, biological mechanism psychological states affect in, 73–74
immune-system cells, 53
immune-system function, measurement of, 55–57

immunocompetence, 6–7, 52–55, 71
counting cells to measure, 53–54
functional tests of, 54–55
immunosuppression, 55, 58, 62–63
Impact of Events Scale, 62
impression management approach, 164
incidence rate, 179
incommunication stage, 255
index case, 283
individual differences
emotional reaction to an event, 35
in health values, 15
individualist culture, 21
infant mortality rate, 292, 306–307
infertility, 157
inflammation, 55, 60, 65, 72, 74
influenza, 7, 67, 298
informational support, 40, 309
information-motivation-behavioural skills model, 158
information-seeking behaviours, 89
injuries, 132–134
insulin, 32
insulin-dependent diabetes (Type 1), 62, 189
intensive care units (ICUs), 11–12, 255–259
communication, importance of, 256–257
discharge planning, 259–260
growth, 255
incommunication stage in, 255
memories of experiences, 256
modern, 256
patient's psychological reaction to, 256
pediatric, 258
psychological impact in, 257
readaptation stage in, 255
reflection stage in, 255
intentions, 13, 16, 18–20
interactions, 80, 82–83
interleukin-6 (IL-6), 66
internal imagery, 130
internality–externality hypothesis, 164
internet, 100–104
intravenous drug users (IDU), 198
intrinsic goals, 131
intrusive memories, 181
invasiveness, 262
in vitro tests, 54
in vivo tests, 54
irrational thinking, 46
irrelevant appraisal, 34
ischemic stroke, 149
isokinetic exercise, 114

isometric exercise, 114
isotonic exercise, 114
ITC project, 144

J

Jackson and Csikszentmihalyi (1999), 117
Jacobson, Edmund, 45
jargon, 86–88
job strain model, 273
Journal of Applied Sport Psychology, 127
Journal of Clinical Sport Psychology, 133
Journal of Sport and Exercise Psychology, The, 108
Journal of the American Medical Association, 264–265

K

kidneys, 11, 31, 230
Kiecolt-Glaser, Janice, 7
kinesthetic imagery, 130
Kübler-Ross, Elisabeth, 176

L

Lalonde, Marc, 304
land-use mix, 299–300
Landy, John, 117
leptin, 162
Ley, Philip, 5–6
life expectancy, 4, 143, 149, 292, 306
Life Experience Survey, 62
life skills, 126
life-threatening illnesses, 3, 6, 12. *See also* chronic illness
lifetime prevalence, 283
limbic system, 31
local anaesthetics, 228
lock-out interval, 254
locus of responsibility, 305, 307, 321
loneliness, 56, 64, 133, 140
longitudinal research, 41, 63, 122
love, 26, 34
LSD (lysergic acid diethylamide), 154–155
lung cancer, 10, 21, 143–144
lymphocytes, 54, 63

M

magnetic resonance imaging (MRI), 46
main effects, 62
malignant neoplasms, 9
malnourishment, 5
malpractice claims, 83–85
mammography, 262–263
marital conflict, 7
massage therapy, 52, 231–232
mastectomy, 178, 183

matching effect, 164
McCreary Centre Society, 102
McGill Pain Questionnaire (MPQ), 223–225
MDMA (3,4-methylenedioxymethamphetamine), 155
medical delay, 245
medical jargon, 86–88
medical level of health promotion, 305
medical procedures, psychological impact of
    colonoscopy, 261–262
    mammography, 262–263
medical school, 11, 87, 264
meditation, 45, 232–233
meditative relaxation, 232
medulla, 30–31
Mega Country Network, 303
mental rehearsal, 130
message framing, 314
metastasized cancer, 178
methamphetamine, 155
micro-inequities, 270
Miller, Greg, 61, 64
Miller, Neal, 3–4, 8
Miller, Suzanne, 6, 250
mindfulness, 131–132
mindfulness-acceptance-commitment (MAC), 47
mindfulness meditation, 233
mindless eating, 170
mineralocorticoids, 32
Minnesota Multiphasic Personality Inventory (MMPI), 70
mitogen, 54
mixed management model of care, 261
modelling, 46
    effect, 139–140, 152, 164
monitors, 6, 187, 250–251
mononucleosis, 55
mood states, 120
    negative, 71, 190, 224
morbidity, 37, 138, 149, 194, 320
mortality, 171, 273, 320
    adherence to drug therapy and, 99
    alcohol consumption and, 149
    behavioural contributors to, 38
    BMI and, 161
    cancer and, 10, 261, 308
    for cardiac patients, 194
    depression and, 65–66, 69, 180, 193
    diabetes and, 189
    heart disease and, 72
    infant, 292, 306–307
    myocardial infarction and, 123
    pessimism and, 70
    prevalence of smoking and, 138, 144

risk for premature, 36
role of physical fitness, 122
social integration and, 308
statistics, twentieth century, 7, 12
Mothers Against Drunk Driving (MADD), 303
motivational models of health behaviour, 12–13
motor vehicle accidents, 303, 316
multidisciplinary pain management programs, 238–239
multilevel explanations, 87–88
multiple sclerosis, 62
multi-stage models, 20–21
muscle dysmorphia, 172–173
mutual aid, 308–309
mutual-participation model, 78–79
myocardial infarction (MI), 66, 123, 143, 149, 156, 192, 194–195, 243, 247
myocardial ischemia, 193

N

narcotics, 227
narrowly biomedical communication patterns, 79
National Population Health Survey, 287, 307
natural killer (NK) cells, 53, 74
    cytotoxic activity assay, 54
    depression and, 64, 66
    lysis, 54
natural-killer (NK) cells, 54
naturally occurring support, 309
nature *vs* nurture debate, 33
nausea, 133, 139, 149, 155–156, 184–185
navigator, 187
negative-affect smokers, 140
negative mood, 64
negative states, 67
negotiated model, 258
neighbourhood, health-related dimensions of a, 299–300
neighbourhood's walkability score, 300
Neonatal Facial Coding System (NFCS), 225
neonatal intensive care unit, 225, 257–258
neonates, 259
nervous system, 30
neuromatrix theory, 211
neurosignature patterns, 211
neurotransmitters, 155, 228
new depression, 72
New Perspective on the Health of Canadians, A, 304
nicotine gum, 146
nicotine inhalers and nicotine nasal sprays, 147
nicotine patch, 146
nicotine-replacement therapy, 146–147
NK cell cytotoxic activity assay, 54
NK cell lysis, 54

nociceptors, 209
"no-claims" primary-care physicians, 84–85
non-adherence, 124
non-compliance, 4
non-discrepant responses, 87
non-insulin-dependent diabetes (Type II), 189
non-narcotic analgesics, 227
noradrenaline, 30–31
norepinephrine, 31
normative standards, 320
novelty, 36
numeric rating scale (NRS), 226
Nunavut Arctic College, 293
nurse practitioners, 278
nurses, 270–273
    advanced training and re-definition of roles in modern nursing, 271
    nature of, 270–272
    stress in nursing, 272–273

O

obesity, 5
    age differences, 159
    among children, 8–9, 159, 166
    behavioural treatments for, 167–168
    biological factors contributing to, 162
    biological system controling food intake, 162
    Body Mass Index (BMI) Nomogram, 160
    in Canada, 159
    definition, 160
    economic burden of, 161
    environmental and hunger cues, 164
    ghrelin and, 162
    health risk classification according to body mass index (BMI), 160
    heridity aspect of, 162
    hormones contributing to body weight regulation, 163
    pharmacological treatment of, 166–167
    prevalence of, 158–159
    prevention and treatment of, 164–168
    psychosocial factors contributing to, 163
    sociocultural factors contributing to, 163–164
occupational therapists, 238, 274
omega-3s (long-chain fatty acids), 74
oncology, 178, 266, 273
operant pain, 215
Organisation for Economic Co-operation and Development (OECD) countries, health status of, 9
organ transplants, 248
orienting statements, 84
Oucher scale, 226
outcome goals, 131

outpatients, 247
overgeneralization, 47, 129
Oxycodone, 156
OxyNEO, 156

P

pain
　acute *vs* chronic, 213–216
　behavioural assessment of, 220–221
　behaviours, 215, 220–221
　brain's role in perception, 211
　cancer, 214, 219, 227, 230
　chronic intractable benign, 214
　chronic progressive, 214
　chronic recurrent, 214
　common complaints in chronic, 215
　culture and, 219–220
　depression and, 216
　endogenous opioids for managing, 211–213
　gender and, 216–219
　in infants and children, assessing, 225–226
　inhibition of, 211–213
　interviews about, 221
　measurement of, 220–227
　neurochemical basis of, 211–213
　in older adults, assessing, 226–227
　operant, 215
　perception of, 209
　phantom limb, 211–212
　psychosocial factors and, 216–220
　rating scales for management of,
　　221–222
　relieving chemicals, 213
　respondent, 215
　self-reports of, 221–225
　significance of, 208–209
　theories of, 210–211
Pain Assessment Checklist for Seniors with Limited Ability
　　to Communicate (PACSLAC), 226–227
pain behaviours, 220
Pain Catastrophizing Scale, 218
pain control techniques
　acupuncture, 230
　anaesthetics, 228
　antidepressants, 228
　centrally acting analgesics, 227
　distraction, 233–236
　guided imagery, 233
　hypnosis, 236–238
　massage, 231–232
　meditation, 232–233
　mindfulness meditation, 233

multidisciplinary pain management programs,
　　238–239
　narcotics, 227
　peripherally acting analgesics, 227
　pharmacological, 227–228
　physical therapy, 230–231
　progressive muscle relaxation, 232
　relaxation, 232–233
　sedatives and tranquillizers, 228
　Shiatsu massage, 231
　surgical treatment, 228
　Swedish massage, 231
　transcutaneous electrical nerve stimulation (TENS),
　　229–230
　virtual snowmen, 234–235
pain questionnaires, 223–225
pain threshold, 217
pain tolerance level, 217
palliative care, 260–261
　common choices for, 260
　compassionate communication and, 260
　hospital, 260
　mixed management model of care, 261
　practitioners and, 261
　staff experiences, 260–261
pancreas, 32
Pap smear test, 18, 308
parasympathetic component of autonomic system, 32
Parents of Multiple Births Association, 101
Parkinson's disease, 82, 199
ParticipAction, 304
participant modelling, 46
passive leisure, 112
passive smoking, 144
patient-centred care, 81, 253
patient-controlled analgesia (PCA), 254
patient delay, 245–247
patient–physician social concordance, 90–91
patient satisfaction with medical care, 83–85
PCP (phencyclidine), 154–155
peaceful talk, 262
peptic ulcers, 33
perceived behavioural control, 19
Percodan, 156
performance accomplishments, 117–118
performance goals, 131
periaqueductal grey area, 211
peripherally acting analgesics, 227
peripheral nervous system, 30, 50, 209, 227
peripheral route, 311–312
personal control, 40–41
personal factors, 273

personality, 37
  coronary heart disease (CHD) and, 37
  health psychology and, 5–6
  health-related behaviours and, 38–39
  roel in stress, 37–39
  role in coping, 37–39
  traits, 37, 141, 171, 243
  Type A, 4–5, 37, 46
  Type B, 37
person variables, 36
persuasion, 311
pessimism, 69–71
phantom limb pain, 211–212
physical activity
  adherence to, 124–126
  age differences, 113
  children's, 113–114
  cognitive functioning and, 119–120
  five components of health and, 112–114
  forms of, 114–115
  gender differences, 113
  injury and, 132–134
  leisure-time, 121
  mood and, 120–122
  nature of, 108–109
  parameters of, 110
  Peter's story, case example, 109–112
  physical benefits of, 122–124
  population-based approach to, 114
  positive health impact of, 113
  in protecting against cancer and stroke, 123–124
  psychological benefits of, 115–122
  psychological factors affecting performance in exercise
    and sport, 126–132
  role of imagery in, 129–130
  self-concept and, 116–119
  walking as a form of, 125
physical disabilities, 199
physical fitness, 109, 116
physical therapy, 230–231
  adherence, 276
  behavioural interventions in, 276
  goal setting, 274–276
physician impairment, 268
physician-patient interaction, 77–91
  active-passive model, 78
  age and education level, effect of, 91
  biomedical–psychosocial continuum, 88
  biopsychosocial communication, 79
  collaborative model, 82
  consumerist communication, 80
  expanded biomedical communication, 79
  guidance-cooperation model, 78
  health information on the Internet and, 103–104
  information giving, 82
  lack of information-seeking behaviours and, 89
  malpractice lawsuits, 83–85
  mutual-participation model, 78–79
  narrowly biomedical communication patterns, 79
  patient behaviours contributing to faulty
    communication, 88
  patient deception, 88–89
  patient participation, 82–83
  patient satisfaction, 83–85
  patients' inability to remember information and,
    89–90
  physician attributes, 81
  physician behaviours contributing to faulty
    communication, 85–86
  physician's use of medical jargon, 86–88
  psychosocial communication pattern, 80
  race-concordant doctor–patient interviews, 91
  time factor, 88
  via e-mail, 90
physicians
  emotional involvement in their work, 264–265
  experiencing burnout, 265
  impairment, 268
  stress or emotional exhaustion, 265–268
physiotherapists, 274–276
phytohemagglutinin (PHA), 54
pituitary gland, 32
pneumonia, 7, 143
pokeweed mitogen (PWM), 54
positive-affect smokers, 140
positive correlation, 59
positive emotions, 41–42
positive psychology, 41
Posluszny, Donna, 7
post-concussion syndrome, 133
post-traumatic growth, 188
post-traumatic stress disorder (PTSD), 58–59, 188,
    257, 272
powerful, 18–19, 79
powerful others, 248
practical support, 309
precede-proceed model, 317–319
predictability, 36
pregnancy, 16–17, 21, 74, 102, 144–145, 158, 161, 197
Present Pain Intensity (PPI) score, 223
prevalence, 138, 169, 174
preventability, 8
primary appraisal, 34–35
primary care, 79–80, 84

primary care physicians, 84
proactive coping, 39
problem-focused coping strategies, 39
process goals, 131
Profile of Mood States (POMS), 67
prognosis, 69, 72, 82
progressive illness, 260
progressive muscular relaxation (PMR), 45, 128, 232
proinflammatory, 65
proliferation, 54
propriety standards, 320–321
prospect theory, 314
prostate cancer, 68, 123, 178
protease inhibitor drug combinations, 198
proximity, 299
psilocybin, 155
psychoeducation, 47, 251, 254
psychological empowerment, 273
psychological methods, 127
psychological skills, 126–127
psychological states, 6–7, 46, 52–53, 66, 195
    disease progression and, 180
    influence on immune system, 73–74
psychoneuroimmunological research, 53–57
    dependent and independent variable, 53
    URTI experiences, 61–62
psychoneuroimmunology (PNI), 6–7
    importance of, 52–53
    overview of research, 57–73
    short-term vs long-term effects, 56, 74
    statistical significance vs clinical significance,
        56–57
psychosocial communication pattern, 80
psychosocial stressors, 31
psychotherapy, 188–189, 199
Public Health Agency of Canada, 280
public health level of health promotion, 305
pychoeducational model for sport psychology, 126

Q
quality of life, 3, 69, 168, 174
quality of life in context of chronic illness, 199–202
    multidimensional or global assessment, 202
    as a subjective phenomenon, 201–202
    tradeoff between duration and, 200–201
quarantine, 67
questionnaires, 195, 201–202
quintiles, 307
quit-smoking programs, 21
quitting smoking, 144–147
    aversion therapies, 147
    behavioural contracting, 147

nicotine-replacement therapy, 146–147
on one's own, 145–146
reasons for, 145
self-management strategies, 147
stimulus control strategies, 147

R
race-concordant doctor–patient interviews, 91
radiation therapy, 183
radical surgery, 182
rapid smoking, 147
rational emotive behaviour therapy (REBT), 46–47, 129
Raynaud's disease, 45
reactance, 249
readaptation stage, 255
reality shock, 272
reappraisal, 34–35
reflection stage, 255
rehabilitation programs, 194
relaxation, 127–128
    for pain control, 232–233
    phase, 48
    progressive muscle, 232
    response, 45
    as a skill in coping with pressure of athletic
        performance, 128
    skills, 128
    techniques, 42, 232
    training, 47, 174, 232
relaxed state, 42
relocation stress, 256
remembering, 89
residency, 213, 266
resilience, 41
resistance, 33
respiratory diseases, 8, 247
    influenza, 7
    negative mood and, 66–68
    pneumonia, 7
    PTSD and, 58–59
    Severe Acute Respiratory Syndrome (SARS), 282–283
    smoking and, 143–144
    smoking cannabis and, 155
    stress and, 60–62
    upper respiratory infections, 58, 64, 66–68
respondent pain, 215
response efficacy belief, 13
restraint theory of eating behaviour, 165
restructuring, 5, 46
reticular formation, 31
retrospective research, 245
rheumatoid arthritis, 62

Ritalin, 156
Rosenman, Ray, 37
rotational injury, 133

S

safe-sex practices, 158
salivary immunoglobulin A antibody (sIgA), 55, 60
Schmale, Arthur, 70
scientific standards of health promotion, 320
Scott, Steve, 117
secondary appraisal, 34–35
second-hand smoke, 144
second-impact syndrome, 133
sedentary lifestyle, effect of, 123–124
seeking medical care. *See also* delaying medical care
    from health care system, 245
    from hospital, 247–261
    interpreting symptoms, 244–245
    perception of symptoms, 242–244
self-accountability, 314
self-awareness model, 151
self-care, 307
self-confidence, 116
self-efficacy, 46, 116, 129, 312
    athletic performance and, 117
    as a function of participation in exercise, 119
    sources of efficacy expectations, 117–118
self-hypnosis, 52
self-management strategies for smoking
    cessation, 147
self-monitoring, 98
self-regulatory model, 127
self-talk, 128–129
Selye, Hans, 28–29, 32–33
    honours, 29
    Stress without Distress, 29
set-point theory, 162
Severe Acute Respiratory Syndrome (SARS), 282–283
sexually transmitted diseases (STDs), 157
Shakespeare, William, 30
short-term stress, 74
sites of cancer, 178
situation variables, 36
smoking
    age and gender differences, 136–137
    becoming a regular smoker, 140–141
    beginning to smoke, 139–140
    cancer risk from, 143–144
    cardiovascular and cerebrovascular disease,
      risk of, 143
    chronic lower respiratory diseases, risk of, 144
    by education level, 138

    environmental tobacco smoke (ETS), 144
    of flavoured tobacco products, 141
    health hazards and economic burden of tobacco
      consumption, 143–144
    health warning labels and, 142–143
    by income level, 138
    link between heredity and, 141
    psychological reasons for, 141
    quitting, 144–147
    reasons for, 139–141
    sociocultural differences, 137–138
social comparison, 187
social concordance, 90–91
social determinants of health, 283–284, 305
social dominance, 37
social ecological model, 280–282, 288, 298
social facilitation approach, 164
social learning model, 151–152
social support, 40–41, 308–310
socioeconomic status
    being physically active, 113, 125
    patient–physician interaction, 91
    prevalence of pain, 214
    smoking behavior, 137
spirituality, 40
splenomegaly, 86
sport psychology, 108
sports
    definition, 109
    models of stress management, 127
    popular, 113
    skills, 126
stage of resistance, 29
stages of change model, 20–21
    and support for government quit-smoking programs, 21
Statistics Canada, 113
stereotypic response, 29
Stewart, Moira, 91
stimulant drug, 156
strain, 30
stress, 251. *See also* general adaptation syndrome (GAS)
    autoimmune diseases and, 62
    body responses to, 32–33
    cancer and, 63
    cognitive transactional models of, 34–37
    cortisol levels during, 32
    environmental factors, 30
    individual's cognitive appraisal and, 28
    issues in defining, 26–30
    long-term effects, 59–60
    in nursing, 272–273
    perception of symptoms, 243

stress (*continued*)

   in persons living with AIDS, 73

   physicians and, 265–268

   psychological impact of exercise and physical activity
     on, 122

   psychology of, 30–32

   role of personality in, 37–39

   social behaviour during, 30

   stress-reduction interventions and immune functioning,
     63–64

   upper respiratory tract infection (URTI) and, 60–62

stress appraisal, 34–36

stress-buffering hypothesis, 40

stress-diathesis model, 33–34

stressful appraisal, 34

stress-inoculation training, 47, 127

stress-intrusion scores, 62

stress literacy, 27

stress management techniques, 42

stressors, 30, 56

stress-related emotional states, 47

stress response, 39

   dampening effect, 151

subjective norms, 16–17

substance abuse

   alcohol, 147–153

   illicit drug use, 153–157

   physician impairment and, 268

   smoking, 136–147

survival of the fittest, 33

sympathetic adrenomedullary (SAM) system, 30

sympathetic nervous system, 30–31

symptoms

   interpreting, 244–245

   perception of, 242–244

systematic desensitization, 46

Szasz, Thomas, 78–79

T

tailoring the regimen, 98

tangible support, 40

task orientation, 131

T cells, 53

temporal uncertainty, 36

tending, 29

tension phase, 48

tension reduction hypothesis, 151

T-helper-cell activity, 72

theories in health psychology

   Bagozzi's goal theory, 20

   behavioural enaction models, 19

   Gollwitzer's implementation intentions model, 20

   health belief model, 13–14

   health beliefs and health values, 14–15

   multi-stage models, 20–21

   stages of change model, 20–21

   theory of planned behaviour, 19

   theory of reasoned action, 16–18

theory of human becoming, 260

theory of planned behaviour, 19, 22, 125, 158, 311

theory of reasoned action, 16–18, 22, 125, 158, 311

   in predicting health behaviour, 18

Thornton, Johnson, 91

threat appraisal, 34

thyroid gland functions during stress, 32

total institution, 249. *See also* hospitals

traits, 37, 66, 73

   conscientiousness-related, 38

   negative, 38, 67

   personality, 37, 141, 171, 243

tranquillizers, 148, 228

transcendent accomplishments, 117

transcendental meditation (TM), 45

transcutaneous electrical nerve stimulation (TENS), 229–230

translocation stress, 256

transtheoretical model, 20, 125

trauma, 28

triage, 253

tumours, 178, 183–184

Twain, Mark, 30

Type A behaviour pattern, 4–5, 37, 46

Type B personality, 37

U

UAB Pain Behavior Scale, 221

ulcers, 33, 245

uncertainty, 254

   anxiety of HIV/AIDS patients and, 197

   event, 36

   as a source of stress, 267–268

   temporal, 36

uniformity myth, 251

unsafe sexual behaviour

   contributing factors to, 157

   effect of sexual arousal on, 158

   failure to use condoms, reasons, 157

   gay and bisexual males, 157

   intoxication and, 157–158

   negative effects of, 157

upper respiratory infections (URI), 58

   negative mood and, 66–68

upper respiratory tract infection (URTI), 60–62, 67–68

urinary bladder, 144

User's Guide to Evidence-Based Medicine, 101

V

vaccinations, 61, 68, 296–298
  psychology of, 296–298
Valium, 156
Valsalva manoeuvre, 43
verbal descriptor scale (VDS), 222–223, 226
verbal persuasion, 117–118
vicarious experience, 117–118
virtual reality analgesia, 234
visual analog scale (VAS), 222, 226
visuomotor behaviour-rehearsal program, 127
vomiting, 133, 149, 155, 168, 184–185
vulnerabilities, 33–34, 310, 318
  in Canada, 285
  concept, 35
  culture and, 289
  health beliefs and, 13
  health-related, 285
  information regarding, 311
  perceived, 13–14, 16
  personal, 13, 312
  of population, 284–285
  positive life events and, 62

W

Waitzkin, Howard, 5–6, 87
water, 44, 110, 208, 235
Western culture, 43, 45, 244

West Haven–Yale Multidimensional Pain Inventory (MPI),
  223–225
withdrawal, 145
  hangovers and, 149, 152
  physiological, 156
  social, 156
World Health Day, 101
World Health Organization (WHO), 102
  Framework Convention on Tobacco Control, 142–143
  health, definition of, 3
  health initiatives, 101
  health promotion, definition of, 303
  health promotion initiatives, 303–304
  obesity prevalence, 158
  political and sociological approaches to health, 303
World Immunization Week, 101

X

Xanax, 156

Y

yoga, 43, 107
yogis, 44
youth
  smoking and, 16, 138, 140–141, 308
  solvent use among, 292–293
  unsafe sexual behaviours, 157
  use of illicit drugs, 154–156